Pg 221
#2-14 even

Holt
Geometry

Eugene D. Nichols
Mervine L. Edwards
E. Henry Garland
Sylvia A. Hoffman
Albert Mamary
William F. Palmer

Holt, Rinehart and Winston, Publishers
New York • Toronto • London • Sydney

Staff Credits

Editorial Development   Eleanor R. Spencer, Everett T. Draper, Earl D. Paisley, Arlene Grodkiewicz

Editorial Processing   Margaret M. Byrne, Regina Chilcoat, Holly L. Massey

Art and Production   Vivian Fenster, Fred C. Pusterla, Robin M. Swenson, Russell Dian, Beverly Silver, Annette Sessa-Galbo, Anita Dickhuth, Donna Bogdanowich, Fran Gugliotti, Louise Hannibal

Product Manager   John W. M. Cooke

Advisory Board   Robert Wolff, Patricia M. Cominsky, José Contreras, Roy V. Eliason, C. Paul Moore, Randolph Ragsdale, Kenneth C. Scupp

Consultants   Patricia M. Cominsky

Researchers   James R. George, Erica S. Fellman

Acknowledgments for Photographs

Cover Photo: Computer-generated block graph "Black Night from Purple Palace", MCA-All. The x-axis is parallel to the spine and the origin is in the center. Both x-values and y-values are from -38 to 38. Colors are 65432170. The equation is $(Y - 4 * \tan(X/8))/(ABS(X) - ABS(X) - ABS(Y) + .001)$. By E. P. Miles, Jr. on an Intecolor 8051 at Florida State University, program by William Jasiniecki, photo by John Owen. © 1980 EPM. All rights reserved. Used by permission.

Pages: 22, 202, 233, 262, 332, 421, 493, 553, HRW photos by Russell Dian; *page x,* Dr. Donald Greenberg, Program of Computer Graphics, Laboratory, Cornell University, Ithaca, New York; *page 17,* New York State Highway Commission; *page 52,* Robert Houser/Photo Researchers; *page 67* left, Bettmann Archive; *page 67* right, Rare Book Division, New York Public Library; *page 97,* Estol/Ezra Stoller; *page 102* left, George Holton/Photo Researchers; *page 102* right, Paolo Koch ©/Photo Researchers; *page 128,* Black Star; *page 177,* U.S. Department of Interior Geological Survey; *page 182,* USDA Soil Conservation Service; *page 207,* German Information Center; *page 263,* Dan McCoy/Rainbow; *page 300,* Redwood Empire Association; *page 380,* Harvard College Observatory; *page 461,* J. Alex Langly/DPI; *page 466,* New York Public Library, Picture Collection; *page 519,* Francis Laping/DPI

Line art prepared by Vantage Art, Inc.

ISBN: 0-03-053866-1
2345   032   9876543

About the Authors

Eugene D. Nichols
Distinguished Professor of Mathematics Education
and Lecturer Mathematics Department
Florida State University
Tallahassee, Florida

Mervine L. Edwards
Chairman of the Mathematics Department
Shore Regional High School,
West Long Branch, New Jersey

E. Henry Garland
Head of the Mathematics Department
Developmental Research School
DRS Professor
Florida State University
Tallahassee, Florida

Sylvia A. Hoffman
Resource Consultant in Mathematics
Illinois State Board of Education
State of Illinois

Albert Mamary
Assistant Superintendent of Schools for Instruction
Johnson City Central School District
Johnson City, New York

William F. Palmer
Professor and Chairman
Department of Education
Catawba College, and
Mathematics Consultant
Salisbury City Schools
Salisbury, North Carolina

Consulting Au for Computer Strand

Barbara L. Kur
Assistant Professor
Director of Acad omputing
Hollins College
Hollins College, V

iii

Contents

4 Proving Triangles Congruent

5 Applying Congruent Triangles

6 Exploring Polygons

7 Quadrilaterals

8 Trapezoids and Symmetric Polygons

9 Similarity

10 Applying Similar Triangles

11 Circles and Lines

12 Areas of Geometric Figures

13 Coordinate Geometry

Symbol List

FIGURES AND MEASURES

These illustrations are called computer graphics displays. Computer graphics shows the use of geometry in design. Each of these displays shows the computer-generated images of a house on a computer graphics system.

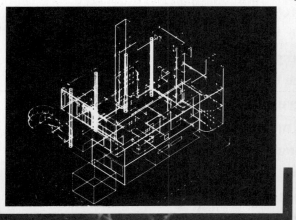

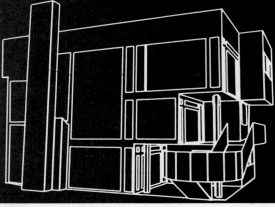

The display on the left above shows all of the planes of the house. The display on the right shows some of the exterior planes of the house. The lower display shows the geometric model of the house in its final setting.

Programmers who develop and use this system know and apply geometric principles.

1.1 Points, Lines, and Planes

To identify and name geometric figures such as points, lines, planes, collinear points, and coplanar points

Geometry is the study of sets of points. When beginning any field of study, you must pay special attention to the meanings of the words you use. When defining words, you must express them in terms of simpler words whose meanings you already know. This means that you must begin with a few simple words that remain undefined but whose meanings are nevertheless understood. Some *undefined terms* of geometry are *point, line,* and *plane.* These terms serve as a basis for defining other geometric terms.

Even though point, line, and plane are not formally defined, the chart below will give you information about identifying and naming them.

Undefined term	Picture	How to name	Other information
point	dot ●	capital letter ● P Read: point *P*	has no length, width, or thickness; occupies no space
line	straight mark with two arrowheads ◀————————▶	two capital letters with a double arrowhead above them, or a lower-case letter ◀—●————————●—▶ *A* *B* ℓ $\overleftrightarrow{AB}$, $\overleftrightarrow{BA}$, or *l* Read: line *AB*, line *BA*, or line *l*	has length, but no width or thickness; is straight; is an infinite set of points that extends indefinitely in two directions
plane	slanted four-sided figure	lowercase letter *m* Read: plane *m*	has length and width, but no thickness; is a flat surface; is an infinite set of points that extends indefinitely in all directions

Example 1

Give seven possible names for the line shown below.

$$R \qquad S \quad T \qquad n$$

The line can be named $\overleftrightarrow{RS}$, $\overleftrightarrow{SR}$, $\overleftrightarrow{RT}$, $\overleftrightarrow{TR}$, $\overleftrightarrow{ST}$, $\overleftrightarrow{TS}$, or n.

Once you have accepted a few basic undefined terms, you can use them to define other terms. Notice that the definitions below are based on the concepts of *point*, *line*, and *plane*.

Definitions:	
Space	*Space* is the set of all points.
Geometric figure	A *geometric figure* is a set of points.
Collinear points	*Collinear points* are points that lie on the same line. Points that do not lie on the same line are **noncollinear.**
Coplanar points	*Coplanar points* are points that lie in the same plane. Points that do not lie in the same plane are **noncoplanar.**

Example 2

In the figure, find 3 collinear points, 3 coplanar points, 3 noncollinear points, and 4 noncoplanar points.

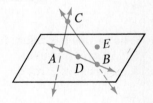

A, D, and B are collinear.
A, B, and E are coplanar.
A, B, and C are noncollinear.
A, B, C, and E are noncoplanar.   (Other answers are possible.)

Observe the different ways in which points, lines, and planes can be positioned. Notice that point P *lies on* line l, but point Q does not. Also, point P *is contained in* line l, or line l *contains* point P.

Notice that lines m and n *intersect* at point A, but lines r and s do not intersect. The *intersection* of lines m and n is point A.

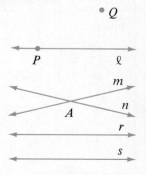

Line *t* *lies in* plane *p*, or line *t* *is contained in* plane *p*. Line *u* *intersects* plane *p* in point *C*. Line *v* does not intersect plane *p*.

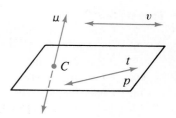

Reading in Geometry

Match each term on the right with its description on the left.
1. Points that line on the same line
2. The set of all points
3. Occupies no space
4. A flat surface
5. Points that lie in the same plane
6. Has length, but no width or thickness

a. line
b. coplanar points
c. plane
d. point
e. collinear points
f. space

Oral Exercises

Give all possible names for each figure shown below.

1.

2. • *S*

3.

4.

What geometric figure is suggested by each of the following?
5. A superhighway
7. A wall of a room

6. A tabletop
8. The intersection of two streets

Written Exercises

Identify the following points as *collinear, coplanar but noncollinear,* or *noncoplanar*.

Ⓐ 1. *R, U, W*
2. *S, T, U, R*
3. *S, U, V*
4. *V, U, S, W*
5. *T, U, V*
6. *S, T, U*

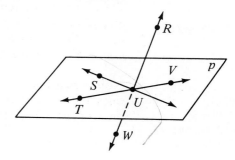

True or false?

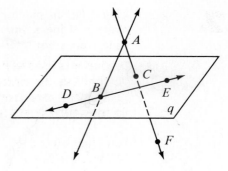

7. $\overleftrightarrow{DE}$ is contained in plane q.
8. $\overleftrightarrow{AC}$ and $\overleftrightarrow{FA}$ are the same line.
9. $\overleftrightarrow{AB}$ and $\overleftrightarrow{DE}$ intersect in point C.
10. B, C, and E are noncoplanar.
11. Point B is the intersection of $\overleftrightarrow{AB}$ and plane q.
12. The intersection of $\overleftrightarrow{AF}$ and plane q is point C.
13. $\overleftrightarrow{CF}$ passes through point E.
14. Point A and plane q do not intersect.
15. $\overleftrightarrow{DE}$ contains point B.

Draw and label each figure described below. Use a straightedge.

B 16. $\overleftrightarrow{MN}$ lying in plane r and point P in plane r but not on $\overleftrightarrow{MN}$

17. $\overrightarrow{TU}$ intersecting plane q in point V

18. $\overleftrightarrow{AB}$ and $\overleftrightarrow{CD}$ lying in plane q such that $\overleftrightarrow{AB}$ and $\overleftrightarrow{CD}$ intersect at point E

19. $\overleftrightarrow{EF}$, $\overleftrightarrow{EG}$, and $\overleftrightarrow{EH}$ intersecting plane p in points F, G, and H, respectively

20. $\overleftrightarrow{MN}$ not intersecting plane r with $\overrightarrow{MQ}$ intersecting plane r in point Q

21. noncollinear points A, B, and C lying in plane p with $\overrightarrow{DC}$ intersecting plane p

Give a brief explanation for each of the following.

C 22. Why is it necessary to begin the study of geometry with undefined terms?

23. Why is it impossible for four noncoplanar points to be collinear?

Algebra Review

OBJECTIVE ▶ **To simplify expressions involving absolute value**

$|n|$ means the *absolute value* of n.

$|n| = n$, if n is a positive number, or 0.
$|n| = -n$, if n is a negative number.

Thus, $|5| = 5$, $|0| = 0$, and $|-4| = -(-4)$, or 4.
Notice that the absolute value of a number cannot be negative.

Example Simplify $|-5 - (-3)|$.

$|-5 - (-3)| = |-5 + 3| = |-2| = -(-2)$, or 2

Simplify.

1. $\|5 - 3\|$	2. $\|9 - 4\|$	3. $\|5 - 13\|$	4. $\|12 - 18\|$
5. $\|0 - (-4)\|$	6. $\|13 - (-9)\|$	7. $\|-9 - (-7)\|$	8. $\|-4 - (-12)\|$
9. $\|-16 - 9\|$	10. $\|-5 - 5\|$	11. $\|-5 - (-5)\|$	12. $\|-8 + 13\|$

1.2 Distance and Length

OBJECTIVES ► **To find the coordinate of a point on a number line**
To find the distance between two points on a number line
To identify and name segments and rays
To measure a segment to the nearest centimeter or millimeter

Sometimes it is useful to assign numbers to the various points of a line. When this is done, the line is called a *number line*. The number assigned to each point is called the *coordinate* of the point.

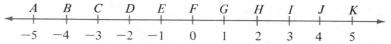

On the number line above, point *D* corresponds to -2, so -2 is the coordinate of *D*. On a given number line, no two points have the same coordinate. There is a *one-to-one correspondence* between the points and the coordinates. The symbol $\leftrightarrow$ is used to show the correspondence between a point and its coordinate. $A \leftrightarrow -5$ means "point *A* corresponds to the number -5."

Example 1 For each point, *A*, *B*, *C*, *D*, find its corresponding coordinate.

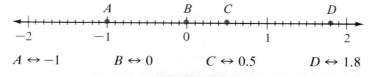

$A \leftrightarrow -1$ $B \leftrightarrow 0$ $C \leftrightarrow 0.5$ $D \leftrightarrow 1.8$

Different one-to-one correspondences between points and numbers can be set up if different number lines are used. On the first number line below, point *W* corresponds to -5. On the second, *W* corresponds to -3.

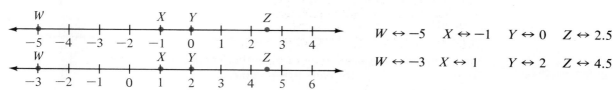

$W \leftrightarrow -5$ $X \leftrightarrow -1$ $Y \leftrightarrow 0$ $Z \leftrightarrow 2.5$

$W \leftrightarrow -3$ $X \leftrightarrow 1$ $Y \leftrightarrow 2$ $Z \leftrightarrow 4.5$

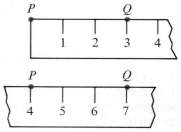

A ruler is like a number line since a number (coordinate) is assigned to every point of the ruler. You can use a ruler to measure the distance between two points. In the diagrams at the right, the distance between points *P* and *Q* is 3 cm, no matter which way the ruler is placed. Note that $3 - 0 = 3$ and $7 - 4 = 3$. The distance is the same as the difference between the coordinates.

DISTANCE AND LENGTH

Definition:	The *distance between two points*, A and B, with coordinates a and b, is $|b - a|$ or $|a - b|$. The symbol AB means "the distance between points A and B."
distance	

Example 2 Find the distance between each pair of points listed below.

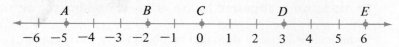

Points	Distance
D and E	$DE = |6 - 3| = |3| = 3$
B and D	$BD = |3 - (-2)| = |5| = 5$
D and A	$DA = |-5 - 3| = |-8| = 8$
B and C	$BC = |0 - (-2)| = |2| = 2$
B and A	$BA = |-5 - (-2)| = |-3| = 3$

In the figure at the right, point C is between points A and B. Neither D nor E is between A and B. The term *between* can be defined in relation to distances.

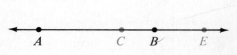

Definition:	Point C is **between** points A and B if C is on $\overleftrightarrow{AB}$ and $AC + CB = AB$.
between	

Two other important geometric figures can now be defined.

Definitions:	*Segment AB* is the set of points consisting of A, B, and all points between A and B. A and B are called the *endpoints* of the segment. Either $\overline{AB}$ or $\overline{BA}$ can be used to name segment AB.
segment	

ray	*Ray AB* is the set of points consisting of $\overline{AB}$ and all points P such that B is between A and P. A is called the *endpoint* of the ray. The symbol $\overrightarrow{AB}$ is used to name ray AB.

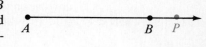

Example 3 Give all other names for each figure named below.

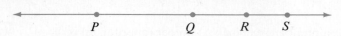

Figure $\overrightarrow{PQ}$; $\overrightarrow{SQ}$; $\overrightarrow{QS}$; $\overrightarrow{SR}$ Other names $\overrightarrow{QP}$; $\overrightarrow{QS}$; $\overrightarrow{QR}$; $\overrightarrow{SQ}$; $\overrightarrow{SP}$

Definition:	The *length* (or *measure*) of $\overline{AB}$ is the distance between points A and B. The symbol AB means "the length of $\overline{AB}$."
length of segment	

CHAPTER ONE

Example 4 Find the length of $\overline{XY}$ to the nearest centimeter (cm) and to the nearest millimeter (mm).

$\overline{XY}$ is about 4 cm long.
$\overline{XY}$ is about 43 mm long.

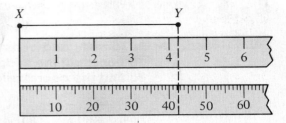

Written Exercises

Give the coordinate of each point.

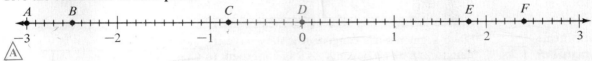

Ⓐ

Find each indicated distance. Use the number line.

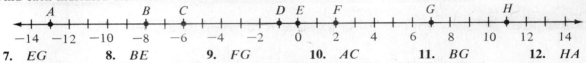

7. *EG*   **8.** *BE*   **9.** *FG*   **10.** *AC*   **11.** *BG*   **12.** *HA*

Give all other names for each figure named below. Use the number line.

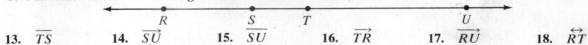

13. $\overline{TS}$ **14.** $\overrightarrow{SU}$ **15.** $\overline{SU}$ **16.** $\overrightarrow{TR}$ **17.** $\overrightarrow{RU}$ **18.** $\overleftrightarrow{RT}$

Measure each segment to the nearest centimeter and to the nearest millimeter.

19. A B **20.** C D **21.** E F

Complete each statement. Use the number line.

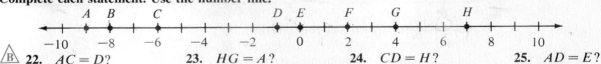

Ⓑ **22.** $AC = D$?   **23.** $HG = A$?   **24.** $CD = H$?   **25.** $AD = E$?

The coordinate of *A* is given. Find all possible coordinates of *B* so that $\overline{AB}$ has the indicated length.

     26. $A \leftrightarrow 6; AB = 8$ **27.** $A \leftrightarrow -3; AB = 4$ **28.** $A \leftrightarrow 1.2; AB = 7$ **29.** $A \leftrightarrow -3.4; AB = 7.8$

Explain each of the following. Use the definition of *between*.

Ⓒ **30.** Why is point *C* not between points *A* and *B*?

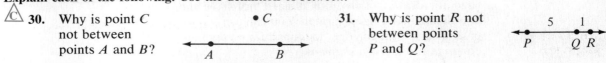

31. Why is point *R* not between points *P* and *Q*?

DISTANCE AND LENGTH

1.3 Congruent Segments

OBJECTIVES ► **To identify and construct congruent segments**
To construct the midpoint of a segment
To find the coordinate of the midpoint of a segment

Two segments can have the same length. In the figure below, $\overline{AB}$ and $\overline{CD}$ are each 2 cm long. $\overline{AB}$ and $\overline{CD}$ are examples of *congruent* segments.

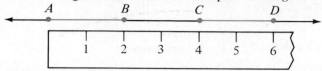

Definition:
congruent
segments

Two **segments** are **congruent** if they have the same length. $\overline{AB} \cong \overline{CD}$ means "$\overline{AB}$ is congruent to $\overline{CD}$." Similar markings are used to indicate congruent segments.

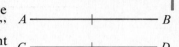

Example 1 Show that each pair of segments is congruent. Use coordinates.

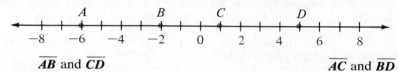

$\overline{AB}$ and $\overline{CD}$ $\overline{AC}$ and $\overline{BD}$

$AB = |-2 - (-6)| = 4$ $AC = |1 - (-6)| = 7$
$CD = |5 - 1| = 4$ $BD = |5 - (-2)| = 7$
The lengths are the same, so $\overline{AB} \cong \overline{CD}$.   The lengths are the same, so $\overline{AC} \cong \overline{BD}$.

Definition:
midpoint

M is the **midpoint** of $\overline{AB}$ if M lies on $\overline{AB}$ and $\overline{AM} \cong \overline{MB}$. The midpoint **bisects** the segment.

Any geometric figure that contains the midpoint of a segment is called a **bisector** of the segment. Thus, a segment may be bisected by a point, a line, a ray, another segment, or any geometric figure. In the diagram, line l bisects $\overline{AB}$.

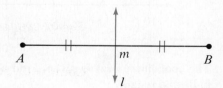

A compass and a straightedge are the basic tools for constructing geometric figures. A straightedge is used for drawing lines, but it need not have the coordinate markings of a ruler. You can use a compass and a straightedge to construct a segment congruent to a given segment.

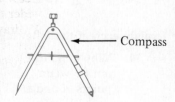
Compass

⌐Construction   A segment congruent to a given segment ─────────────────────────────┐

Given: $\overline{AB}$
Construct: $\overline{CD} \cong \overline{AB}$ on line l

A •─────────────────• B

Adjust the compass to correspond to A and B.

Place compass point on any point C of line l. Mark D with compass pencil.

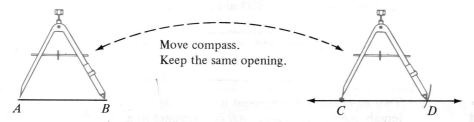

Move compass.
Keep the same opening.

Conclusion: $\overline{CD} \cong \overline{AB}$

Similar procedures can be used to carry out more complicated constructions.

Example 2   Construct a segment with a length equal to the sum of the lengths of two given segments, $\overline{AB}$ and $\overline{CD}$.

A ─────────── B   C ─────── D

Construct $\overline{PO} \cong \overline{AB}$, as shown at the right. Then construct $\overline{OQ} \cong \overline{CD}$.

$PO = AB$ and $OQ = CD$

Thus, $PQ = AB + CD$.

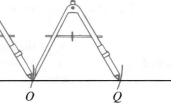

P O Q

Equidistant means "the same distance from."

Example 3   Construct a point P equidistant from two given points.

Let X and Y be two given points. Open your compass wider than one-half of XY. With the compass point on X, draw an arc. With the same compass opening and with the compass point on Y, draw a second arc that intersects the first arc at P.

P

• X • Y

Conclusion: $XP = YP$

CONGRUENT SEGMENTS   **9**

Construction   The midpoint of a given segment

Given: $\overline{AB}$
Construct: M, the midpoint of $\overline{AB}$

A ———————————— B

Construct P so that $AP = BP$.

✗ P

A ———————————— B

Construct Q different from P so that $AQ = BQ$.

✗ P

A ———————————— B

✗ Q

Draw $\overleftrightarrow{PQ}$ intersecting $\overline{AB}$ at M.

✗ P

M

A ———————————— B

Q

Conclusion: M is the midpoint of $\overline{AB}$.

Written Exercises

Which pairs of segments are congruent? Use a ruler to decide.

Ⓐ 1.   2.   3.   4.

Which pairs of segments are congruent? Use a compass to decide.

5.   6.   7.   8.

Which pairs of segments are congruent? Use coordinates to decide.

```
    A   B   C   D   E   F   G   H   I   J   K   L   M   N   O   P   Q   R   S   T   U
◄───┼───┼───┼───┼───┼───┼───┼───┼───┼───┼───┼───┼───┼───┼───┼───┼───┼───┼───┼───┼───┼───►
      −10     −8      −6      −4      −2       0       2       4       6       8      10
```

9. $\overline{AE}$ and $\overline{GK}$

10. $\overline{GM}$ and $\overline{MQ}$

11. $\overline{BH}$ and $\overline{KQ}$

12. $\overline{GN}$ and $\overline{LR}$

13. $\overline{BP}$ and $\overline{UG}$

14. $\overline{QD}$ and $\overline{TG}$

Construct a segment $\overline{AB}$ congruent to each given segment. Then construct a point P equidistant from the endpoints of $\overline{AB}$.

15. Z   Y

16. X   W

Construct a segment $\overline{MN}$ congruent to each given segment. Then construct the midpoint of $\overline{MN}$.

17. P   Q

18. R   S

Find the coordinate of the midpoint of the segment whose endpoints have the given coordinates.

Example

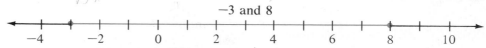

−3 and 8

Step 1 Find the distance between the points with coordinates −3 and 8: $|-3-8| = 11$

Step 2 Find one-half of the distance: $\frac{1}{2}(11) = 5\frac{1}{2}$

Step 3 Add it to the smaller coordinate: $-3 + 5\frac{1}{2} = 2\frac{1}{2}$

Thus, $2\frac{1}{2}$ is the coordinate of the midpoint.

 B

19. 5 and 17   **20.** 5 and −5   **21.** 0 and 12

22. −9 and −4   **23.** −5.6 and −8.4   **24.** −4.6 and 3.5

25. $2\frac{1}{2}$ and $3\frac{1}{4}$ **26.** $-5\frac{1}{3}$ and $6\frac{2}{3}$ **27.** $-3\frac{1}{8}$ and $-7\frac{3}{4}$

Construct each of the following.

28. A segment whose length is $MN + OP$

$\overline{M \quad\quad N} \quad\quad \overline{O \quad\quad\quad P}$

29. A segment whose length is $AB - CD$

$\overline{A \quad\quad\quad\quad B} \quad \overline{C \quad D}$

30. A segment twice as long as $\overline{XY}$.

$\overline{X \quad\quad\quad\quad\quad Y}$

31. A segment whose length is one fourth the length of $\overline{PQ}$

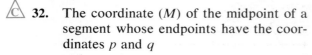

$\overline{P \quad\quad\quad\quad\quad\quad\quad\quad\quad Q}$

Write a formula for finding each of the following.

 C

32. The coordinate (M) of the midpoint of a segment whose endpoints have the coordinates p and q

33. The coordinate (q) of the second endpoint of a segment whose first endpoint has the coordinate p and whose midpoint has the coordinate m

34. The coordinate (r) of the point $\frac{1}{4}$ of the way from the point whose coordinate is p to the point whose coordinate is q if $p < q$

35. The coordinate (r) of the point $\frac{3}{4}$ of the way from the point whose coordinate is p to the point whose coordinate is q if $p < q$

A Challenge To You

Examine the figure at the right.

1. How many different lines are determined?
2. How many different segments are determined?
3. How many different rays are determined?

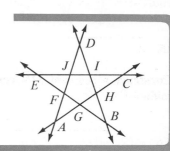

CONGRUENT SEGMENTS

1.4 Angles

OBJECTIVES ► To measure an angle
To construct congruent angles and the bisector of an angle
To apply the definition of the bisector of an angle

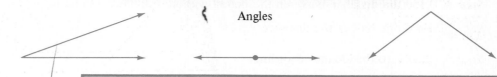

Angles

**Definition:
angle**

> An *angle* is the union of two rays with a common endpoint. The rays are the *sides* of the angle. The common endpoint is the *vertex* of the angle.

The symbol ∠ means "angle." An angle may be named in several different ways. Usually three capital letters are used. The middle letter names the vertex. The other letters name a point on each side of the angle. An angle may also be named by the vertex alone or by a lowercase letter placed between the rays.

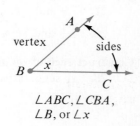

∠ABC, ∠CBA, ∠B, or ∠x

A *protractor* is used to measure an angle. The protractor assigns a number from 0 through 180 to the angle. The number is called the *measure* of the angle. Every angle has a degree measure m such that $0 < m \leq 180$.

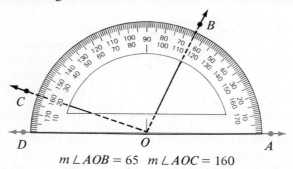

$m\angle AOB = 65$ $m\angle AOC = 160$

Example 1 Find the measure of ∠COD, ∠AOB, ∠AOC, and ∠BOC.

m ∠COD = 70
m ∠AOB = 60
m ∠AOC = 110
m ∠BOC = 120 − 70 = 50

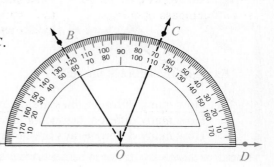

A protractor can be used to draw an angle with a given measure.

Example 2 Draw ∠XYZ so that m ∠XYZ = 130. Use a protractor.

Step 1 Draw a ray, $\overrightarrow{YX}$.
Step 2 Place the protractor center on Y with $\overrightarrow{YX}$ pointing to 0°.
Step 3 Mark Z at 130°.
Step 4 Draw $\overrightarrow{YZ}$.

m ∠XYZ = 130

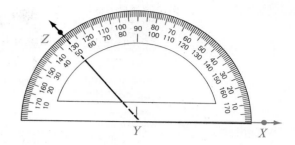

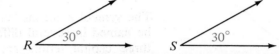

The two angles at the right have the same measure. They are examples of *congruent* angles.

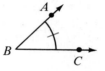

Definition: congruent angles ✓

Two angles are *congruent* if they have the same measure. ∠ABC ≅ ∠DEF means "∠ABC is congruent to ∠DEF." Similar markings are used to indicate congruent angles.

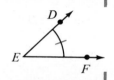

You can construct an angle congruent to a given angle using only a compass and a straightedge.

┌Construction An angle congruent to a given angle ─────────────

Given: ∠ABC
Construct: ∠DEF ≅ ∠ABC

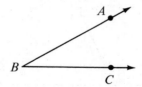

Construct an arc with center B. Use any compass opening.

On a line, pick a point E. Using the same compass opening, construct an arc with center E.

Open the compass to the length PQ. Construct an arc with center F. Draw $\overrightarrow{ED}$.

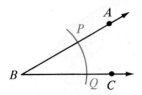

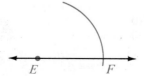

Conclusion: ∠DEF ≅ ∠ABC

ANGLES

An angle in a plane separates the plane into three sets of points: the *angle* itself, the *interior* of the angle, and the *exterior* of the angle. (This does not apply to an angle which measures 180°.) The interior of the angle is the part which contains no lines. The exterior is the other part. The concept of interior is applied in the next definition.

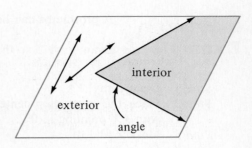

Definition:
bisector of angle

$\overrightarrow{OP}$ bisects $\angle AOB$ if P is in the interior of $\angle AOB$ and $\angle AOP \cong \angle POB$. $\overrightarrow{OP}$ is the **bisector** of $\angle AOB$.

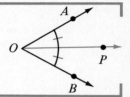

Construction   The bisector of a given angle

Given: $\angle XOY$
Construct: $\overrightarrow{OP}$, the bisector of $\angle XOY$

Draw an arc with center O.

Open the compass to the length AB.
Draw an arc with center A.
Draw an arc with center B.

Draw $\overrightarrow{OP}$.

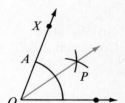

Conclusion: $\overrightarrow{OP}$ is the bisector of $\angle XOY$.

Example 3   Given: $\overrightarrow{BD}$ bisects $\angle ABC$; m $\angle ABD = 2x + 5$, and m $\angle DBC = 3x - 12$.
Find m $\angle ABD$.

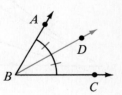

$\angle ABD \cong \angle DBC$ so   m $\angle ABD =$ m $\angle DBC$
$$2x + 5 = 3x - 12$$
$$x = 17$$

Thus, m $\angle ABD = 2x + 5 = 2 \cdot 17 + 5$, or 39.

Reading in Geometry

Translate each sentence into symbols.

1. The measure of angle *RST* is equal to 72 degrees.
2. The measure of angle *C* is equal to the measure of angle *D*.
3. Angle *ABC* is congruent to angle *XYZ*.
4. Point *W* corresponds to negative 4.
5. Segment *EF* is congruent to segment *GH*.
6. The length of segment *PQ* is equal to the length of segment *RS*.

Oral Exercises

1. Name the vertex and the sides of ∠*PQR*.
2. Give ten names for the angle.

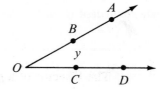

Written Exercises

Find the measure of each angle. Use the protractor pictured below.

△ 1. ∠*AOB*
2. ∠*EOF*
3. ∠*BOD*
4. ∠*COF*
5. ∠*EOB*
6. ∠*AOF*

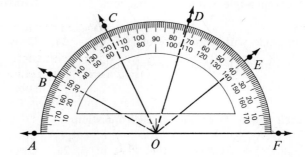

Find the measure of each angle. Use a protractor.

7.

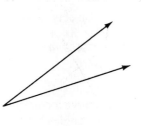

8.

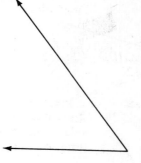

9.

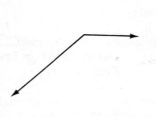

10.

ANGLES

Use a protractor to determine which pairs of angles are congruent.

11. 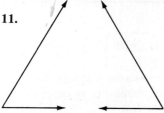 **12.** 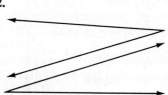 **13.**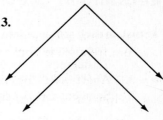

Use a protractor to draw angles having each given measure. Then use a compass and straightedge to bisect each angle.

14. m $\angle ABC = 38$ **15.** m $\angle DEF = 76$ **16.** m $\angle PQR = 90$ **17.** m $\angle JKL = 172$

Construct an angle congruent to each given angle. (Ex. 18−20)

18. 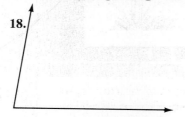   **19.**    **20.**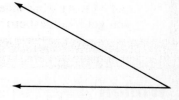

B **21.** Draw an angle with a measure of 100°. Construct an angle with $\frac{1}{4}$ of this measure.

22. Draw an angle with a measure of 136°. Construct an angle with $\frac{1}{8}$ of this measure.

23. Draw an angle with a measure of 70°. Construct an angle with $\frac{3}{4}$ of this measure.

24. Draw an angle with a measure of 136°. Construct an angle with $\frac{5}{8}$ of this measure.

Draw and label each figure. Then answer each question.

25. Draw $\angle ABC \cong \angle CBD$ so that C is in the interior of $\angle ABD$. Is $\overrightarrow{BC}$ the bisector of $\angle ABD$? Why or why not?

26. Draw $\angle ABC \cong \angle CBD$ so that C is in the exterior of $\angle ABD$. Is $\overrightarrow{BC}$ the bisector of $\angle ABD$? Why or why not?

Find the measure of each indicated angle. (Ex. 27−28)

27. Given: $\overrightarrow{OB}$ bisects $\angle AOC$, m $\angle AOB = 5x + 2$ and, m $\angle BOC = 6x - 3$. Find m $\angle AOB$.

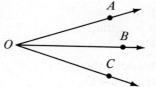

28. Given: $\overrightarrow{OB}$ bisects $\angle AOC$, m $\angle AOB = 8x + 3$, and m $\angle BOC = 9x - 4$. Find m $\angle BOC$.

C **29.** Can the interior and exterior of an angle with a measure of 180° be defined? Explain.

30. Can three coplanar angles have a common side? Three noncoplanar angles? Illustrate, if possible.

CHAPTER ONE

Applications

Read → Plan → Solve → Interpret

Mileposts on interstate highways indicate the number of miles you are from some point of reference, usually the state line.

1. How far is it from Milepost 38 to Milepost 96?

2. How far is it from Milepost 214 to Milepost 79?

3. If you drive 57 miles from Milepost 0, at what milepost will you be?

4. If you drive 78 miles toward the state line from Milepost 246, at what milepost will you be?

5. Jonesboro is halfway between Mileposts 37 and 193. At what milepost will you be when you get to Jonesboro?

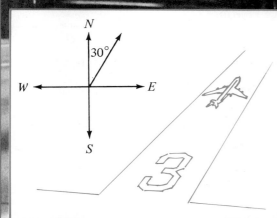

Airport runways are numbered to indicate angle measures with North. In clockwise direction from North, the degree measure is 10 times the runway number. For example, Runway 3 is 30° from North.

6. What is the measure of the angle that Runway 16 makes with North?

7. What is the runway number if the angle measure from North is 100°?

8. If each runway in Exercises 6 and 7 is approached from the opposite direction, what would each runway number be?

The yardline numbers on a football field are coordinates. However, there are some differences in the arrangement of these coordinates and the arrangement of the coordinates on a number line.

9. On a number line, the coordinate of the center point is usually 0. What yardline corresponds to this coordinate?

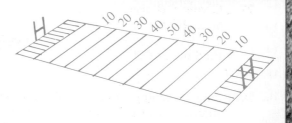

10. How many yards are there between the home team's 20-yardline and the visitor's 40?

11. Write a formula for the distance between any two yardlines.

Chapter One Review

Vocabulary

point [1.1], line [1.1], plane [1.1], space [1.1], geometric figure [1.1], collinear [1.1], coplanar [1.1], coordinate [1.2], distance [1.2], segment [1.2], ray [1.2], length [1.2], congruent [1.3], bisector [1.3], equidistant [1.3], angle [1.4], interior [1.4], exterior [1.4]

Give all possible names for each figure. [1.1]

1.

2.

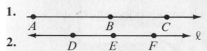

Identify each set of points as collinear, coplanar but noncollinear, or noncoplanar. [1.1]

3. *H, L*

4. *G, K*

5. *H, I, L*

6. *H, I, G*

7. *H, I, K, L*

8. *H, J, K, G*

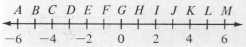

Use the number line (Ex. 9–15). [1.2, 1.3]

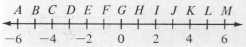

9. Find *FJ*.

10. Find *GK*.

11. Find *BH*.

12. Find the midpoint of $\overline{BL}$.

13. Find the midpoint of $\overline{AG}$.

14. Is $\overline{AE}$ congruent to $\overline{EJ}$?

15. Is $\overline{CG}$ congruent to $\overline{EI}$?

*16. Find the coordinate (*r*) of the point $\frac{2}{3}$ of the distance from the point with coordinate *x* to the point with coordinate *y* if *x* < *y*. [1.4]

Use a protractor to find the measure of each angle (Ex. 17–18). [1.4]

17.   18.

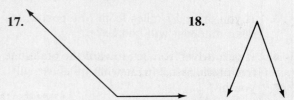

19. Construct a segment congruent to $\overline{AB}$. [1.3]

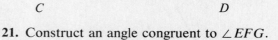

20. Construct the midpoint of $\overline{CD}$. [1.3]

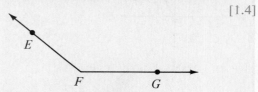

21. Construct an angle congruent to ∠*EFG*. [1.4]

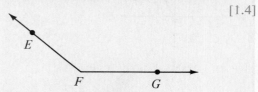

22. Construct the bisector of ∠*HIJ*. [1.4]

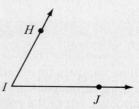

23. Given: $\overrightarrow{KL}$ bisects ∠*MKN*, m ∠*MKL* = 5*x* + 3, and m ∠*LKN* = 6*x* − 4. Find m ∠*MKL*. [1.4]

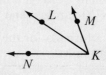

Chapter One Test

Give all possible names for each figure.

1.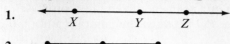

2.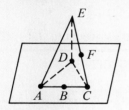

Identify each set of points as collinear, coplanar but noncollinear, or noncoplanar.

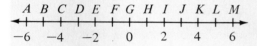

3. *A, D*
4. *B, F*
5. *A, B, C*
6. *A, F, C*
7. *A, B, C, D*
8. *A, C, D, E*

Use the number line for Items 9-15.

9. Find *GM*.
10. Find *IL*.
11. Find *BJ*.
12. Find the midpoint of $\overline{GM}$.
13. Find the midpoint of $\overline{BJ}$.
14. Is $\overline{BF}$ congruent to $\overline{HM}$?
15. Is $\overline{BJ}$ congruent to $\overline{DM}$?

Use a protractor to find the measure of each angle. (Items 16-17)

16.

17.

18. Construct a segment congruent to $\overline{XY}$.

   X ——————— Y

19. Construct an angle congruent to ∠*UVW*.

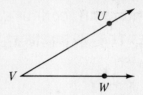

20. Construct the midpoint of $\overline{ST}$.

   S ————————————— T

21. Construct the bisector of ∠*PQR*.

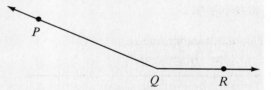

22. Given: $\overrightarrow{IJ}$ *bisects* ∠*HIK*; m ∠*HIJ* = 5x − 3; and m ∠*JIK* = 3x + 15. Find m ∠*JIK*.

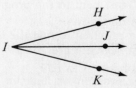

*23. Find the coordinate (*r*) of the point $\frac{1}{3}$ of the way from the point whose coordinate is *p* to the point whose coordinate is *q* if *p* < *q*.

Computer Activities

Computers are often used to help solve problems involving measurements. Engineers and architects rely on computers for determining specifications of buildings, machines, bridges, aircraft, and so forth.

Following is a program that you can use to compute the length of a segment, given the coordinates of the endpoints. Since the length of a segment $\overline{PQ}$ is the distance PQ between the points P and Q, the BASIC function ABS(x) is used in the program.

For example, ABS(7) = 7   ABS(−8) = 8   ABS(x) = 32 when x is −32.

See the computer section on p. 560 for more information.

PROGRAM

```
10 PRINT "PROGRAM COMPUTES LENGTH OF SEGMENT XY"
20 PRINT "ENTER X POINT, Y POINT"
30 INPUT X, Y
40 LET L = X - Y
50 LET D = ABS(L)
60 PRINT "LENGTH OF SEGMENT XY IS"; D
70 END
```

Exercises

Type in the program above and run it for each of the following endpoints. (Ex. 1–8)

1. $x = 12$ and $y = 18$
2. $x = -7$ and $y = 3$
3. $x = 512$ and $y = -833$
4. $x = -34$ and $y = -22$
5. $x = 9.2$ and $y = 15.4$
6. $x = -1.5$ and $y = 3.4$
7. $x = -25.3$ and $y = -14.6$
8. $x = -15.4$ and $y = -6.1$
9. Add a statement to the program above so that it will also print the endpoints, x and y.

10. Write a program to find the length of a segment congruent to a given segment if the endpoints of the first segment are given.

11. Write a program to find the missing endpoint of a segment congruent to a given segment if the endpoints of the first segment and one endpoint of the other segment are given.

ACTIVITY: MEASUREMENT

College Prep Test

Directions: Choose the one best answer to each question or problem.

1. Which of the following is true of a ray but not true of a segment?

   (A) Can be named by two points
   (B) Extends indefinitely in two directions
   (C) Has a definite length
   (D) Has two endpoints
   (E) Has only one endpoint

2. Which of the following is another name for $\overrightarrow{BE}$?

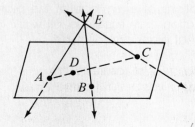

   (A) $\overrightarrow{EB}$
   (B) $\overrightarrow{BC}$
   (C) $\overrightarrow{AB}$
   (D) $\overrightarrow{BD}$
   (E) $\overrightarrow{BA}$

3. In the figure shown, which of the following is not true?

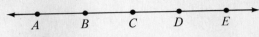

   (A) A, B, and C are coplanar.
   (B) A, D, and C are coplanar.
   (C) A and B are collinear.
   (D) A, B, C, and E are coplanar.
   (E) A, E, and C are coplanar.

4. 53 m is equivalent to

   (A) .53 cm   (B) .53 mm   (C) .53 km
   (D) 53 mm   (E) None of these

5. Which of the following are true? Use the number line.

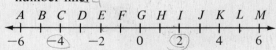

   $\overline{BH}$ is congruent to
   I. $\overline{DJ}$
   II. $\overline{GM}$
   III. $\overline{EL}$

   (A) I only   (B) II only   (C) III only
   (D) I and II only   (E) I, II, and III

6. Which of the following are not true? Use the number line for exercise 5.
   I. $CI = -2$
   II. $CI = 6$
   III. The mid point of $\overline{CI}$ is 0.

   (A) I only   (B) II only   (C) III only
   (D) I and III only   (E) II and III only

7. Which of the following figures has an interior?

   (A) An angle   (B) A circle
   (C) A closed figure   (D) All of these
   (E) None of these

8.

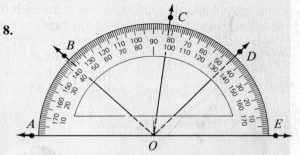

   Which of the following is true?

   (A) $\angle AOB \cong \angle BOC$ (B) $\angle BOC \cong \angle COD$
   (C) $\angle COD \cong \angle DOE$ (D) $\angle AOB \cong \angle COD$
   (E) None of these

2 INTRODUCING PROOFS

Mathematics in Architecture

Architects provide a variety of services related to building. They prepare the working drawings and specifications showing the exact dimensions and locations of every part of the plan. During construction they supervise all work to make certain that plans are followed.

A new supermarket is opening in Jonesboro. The parking lot measures 80m by 50m. How should the parking spaces and the access drives be laid out so that the maximum number of cars can be parked?

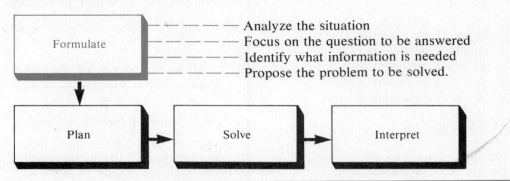

Formulate
— Analyze the situation
— Focus on the question to be answered
— Identify what information is needed
— Propose the problem to be solved.

Plan → Solve → Interpret

2.1 Types of Angles

OBJECTIVES ► **To classify angles by their measures**
To identify angles as adjacent or vertical

The degree measure m of an angle must be greater than 0 and less than or equal to 180. You can classify angles into four categories by their measures.

Definitions:
acute angle
right angle
obtuse angle
straight angle

An *acute* angle is an angle with degree measure m such that 0 < m < 90.
A *right* angle is an angle with degree measure m = 90.
An *obtuse* angle is an angle with degree measure m such that 90 < m < 180.
A *straight* angle is an angle with degree measure m = 180.

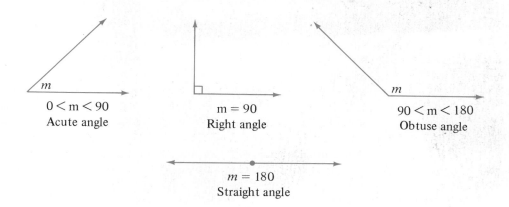

| 0 < m < 90 | m = 90 | 90 < m < 180 |
| Acute angle | Right angle | Obtuse angle |

m = 180
Straight angle

Notice how the symbol ⌐ is used to indicate a right angle. This symbol will be used throughout this book. The picture of the straight angle is also the picture of a line. You may find it useful sometimes to think of a line as a type of angle.

Example 1 Measure each angle with a protractor. Classify each as acute, right, or obtuse.

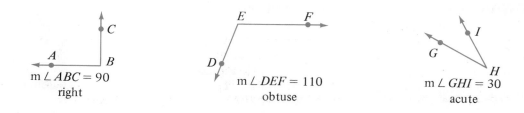

m ∠ ABC = 90
right

m ∠ DEF = 110
obtuse

m ∠ GHI = 30
acute

Sometimes pairs of angles are classified not by their measures but by their positions with respect to each other. *Adjacent* angles and *vertical* angles are such angles.

Definition:
adjacent angles

> *Adjacent angles* are two coplanar angles that have a common side between them but have no interior points in common.

Adjacent angles must have a common side, which means they must also have a common vertex. $\angle XOY$ and $\angle YOZ$ share a common side $\overrightarrow{OY}$ and are adjacent; $\angle KUL$ and $\angle MUN$ do not share a common side and are not adjacent. Although $\overrightarrow{IS}$ is shared by $\angle RAS$ and $\angle SIT$, $\overrightarrow{AS}$ is not shared. The two angles do not have a common vertex. They are not adjacent angles.

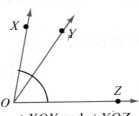

$\angle XOY$ and $\angle YOZ$
are adjacent.

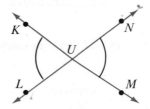

$\angle KUL$ and $\angle MUN$
are not adjacent.

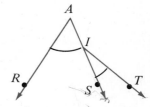

$\angle RAS$ and $\angle SIT$
are not adjacent.

Adjacent angles must be coplanar, and they must have no interior points in common. $\angle BAC$ and $\angle CAD$ are adjacent. $\angle LOM$ and $\angle MON$ are not coplanar and are not adjacent. P is in the interior of both $\angle QIS$ and $\angle QIR$. They are not adjacent.

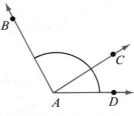

$\angle BAC$ and $\angle CAD$
are adjacent.

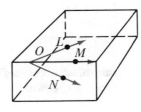

$\angle LOM$ and $\angle MON$
are not adjacent.

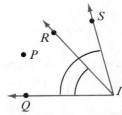

$\angle QIS$ and $\angle QIR$
are not adjacent

Example 2 Is each of the given pairs of angles adjacent? If not, why not?

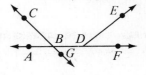

	Answers
$\angle ADE$ and $\angle EDF$	Adjacent
$\angle CBA$ and $\angle FBG$	Not adjacent

No common side

Definition:
vertical angles

Vertical angles are nonadjacent angles formed by two intersecting lines.

∠*XOW* and ∠*YOZ* are vertical angles. So are ∠*WOZ* and ∠*XOY*. ∠*AOB* and ∠*COD* are not vertical angles, since they are not formed by intersecting lines. Neither are ∠*BOC* and ∠*DOA*.

Vertical angles

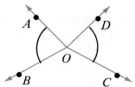

Not vertical angles

Example 3 Name the second angle in each pair of vertical angles.

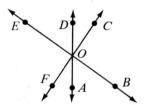

	Answers
∠*BOC*	∠*EOF*
∠*AOE*	∠*DOB*
∠*COA*	∠*FOD*

Oral **Exercises**

Does the angle appear to be acute, right, obtuse, or straight?

1.  2.   3.  4.

Name a second angle to form a pair of adjacent angles.

5. ∠*XYW* and _____   6. ∠*CBD* and _____   7. ∠*FGH* and _____

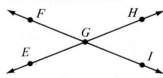

Name a second angle to form a pair of vertical angles.

8. ∠*KLJ* and _____   9. ∠*QOR* and _____   10. ∠*YAZ* and _____

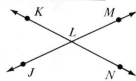 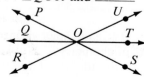 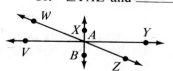

TYPES OF ANGLES

25

Written Exercises _____

Using the picture, name an angle of each kind and find its measure.

△ 1.   An acute angle
3.   A right angle

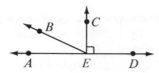

2.   An obtuse angle
4.   A straight angle

Is each of the given pairs of angles adjacent? If not, why not?

5.   ∠GIF and ∠HIJ   6.   ∠LPK and ∠NPK   7.   ∠QSR and ∠RST   8.   ∠VUW and ∠WUX
9.   ∠FIJ and ∠FIG   10.   ∠MON and ∠KPN   11.   ∠QST and ∠RST   12.   ∠WUX and ∠XUY

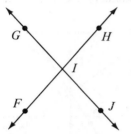 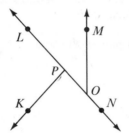 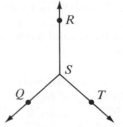 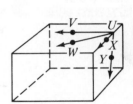

Draw a picture to illustrate each of the following.

13.   Two vertical angles
15.   Two angles with a common vertex but no common side

14.   Two adjacent angles
16.   Two angles with a common side which are not adjacent

True or false? For each false statement, draw a picture showing why it is false.

 17.   A right angle and an acute angle ⤴ cannot be adjacent.
19.   Two lines that form vertical angles also form adjacent angles.
21.   Two noncoplanar angles cannot be vertical angles.
23.   If the noncommon sides of two adjacent angles form a straight angle, then both angles must be right angles.

18.   An obtuse angle and a right angle cannot be vertical angles.
20.   Two right angles cannot be vertical.
22.   Any two angles with a common vertex are vertical angles.
24.   If the noncommon sides of two adjacent angles form a straight angle, then one angle can be obtuse and the other can be acute.

Cumulative Review _____

1.   Are there any geometric figures that have lines in both their interiors and exteriors?
2.   What are some undefined terms of geometry?
3.   Find the length of a segment whose endpoints have the coordinates −5 and −12.

2.2 Supplementary and Complementary Angles

OBJECTIVE ►

To identify supplementary and complementary angles and find their measures

You learned that a straight angle has a measure of 180° and a right angle has a measure of 90°. Some pairs of angles, called *supplementary* or *complementary*, are related to straight angles or right angles, respectively.

Definitions:
supplementary angles and linear pair

> Two angles are *supplementary* if the sum of their measures is 180°. Each angle is called a supplement of the other. If the angles are adjacent and supplementary, then they are called a *linear pair*.

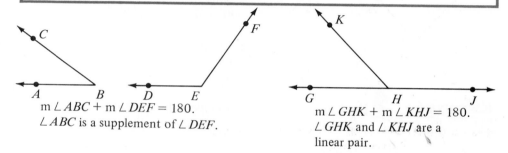

m ∠ *ABC* + m ∠ *DEF* = 180.
∠ *ABC* is a supplement of ∠ *DEF*.

m ∠ *GHK* + m ∠ *KHJ* = 180.
∠ *GHK* and ∠ *KHJ* are a linear pair.

Supplementary angles do not have to be adjacent. If they are adjacent, then the sides of the two angles that are not the common side form a straight angle.

Example 1 Which are measures of supplementary angles?

	Answers
30° and 160°	not supplementary
103° and 67°	not supplementary
86° and 94°	supplementary

Complementary angles are related to right angles.

Definition:
complementary angles

> Two angles are *complementary* if the sum of their measures is 90°. Each angle is called a *complement* of the other.

Complementary angles do not have to be adjacent. If they are adjacent, then the sides of the two angles that are not the common side form a right angle.

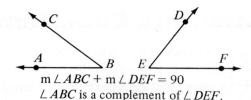

$m \angle ABC + m \angle DEF = 90$
$\angle ABC$ is a complement of $\angle DEF$.

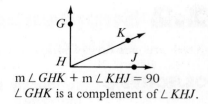

$m \angle GHK + m \angle KHJ = 90$
$\angle GHK$ is a complement of $\angle KHJ$.

Example 2 Find the measure of a complement of each angle, if possible.
Find the measure of a supplement.

Answers

Measure of angle	Measure of complement	Measure of supplement
60°	30°	120°
95°	none	85°
m	$90 - m$	$180 - m$

You will use the representations m, $90 - m$, and $180 - m$ to solve problems about angles.

Example 3 Find the measure of an angle if its measure is 60° more than the measure of its complement.

The sum of the measures is 90°. ▶ Let $m =$ measure of the angle
$90 - m =$ measure of its complement
$m = (90 - m) + 60$
$2m = 150$
$m = 75$ **Thus, the angle measure is 75°.**

Example 4 Find the measure of an angle if its measure is twice that of its supplement.

The sum of the measures is 180°. ▶ Let $m =$ measure of the angle
$180 - m =$ measure of its supplement
$m = 2(180 - m)$
$m = 360 - 2m$
$3m = 360$
$m = 120$ **Thus, the angle measure is 120°.**

Example 5 Find the measure of an angle if its measure is 40° less than four times the measure of its complement.

Let $m =$ measure of the angle
$90 - m =$ measure of its complement
$m = 4(90 - m) - 40$
$m = 360 - 4m - 40$
$5m = 320$
$m = 64$ **Thus, the angle measure is 64°.**

Oral Exercises

Which are measures of complementary angles? supplementary angles? neither?

1. 60° and 30°
2. 130° and 50°
3. 114° and 66°
4. 92° and 2°
5. 53° and 47°
6. 87° and 87°
7. 65° and 25°
8. 69° and 21°
9. 57° and 122°
10. 97° and 93°
11. 45° and 45°
12. 26° and 154°

What is the measure of a complement of each angle whose measure is given?

13. 45°
14. 20°
15. 78°
16. 46°
17. 8°
18. 38°

What is the measure of a supplement of each angle whose measure is given?

19. 90°
20. 70°
21. 160°
22. 97°
23. 9°
24. 108°

Which of the following is a picture of a linear pair?

25.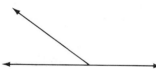
26.
27.

Written Exercises

Find the measure of a complement and a supplement, if possible, of each angle whose degree measure is given.

1. 30°
2. 75°
3. 5°
4. 98°
5. 128°
6. 180°
7. 140°
8. x
9. 22.5°
10. 85.2°
11. $m - 5$
12. $10 - x$

Find the measure of the angle if its measure is as given.

13. 50° more than that of its complement
14. 60° more than that of its supplement
15. 20° less than that of its supplement
16. 78° less than that of its complement
17. Twice that of its complement
18. Three times that of its supplement
19. Equal to that of its complement
20. Equal to that of its supplement

Find the measure of the angle if the measure of its supplement or complement is as given.

21. The measure of its complement is one fourth that of its supplement
22. The measure of its supplement is 3 times that of its complement.
23. Its measure is 24° less than twice that of its complement.
24. Its measure is 81° more than twice that of its supplement.
25. Its measure is 26° less than three times that of its complement.
26. Its measure is 18° more than half that of its supplement.
27. The measure of its supplement is 52° more than twice that of its complement.
28. The measure of its supplement is 10° more than 3 times that of its complement.
29. Five times the measure of its complement is 24° less than twice the measure of its supplement.
30. Four times the measure of its complement is 12° more than twice the difference between the measures of its supplement and its complement.

SUPPLEMENTARY AND COMPLEMENTARY ANGLES

2.3 Drawing Conclusions

OBJECTIVES ▶ **To draw conclusions about angles using given information**
To use the transitive and substitution properties of congruence.

If you know certain things about angles, you can often discover other things about them. For example, suppose that m $\angle ABC = 105$ and m $\angle DEF = 105$. Since the angle measures are equal, you can conclude that the two angles are congruent.

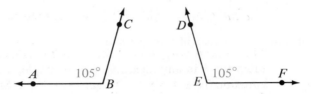

Since m $\angle ABC = 105$ and m $\angle DEF = 105$, $\angle ABC \cong \angle DEF$.

Example 1 $\overrightarrow{HJ}$ bisects $\angle GHI$. What conclusions can you draw about the angles formed?

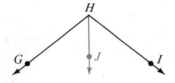

A bisector forms two congruent angles.

Thus, $\angle GHJ \cong \angle JHI$ and m $\angle GHJ =$ m $\angle JHI$.

In algebra you learned about the *transitive property of equality*. This states that if $x = y$ and $y = z$, then $x = z$, for all numbers x, y, and z. Since the measures of angles and segments are numbers, the transitive property is true for all such measures.

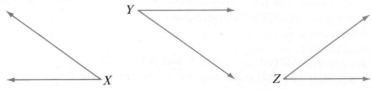

Suppose that $\angle X \cong \angle Y$ and $\angle Y \cong \angle Z$. This means that m $\angle X =$ m $\angle Y$ and m $\angle Y =$ m $\angle Z$. By the transitive property, m $\angle X =$ m $\angle Z$. Since the measures are equal, $\angle X \cong \angle Z$. A similar argument can be given to show that if $\overline{AB} \cong \overline{CD}$ and $\overline{CD} \cong \overline{EF}$, then $\overline{AB} \cong \overline{EF}$. This leads to the transitive property of congruence, which is true for all angles or segments.

| **Transitive property of congruence** | If $\angle X \cong \angle Y$ and $\angle Y \cong \angle Z$, then $\angle X \cong \angle Z$.

If $\overline{AB} \cong \overline{CD}$ and $\overline{CD} \cong \overline{EF}$, then $\overline{AB} \cong \overline{EF}$. |

Example 2 If $\angle AOB \cong \angle BOC$ and $\angle BOC \cong \angle COD$, which other angles are congruent?

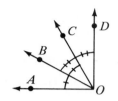

Use the transitive property. ► $\angle AOB \cong \angle COD$

The *substitution property of equality* states that if $a = b$, then a can be substituted for b in any equation. For example, if $x = y + 1$, you can substitute in the equation $3x + 4 = y + 1$ to get $3x + 4 = x$. Since any congruence statement such as $\angle A \cong \angle B$ or $\overline{AB} \cong \overline{CD}$ can be changed into a statement of equality (m $\angle A =$ m $\angle B$ or $AB = CD$), there is a similar substitution property of congruence.

| **Substitution property of congruence** | If $\angle A \cong \angle B$, then $\angle A$ can be substituted for $\angle B$ in any congruence statement.

If $\overline{AB} \cong \overline{CD}$, then $\overline{AB}$ can be substituted for $\overline{CD}$ in any congruence statement. |

Example 3 Given: m $\angle T = 53$ and m $\angle V = 53$. Draw a picture to show this. What conclusion can you draw about the angles? Give a reason for your conclusion.

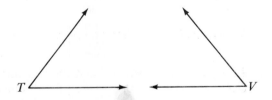

Since m $\angle T = 53$ and m $\angle V = 53$, by the substitution property, m $\angle T =$ m $\angle V$. Therefore, $\angle T \cong \angle V$.

Example 4 Given: $\overline{GH} \cong \overline{KL}$ and $\overline{RT} \cong \overline{KL}$.
Which other segments are congruent?

Substitute $\overline{GH}$ for $\overline{KL}$. ► $\overline{RT} \cong \overline{GH}$

You will use both the transitive property and the substitution property in showing other relationships between angles or segments.

Reading in Geometry

Write the word from the list that completes each sentence so that the paragraph has meaning.

Geometry often involves using information that is known to discover other _____. This is called drawing _____. For example, if you know that $\overrightarrow{AB}$ _____ $\angle CAD$, then you know that $\angle CAB$ is congruent to $\angle BAD$. Similarly, if P is the _____ of $\overline{AB}$, then you know that $\overline{AP}$ is congruent to $\overline{PB}$.

bisects
information
pictures
midpoint
conclusions
point

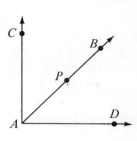

Written Exercises

In each of the following, which other angle measures are equal?

⚠ **1.** m $\angle AOB$ = m $\angle AOD$, m $\angle AOD$ = m $\angle DOC$, m $\angle DOC$ = m $\angle BOC$

2. m $\angle EOF$ = m $\angle HOI$, m $\angle FOG$ = m $\angle GOH$, m $\angle FOG$ = m $\angle HOI$.

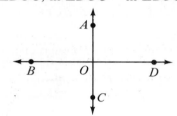

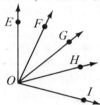

What conclusion can you draw based on each set of given information? Give a reason for your conclusion.

3. $\overrightarrow{KL}$ bisects $\angle JKM$.

4. $\angle NOP \cong \angle POQ$, $\angle POQ \cong \angle QOR$.

5. U is in the interior of $\angle STV$. $\angle STU \cong \angle UTV$.

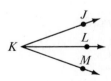

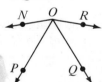

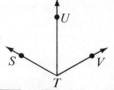

6. B is the midpoint of $\overline{AC}$.

7. E is between D and F, $\overline{DE} \cong \overline{EF}$.

8. $\overline{GH} \cong \overline{HI}$, $\overline{HI} \cong \overline{IJ}$.

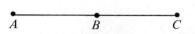

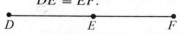

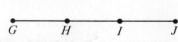

Draw a diagram for each of the following. What conclusion can you draw based on the given information. Give a reason for your conclusion.

⚠ **9.** m $\angle a$ = 48, $\angle a$ and $\angle b$ are complementary.

10. m $\angle c$ = 83, $\angle c$ and $\angle d$ are adjacent angles.

11. m $\angle e$ = 104, $\angle e$ and $\angle f$ are supplementary.

12. $\angle A \cong \angle B$, $\angle A$ and $\angle B$ are complementary.

13. $\angle C \cong \angle D$, $\angle C$ and $\angle D$ are supplementary.

14. m $\angle E$ = 38, $\angle E \cong \angle F$.

Based on the given information, is each stated conclusion correct? Why or why not?

Example $\angle x$ and $\angle y$ are complementary
conclusion: m $\angle x = 45$

No: The conclusion assumes that $\angle x \cong \angle y$.

15. m $\angle XYZ = 100$, m $\angle ZYW =$ 100. Conclusion: $\overline{YZ}$ bisects $\angle XYW$.

16. m $\angle M = 71$, $\angle M \cong \angle N$, $\angle N$ and $\angle O$ are supplementary. Conclusion: m $\angle O = 109$.

17. m $\angle S = 45$, $\angle S$ and $\angle T$ are complementary. Conclusion: $\angle S \cong \angle T$.

Cumulative Review

1. Find the measure of a supplement of a 70° angle.
2. What is the measure of a right angle?
3. What are congruent segments?

 CALCULATOR ACTIVITIES

1. Astronomers use angle measures to three decimal places. If $\angle A$ measures 41.238°, find the measure of a complement and a supplement of $\angle A$.

2. If the measure of $\angle A$ in Activity 1 is doubled, then what is the measure of a complement and a supplement of $\angle A$?

A Challenge To You

Some geometry procedures use step-by-step substitutions. This word change game uses a similar process.

Changing exactly one letter at a time and using only commonly accepted words, the word *FISH* can be changed to the word *CATS* in six steps.

	FISH			*FISH*
Change *F* to *D*.	*DISH*		Change *H* to *T*.	*FIST*
Change *I* to *A*.	*DASH*		Change *I* to *A*.	*FAST*
Change *D* to *M*.	*MASH*	or	Change *F* to *P*.	*PAST*
Change *H* to *S*.	*MASS*		Change *T* to *S*.	*PASS*
Change *S* to *T*.	*MATS*		Change *S* to *T*.	*PATS*
Change *M* to *C*.	*CATS*		Change *P* to *C*.	*CATS*

Try these.

1. *COW* to POT
2. *CAR* to *TAX*
3. *BALL* to *BELT*
4. *HORSE* to *MOUSE*
5. *EAT* to *RUN*
6. *TOY* to *POP*
7. *MEAT* to *BEEF*
8. *HOME* to *CAMP*
9. *WARM* to *COLD*

2.4 Writing Proofs

► **To write reasons for statements**
To write simple geometric proofs using properties of equations

In geometry you should be able to give a reason for any statement that you make or for any conclusion that you draw. There are many types of reasons that you may use. Sometimes the reason for a statement may be a geometric property or definition that you have learned. Other reasons may involve algebraic properties or methods, or arithmetic facts. Later you will learn about other types of reasons.

In algebra you learned that if you add the same number to both sides of an equation, or subtract the same number from both sides, the resulting equation is still true. Similarly, if you multiply both sides by the same number or divide by the same number (except 0), the equality is unchanged. Since you will use these equation properties throughout your work in geometry, they are stated below.

Equation Properties

Addition: If $a = b$, then $a + c = b + c$ for all numbers a, b, and c.
Subtraction: If $a = b$, then $a - c = b - c$ for all numbers a, b, and c.
Multiplication: If $a = b$, then $a \cdot c = b \cdot c$ for all numbers a, b, and c.
Division: If $a = b$, then $\dfrac{a}{c} = \dfrac{b}{c}$ for all numbers a, b, and c ($c \neq 0$).

Example 1 What reason can you give for the given conclusion?
If m $\angle AOB =$ m $\angle COD$,
then m $\angle AOB +$ m $\angle BOC =$ m $\angle COD +$ m $\angle BOC$.

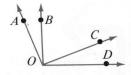

Addition property of equality.
(m $\angle BOC$ is added to both sides of the equation.)

Example 2 What reason can you give for the given conclusion?
If 2m $\angle PML = 80$, then m $\angle PML = 40$.

Division property of equality.
(Both sides of the equation were divided by 2.)

The reasons for any statements or conclusions should be written and labeled clearly. The symbol ∴ is used to mean *therefore* and usually indicates the conclusion. Example 3 shows you how geometric statements or conclusions and their corresponding reasons should be written.

Example **3** What conclusion can you draw based on the given information? Give a reason for each statement.

Given: $\overrightarrow{OP}$ bisects $\angle AOB$.

Conclusion: $\angle AOP \cong \angle POB$

Statements	Reasons
1. $\overrightarrow{OP}$ bisects $\angle AOB$	1. Given
2. $\therefore \angle AOP \cong \angle POB$	2. Definition of $\angle$ bisector

A **proof** is a formal argument that shows how a conclusion follows logically from other statements. A standard style or format is usually used in writing a geometric proof. You should write what is known or given, followed by steps which lead to the desired conclusion. You will usually use a two-column pattern. In this book, colored arrows will be used to show which step or steps in a proof lead to succeeding steps.

Example **4** Write a complete proof of the following.

Given: m $\angle X = 38$, m $\angle Y = 38$
Prove: $\angle X \cong \angle Y$

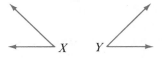

Proof

The colored arrows show which statements follow from other statements.

Statements	Reasons
1. m $\angle X = 38$	1. Given
2. m $\angle Y = 38$	2. Given
3. m $\angle X =$ m $\angle Y$	3. Substitution property
4. $\therefore \angle X \cong \angle Y$	4. Definition of $\cong$ angles

Example **5** Give a reason for each step in the following proof.

Given: m $\angle AOB +$ m $\angle BOC =$ m $\angle COD +$ m $\angle BOC$
Prove: $\angle AOB \cong \angle COD$

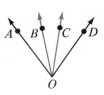

Proof

Subtract m $\angle BOC$.

Statements	Reasons
1. m $\angle AOB +$ m $\angle BOC =$ m $\angle COD +$ m $\angle BOC$	1. Given
2. m $\angle AOB =$ m $\angle COD$	2. Subtraction property of equality
3. $\therefore \angle AOB \cong \angle COD$	3. Definition of $\cong$ angles

Example 6

Draw a diagram based on the given information. Write the missing statements in the proof.

Given: $\overline{AB} \cong \overline{BC}$, $\overline{BC} \cong \overline{CD}$, and $AB = 21$
Prove: $CD = 21$

Proof

Statements	Reasons
1. $\overline{AB} \cong \overline{BC}$	1. Given
2. $\overline{BC} \cong \overline{CD}$	2. Given
3. $\overline{AB} \cong \overline{CD}$	3. Transitive property
4. $AB = CD$	4. Definition of $\cong$ segments
5. $AB = 21$	5. Given
6. $\therefore CD = 21$	6. Substitution property

Oral Exercises

If each statement in the first column is given information, what is the reason for each corresponding conclusion?

Given

1. $XY = ZW$ and $ZW = AB$
2. $AB = CD$ and $AB = 8$
3. $\angle XYZ \cong \angle ABC$ and $\angle ABC \cong \angle RPG$
4. $m \angle ROA = m \angle POW$ and $m \angle POW = 78$
5. $RT + LM = 19$ and $LM = 7$
6. $m \angle SLC + m \angle RTU = 127$ and $m \angle SLC = 18$
7. $m \angle RTU = 18$ and $m \angle HJK = 37$
8. $m \angle NMJ = 83$
9. $AZ = 26$
10. $\overrightarrow{LM}$ bisects $\angle ALZ$.

Conclusion

$XY = AB$
$CD = 8$
$\angle XYZ \cong \angle RPG$
$m \angle ROA = 78$
$RT = 12$
$m \angle RTU = 109$
$m \angle RTU + m \angle HJK = 55$
$2(m \angle NMJ) = 166$
$\dfrac{AZ}{2} = 13$
$\angle ALM \cong \angle MLZ$

Written Exercises

Write the missing statements in each proof.

△ 1. Given: $AB = 9$, $CD = 9$
Prove: $\overline{AB} \cong \overline{CD}$

$\overline{}$
$A \qquad B \quad C \qquad D$

Proof

Statements	Reasons
1. $AB = 9$	1. Given
2. $CD = 9$	2. Given
3. $AB = ?$	3. Substitution property
4. $\therefore ?$	4. Definition of $\cong$ segments

2. Given: $\overline{AB} \cong \overline{CD}$, $CD = 12$
Prove: $\overline{AB} = 12$

$\overline{}$
$A \qquad B \quad C \qquad D$

Proof

Statements	Reasons
1. $\overline{AB} \cong \overline{CD}$	1. Given
2. ?	2. Definition of $\cong$ segments
3. $CD = 12$	3. Given
4. $\therefore ?$	4. Substitution property

Give a reason for each statement in each proof.

3. Given: $AB + BC = 12$ and $\overline{AB} \cong \overline{CD}$
   Prove: $CD + BC = 12$

$$A \quad B \quad C \quad D$$

Proof

Statements	Reasons
1. $\overline{AB} \cong \overline{CD}$	1. ?
2. $AB = CD$	2. ?
3. $AB + BC = 12$	3. ?
4. $\therefore CD + BC = 12$	4. ?

4. Given: $AB = 8$, $\overline{AB} \cong \overline{BC}$ and $\overline{BC} \cong \overline{CD}$
   Prove: $CD = 8$

$$A \quad B \quad C \quad D$$

Proof

Statements	Reasons
1. $\overline{AB} \cong \overline{BC}$	1. ?
2. $\overline{BC} \cong \overline{CD}$	2. ?
3. $\overline{AB} \cong \overline{CD}$	3. ?
4. $AB = CD$	4. ?
5. $AB = 8$	5. ?
6. $\therefore CD = 8$	6. ?

Write a proof for each, using the pattern shown in this lesson.

5. Given: m $\angle A =$ m $\angle B$ and m $\angle B =$ m $\angle C$
   Prove: $\angle A \cong \angle C$

6. Given: m $\angle D = 79$ and m $\angle E = 79$
   Prove: $\angle D \cong \angle E$

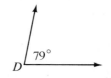

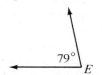

7. Given: m $\angle WOX +$ m $\angle XOY =$
   m $\angle ZOY +$ m $\angle XOY$
   Prove: $\angle WOX \cong \angle ZOY$

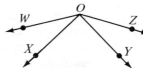

8. Given: $\angle WOX \cong \angle ZOY$
   Prove: m $\angle WOX +$ m $\angle XOY =$
   m $\angle ZOY + \angle XOY$

Draw a diagram based on the given information. Then write a proof for each.

9. Given: m $\angle A +$ m $\angle B =$ 103, and m $\angle B +$ m $\angle C = 103$
   Prove: m $\angle A =$ m $\angle C$

10. Given: m $\angle D -$ m $\angle E = 13$, and m $\angle F -$ m $\angle E = 13$
   Prove: m $\angle D =$ m $\angle F$

11. Given: m $\angle G = 35$, m $\angle H = 2($m $\angle G)$, and m $\angle I = 70$
   Prove: $\angle H \cong \angle I$

12. Given: $JK + KL = 18$ and $KL + LM = 18$
   Prove: $JK = LM$

13. Given: $NO - RS = 25$ and $PQ - RS = 25$
   Prove: $NO = PQ$

14. Given: $AB = 7$, $CD = 2(AB)$, and $EF = 14$
   Prove: $\overline{CD} \cong \overline{EF}$

15. Given: m $\angle XYZ = \frac{1}{2}($m $\angle WYZ)$, m $\angle RST = \frac{1}{2}($m $\angle QST)$, and $\angle WYZ \cong \angle QST$
   Prove: $\angle XYZ \cong \angle RST$

16. Given: $JK = \frac{1}{2}(LM)$, $NO = \frac{1}{2}(PQ)$, and $\overline{LM} \cong \overline{PQ}$
   Prove: $\overline{JK} \cong \overline{NO}$

2.5 Postulates and Theorems

OBJECTIVE ▶ **To use postulates and theorems involving points, lines, and planes**

In geometry, it is impossible to prove every statement. You must accept some basic statements as reasonable without a formal argument to show that they are true. Statements that are accepted without proof are called *postulates*.

> **Postulate 1** For any two points, there is exactly one line containing them.

It is accepted without proof that two given points are contained in exactly one line. From this, you can give an argument to prove another statement.

Example 1 Can two lines intersect in two points?

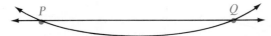

No. If they did, then there would be two different lines containing the two points. This contradicts postulate 1.

Such statements that are proved are called *theorems*. Most of the proofs of theorems in this book will use the formal pattern consisting of statements and reasons as presented in the last lesson. However, some proofs will be given using an informal, indirect way. The argument given in Example 1 is an indirect proof of your first theorem.

> **Theorem 2.1** Two lines intersect in at most one point.

The next postulate involves points and a plane.

> **Postulate 2** Three noncollinear points are contained in exactly one plane.

Many planes contain two given points, but only one plane contains three non-collinear points.

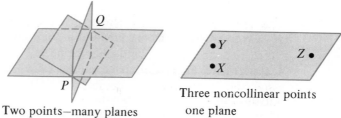

Two points—many planes

Three noncollinear points one plane

Three other postulates involving points, lines, and planes are generally accepted.

Postulate 3 If two points of a line are in a given plane, then the line itself is in the plane.

Postulate 4 If two planes intersect, then they intersect in exactly one line.

Postulate 5 Space contains an infinite number of points, not all co-planar. A plane contains an infinite number of points, not all collinear. A line contains an infinite number of points.

Example 2 What are the possible intersections of a line and a plane? Draw a picture of each.

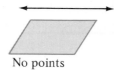

No points

Exactly one point
(Postulate 3 suggests these.)

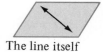

The line itself

Example 3 What are the possible intersections of two planes?
Draw a picture of each.

Planes do not intersect.

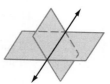

Planes intersect in a line.

(Postulate 4 suggests these.)

You can use these postulates to prove other theorems about points, lines, and planes.

Theorem 2.2   A line and a point not on the line are contained in exactly one plane.

Given: Line *l* and point *P* not on *l*
Prove: Exactly one plane contains *l* and *P*.

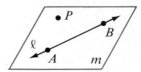

Proof

Statements	Reasons
1. Line *l* and point *P* not on *l*	1. Given
2. *l* contains at least 2 points. Name them *A* and *B*.	2. Postulate 5
3. *P*, *A*, and *B* are noncollinear	3. Definition of noncollinear points
4. *P*, *A*, and *B* are in exactly one plane. Name it *m*.	4. Postulate 2
5. *l* is in *m*.	5. Postulate 3
6. ∴ Exactly one plane contains *l* and *P*.	6. Steps 4 and 5

The proofs of two other theorems are similar to the proofs of Theorems 2.1 and 2.2, respectively. These proofs are to be completed as Exercises 22 and 23.

Theorem 2.3   If a line intersects a plane, but is not contained in the plane, then the intersection is exactly one point. (See Exercise 22.)

Theorem 2.4   Two intersecting lines are contained in exactly one plane. (See Exercise 23.)

Example 4 True or false? An angle (other than a straight angle) is contained in exactly one plane.
Draw a picture and give an argument.

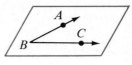

True.
The angle consists of two rays which determine two intersecting lines.
By Theorem 2.4, the lines are contained in exactly one plane.

Written Exercises

True or false?

1. Two points are in exactly one line.
3. Two points are in exactly one plane.
5. Two planes can intersect in exactly one line.
7. Two planes must intersect in exactly one line.
9. Two lines must intersect in exactly one point.
11. Postulates are statements to be proved.
13. Theorems are statements to be proved.

2. Three noncollinear points are in exactly one plane.
4. Four points are in exactly one plane.
6. Two planes can intersect in exactly one point.
8. A line and a plane must intersect in exactly one point.
10. Two lines can intersect in exactly one point.
12. Since postulates are not proved, they may not be used as reasons in proofs.

Answer each question. Draw a picture to illustrate. (Ex. 14–21)

14. Can a curve intersect a line in exactly two points?
16. Can more than one plane contain three given points?
18. How many different lines are determined by four noncollinear points?
20. Is it possible for exactly two lines to be determined by three points?
22. Prove Theorem 2.3. Use postulates 3 and 5.

15. Can a curve intersect a plane in exactly two points?
17. Can three points ever be noncoplanar?
19. How many different planes are determined by four noncoplanar points?
21. Is it possible to have an angle that is not in a single plane?
23. Prove Theorem 2.4. Use postulates 2, 3, and 5.

Algebra Review

OBJECTIVE ► To evaluate algebraic expressions

To evaluate an algebraic expression:
(1) Substitute the value for each variable.
(2) Simplify any powers.
(3) Do multiplications and divisions.
(4) Do additions and subtractions.

Example Evaluate $x^3 + 3x^2 + 4$ if $x = -3$.

$(-3)^3 + 3(-3)^2 + 4$

$-27 + 3(9) + 4$

$-27 + 27 + 4$, or 4

Evaluate.

1. $x^2 - 2x + 7$ if $x = 2$
4. $(a + 2)^2 + 4$ if $a = -3$

2. $3b^2 - 6b + 7$ if $b = -3$
5. $n^3 + (n - 3)(n + 4)$ if $n = 0$

3. $2t^3 + t^2 - 3t + 4$ if $t = 1$
6. $2(y - 1)^2 + y + 3$ if $y = 4$

POSTULATES AND THEOREMS

2.6 Angle and Segment Addition

OBJECTIVES ► **To use the angle addition postulate**
To use segment addition

When you measure segments or angles, you are assuming that there are segments congruent to those marked on your ruler and that there are angles congruent to those indicated on your protractor. Two postulates guarantee that angles and segments of any given measure do exist.

Postulate 6 On every line, there is a segment with a given point as an endpoint congruent to any given segment.

Postulate 7 For every ray, there is an angle with the given ray as a side congruent to any given angle.

When you bisect a segment or an angle, you are assuming that there actually is a midpoint of the segment or a bisector of the angle.

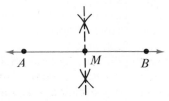

M is the midpoint of AB.

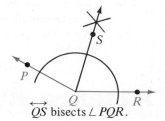

$\overleftrightarrow{QS}$ bisects $\angle PQR$.

Postulate 8 Every segment has exactly one midpoint.

Postulate 9 Every angle, except a straight angle, has exactly one bisector.

You may need to find the measure of an angle from what is known about the measures of other angles. You may know that m $\angle XYZ = 40$ and m $\angle ZYW = 60$. Using a protractor, m $\angle XYW$ is found to be 100. In this case, the sum of the measures of the two smaller angles is the measure of the larger angle. This leads to the statement of the next postulate.

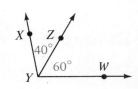

Postulate 10 Angle Addition Postulate

If D is in the interior of $\angle ABC$,
then m $\angle ABC =$ m $\angle ABD +$ m $\angle DBC$.

m $\angle ABD +$ m $\angle DBC$ is not always equal to m $\angle ABC$. In the figure below, D is not in the interior of $\angle ABC$. In this case, the Angle Addition Postulate does not apply.

m $\angle ABD = 160$, m $\angle DBC = 155$.
But, m $\angle ABC = 45$, not 315.

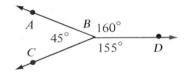

Example 1

Given: m $\angle DOF = 124$, m $\angle DOE = 36$.
Find m $\angle EOF$

m $\angle DOE +$ m $\angle EOF =$ m $\angle DOF$
        m $\angle EOF =$ m $\angle DOF -$ m $\angle DOE$
Thus, m $\angle EOF = 124 - 36$ or 88.

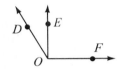

A geometric figure can be rather complicated. Several angles in the figure may have the same vertex. In such cases, it often is helpful to number the angles, as shown below. Thus, $\angle AOB$ can also be called $\angle 1$. Labeling angles in this way helps avoid confusion and saves time in writing proofs.

$\angle 1 \cong \angle AOB$
$\angle 2 \cong \angle BOC$
$\angle 3 \cong \angle COD$

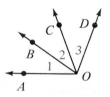

The *reflexive property of equality* states that a number is equal to itself: $a = a$, for any number a. Since congruence statements are actually statements about measures, which are numbers, there is a similar reflexive property for congruence statements.

Reflexive property of congruence

$\angle A \cong \angle A$ and $\overline{AB} \cong \overline{AB}$, for any angle A and any segment $\overline{AB}$.

You will use the reflexive property in many proofs.

Example 2 Give a reason for each step in the following proof.

Given: m ∠1 = m ∠3
Prove: ∠WOY ≅ ∠ZOX

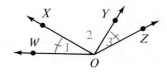

Proof

Add m ∠2 to both sides of equation. ▶

Statements	Reasons
1. m ∠1 = m ∠3	1. Given
2. m ∠2 = m ∠2	2. Reflexive property
3. m ∠1 + m ∠2 = m ∠3 + m ∠2	3. Addition property of equality
4. m ∠WOY = m ∠1 + m ∠2, m ∠ZOX = m ∠3 + m ∠2	4. Angle addition postulate
5. m ∠WOY = m ∠ZOX	5. Substitution property
6. ∴∠WOY ≅ ∠ZOX	6. Definition of ≅ angles

You learned to add the measures of angles, using the angle addition postulate. The definition of *between* accepted in Chapter 1 allows the same type of addition with segments. If point P is between points A and B, then $AP + PB = AB$. You can assume betweenness from the picture used with the proof.

$$AP + PB = AB$$

If P is not between A and B, then $AP + PB \neq AB$. Below, if $AP = 15$, and $PB = 6$, then $AB = 9$, not 21.

Example 3 Given: $AB = CD$
Prove: $AC = BD$

Proof

Statements	Reasons
1. $AB = CD$; $BC = BC$	1. Given; reflexive property
2. $AB + BC = CD + BC$	2. Addition property of equality
3. $AC = AB + BC$	3. Definition of between
4. $BD = BC + CD$	4. Definition of between
5. ∴ $AC = BD$	5. Substitution property

Written Exercises

Give another name for each angle.

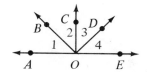

A 1. ∠1

2. ∠BOC

3. ∠4

4. ∠COD

Find each indicated length.

5. XY = 7 cm, YZ = 4 cm, XZ = ?

6. XZ = 9 cm, XY = 6 cm, YZ = ?

7. XY = 5 m, YZ = 3 m, XZ = ?

8. XZ = 15 m, YZ = 6 m, XY = ?

X ———— Y · Z

W is in the interior of ∠XYZ. Find each indicated angle measure. (Ex. 9–11)

9. Given: m ∠XYW = 40, and m ∠WYZ = 60, Find m ∠XYZ.

10. Given: m ∠XYZ = 113, and m ∠XYW = 42, Find m ∠WYZ.

11. Given: m ∠XYZ = 94, and m ∠WYZ = 32, Find m ∠XYW.

12. Given: m ∠1 = 55, m ∠ 2 = 20, and m 1 = m∠3 Find m ∠GOI.

13. Given: m ∠1 = m ∠3 and m ∠GOI = 78 Find m ∠FOH.

14. Given: JK = 4 cm, KL = 7 cm, and JK = LM Find KM.

15. Given: JK = LM and JL = 20 mm Find KM.

Write the missing statements or reasons in each proof. (Ex. 16–17)

16. Given: m ∠1 = m ∠3
Prove: m ∠NRP = m ∠ORQ

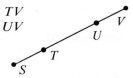

17. Given: SU = TV
Prove: ST = UV

Proof

Statements	Reasons
1. ?	1. Given
2. m ∠1 + m ∠2 = m ∠3 + m ∠2	2. ?
3. m ∠NRP = m ∠1 + m ∠2	3. ?
4. ?	4. Angle addition postulate
5. ∴ ?	5. Substitution property

Proof

Statements	Reasons
1. SU = TV	1. ?
2. ST + TU = SU	2. ?
3. ?	3. Definition of between
4. ST + TU = TU + UV	4. ?
5. ∴ ?	5. Subtraction property of equality

18. Given: AB = DE
Prove: AD = BE

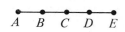

19. Given: AC = BD
Prove: AB = CD

ANGLE AND SEGMENT ADDITION

B **20.** Given: $\angle 1 \cong \angle 3$
Prove: $\angle AOC \cong \angle DOB$

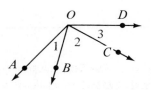

21. Given: $\angle AOC \cong \angle DOB$
Prove: $\angle 1 \cong \angle 3$

22. Given: $\overline{EH} \cong \overline{FI}$, and $\overline{HG} \cong \overline{IG}$
Prove: $\overline{EG} \cong \overline{FG}$

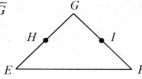

23. Given: $\overline{EG} \cong \overline{FG}$, and $\overline{EH} \cong \overline{FI}$
Prove: $\overline{HG} \cong \overline{IG}$

24. Given: $\overline{JL} \cong \overline{NL}$
$JK = \frac{1}{2}JL$, and $NM = \frac{1}{2}NL$
Prove: $\overline{JK} \cong \overline{NM}$

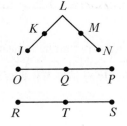

25. Given: $\overline{JK} \cong \overline{NM}$,
$JK = \frac{1}{2}JL$, and $NM = \frac{1}{2}NL$
Prove: $\overline{JL} \cong \overline{NL}$

C **26.** Given: Q bisects $\overline{OP}$, T bisects $\overline{RS}$, and $\overline{OP} \cong \overline{RS}$
Prove: $\overline{OQ} \cong \overline{TS}$

27. Given: $\overline{OQ} \cong \overline{QP}$, $\overline{OQ} \cong \overline{RT}$, and $\overline{OP} \cong \overline{RS}$
Prove: T bisects $\overline{RS}$

A Challenge To You

Mona has to drive from Metropolis to Century Village. According to the highway map, there are several different routes. How many different routes are there? What is the shortest route?

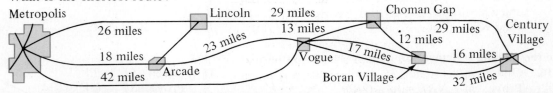

Algebra Review

OBJECTIVE ► **To multiply polynomials**

To multiply polynomials, use the Distributive Property:
$$a(b + c) = ab + ac.$$

Example

Multiply $3x(x^2 + 5)$.
$$3x \cdot x^2 + 3x \cdot 5$$
$$3x^3 + 15x$$

Multiply $(3y + 4)(y - 3)$
$$(3y + 4) \cdot y + (3y + 4) \cdot (-3)$$
$$3y^2 + 4y - 9y - 12$$
$$3y^2 - 5y - 12$$

Multiply.

1. $3(x + 4)$
2. $6a(2a^2 + 3a)$
3. $2x^2(4x^3 - 5)$
4. $(3t - 2s)(-5)$
5. $(6x^2 - 4x)(-4x^3)$
6. $(2z + 1)(z - 3)$
7. $(3x + 5)(2x - 3)$
8. $(2r + 3)(2r + 3)$
9. $(p - q)(p + q)$
10. $(3c - 4)(3c + 4)$
11. $(4c^2 - 3b)(4c^2 + 3b)$
12. $(5x + 3y^2)(5x + 3y^2)$

2.7 Perpendiculars

OBJECTIVES ► **To identify perpendicular lines, rays, and segments**
To prove statements about perpendiculars
To construct perpendicular lines

You learned earlier that a right angle has a measure of 90°. Sometimes lines intersect to form a right angle.

Definition:
perpendicular

Two lines are *perpendicular* if they intersect to form a right angle.

$\overleftrightarrow{AB} \perp \overleftrightarrow{XY}$ means that $\overleftrightarrow{AB}$ is perpendicular to $\overleftrightarrow{XY}$. The symbol $\not\perp$ means *is not perpendicular to*. In the figure, the symbol ⌐ is used to show that the lines are perpendicular.

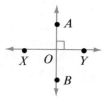

Since the measure of a straight angle is 180°, it seems reasonable to assume that the sum of the measures of certain angles on one side of a line is 180°.

Postulate 11
The sum of the measures of the angles with the same vertex on one side of a line and with no interior points in common is 180°. The sum of the measures of all angles around a common vertex and with no interior points in common is 360°.

You should try to write proofs of the following theorems about right angles and perpendiculars.

Theorem 2.5 All right angles are congruent.

Theorem 2.6 Two perpendicular lines form four congruent right angles.

Segments and *rays* are *perpendicular* if the lines that contain them are perpendicular.

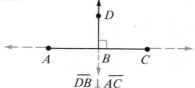

$\overline{DB} \perp \overline{AC}$

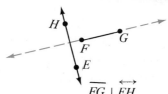

$\overline{FG} \perp \overleftrightarrow{EH}$

Example 1 Which of the following appear to be perpendicular?

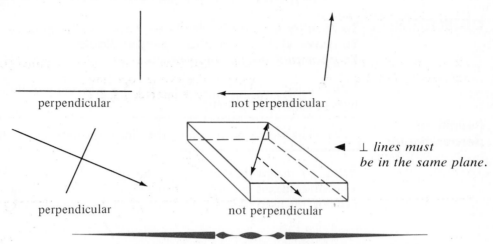

perpendicular   not perpendicular

◀ ⊥ *lines must be in the same plane.*

perpendicular   not perpendicular

A line can be constructed perpendicular to a given line.

Construction   A line perpendicular to a given line through a point not on the line

Given: Line *l* and *P* not on *l*
Construct: $\overleftrightarrow{PQ} \perp l$

• *P*

l ◀——————▶

Draw an arc with center *P* intersecting *l* at *A* and *B*.

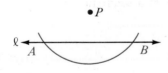

Using *A* and *B* as centers, and keeping the same opening, draw two arcs intersecting at *Q*.

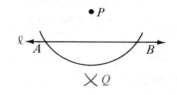

Draw $\overleftrightarrow{PQ}$.

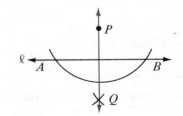

Conclusion: $\overleftrightarrow{PQ} \perp l$

The construction above involves a perpendicular from a point not on the line. You can also construct a perpendicular through a point on a given line.

┌─Construction   A line perpendicular to a given line through a point on ────┐
                       the line

Given: Line *l* and point *P* on *l*
Construct: $\overleftrightarrow{QP} \perp l$

Draw an arc with center *P* intersecting *l* at *A* and *B*.	Using *A* and *B* as centers, and keeping the same opening, draw two arcs intersecting at *Q*.	Draw $\overleftrightarrow{QP}$.
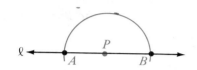	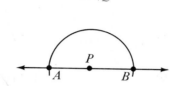	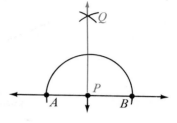

Conclusion: $\overleftrightarrow{QP} \perp l$

It seems reasonable to conclude that there is exactly one line through any given point which is perpendicular to a given line.

┌─ Postulate 12   For a given point and a line in a plane, there is exactly ─┐
                      one line through the point which is perpendicular to
                      the given line.

In the construction above and the one on page 48, $\overleftrightarrow{QP}$ is the *perpendicular bisector* of $\overline{AB}$. This means that it both bisects the segment $\overline{AB}$ and is perpendicular to it. You should modify these constructions to complete the following.

┌─Construction   The perpendicular bisector of a segment ────┐
                         (See Exercise 5.)

Example 2 Construct a 45° angle.

Construct $\overleftrightarrow{AO} \perp \overrightarrow{OB}$
Bisect $\angle AOB$.   ▶

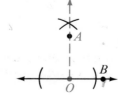   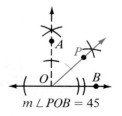

$m\angle POB = 45$

PERPENDICULARS

Example 3 In the given figure, which pairs of rays are perpendicular? Which pairs form a straight angle?

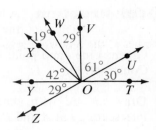

m ∠ZOW = 90
m ∠YOV = 90
m ∠WOU = 90
m ∠ZOU = 180

► $\overrightarrow{OZ} \perp \overrightarrow{OW}$
$\overrightarrow{OY} \perp \overrightarrow{OV}, \overrightarrow{OW} \perp \overrightarrow{OU}$
$\overrightarrow{OZ}$ and $\overrightarrow{OU}$ form a straight angle.

You can fold a piece of paper to form perpendicular edges. Fold any piece of paper and crease it to form a straight edge. Fold this edge at some point back on itself and crease the paper again. You have formed two congruent angles which are a linear pair. You can prove that these must be right angles.

Theorem 2.7 If two lines form congruent adjacent angles, then the lines are perpendicular.

Given: ∠DOA ≅ ∠DOC
Prove: $\overleftrightarrow{DB} \perp \overleftrightarrow{AC}$

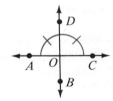

Analysis: Lines are ⊥ if a right angle is formed.

Proof

Statements	Reasons
1. ∠DOA ≅ ∠DOC	1. Given
2. m ∠DOA = m ∠DOC	2. Definition of congruent angles
3. m ∠DOA + m ∠DOC = 180	3. Sum of measures of angles with the same vertex on one side of a line and with no interior points in common is 180°
4. m ∠DOA + m ∠DOA = 180	4. Substitution property
5. 2 m ∠DOA = 180	5. Addition
6. m ∠DOA = 90	6. Division property of equality
7. ∠DOA is a right angle	7. Definition of right angle
8. ∴ $\overleftrightarrow{DB} \perp \overleftrightarrow{AC}$	8. Definition of perpendicular

CHAPTER TWO

Oral Exercises

Which of the following appear to be perpendicular?

1.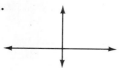
2.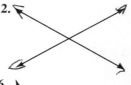
3.
4.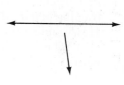

5.
6.
7.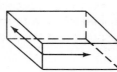
8.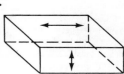

Written Exercises

In each figure, which pairs of rays are perpendicular? Which pairs form a straight angle? (Ex. 1–2)

Ⓐ 1.

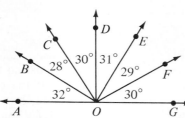

2.

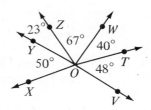

3. Draw a line and a point not on the line. Construct a perpendicular to the line through the point.

4. Draw a line. Mark a point on the line. Construct a perpendicular to the line through the point.

5. Draw a segment. Construct its perpendicular bisector.

6. Given: $\angle AOB$ and $\angle BOC$ are complementary.
Prove: $\overrightarrow{OC} \perp \overleftrightarrow{AD}$

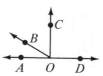

7. Given: $\angle XYT \cong \angle WZV$. $\angle XYT$ and $\angle WZV$ are supplementary.
Prove: $\overrightarrow{ZV} \perp \overleftrightarrow{XW}$

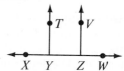

Construct an angle for each of the given measures.

Ⓑ 8. $45°$

9. $135°$

10. $22\frac{1}{2}°$

Draw a picture and write a proof for each of the following.

11. Given: $\overleftrightarrow{AB} \perp \overleftrightarrow{CD}$ intersecting at E
Prove: $\angle AEC \cong \angle AED$

12. Given: $\overleftrightarrow{AB} \perp \overleftrightarrow{CD}$ intersecting at E
Prove: m $\angle AED$ + m $\angle DEB$ = 180

PERPENDICULARS

Applications

Read → Plan → Solve → Interpret

1. A carpenter suspects that her homemade framing square does not show a right angle. How could she use her knowledge of supplementary angles to check this? What experiment could she set up to check the accuracy of the square?

2. A contractor has to pour a concrete floor for a new building. After the fresh concrete is poured in place, it must be leveled and smoothed flat. How can this be done? How can the contractor's knowledge of properties of points, lines, and planes help him?

3. A carpenter must place a post so that it is perpendicular to the floor. If the only tool available is a framing square, how can the job be done accurately? How many measurements with the square are necessary if the floor is perfectly flat?

4. A base has to be made out of the pipes for an outdoor around tabletop. The top does not have to be perfectly level, but should not wobble. The legs can be set in concrete. The top will be a heavy piece of slate resting on the pipes. Which combination of legs shown will guarantee that the table will sit rigidly and not wobble? Why?

2.8 Proving Theorems About Angles

OBJECTIVE ► **To prove and use theorems about angles**

One angle is a supplement of another if their measures total 180°. Suppose that two given angles are each supplements of two congruent angles whose measures are 73°. Each of the two given angles must have a measure of 107° to be a supplement of a 73° angle. If both given angles have a measure of 107°, then they are congruent to each other. This result is generalized in the following theorem.

Theorem 2.8 Supplements of congruent angles are congruent.

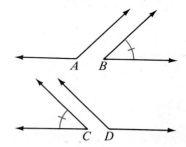

Given: ∠A is a supplement of ∠B,
 ∠D is a supplement of ∠C,
 ∠B ≅ ∠C
Prove: ∠A ≅ ∠D

Proof

Statements	Reasons
1. ∠A is a supplement of ∠B.	1. Given
2. ∠D is a supplement of ∠C.	2. Given
3. m ∠A + m ∠B = 180, m ∠D + m ∠C = 180	3. Definition of supplementary angles
4. m ∠A + m ∠B = m ∠D + m ∠C	4. Substitution property
5. ∠B ≅ ∠C	5. Given
6. m ∠B = m∠C	6. Definition of congruent angles
7. m ∠A = m ∠D	7. Substitution and subtraction properties
8. ∴ ∠A ≅ ∠D	8. Definition of congruent angles

A **corollary** of a theorem is a theorem whose proof requires only a few simple statements in addition to the proof of the original theorem. The statement below is a corollary of Theorem 2.8.

Corollary   Supplements of the same angle are congruent.

Two angles are complements of each other if their measures total 90°. An argument similar to that of Theorem 2.8 can be given to prove that complements of congruent angles are also congruent.

Theorem 2.9   Complements of congruent angles are congruent.

Given: ∠A is a complement of ∠B
∠D is a complement of ∠C
∠B ≅ ∠C
Prove: ∠A ≅ ∠D

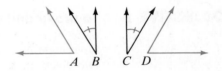

Proof

Statements	Reasons
1. ∠A is a complement of ∠B.	1. Given
2. ∠D is a complement of ∠C.	2. Given
3. m ∠A + m ∠B = 90, m ∠D + m ∠C = 90	3. Definition of complementary angles
4. m ∠A + m ∠B = m ∠D + m ∠C	4. Substitution property
5. ∠B ≅ ∠C	5. Given
6. m ∠B = m ∠C	6. Definition of congruent angles
7. m ∠A = m ∠D	7. Substitution and subtraction properties
8. ∴ ∠A ≅ ∠D	8. Definition of congruent angles

Corollary   Complements of the same angle are congruent.

Example 1

Given: m ∠BOC = 40, m ∠COD = 40,
$\overrightarrow{OC} \perp \overleftrightarrow{AE}$

What conclusion can you
draw about ∠AOB and ∠DOE?

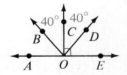

∠AOB ≅ ∠DOE

◄ *Complements of congruent angles are congruent.*

Example 2

Give a reason for each step in the following proof.
Given: m ∠HOI = 40
Prove: ∠GOH ≅ ∠FOI

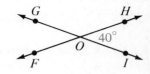

Proof

Statements	Reasons
1. m ∠HOI = 40	1. Given
2. m ∠HOI + m ∠GOH = 180 m ∠HOI + m ∠FOI = 180	2. The sum of the measures of angles with the same vertex on one side of a line is 180°.
3. m ∠GOH = 140 m ∠FOI = 140	3. Substitution and subtraction properties of equality
4. ∴ ∠GOH ≅ ∠FOI	4. Definition of congruent angles

Example 2 suggests the following theorem about vertical angles.

Theorem 2.10 Vertical angles are congruent. ─────────

Given: ∠1 and ∠3 are vertical angles.
Prove: ∠1 ≅ ∠3

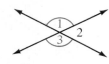

Analysis: ∠1 and ∠3 are both
supplements of ∠2.

Proof

Statements	Reasons
1. ∠1 and ∠3 are vertical angles.	1. Given
2. m ∠1 + m ∠2 = 180 m ∠3 + m ∠2 = 180	2. Sum of measures of angles with the same vertex on one side of a line is 180°.
3. ∠1 is a supplement of ∠2 ∠3 is a supplement of ∠2	3. Definition of supplementary ∠'s
4. ∴ ∠1 ≅ ∠3	4. Supplements of the same angle are congruent.

Theorem 2.10 can sometimes be used to find the measures of vertical angles.

Example 3 Given: m ∠RHM = 3x,
              m ∠AHQ = 4x − 23
              Find m ∠RHM.

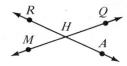

m ∠AHQ = m ∠RHM ◄ *Vertical angles are congruent.*
    4x − 23 = 3x
         x = 23
        3x = 69   **Thus, m ∠RHM = 69.**

Oral Exercises _____

Complete each statement. Give a reason for your answer.

1. ∠DOA ≅ ?   2. ∠HOI ≅ ?   3. ∠JKN ≅ ?

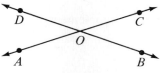
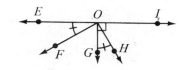
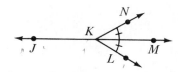

4. m ∠POQ = ?   5. m ∠STV = ?   6. m ∠ZOW = ?

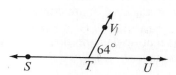
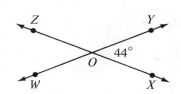

PROVING THEOREMS ABOUT ANGLES

Written Exercises

 1. Given: m $\angle SOP = 5x$, and
   m $\angle ROQ = 4x + 10$
   Find m $\angle SOP$.
3. Given: m $\angle SOR = 7y - 12$, and m $\angle POQ = 5y + 12$
   Find m $\angle SOR$

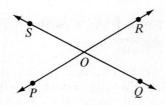

2. Given: m $\angle SOP = 7x + 9$,
   m $\angle ROQ = 8x$
   Find m $\angle ROQ$.
4. Given: m $\angle SOR = 8y + 8$,
   and m $\angle POQ = 10y - 12$
   Find m $\angle POQ$.

What conclusions can you draw about the given angles? (Ex. 5–7)

5. Given: $\angle 1 \cong \angle 4$

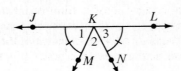

6. Given: $\angle 1 \cong \angle 3$

7. Given: $\angle 1 \cong \angle 4$

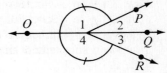

Give a reason for each step in each proof. (Ex. 8–9)

8. Given: $\angle TOP \cong \angle TOQ$
   Prove: $\angle POS \cong \angle QOS$

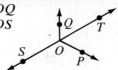

9. Given: $\angle ABD \cong \angle CBF$,
   m $\angle ABD +$ m $\angle DBE = 90$, and
   m $\angle CBF +$ m $\angle FBE = 90$
   Prove: $\angle DBE \cong \angle FBE$

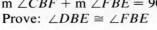

Proof

Statements	Reasons
1. $\angle TOP \cong \angle TOQ$	1. ?
2. m $\angle QOS +$ m $\angle TOQ = 180$	2. ?
3. m $\angle POS +$ m $\angle TOP = 180$	3. ?
4. $\angle QOS$ is a supplement of $\angle TOQ$.	4. ?
5. $\angle POS$ is a supplement of $\angle TOP$.	5. ?
6. $\therefore \angle POS \cong \angle QOS$	6. ?

Proof

Statements	Reasons
1. $\angle ABD \cong \angle CBF$	1. ?
2. m $\angle ABD +$ m $\angle DBE = 90$	2. ?
3. m $\angle CBF +$ m $\angle FBE = 90$	3. ?
4. $\angle ABD$ is a complement of $\angle DBE$.	4. ?
5. $\angle CBF$ is a complement of $\angle FBE$.	5. ?
6. $\therefore \angle DBE \cong \angle FBE$	6. ?

B 10. Given: $\angle 3 \cong \angle 5$
    Prove: $\angle 1 \cong \angle 5$

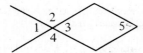

11. Given: $\angle 1 \cong \angle 5$
    Prove: $\angle 2$ is a supplement of $\angle 5$.

Cumulative Review

1. Give an example of the division property of equality.
2. An angle has a measure of 89°. Is the angle an acute angle, a right angle, an obtuse angle, or a straight angle?
3. If the noncommon sides of two adjacent angles are perpendicular, what is the sum of the measures of the two angles?

2.9 Setting Up Proofs

OBJECTIVES ► **To set up a proof from a verbal statement**
To prove theorems

Theorems are statements that can be proved. Before beginning to write a proof for a given theorem, you should draw a diagram, label it, and then restate the theorem in terms of the diagram. The restatement should indicate what is *given* and what is to be *proved*. It should use the specific segments, rays, angles, and other geometric parts from your diagram.

Sometimes the statement of a theorem is written in a general way as a simple declarative sentence. In that case, the subject of the sentence becomes the *Given* and the verb and the remainder of the sentence become the *Prove*. Example 1 shows you how to set up a proof of a theorem stated this way.

Example 1 Draw a labeled diagram. Restate the theorem in terms of the diagram. State what is given and what is to be proved.

The bisectors of two adjacent supplementary angles are perpendicular.

Given: ∠AOC and ∠COB are
supplementary, $\overrightarrow{OD}$
bisects ∠AOC, $\overrightarrow{OE}$
bisects ∠COB.
Prove: $\overrightarrow{OD} \perp \overrightarrow{OE}$

The diagram includes adjacent angles which are supplementary and bisectors which are ⊥.

Sometimes a theorem is written in an "If . . ., then . . ." form. The "if" part of the sentence is the *Given;* the "then" part of the sentence is the *Prove.*

Example 2 Draw a labeled diagram. Restate the theorem in terms of the diagram. State what is given and what is to be proved.

If two congruent angles are supplementary, then they are right angles.

Given: ∠ABC ≅ ∠FED,
∠ABC and ∠FED
are supplementary.
Prove: ∠ABC and
∠FED are right
angles.

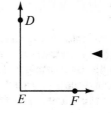

The diagram includes two angles which are congruent and supplementary, and are right angles.

You may find it helpful to write an *analysis* of the proof before you try to prove a theorem. The analysis is a statement of key steps necessary to prove your final outcome. You may wish to list several possible ways of showing this final result. Essentially, in an *analysis* you work backwards from what is to be proved to try to see what will work.

Example 3 Write an analysis for the given theorem.

If two lines are perpendicular, then they form congruent angles.

Analysis: Show that two angles have equal measures.
Measures are equal if both are right angles.

An analysis is provided in many of the proofs in this book.

Written Exercises

Draw a labeled diagram for each of the following. Restate the theorem in terms of the diagram. State what is given and what is to be proved.

 1. If two angles are each congruent to a third angle, then they are congruent to each other.

2. If two segments are each congruent to a third segment, then they are congruent to each other.

3. Supplements of vertical angles are congruent.

4. Complements of vertical angles are congruent.

5. If two angles are adjacent to and supplements of the same angle, then the two angles are vertical angles.

6. If two angles are vertical angles, then they are adjacent to and supplements of the same angle.

Draw a labeled diagram for each of the following. Restate the theorem in terms of the diagram. State what is given and what is to be proved. Write an analysis and prove each theorem.

 7. If the complements of two given angles are congruent, then the supplements of the given angles are also congruent.

8. If the supplements of two given angles are congruent, then the complements of the given angles are also congruent.

9. If two angles are complementary and congruent, then each angle has a measure of 45°.

10. If two lines are perpendicular, then they form congruent adjacent angles.

Cumulative Review

1. Simplify $|3 - 7|$.
2. Is it possible for two planes to intersect in exactly one line?
3. True or false: An angle is a coplanar figure.

2.10 Dihedral Angles

OBJECTIVES ► **To identify and measure dihedral angles**
To recognize perpendicular lines and planes in space

An angle was defined as the union of two rays with a common end point. There are angles in space which share some of the properties of angles in a single plane. These are called *dihedral angles*. Two lines intersect to form four angles; two planes intersect to form four dihedral angles.

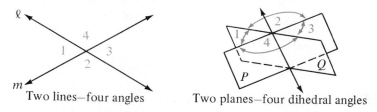

Two lines—four angles   Two planes—four dihedral angles

Each dihedral angle has two faces and an edge. Each face is a half-plane. Each edge is a line.

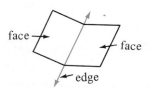

Dihedral angles are named by a point in each face and by the edge.

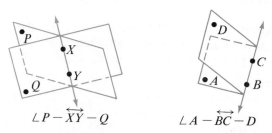

$\angle P - \overleftrightarrow{XY} - Q$ $\angle A - \overleftrightarrow{BC} - D$

It is possible to have *adjacent dihedral angles*. These share a common face and a common edge.

$\angle A - \overleftrightarrow{PQ} - B$ and $\angle B - \overleftrightarrow{PQ} - C$ are adjacent dihedral angles.

Many common objects are models of dihedral angles. Two pages of a book and the inside part of a cake with a slice cut out are two examples.

A dihedral angle is measured by its *plane angles*. A *plane angle* is the union of the two rays, one in each face, which are perpendicular to the edge at the same point.

$\overrightarrow{VU} \perp \overleftrightarrow{VY}$ at V.
$\overrightarrow{XY} \perp \overleftrightarrow{VY}$ at Y.

$\overrightarrow{VW} \perp \overleftrightarrow{VY}$ at V.
$\overrightarrow{YZ} \perp \overleftrightarrow{VY}$ at Y.

Plane angles: $\angle UVW$ and $\angle XYZ$

The following theorem about dihedral angles can be proved. The proof involves some ideas you have not yet studied, so it will not be given here.

┌ **Theorem 2.11**   Any two plane angles of a dihedral angle are con- ┐
                     gruent.
└   ┘

The measure of a dihedral angle is the measure of any one of its plane angles.

Example 1 Given: The measure of plane angle ABC is 130.
Find the measure of plane angle DEF.

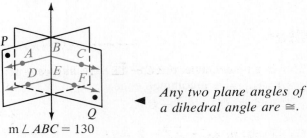

◄ *Any two plane angles of a dihedral angle are $\cong$.*

m $\angle ABC = 130$

Example 2 If $\angle ABC$ is a plane angle of $\angle C - \overleftrightarrow{BE} - D$ and m $\angle ABC = 85$, find the measure of $\angle C - \overleftrightarrow{BE} - D$.

m $\angle C - \overleftrightarrow{BE} - D = 85$ ◄ *The measure of a dihedral angle is the measure of one of its plane angles.*

Definition:
perpendicular
planes

Two *planes* are *perpendicular* if they intersect to form a right dihedral angle.

If plane p is perpendicular to plane q, then any one of the dihedral angles formed is a right dihedral angle. This also means that any of the plane angles formed are right angles.

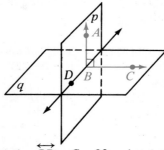

If $p \perp q$, then m $\angle A - \overleftrightarrow{BD} - C = 90$ and m $\angle ABC = 90$

Definition:
line
perpendicular
to a plane

A line is *perpendicular to a plane* if it is perpendicular to all lines in the plane which intersect it.

Later, you will be able to prove that if l is perpendicular to any two lines in plane p, it is perpendicular to all the lines in p that intersect it.

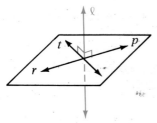

Written Exercises

If $\angle UYV$ is a plane angle of $\angle C - \overleftrightarrow{XZ} - B$, find each of the following: (Ex. 1–8)

1. Given: m $\angle UYV = 82$
   Find m $\angle C - \overleftrightarrow{XZ} - B$.

2. Given: m $\angle TYU = 127$
   Find m $\angle A - \overleftrightarrow{XZ} - C$.

3. Given: m $\angle C - \overleftrightarrow{XZ} - B = 81$
   Find m $\angle UYV$.

4. Given: m $\angle A - \overleftrightarrow{XZ} - C = 149$
   Find m $\angle TYU$.

5. Given: m $\angle UYV = 69$
   Find m $\angle C - \overleftrightarrow{XZ} - A$

6. Given: m $\angle TYU = 132$
   Find m $\angle C - \overleftrightarrow{XZ} - B$

7. Given: m $\angle A - \overleftrightarrow{XZ} - C = 127$
   Find m $\angle UYV$.

8. Given: m $\angle C - \overleftrightarrow{XZ} - B = 59$
   Find m $\angle TYU$.

DIHEDRAL ANGLES

True or false?

 9. Any angle whose sides are contained in the faces of a dihedral angle is a plane angle of the dihedral angle.

10. Any angle whose vertex is on the edge of a dihedral angle is a plane angle of the dihedral angle.

11. The measures of all plane angles of a dihedral angle are equal.

12. Adjacent dihedral angles can have adjacent plane angles.

13. All angles with sides in the faces of a dihedral angle and vertices on its edge are congruent.

14. If a plane is perpendicular to a second plane, then it is perpendicular to every line in the second plane.

If possible give the measure of each angle. If not enough information is given, state what additional information is needed. (Ex. 15–22)

15. Given: m $\angle WOZ = 90$
Find m $\angle W - \overleftrightarrow{AB} - Z$.

16. Given plane $p \perp$ plane q
Find m $\angle ZOF$.

17. Given: plane $\angle ZOX$, and m $\angle ZOX = 90$
Find m $\angle Z - \overrightarrow{AB} - X$.

18. Given: plane $\angle WOZ$, and m $\angle EOZ = 90$
Find m $\angle Z - \overleftrightarrow{AB} - W$.

19. Given: m $\angle EOW = 30$
Find m $\angle WOF$.

20. Given: plane $p \perp$ plane q, and plane $\angle ZOW$
Find m $\angle ZOW$.

21. Given: plane $\angle WOZ$, and $\overleftrightarrow{EF} \perp \overleftrightarrow{ZY}$
Find m $\angle W - \overleftrightarrow{AB} - Z$.

22. Given: plane $\angle WOZ$, and m $\angle W - \overleftrightarrow{AB} - Z = 88$
Find m $\angle ZOX$.

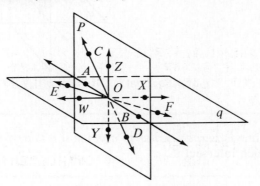

p: contains A, B, C, D, O, Y, Z
q: contains A, B, E, F, O, X, W

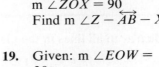
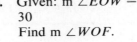
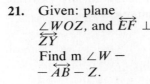

 23. Prove: If a line is perpendicular to a plane, then every plane that contains the line is also perpendicular to the given plane.

Algebra Review

OBJECTIVE ► **To add and subtract polynomials**

To simplify polynomials, combine like terms.

Example   Simplify. $(5x^4 + 3x^2 + 5) - (2x^3 + 2x^2 - x + 3)$
$$5x^4 + 3x^2 + 5 - 2x^3 - 2x^2 + x - 3 = 5x^4 - 2x^3 + x^2 + x + 2$$

Simplify.
1. $(5x^2 + 2x - 1) + (3x^2 - 3x + 4)$
2. $(2x^3 + 5x^2 + 7) + (4x^3 + 3x^2 - 4x)$
3. $(7x^4 + 3x^3 + 4x^2) - (3x^4 - 2x^3 + 2x^2)$
4. $(4x^4 + x^3 + x) - (2x^4 - x^3 - x^2)$
5. $(1 + 3x + x^2) + (2 + 4x + x^3)$
6. $(7 - 2x^2 + x^3) - (3 + 2x + x^3)$

Computer Activities

In geometry, it often is important to derive additional facts from given figures and measures. For example, it is important to decide whether two angles are complementary, supplementary, or neither. In the program below, you will use the IF . . . THEN statement to compare sums of angle measures to 90° and 180°. You will recall that:

> Two angles are *complementary* if the sum of their measures is 90°.
> Two angles are *supplementary* if the sum of their measures is 180°.

See the computer section on p. 560 for more information.

PROGRAM

```
10 PRINT "PROGRAM DETERMINES IF PAIR OF ANGLES IS"
20 PRINT "COMPLEMENTARY, SUPPLEMENTARY, OR NEITHER"
30 PRINT "ENTER MEASURES OF TWO ANGLES"
40 INPUT X, Y
50 LET S = X + Y
60 IF S = 90 THEN 100
70 IF S = 180 THEN 120
80 PRINT "ANGLES ARE NEITHER COMPLEMENTARY NOR SUPPLEMENTARY"
90 GO TO 130
100 PRINT "ANGLES X AND Y ARE COMPLEMENTARY"
110 GO TO 130
120 PRINT "ANGLES X AND Y ARE SUPPLEMENTARY"
130 END
```

Exercises

Type in the program above and run it for the following angle measures. (Ex. 1–4)

1. $m \angle x = 66$ and $m \angle y = 24$

2. $m \angle x = 36$ and $m \angle y = 45$

3. $m \angle x = 112$ and $m \angle y = 68$

4. $m \angle x = 89$ and $m \angle y = 111$

5. Write a program to determine if Angle x is an acute angle, an obtuse angle, or a right angle. For comparison, use IF . . . THEN statements in the program:

6. Write a program to find the missing angle measure, given that the sum of the degree measures of four angles is 180.

Chapter Two Review

Classify each angle as acute, right, obtuse, or straight. [2.1]
1. m $\angle ABC = 57$
2. m $\angle DEF = 180$
3. m $\angle GHI = 90$
4. m $\angle JKL = 179$

Which are measures of complementary angles? Supplementary angles? Neither? [2.2]
5. m $\angle A = 58$, m $\angle B = 42$
6. m $\angle C = 132$, m $\angle D = 48$
7. m $\angle E = 72$, m $\angle F = 18$

Find the degree measure of each angle. [2.2]
8. Its measure is 30° less than that of its complement.
9. Its measure is 100° less than three times the measure of its supplement.

True or false?
10. Vertical angles are congruent. [2.8]
11. Exactly one plane contains two given points. [2.5]
12. All acute angles are congruent. [2.1]
13. All right angles are congruent. [2.7]
14. Three points may be in more than one plane. [2.5]

Find the indicated measure of each angle. [Ex. 15-16]

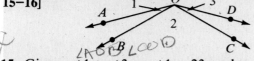

15. Given: $\angle 1 \cong \angle 3$, m $\angle 1 = 23$, and m $\angle 2 = 131$. [2.3]
    Find m $\angle BOD$.
16. Given: $\angle 1 \cong \angle 3$, m $\angle AOC = 137$, and m $\angle 2 = 98$. Find m $\angle 3$.

Vocabulary
acute angle [2.1], adjacent angles [2.1]
complement [2.2], obtuse angle [2.1]
perpendicular [2.7], right angle [2.1]
straight angle [2.1], supplement [2.2]
vertical angles [2.1]

17. Give the reason for each statement in the proof. [2.6, 2.8]
Given: $\angle WXU \cong \angle ZYV$
Prove: $\angle YXU \cong \angle XYV$

Proof

Statements	Reasons
1. m $\angle WXU +$ m $\angle YXU = 180$	1. ?
2. m $\angle ZYV +$ m $\angle XYV = 180$	2. ?
3. $\angle WXU$ is a supp. of $\angle YXU$	3. ?
4. $\angle ZYV$ is a supp. of $\angle XYV$	4. ?
5. $\angle WXU \cong \angle ZYV$	5. ?
6. $\therefore \angle YXU \cong \angle XYV$	6. ?

Construct each of the following (Ex 18-19).
18. A line perpendicular to a given line through a point on the line. [2.7]
19. An angle with a measure of 135°.

Draw a labeled diagram. State what is given and what is to be proved in terms of the diagram. (Ex. 20-21)
20. If the noncommon sides of two adjacent angles are perpendicular, then the angles are complements. [2.2, 2.9]
21. Two intersecting lines are coplanar. [2.5, 2.9]

22. Given: $AB = CD$ [2.6]
    Prove: $AB + BC = CD + BC$
23. Given: $\angle 1 \cong \angle 2$, and $\angle 2 \cong \angle 3$ [2.8]
    Prove: $\angle 1 \cong \angle 3$

24. Prove: Supplements of the same angle are congruent.

Chapter Two Test

Classify each angle as acute, right, obtuse, or straight.

1. m ∠ABC = 87

2. m ∠DEF = 146

Which are measures of complementary angles? supplementary angles? neither?

3. m ∠U = 27, m ∠V = 73

4. m ∠W = 124, m ∠X = 66

5. m ∠Y = 50, m ∠Z = 40

Find the measure of each angle.

6. Its measure is 50° less than its supplement.

7. Its measure is 30° more than twice that of its complement.

True or false?

8. Two lines can intersect in exactly two points.

9. Two planes can intersect in exactly one point.

10. Two angles that are supplements of each other must be a linear pair.

11. Vertical angles cannot be adjacent angles.

12. Perpendicular lines must form four congruent angles.

13. Complementary angles are also adjacent.

Find the indicated measure of each angle. [Ex. 14–15].

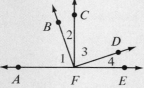

14. Given: $\overrightarrow{FC} \perp \overleftrightarrow{AE}$, m ∠1 = 70, and ∠2 ≅ ∠4
Find m ∠3

15. Given: m ∠AFC = 90, m ∠BFD = 90, and m ∠2 = 20. Find m ∠AFD

16. Give the reason for each statement in the proof.
Given: ∠XOY ≅ ∠YOZ,
∠YOZ ≅ ∠ZOW, and
m ∠XOY = 32

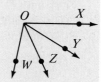

Proof

Statements	Reasons
1. ∠XOY ≅ ∠YOZ	1. ?
2. ∠YOZ ≅ ∠ZOW	2. ?
3. ∠XOY ≅ ∠ZOW	3. ?
4. m ∠XOY = m ∠ZOW	4. ?
5. m ∠XOY = 32	5. ?
6. ∴ m ∠ZOW = 32	6. ?

Construct each of the following. (Ex. 17–18)

17. Draw a line and a point P not on the line. Construct the perpendicular from the point to the line.

18. Construct an angle with a measure of 45°.

19. Draw a labeled diagram for the given statement. State what is given and what is to be proved in terms of the diagram.
If two lines form congruent adjacent angles, then they are perpendicular.

20. Given: $\overrightarrow{OS} \perp \overleftrightarrow{PQ}$, and ∠POR ≅ ∠SOT
Prove: ∠ROS ≅ ∠TOQ

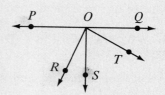

21. Prove: Complements of the same angle are congruent.

College Prep Test

Directions: Choose the one best answer to each question or problem.

1. An angle with a measure of 72.9° is
   (A) acute (B) right (C) obtuse
   (D) straight
   (E) neither of these

2. An obtuse angle could have a measure of
   - I. 89.99°
   - II. 90.001°
   - III. 135°

   (A) I only (B) II only (C) III only
   (D) I and II only
   (E) II and III only

3. If $\angle A$ and $\angle B$ are supplementary, which of the following could be true?
   - I. m $\angle A = 71.4$, m $\angle B = 18.6$
   - II. m $\angle A = 82.4$, m $\angle B = 87.6$
   - III. m $\angle A = 56.2$, m $\angle B = 123.8$

   (A) I only (B) II only
   (C) III only (D) I and II only
   (E) II and III only

4. If m $\angle A = 45$ and m $\angle B = 45$, then
   (A) $\angle A$ and $\angle B$ are complementary.
   (B) $\angle A$ and $\angle B$ are congruent.
   (C) $\angle A$ and $\angle B$ are supplementary.
   (D) $\angle A$ and $\angle B$ are congruent and complementary.
   (E) $\angle A$ and $\angle B$ are congruent and supplementary.

5. If the measure of an angle is 30° less than 4 times that of its supplement, then its measure is
   (A) 66° (B) 75° (C) 138° (D) 165°
   (E) 250°

6. If P is between A and B, and $AP = 7$ and $PB = 12$, then
   (A) $AP - PB = 5$ (B) $AB = 5$
   (C) $AB = 17$ (D) $AB < 17$
   (E) $AB > 17$

7. Two given angles cannot be both
   (A) congruent and complementary.
   (B) congruent and supplementary.
   (C) vertical and congruent.
   (D) adjacent and congruent.
   (E) vertical and adjacent.

8. The intersection of two planes could be
   - I. the empty set.
   - II. a point.
   - III. a line.

   (A) I only (B) II only
   (C) III only (D) I and II only
   (E) I and III only

9. Which of the following are always contained in exactly one plane?
   - I. Any three points
   - II. Two intersecting lines
   - III. A line and a point not on the line

   (A) I only (B) II only
   (C) III only (D) II and III only
   (E) I, II, and III.

10. In the given proof, what is the missing step?
    Given: $\angle 1$ and $\angle 3$ are supplementary
    Prove: $\angle 1 \cong \angle 4$

    Proof:
    1. $\angle 1$ and $\angle 3$ are supplementary
    2. ?
    3. $\therefore \angle 1 \cong \angle 4$

    (A) m $\angle 1 +$ m $\angle 3 = 180$
    (B) m $\angle 1 +$ m $\angle 3 = 90$
    (C) $\angle 1$ and $\angle 2$ are supplementary.
    (D) $\angle 3$ and $\angle 4$ are supplementary.
    (E) m $\angle 1 =$ m $\angle 4$

PARALLELS 3

Famous Mathematicians: Euclid

Euclid was one of the most famous mathematicians of all times. Living in Greece about 300 B.C., he was the first mathematician known to have proved geometric statements in a logical pattern, starting from a few assumptions or postulates.

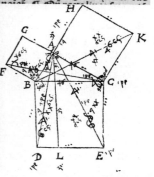

Euclid was a great organizer. He collected and arranged logically essentially all of the important mathematical knowledge of his time. His most famous work is his *Elements*. Many geometry textbooks are based on the *Elements*.

3.1 Parallel and Skew Lines

OBJECTIVES ► To identify parallel lines, rays, and segments
To identify skew lines

Some lines intersect; others do not. Lines that do not intersect may be in the same plane or in different planes.

Definition:
Parallel Lines

> *Parallel lines* are coplanar lines that do not intersect.

$\overleftrightarrow{AB} \parallel \overleftrightarrow{CD}$ means $\overleftrightarrow{AB}$ *is parallel to* $\overleftrightarrow{CD}$. $\overleftrightarrow{EF} \not\parallel \overleftrightarrow{GH}$ means $\overleftrightarrow{EF}$ *is not parallel to* $\overleftrightarrow{GH}$.

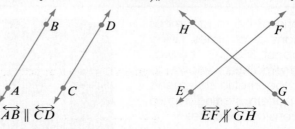

Lines that do not lie in the same plane have a special name.

Definition:
Skew Lines

> *Skew lines* are noncoplanar lines.

Since skew lines are not in the same plane, they cannot intersect. For the same reason, skew lines cannot be parallel. Parallel lines must be *coplanar* lines.

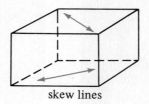

skew lines

Example 1 Which pairs of lines appear to be parallel? Which appear to be skew?

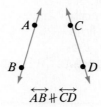

$\overleftrightarrow{AB} \not\parallel \overleftrightarrow{CD}$

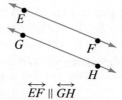

$\overleftrightarrow{EF} \parallel \overleftrightarrow{GH}$

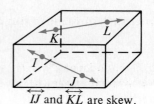

$\overleftrightarrow{IJ}$ and $\overleftrightarrow{KL}$ are skew.

Segments or rays can also be parallel. However, segments or rays that do not intersect are not necessarily parallel. This depends on the lines that contain them.

**Definition:
parallel
segments
and rays**

> *Segments* or *rays* are *parallel* if the lines that contain them are parallel.

Even though $\overline{XY}$ and $\overrightarrow{VW}$ do not intersect, they are not parallel since $\overleftrightarrow{XY}$ and $\overleftrightarrow{VW}$ are not parallel. If $\overleftrightarrow{RS} \parallel \overleftrightarrow{TU}$, then $\overline{RS} \parallel \overline{TU}$.

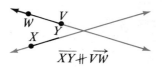

$\overline{XY} \nparallel \overrightarrow{VW}$

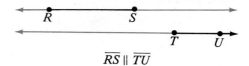

$\overline{RS} \parallel \overline{TU}$

Example 2 Which pairs of segments or rays appear to be parallel?

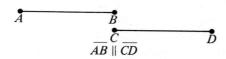

$\overline{AB} \parallel \overline{CD}$

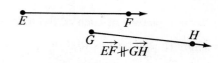

$\overrightarrow{EF} \nparallel \overrightarrow{GH}$

Example 3 True or false? Draw a picture to defend your answer.
Two coplanar rays that do not intersect are parallel.

False $\overrightarrow{AB}$ does not intersect $\overrightarrow{CD}$,
but $\overleftrightarrow{AB}$ does intersect $\overleftrightarrow{CD}$.

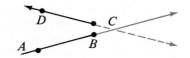

Reading in Geometry

Find a word in this lesson that means each of the following.
1. Lines that are not coplanar.
2. Lines that are coplanar but not parallel.
3. Lines that are both coplanar and nonintersecting.

Explain what each of the following symbols means.
4. ‖   5. ⫲

Find each of the following words in a standard dictionary. Which of the definitions listed for each word applies to this lesson?
6. vertical   7. horizontal

PARALLEL AND SKEW LINES

Oral Exercises

Which pairs of lines, rays, or segments appear to be parallel? Which appear to be skew?

1. 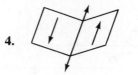   **2.** 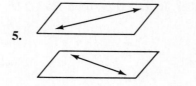   **3.**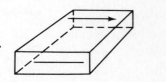

4.   **5.**   **6.**

Written Exercises

Draw a picture of each of the following.

 1. Two lines that do not intersect.

2. Two parallel rays.

3. Two nonintersecting rays that are not parallel.

4. Two nonintersecting lines that are not parallel.

True or false? Draw a picture to defend your answer.

5. Two parallel lines are coplanar.

6. Two coplanar lines are parallel.

7. Skew lines do not intersect.

8. Nonintersecting segments are parallel.

9. Two rays contained in parallel lines are parallel.

10. Two segments contained in parallel rays are parallel.

11. Two segments, that are not skew and that do not intersect are parallel.

12. Two lines that are not skew and that do not intersect are parallel.

Always true, sometimes true, or never true? (Ex. 13–16)

 13. A segment that does not intersect a line is parallel to the line.

14. Two lines parallel to a third line are parallel to each other.

15. Coplanar lines cannot be skew lines.

16. A line parallel to one of two skew lines is parallel to the other.

 17. Define vertical and horizontal lines. Can two vertical lines be parallel? Can two horizontal lines be parallel?

Cumulative Review

1. Draw a figure with an interior and an exterior and whose sides are rays.

2. Draw a segment 20 cm long. Construct its midpoint.

3. Is it possible for the union of two rays to be a line? Why or why not?

3.2 Transversals and Special Angles

OBJECTIVES ► **To identify transversals**
To identify angles formed by lines and their transversals

Line *t* intersects line *l* at *P* and line *m* at *Q*. Line *t* is called a *transversal* of *l* and *m*.

Definition:
transversal

A *transversal* is a line that intersects two or more coplanar lines in two or more distinct points.

Example 1 Is line *t* a transversal? Give a reason for each answer.

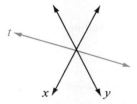

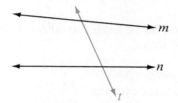

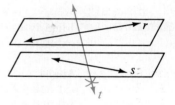

No, line *t* intersects *x* and *y* in one point.

Yes, line *t* intersects *m* and *n* in different points.

No, lines *r* and *s* are not coplanar lines.

Example 2 Identify each transversal in the figure.

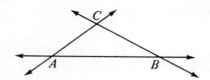

$\overleftrightarrow{AB}$ is a transversal of $\overleftrightarrow{AC}$ and $\overleftrightarrow{BC}$.
$\overleftrightarrow{BC}$ is a transversal of $\overleftrightarrow{AB}$ and $\overleftrightarrow{AC}$.
$\overleftrightarrow{CA}$ is a transversal of $\overleftrightarrow{BC}$ and $\overleftrightarrow{AB}$.

When a transversal intersects two lines, some special pairs of angles are formed.

Special Pairs of Angles
Formed by Two Lines and a Transversal

Alternate Interior Angles	Corresponding Angles	Alternate Exterior Angles

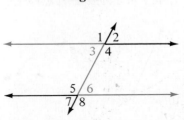 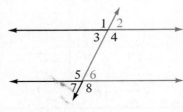 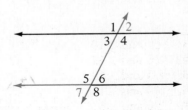

∠3 and ∠6 are alternate interior angles.

Other pair: ∠4 and ∠5

∠2 and ∠6 are corresponding angles.

Other pairs: ∠1 and ∠5, ∠4 and ∠8, ∠3 and ∠7

∠2 and ∠7 are alternate exterior angles.

Other pair: ∠1 and ∠8

Example 3 Identify each given pair of angles as alternate interior, corresponding, alternate exterior, or none of these.

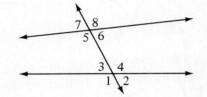

Angles	Answers
∠1 and ∠8	alternate exterior
∠3 and ∠7	corresponding
∠4 and ∠5	alternate interior
∠2 and ∠8	none of these
∠3 and ∠5	none of these

Written Exercises

Identify each transversal in each figure.

Ⓐ **1.**

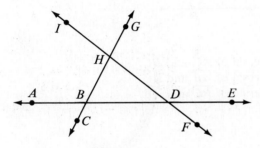

2.

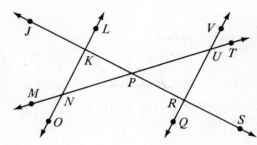

CHAPTER THREE

Identify each given pair of angles as alternate interior, corresponding, alternate exterior, or none of these.

3. ∠2 and ∠4
4. ∠1 and ∠8
5. ∠4 and ∠5
6. ∠1 and ∠5
7. ∠3 and ∠5

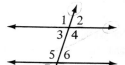

8. ∠2 and ∠7
9. ∠4 and ∠8
10. ∠1 and ∠8
11. ∠1 and ∠5
12. ∠4 and ∠7

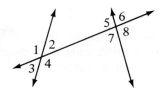

13. ∠1 and ∠10
14. ∠6 and ∠12
15. ∠8 and ∠10
16. ∠4 and ∠11
17. ∠2 and ∠8
18. ∠5 and ∠7

19. ∠1 and ∠6
20. ∠5 and ∠13
21. ∠7 and ∠16
22. ∠8 and ∠14
23. ∠2 and ∠12
24. ∠6 and ∠8

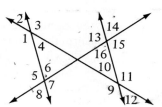

Which of the capital letters listed below contain each of the following?

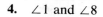 25. A transversal
27. Parallel segments

26. Corresponding angles
28. Alternate interior angles

A E F H K L M N T V W X Y Z

Algebra Review

OBJECTIVE ► **To solve linear equations containing parentheses**

To solve a linear equation containing parentheses:
1) Remove parentheses;   2) combine like terms, and   3) get the variable alone.

Example

Solve $5(x - 3) = 2 - (2 - 2x)$
$5x - 15 = 2 - 2 + 2x$ ◄ $-(2 - 2x) = -1 (2 - 2x) = -2 + 2x$
$5x - 15 = 2x$
$3x = 15$
$x = 5$ **Thus,** the solution is 5.

Solve each equation.

1. $3(x - 1) = x + 7$
2. $4(x + 3) = 2x - 8$
3. $3(x - 1) = 2(x + 4)$
4. $2(2x + 1) = 3(x - 2)$
5. $5x - (2x + 1) = x + 3$
6. $5(2x - 1) - (x + 2) = 2$
7. $3(2x + 3) - 2(x + 4) = 6$
8. $4(3 - 2x) + 2(x + 1) = 5$
9. $3(2 - 3x) - (4 - x) = 6$
10. $\frac{1}{2}(4x + 6) - \frac{2}{3}(6x + 9) = 4$
11. $\frac{2}{3}(9 - 6x) - 2 = \frac{3}{4}(8 - 4x)$
12. $5x - \frac{1}{2}(14 + 2x) = \frac{3}{2}(6x + 6) - x$

3.3 Transversals and Parallel Lines

OBJECTIVES ▶ **To apply the alternate interior angle postulate**
To prove and apply theorems about angles formed by parallel lines and a transversal.

When a transversal intersects two lines, two pairs of alternate interior angles are formed. At the right, line *l* is parallel to line *m*. If you measure the alternate interior angles, ∠*w* and ∠*z*, you will find that m ∠*w* = 57 and m ∠*z* = 57. Thus, ∠*w* and ∠*z* are congruent. Similarly, the alternate interior angles, ∠*x* and ∠*y*, are congruent.

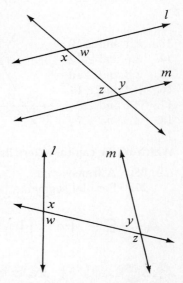

At the right, line *l* is not parallel to line *m*. If you measure the alternate interior angles, ∠*w* and ∠*y*, you will find that m ∠*w* = 77 and m ∠*y* = 62. These angles are not congruent. Similarly, ∠*x* and ∠*z* are not congruent, since their measures are 103° and 118°, respectively.

From your measurements, it appears that the pairs of alternate interior angles are congruent only when the two lines intersected by the transversal are parallel.

Postulate 13 Alternate Interior Angle Postulate

If two parallel lines are intersected by a transversal, then the alternate interior angles are congruent.

You can use Postulate 13 to find the measures of certain angles.

Example 1 Given: *l* ∥ *m*, *r* ∥ *s*, and m ∠1 = 115
Find m ∠2 and m ∠3.

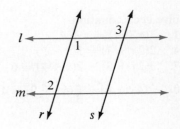

∠1 ≅ ∠2 ◀ *∠1 and ∠2 are alternate interior angles.*
m ∠2 = m ∠1 = 115
∠1 ≅ ∠3 ◀ *∠1 and ∠3 are alternate interior angles.*
m ∠3 = m ∠1 = 115

Thus, m ∠2 = 115 and m ∠3 = 115.

You can use Postulate 13 to show that certain other pairs of angles formed by parallel lines and a transversal are also congruent.

At the right, $l \parallel m$ and m $\angle 1 = 140$. Since $\angle 1$ and $\angle 2$ are alternate interior angles, m $\angle 2 = 140$. Since $\angle 2$ and $\angle 3$ are vertical angles, m $\angle 3 = 140$. Thus, the corresponding angles, $\angle 1$ and $\angle 3$, are congruent. This result is summarized in Theorem 3.1.

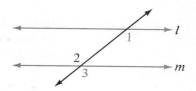

Theorem 3.1 If two parallel lines are intersected by a transversal, then the corresponding angles are congruent.

Given: $\overleftrightarrow{AB} \parallel \overleftrightarrow{CD}$
Prove: $\angle 1 \cong \angle 3$

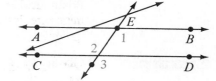

Proof

Statements	Reasons
1. $\overleftrightarrow{AB} \parallel \overleftrightarrow{CD}$	1. Given
2. $\angle 1 \cong \angle 2$	2. Alt. int. $\angle$'s of $\parallel$ lines are $\cong$.
3. $\angle 2 \cong \angle 3$	3. Vert. $\angle$'s are $\cong$.
4. $\therefore \angle 1 \cong \angle 3$	4. Transitive property

In the proof of Theorem 3.1, a previously proved theorem was used as a reason for Step 3. Once a theorem has been proved, it can be used in the proof of another theorem. Abbreviations were also used in writing reasons.

Example 2 Given: $l \parallel m$,
m $\angle 1 = 3x + 15$ and
m $\angle 2 = 2x + 35$
Find m $\angle 1$.

m $\angle 1 =$ m $\angle 2$ ◄ *Corr. $\angle$'s of $\parallel$ lines are $\cong$.*
$3x + 15 = 2x + 35$
$x = 20$

Thus, m $\angle 1 = 3 \cdot 20 + 15$, or 75.

Postulate 13 will be used to prove the next theorem, which states a relationship between the interior angles on the same side of a transversal that intersects two parallel lines.

Theorem 3.2 If two parallel lines are intersected by a transversal, then the interior angles on the same side of the transversal are supplementary.

Given: $l \parallel m$
Prove: $\angle 1$ and $\angle 3$ are supplementary.

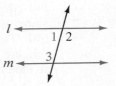

Proof: (See Exercise 13.)

Postulate 13, Theorem 3.1, and Theorem 3.2 can be used to find unknown angle measures and as reasons in other proofs.

Example 3 Given: $\overleftrightarrow{PQ} \parallel \overleftrightarrow{RS}$,
m $\angle y = 4x - 20$, and
m $\angle z = 3x + 25$.
Find m $\angle y$.

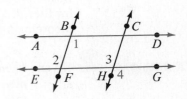

$\begin{aligned} \text{m } \angle y + \text{m } \angle z &= 180 \\ (4x - 20) + (3x + 25) &= 180 \\ 7x + 5 &= 180 \\ 7x &= 175 \\ x &= 25 \end{aligned}$ ◀ *Use Theorem 3.2 and def. of suppl. $\angle$'s.*

Thus, m $\angle y = 4 \cdot 25 - 20$ or 80.

Example 4 Given: $\overleftrightarrow{AD} \parallel \overleftrightarrow{EG}$ and $\overleftrightarrow{BF} \parallel \overleftrightarrow{CH}$
Prove: $\angle 1 \cong \angle 4$

Proof

Statements	Reasons
1. $\overleftrightarrow{AD} \parallel \overleftrightarrow{EG}$ and $\overleftrightarrow{BF} \parallel \overleftrightarrow{CH}$	1. Given
2. $\angle 1 \cong \angle 2$	2. Alt. int. $\angle$'s of $\parallel$ lines are $\cong$.
3. $\angle 2 \cong \angle 3$	3. Corr. $\angle$'s of $\parallel$ lines are $\cong$.
4. $\angle 3 \cong \angle 4$	4. Vertical $\angle$'s are $\cong$.
5. $\therefore \angle 1 \cong \angle 4$	5. Transitive property

You may have to determine if enough information is given to enable you to find the measures of unknown angles. Before a theorem can be used to find such angle measures, you must be sure that all of the conditions of the theorem are satisfied.

Example 5

Based only on the information given, find each indicated angle measure. If not enough information is given, state this fact.

Given: $\overleftrightarrow{AB} \parallel \overleftrightarrow{CD}$ and m $\angle AFG = 102$
Find m $\angle FGD$ and m $\angle FGC$.

Given: m $\angle MPQ = 81$
Find m $\angle PQY$, m $\angle XQR$, and m $\angle OPN$.

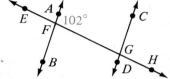
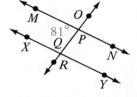

m $\angle FGD = 102$ *The lines are not*   ▶ m $\angle PQY$ — not enough information
m $\angle FGC = 78$ *known to be* ‖.   ▶ m $\angle XQR$ — not enough information
                                                 m $\angle OPN = 81$.

Reading in Geometry

Abbreviations are often used in writing reasons for steps in proofs. Write out in full the statement that each abbreviation represents. Then indicate whether each statement is true or false.

1. Vert. $\angle$'s are $\cong$.

3. Corr. $\angle$'s of ‖ lines are $\cong$.

2. Alt. int. $\angle$'s of ‖ lines are $\cong$.

4. Int. $\angle$'s on same side of transv. are supp.

Written Exercises

Find each indicated angle measure.

Ⓐ **1.** Given: $\overleftrightarrow{AB} \parallel \overleftrightarrow{CD}$ and
m $\angle v = 63$
Find m $\angle w$ and m $\angle z$.

3. Given: $\overleftrightarrow{AB} \parallel \overleftrightarrow{CD}$ and
in $\angle s = 71$
Find m $\angle w$ and m $\angle z$.

5. Given: $\overleftrightarrow{AB} \parallel \overleftrightarrow{CD}$,
m $\angle v = 2x + 10$, and
m $\angle w = 3x - 20$
Find m $\angle v$ and m $\angle w$.

2. Given: $\overleftrightarrow{AB} \parallel \overleftrightarrow{CD}$, and
m $\angle x = 128$
Find m $\angle t$ and m $\angle v$.

4. Given: $\overleftrightarrow{AB} \parallel \overleftrightarrow{CD}$
m $\angle u = 113$
Find m $\angle w$ and m $\angle z$.

6. Given: $\overleftrightarrow{AB} \parallel \overleftrightarrow{CD}$, m $\angle v$
m $\angle v = n$, and
m $\angle x = 5n$.
Find m $\angle v$ and m $\angle x$.

Based only on the information given, find each indicated angle measure. If not enough information is given, state this fact.

7. Given: $\overleftrightarrow{AC} \parallel \overleftrightarrow{DG}$ and m $\angle BEF +$
m $\angle BFE = 158$
Find m $\angle EBF$, m $\angle ABE$ and m $\angle CBF$.

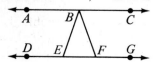

8. Given: $\overleftrightarrow{AD} \parallel \overleftrightarrow{GI}$ and m $\angle EBC = 67$
Find m $\angle EHI$, m $\angle FCD$ and m $\angle GHJ$.

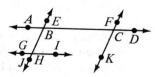

TRANSVERSALS AND PARALLEL LINES

Complete the steps of each given proof. (Ex. 9–10)

9. Given: $\overleftrightarrow{AD} \parallel \overleftrightarrow{EK}$ and $\overleftrightarrow{CG} \parallel \overleftrightarrow{JH}$
   Prove: $\angle ABC \cong \angle EIJ$

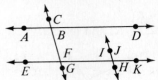

Proof

Statements	Reasons
1. $\overleftrightarrow{AD} \parallel \overleftrightarrow{EK}$ and $\overleftrightarrow{CG} \parallel \overleftrightarrow{JH}$	1. ?
2. $\angle ABC \cong$ $\angle EFC$	2. ?
3. $\angle EFC \cong$?	3. Corr. $\angle$'s of $\parallel$ lines are $\cong$.
4. $\therefore$?	4. ? trans.

10. Given: $\overleftrightarrow{AC} \parallel \overleftrightarrow{DF}$ and $\overleftrightarrow{DF} \parallel \overleftrightarrow{GJ}$
    Prove: m $\angle BEH =$ m $\angle CBE +$ m $\angle EHJ$

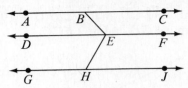

Proof

Statements	Reasons
1. ?	1. Given
2. m $\angle BEH =$ m $\angle BED +$?	2. ?
3. $\angle CBE \cong \angle BED$	3. ?
4. $\angle EHJ \cong$?	4. Alt. int. $\angle$'s of $\parallel$ lines are $\cong$.
5. $\therefore$?	5. Substitution property

B 11. Given: $\overrightarrow{AB} \parallel \overrightarrow{CD} \parallel \overrightarrow{EF}$
   Prove: m $\angle 1 +$ m $\angle 2 +$ m $\angle 3 +$ m $\angle 4 = 360$

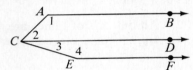

12. Given: $\overleftrightarrow{GI} \parallel \overleftrightarrow{JM}$
    Prove: m $\angle 2 +$ m $\angle 4 +$ m $\angle 5 = 180$

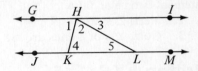

13. Complete the proof of Theorem 3.2.
14. Prove: If two parallel lines are intersected by a transversal, then the alternate exterior angles are congruent.
15. Prove: If a transversal is perpendicular to one of two parallel lines, then it is perpendicular to the other.

Find the measure of each angle using only the information given.

16. Given: $\overleftrightarrow{AB} \parallel \overleftrightarrow{CD}$, m $\angle m = 63$, and $\angle n$ and $\angle q$ are supplementary.

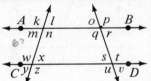

17. Given: $\overleftrightarrow{AB} \parallel \overleftrightarrow{CD}$, m $\angle n = 2a$, m $\angle x = 3a - 10$, m $\angle p = 2b + 15$, and m $\angle t = 3b - 7$.

Contradictory information is given for each figure below. Determine what is contradictory.

C 18. Given: $\overleftrightarrow{AF} \parallel \overleftrightarrow{GM}$, $\angle ABC \cong \angle DEF$, $\angle JBF$ is a supplement of $\angle AEK$, and m $\angle MLK = 88$.

19. Given: $\overrightarrow{AF} \parallel \overleftrightarrow{GM}$, $\overleftrightarrow{CJ} \parallel$ $\overleftrightarrow{DK}$, m $\angle ABC = 48$, m $\angle DLM = 132$, and $\angle AED$ is a complement of $\angle JHM$.

20. Given: $\overrightarrow{BA} \parallel \overrightarrow{CE}$, $\angle 1$ is a complement of $\angle 2$, m $\angle 3 = 48$, and m $\angle 5 = 97$.

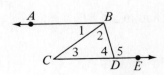

21. Given: $\overrightarrow{BA} \parallel \overrightarrow{CE}$, $\angle 1$ is a complement of $\angle 3$, m $\angle 2 = 42$, and m $\angle 3 = 42$.

CHAPTER THREE

3.4 Proving Lines Parallel

OBJECTIVES ▶ **To form converses of statements**
To prove that certain lines are parallel

Most sentences when turned around have different meanings. "If it is raining, then the streets are wet" does not mean the same thing as "If the streets are wet, then it is raining." The truth of one of these sentences does not guarantee the truth of the other; the two statements just considered are *converses* of each other. The converse of a statement in the "If . . ., then" form is obtained by interchanging the "if" clause with the "then" clause.

Example 1 Write the converse of, "If two lines are parallel, then the alternate interior angles are congruent."

Converse: If the alternate interior angles are ◀ *Interchange the "if"*
congruent, then the two lines are parallel. *and the "then" clauses.*

Example 2 Write the converse of, "If an animal is a dog, then it has four legs." Is the converse true or false?

Converse: If an animal has four legs, then it is a dog. False.

Example 2 shows that the converse of a true statement is not necessarily true. You must deal with the converse as a completely independent statement. Postulate 14 which follows is the converse of Postulate 13 and is an example of a true statement whose converse is true.

Postulate 14 If two lines are intersected by a transversal so that the alternate interior angles are congruent, then the lines are parallel.

Postulate 14 gives you one way to determine if lines are parallel.

Example 3 Tell if each pair of lines is parallel. Give a reason for your answer.

$l \not\parallel m$, Alternate interior ∠'s
are not ≅.

$r \parallel s$, Alternate interior ∠'s
are ≅.

PROVING LINES PARALLEL

You proved that if two parallel lines are intersected by a transversal, then the corresponding angles are congruent. You can use Postulate 14 to prove the converse of this statement.

Theorem 3.3 If two lines are intersected by a transversal so that the corresponding angles are congruent, then the lines are parallel.

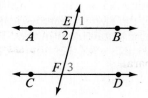

Given: ∠1 ≅ ∠3
Prove: $\overleftrightarrow{AB} \parallel \overleftrightarrow{CD}$

Analysis: Lines are ‖ if alt. int. ∠'s are ≅.

Proof

Statements	Reasons
1. ∠2 ≅ ∠1	1. Vert. ∠'s are ≅.
2. ∠1 ≅ ∠3	2. Given
3. ∠2 ≅ ∠3	3. Transitive property
4. ∴ $\overleftrightarrow{AB} \parallel \overleftrightarrow{CD}$	4. If. alt. int. ∠'s are ≅, then lines are ‖.

In Theorem 3.3, if $\overleftrightarrow{AB}$ and $\overleftrightarrow{CD}$ are both perpendicular to $\overleftrightarrow{EF}$, then the corresponding angles formed are congruent right angles and so the two lines are parallel. This special case of Theorem 3.3 is stated in the following corollary.

Corollary If two coplanar lines are perpendicular to the same line, then they are parallel.

The next theorem is the converse of Theorem 3.2. You can use Theorem 3.3 in its proof.

Theorem 3.4 If two lines are intersected by a transversal so that the interior angles on the same side of the transversal are supplementary, then the lines are parallel. (See Exercise 19.)

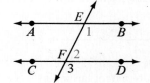

Given: ∠1 and ∠2 are supplementary.
Prove: $\overleftrightarrow{AB} \parallel \overleftrightarrow{CD}$

Analysis: Lines are ‖ if corr. ∠'s are ≅.

Example 4 If m $\angle z = 75$ and m $\angle y = 105$, are lines l and m parallel? Give a reason for your answer.

m $\angle z$ + m $\angle y = 75 + 115$ or 180, and
$\angle z$ and $\angle y$ are supplementary.
$\therefore l \parallel m$ by Theorem 3.4.

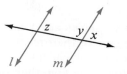

Certain other relationships between special pairs of angles that are formed by intersecting lines can guarantee that the lines are parallel. Example 5 shows that if exterior angles on the same side of a transversal are supplementary, the lines are parallel.

Example 5 Given: $\angle 1$ and $\angle 4$ are supplementary.
Prove: $l \parallel m$

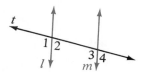

Proof

Statements	Reasons
1. m $\angle 3$ + m $\angle 4 = 180$	1. Sum of meas. of $\angle$'s with same vertex on one side of a line is 180°.
2. $\angle 3$ and $\angle 4$ are supplementary.	2. Def. of suppl. $\angle$'s
3. $\angle 1$ and $\angle 4$ are supplementary.	3. Given
4. $\angle 3 \cong \angle 1$	4. Suppl. of same $\angle$ are $\cong$.
5. $\therefore l \parallel m$	5. If corr. $\angle$'s are $\cong$, then lines are $\parallel$.

Oral Exercises

State the converse of each statement.

1. If Pat and Bobbie practice, then they will become good tennis players.

2. If guitars play, then people dance.
3. If mice appear, then elephants run.

If possible, tell if each pair of lines is parallel.

4.
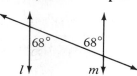

5.
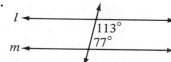

6.
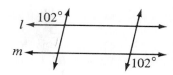

7.
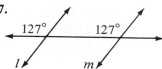

8.
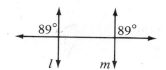

9.
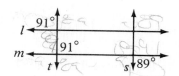

PROVING LINES PARALLEL

Written Exercises _____

Write the converse of each statement. If possible, determine if the converse is true or false.

A 1. If two angles are complementary, then the sum of their measures is 90°.

2. If two lines are perpendicular, then they form a right angle.

3. If two coplanar lines are perpendicular to the same line, then they are parallel.

4. If two lines are intersected by a transversal, then the lines are parallel.

For each of the following, tell which lines or rays are parallel and which angles are congruent. Give a reason for your answer. (Ex. 5-6)

5. Given: $\overrightarrow{BC} \perp \overleftrightarrow{AH}$ and $\overrightarrow{EG} \perp \overleftrightarrow{AH}$

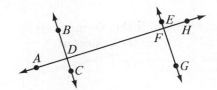

6. Given: $\overrightarrow{BG}$ bisects $\angle ABE$, $\overrightarrow{EH}$ bisects $\angle BEF$, and $\overleftrightarrow{AC} \parallel \overleftrightarrow{DF}$.

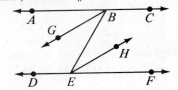

7. Given: $l \parallel m$, and $\angle 1 \cong \angle 4$
   Prove: $t \parallel s$

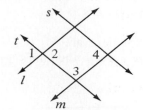

8. Given: $\overrightarrow{FD} \parallel \overrightarrow{CG}$, and $\angle F$ and $\angle C$ are supplements.
   Prove: $\overrightarrow{CA} \parallel \overrightarrow{FE}$

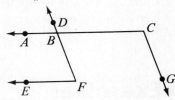

Based on the given information for each of the following, which lines *cannot* be parallel? (Ex. 9-14)

9. m $\angle 2 = 127$, m $\angle 3 = 63$

11. m $\angle 3 = 76$, m $\angle 8 = 114$

13. m $\angle 1 = 111$, m $\angle 5 = 59$

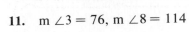

10. m $\angle 3 = 69$, m $\angle 7 = 71$

12. m $\angle 1 = 103$, m $\angle 4 = 105$

14. m $\angle 1 = 123$, m $\angle 8 = 132$

15. Given: $\overline{AB} \parallel \overline{DC}$, and $\angle ADC \cong \angle ABC$.
    Prove: $\overline{BC} \parallel \overline{AD}$

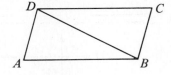

17. Prove Theorem 3.4.

16. Given: $\angle 3 \cong \angle 4$, $\angle 2 \cong \angle 3$, and $\overrightarrow{FJ}$ bisects $\angle IFG$
    Prove: $\overleftrightarrow{EG} \parallel \overleftrightarrow{HK}$

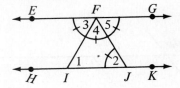

Prove each of the following.

18. If two parallel lines are intersected by a transversal, then the bisectors of a pair of alternate interior angles are parallel.

19. If two parallel lines are intersected by a transversal, then the bisectors of a pair of corresponding angles are parallel.

20. If two lines are intersected by a transversal so that the bisectors of a pair of corresponding angles are parallel, then the lines are parallel.

21. If two lines are intersected by a transversal so that the bisectors of a pair of alternate interior angles are parallel, then the lines are parallel.

A Challenge To You

Below is a scale drawing of a 3 ft-by-4 ft pool table. A ball is shot from corner A along a 45° path, as shown. The ball will eventually drop in the pocket at B.

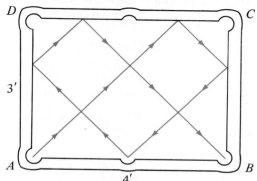

1. Suppose the ball is shot from corner B along a 45° path. Into which pocket will it eventually drop?

Below are scale drawings of pool tables of two different sizes. Assume that a ball is shot from corner A along a 45° path. Into which pocket will it eventually drop? (You may use squared paper to help you decide.)

2.

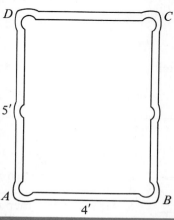

3.

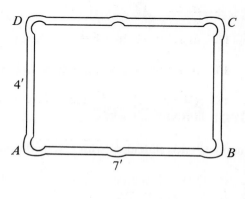

3.5 Using the Parallel Postulate

OBJECTIVE ► **To apply the parallel postulate**

Is it possible for both $\overleftrightarrow{AP}$ and $\overleftrightarrow{BP}$ to be parallel to $\overleftrightarrow{CD}$?

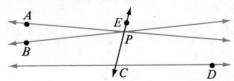

If $\overleftrightarrow{AP} \parallel \overleftrightarrow{CD}$, then $\angle APC \cong \angle PCD$, since parallel lines determine congruent alternate interior angles. If $\overleftrightarrow{BP} \parallel \overleftrightarrow{CD}$, then $\angle BPC \cong \angle PCD$ for the same reason. This means that $\angle APC \cong \angle BPC$. But since B is in the interior of $\angle APC$, $\angle APC$ cannot be congruent to $\angle BPC$. The assumption that $\overleftrightarrow{AP} \parallel \overleftrightarrow{CD}$ results in a conclusion that $\angle APC \cong \angle PCD$ and $\angle APC$ is not congruent to $\angle PCD$. Obviously, this is a contradiction. **Thus, $\overleftrightarrow{AP}$ is not parallel to $\overleftrightarrow{CD}$.**

┌─ **Postulate 15   The Parallel Postulate**   Through a point ─┐
      not on a line, there is exactly one line parallel to the
      given line.
└──┘

Using the parallel postulate, you can determine if certain angle measures are possible or if lines can be parallel.

Example 1 Complete the statement with =, ≠, or "cannot tell."

If $l \parallel n$, and m $\angle y = 130$, then m $\angle z$ _____ 130.

m $\angle z \neq 130$ ◄ $l \not\parallel m$

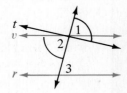

Example 2 Complete the statement with ∥, ∦, or "cannot tell."

If $\angle 1 \not\cong \angle 3$, then v _____ r.

$\angle 2$ could be $\cong$ to $\angle 3$. ► cannot tell

Oral Exercises

Complete each statement with ∥, ∦, or "cannot tell."

1. If $\angle 2 \cong \angle 4$, then r _____ t.
3. If $r \parallel s$, then r _____ t.
5. If $\angle 2 \cong \angle 3$, then r _____ s.

2. If $\angle 1 \cong \angle 4$, then r _____ t.
4. If $r \not\parallel t$, then r _____ s.
6. If $\angle 2 \not\cong \angle 3$, then r _____ s.

Written Exercises _____

Complete each statement with =, ≠, or "cannot tell."

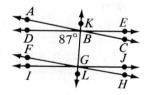

A 1. If $\overleftrightarrow{AC} \parallel \overleftrightarrow{FH}$, and m $\angle DBL =$ 87, then m $\angle KGJ$ _____ 87.

3. If $\overleftrightarrow{AC} \parallel \overleftrightarrow{FH}$, $\overleftrightarrow{DE} \parallel \overleftrightarrow{IJ}$, and m $\angle DBL = 87$, then m $\angle FGL$ _____ 87.

2. If $\overleftrightarrow{DE} \parallel \overleftrightarrow{IJ}$, and m $\angle DBL =$ 87, then m $\angle KGJ$ _____ 87.

4. If $\overleftrightarrow{AC} \parallel \overleftrightarrow{FH}$, $\overleftrightarrow{DE} \parallel \overleftrightarrow{IJ}$, and m $\angle DBL = 87$, then m $\angle FGK$ _____ 93.

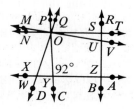

5. If $\overleftrightarrow{NT} \parallel \overleftrightarrow{WA}$, and m $\angle PYA =$ 92, then m $\angle SZA$ _____ 92.

7. If $\overleftrightarrow{NT} \parallel \overleftrightarrow{WA}$, $\overleftrightarrow{PC} \parallel \overleftrightarrow{SB}$ and m $\angle PYA = 92$, then m $\angle VUZ$ _____ 88.

6. If $\overleftrightarrow{PC} \parallel \overleftrightarrow{SB}$, and m $\angle PYA =$ 92, then m $\angle SZW$ _____ 88.

8. If $\overleftrightarrow{MV} \parallel \overleftrightarrow{WA}$, $\overleftrightarrow{PC} \parallel \overleftrightarrow{SB}$, and m $\angle PYA = 92$, then m $\angle VUZ$ _____ 88.

Complete each statement with ∥, ∦, or "cannot tell." (Ex. 9–14)

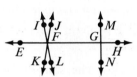

9. If $\overleftrightarrow{IL} \not\parallel \overleftrightarrow{MN}$, then $\overleftrightarrow{JK}$ _____ $\overleftrightarrow{MN}$

11. If $\angle IFH \cong \angle MGH$, then $\overleftrightarrow{IL}$ _____ $\overleftrightarrow{MN}$.

13. If $\angle JFE \cong \angle HGN$, then $\overleftrightarrow{JK}$ _____ $\overleftrightarrow{MN}$.

10. If $\overleftrightarrow{MN} \parallel \overleftrightarrow{JK}$, then $\overleftrightarrow{IL}$ _____ $\overleftrightarrow{MN}$.

12. If $\angle JFH$ and $\angle EGN$ are supplements, then $\overleftrightarrow{JK}$ _____ $\overleftrightarrow{MN}$.

14. If $\overleftrightarrow{JK} \perp \overleftrightarrow{EH}$ and $\overleftrightarrow{MN} \perp \overleftrightarrow{EH}$, then $\overleftrightarrow{JK}$ _____ $\overleftrightarrow{MN}$.

 15. Prove: In a plane, if one of two parallel lines is intersected by a third line, then the second is also intersected by the third line.

16. Prove Postulate 13 using Postulate 15.

A Challenge To You

Some figures can be divided into four parts, all having the same size and shape. One of these is shown. Can you divide the other figures?

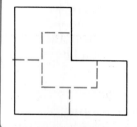

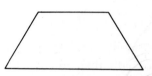

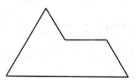

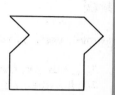

3.6 Measuring Angles in a Triangle

OBJECTIVE ► **To prove and apply the theorem about the sum of the angle measures of a triangle**

You can use the properties of angles formed by parallel lines and a transversal to prove other important theorems.

Suppose that $\overleftrightarrow{CD}$ is parallel to the base $\overline{AB}$ of $\triangle ABC$. If m $\angle A = 61$ and m $\angle B = 46$, then the measure of the third angle of the triangle can be found.

$$\text{m } \angle 1 + \text{m } \angle 2 + \text{m } \angle 3 = 180$$
$$\downarrow \qquad\qquad\qquad \downarrow$$
$$\text{m } \angle A + \text{m } \angle 2 + \text{m } \angle B = 180$$
$$61 + \text{m } \angle 2 + 46 = 180$$
$$\textbf{Thus, m } \angle 2 = 73.$$

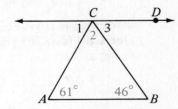

This suggests a proof of one of the most widely used theorems in geometry. The proof of this theorem requires a line which is not part of the original triangle. This line $\overrightarrow{DC}$ is called an *auxiliary* line and is indicated with a dashed line in the figure of the proof.

┌ **Theorem 3.5** The sum of the measures of the angles of a triangle is 180°. ┐

Given: $\triangle ABC$
Prove: m $\angle x +$ m $\angle y +$ m $\angle z = 180$

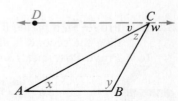

Proof

Statements	Reasons
1. $\triangle ABC$	1. Given
2. Draw $\overrightarrow{DC} \parallel \overline{AB}$.	2. Parallel postulate
3. m $\angle x =$ m $\angle v$	3. Alt. int. $\angle$'s of $\parallel$ lines are $\cong$.
4. m $\angle y =$ m $\angle w$	4. Alt. int. $\angle$'s of $\parallel$ lines are $\cong$.
5. m $\angle v +$ m $\angle z +$ m $\angle w = 180$	5. Sum of meas. of $\angle$'s with the same vertex on one side of a line $= 180°$.
6. $\therefore$ m $\angle x +$ m $\angle y +$ m $\angle z = 180$	6. Substitution

You can use Theorem 3.5 to find unknown angle measures in a triangle.

CHAPTER THREE

Example **1** Find the measure of the third angle of the triangle.

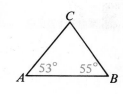

$$53 + 55 + m \angle C = 180$$

Thus, m $\angle C = 72$.

Example **2** Given: m $\angle A = x + 2$, m $\angle B = 3x - 10$, and
m $\angle C = 4x - 4$
Find m $\angle B$ and m $\angle C$.

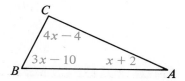

$(x + 2) + (3x - 10) + (4x - 4) = 180$ ◄ *The sum of the measures of all 3 angles is 180°*
$8x - 12 = 180$
$8x = 192$
$x = 24$

Thus, m $\angle B = 3 \cdot 24 - 10$, or 62,
and m $\angle C = 4 \cdot 24 - 4$, or 92.

You can prove the following theorem about the measures of corresponding angles in two triangles, using Theorem 3.5 in the proof.

Theorem 3.6 If two angles of one triangle are congruent to two angles of a second triangle, then the third angles are congruent.

Given: $\triangle ABC$, $\triangle DEF$,
$\angle A \cong \angle D$, and $\angle B \cong \angle E$
Prove: $\angle C \cong \angle F$

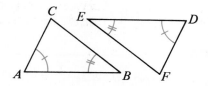

Proof

Statements	Reasons
1. $\triangle ABC$, $\triangle DEF$, $\angle A \cong \angle D$, $\angle B \cong \angle E$	1. Given
2. m $\angle A =$ m $\angle D$, m $\angle B =$ m $\angle E$	2. Def. of $\cong \angle$'s
3. m $\angle A +$ m $\angle B +$ m $\angle C = 180$, m $\angle D +$ m $\angle E +$ m $\angle F = 180$	3. Sum of meas. of $\angle$'s of a $\triangle = 180°$.
4. m $\angle A +$ m $\angle B +$ m $\angle C =$ m $\angle D +$ m $\angle E +$ m $\angle F$	4. Substitution property
5. m $\angle A +$ m $\angle B =$ m $\angle D +$ m $\angle E$	5. Addition property of equality
6. m $\angle C =$ m $\angle F$	6. Subtraction property of equality
7. $\therefore \angle C \cong \angle F$	7. Def. of $\cong \angle$'s

MEASURING ANGLES IN A TRIANGLE

Example 3 Given: $\angle A \cong \angle D$, $\angle G \cong \angle E$
m $\angle GCA = 2x - 30$,
and m $\angle EBD = x + 5$
Find m $\angle GCA$.

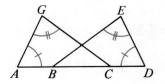

Use Th. 3.6. ► $\angle GCA \cong \angle EBD$
$2x - 30 = x + 5$
$x = 35$

Thus, m $\angle GCA = 2 \cdot 35 - 30$, or 40.

Oral Exercises

Find the measure of the third angle of $\triangle ABC$.

1. m $\angle A = 60$, m $\angle B = 60$, m $\angle C = ?$
3. m $\angle A = 30$, m $\angle B = 60$, m $\angle C = ?$

2. m $\angle A = 45$, m $\angle B = 45$, m $\angle C = ?$
4. m $\angle A = 100$, m $\angle B = 40$, m $\angle C = ?$

Find the measure of the third angle of each triangle.

5.
6.
7.
8.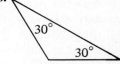

9.
10.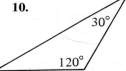
11.
12.

Written Exercises

Find the measure of each angle in $\triangle ABC$. (Ex. 1–4)

Ⓐ 1. m $\angle A = x$
m $\angle B = x$
m $\angle C = 2x$

2. m $\angle A = 2x + 15$
m $\angle B = 3x - 5$
m $\angle C = 4x + 35$

3. m $\angle A = x$
m $\angle B = x + 10$
m $\angle C = x + 20$

4. m $\angle A = 2x + 28$
m $\angle B = x + 13$
m $\angle C = 4x - 15$

5. Given: $\angle A \cong \angle D$, $\angle B \cong \angle E$,
m $\angle C = x$, and m $\angle F = 2x - 30$
Find m $\angle C$.

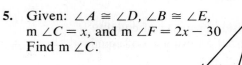

6. Given: $\angle A \cong \angle D$, $\angle C \cong \angle F$,
m $\angle B = 4y + 20$, and m $\angle E = y + 80$
Find m $\angle E$.

7. Given: $\overline{BC} \perp \overline{CA}$
Prove: m $\angle A$ + m $\angle B$ = 90

8. Given: A, C, and E are collinear.
Prove: m $\angle s$ = m $\angle x$ + m $\angle y$

9. Given: $\angle D \cong \angle C$
Prove: $\angle A \cong \angle E$

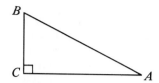

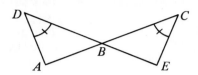

B 10. Given: $\angle A \cong \angle B$
and $\overrightarrow{CD} \perp \overrightarrow{AB}$
Prove: $\overrightarrow{CD}$ bisects $\angle ACB$.

11. Given: $\angle CDE \cong \angle CED$
and $\angle A \cong \angle B$
Prove: $\overline{DE} \parallel \overline{AB}$

12. Given: $\overline{FD} \perp \overline{AB}$
and $\angle A \cong \angle B$
Prove: $\angle F \cong \angle CEF$

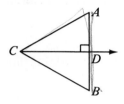

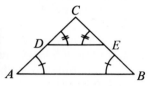

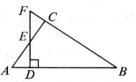

Use the information given to find each indicated angle measure. If not enough information is given, write "too little information."

Given: m $\angle BEG$ = 61 and m $\angle DFB$ = 52
13. Find m $\angle EBF$.
14. Find m $\angle BFG$.
15. Find m $\angle ABE$.

Given: $\overleftrightarrow{AB} \parallel \overleftrightarrow{DE}$, $\overline{BD} \parallel \overline{EC}$, $\overline{EB} \perp \overline{AB}$, and m $\angle BDE$ = 76
16. Find m $\angle DBE$.
17. Find m $\angle ACE$.
18. Find m $\angle ABC$.

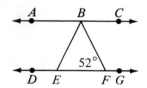

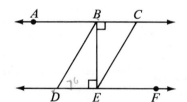

For each figure, determine whether or not contradictory information is given. If so, what information is contradictory?

C 19. Given: $\overleftrightarrow{AC} \not\parallel \overleftrightarrow{FJ}$, m $\angle ABD$ = 27, m $\angle HBK$ = 105, and m $\angle EGJ$ = 48

20. Given: $\overleftrightarrow{AE} \parallel \overleftrightarrow{PM}$, $\overleftrightarrow{CL} \perp \overleftrightarrow{AE}$, $\angle CKM$ is a supplement of $\angle CBE$, m $\angle PKC$ = 92, and m $\angle QGC$ + m $\angle ADQ$ = 180

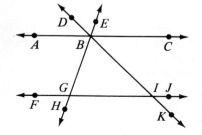

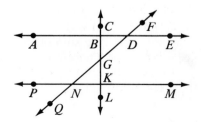

MEASURING ANGLES IN A TRIANGLE

3.7 Indirect Proof

► **To apply the method of indirect proof**

The proofs of almost all of the theorems presented so far have been what are called *direct* proofs. Sometimes, however, a theorem can more easily be proved by an *indirect* proof. In an indirect proof, two possibilities exist. To prove that possibility A is true, you must show that possibility B cannot be true. This leaves possibility A as the only true one.

The following proof of Theorem 3.7 uses an indirect proof. Notice that the proof is written in paragraph form, rather than in the usual two-column format. This often is a more natural approach.

┌─ **Theorem 3.7**   In a plane, two lines parallel to the same line are ─┐
                     parallel to each other.

Given: $\overleftrightarrow{AB} \parallel \overleftrightarrow{EF}$ and $\overleftrightarrow{CD} \parallel \overleftrightarrow{EF}$;
       $\overleftrightarrow{AB}$, $\overleftrightarrow{CD}$, and $\overleftrightarrow{EF}$ are
       coplanar.
Prove: $\overleftrightarrow{AB} \parallel \overleftrightarrow{CD}$

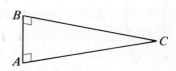

Proof

Suppose that $\overleftrightarrow{AB}$ and $\overleftrightarrow{CD}$ are not parallel. Then they intersect at a point P. But this means that there are two lines through P parallel to $\overleftrightarrow{EF}$. This contradicts postulate 15. Therefore, $\overleftrightarrow{AB}$ and $\overleftrightarrow{CD}$ must be parallel.

Example   Give an indirect proof.
A triangle cannot have two right angles.

Given: $\triangle ABC$
Prove: $\angle A$ and $\angle B$ cannot both be right angles.

Suppose that $\angle A$ and $\angle B$ are both right angles. Then m $\angle A$ + m $\angle B = 180$ and m $\angle A$ + m $\angle B$ + m $\angle C > 180$. This contradicts Theorem 3.5 which states that the sum of the angle measures of a triangle is 180°.
Therefore, $\angle A$ and $\angle B$ cannot both be right angles.

Written **Exercises**

Give an indirect proof of each of the following. (Ex. 1–14)

Ⓐ **1.** Given: $l \nparallel m$
    Prove: $\angle 1 \not\equiv \angle 2$

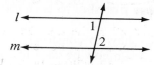

2. Given: $\angle 1 \not\equiv \angle 2$
    Prove: $l \nparallel m$

3. Given: $\angle 3 \not\equiv \angle 4$
    Prove: $t \not\perp s$

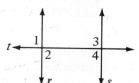

4. Given: $t \not\perp s$
    Prove: $\angle 3 \not\equiv \angle 4$

5. Given: $r \perp t, s \not\perp t$
    Prove: $r \nparallel s$

6. Given: $r \perp t, r \nparallel s$
    Prove: $s \not\perp t$

7. Given: m $\angle 1$ + m $\angle 2$ = 176
    Prove: $l \nparallel m$

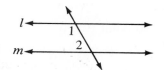

8. Given: $l \nparallel m$
    Prove: m $\angle 1$ + m $\angle 2 \ne$ 180

9. A triangle cannot have more than one obtuse angle.

10. A triangle cannot have both a right angle and an obtuse angle.

11. A triangle cannot have two parallel sides.

12. Skew lines do not intersect.

Ⓑ **13.** Given: $r \parallel s, s \nparallel t$
    Prove: $r \nparallel t$

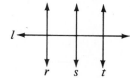

14. Given: $r \parallel s, s \perp l, t \perp l$
    Prove: $r \nparallel l$

Ⓒ **15.** Give an indirect proof of Theorem 3.6.

CALCULATOR ACTIVITIES

1. In $\triangle ABC$, m $\angle A = 26.437°$ and m $\angle B = 48.596°$. Find m $\angle C$.

2. In $\triangle DEF$, m $\angle D = 17.398°$ and m $\angle E = 2 \cdot$ m $\angle D$. Find m $\angle F$.

A Challenge To You

An architect is designing a floor plan as shown with 13 wall sections. By rearranging the rooms to form a square, only twelve wall sections are needed. Design some floor plans including one with five rooms, one with six rooms, one with seven rooms, and one with eight rooms. In each case, each room must share at least one wall section with another room. For each plan, what is the least number and the greatest number of wall sections needed?

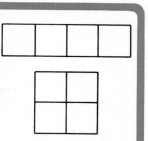

INDIRECT PROOF

3.8 Constructing Parallels

OBJECTIVE ► **To construct a line parallel to a given line**

You learned earlier how to construct an angle congruent to a given angle. A similar construction can now be used to construct a line parallel to a given line, using congruent corresponding angles.

⌐Construction A line parallel to a given line through a point not on ⌐
the given line.

• *P*

Given: line *l* and point *P*
Construct: $\overleftrightarrow{PT} \parallel l$

←————————————→ *l*

Draw $\overleftrightarrow{PQ}$ through any point *Q* on line *l*.

Construct a corresponding angle at *P* congruent to ∠ 1.

Draw $\overleftrightarrow{PT}$

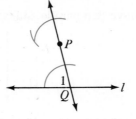
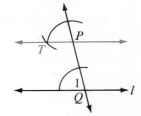

Conclusion: $\overleftrightarrow{PT} \parallel l$

Since both congruent alternate interior angles and congruent corresponding angles assure that two lines will be parallel, you may use either of these to construct parallel lines.

Example 1 Through *A*, construct a line parallel to $\overline{BC}$ by constructing. congruent alternate interior angles.

Use AC as a transversal. ►

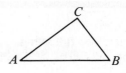

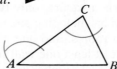

Conclusion: $\overleftrightarrow{AD} \parallel \overline{BC}$

Written **Exercises** _____

1. Construct a line through
A parallel to *l*.

2. Construct a <u>line</u> through
C parallel to $\overline{BD}$.

3. Construct a <u>line</u> through
E parallel to $\overrightarrow{FG}$.

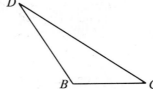

4. Construct $\overleftrightarrow{JK} \parallel \overleftrightarrow{HI}$ and
$\overleftrightarrow{HL} \parallel \overleftrightarrow{JI}$.

5. Construct *M*, the midpoint of $\overline{NO}$. Through *M*,
construct $\overrightarrow{MQ} \parallel \overline{NP}$ and
$\overleftrightarrow{MR} \parallel \overline{OP}$.

6. Construct $\triangle VWX$ such
that $\overline{VW} \parallel \overline{ST}$, $\overline{WX} \parallel \overline{TU}$
and $\overline{XV} \parallel \overline{US}$.

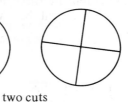

A Challenge To You

A pie can be cut into two pieces with one straight cut. Two straight cuts will
form a minimum of three pieces and a maximum of four pieces. Three straight cuts
will form a minimum of four pieces and a maximum of seven pieces. How many
pieces will there be with four cuts? with five cuts? with *n* cuts?

one cut   two cuts   three cuts

Complete the following:

Number of Cuts	Smallest Number of Pieces	Largest Number of Pieces
1	2	2
2	3	4
3		7
4		
5		
.		
n		

CONSTRUCTING PARALLELS   **93**

3.9 Parallel Planes

To identify true statements about parallel lines and planes
To prove statements about parallel lines and planes

You learned that two given lines can be parallel, intersecting, or skew. Two planes, on the other hand, must be either intersecting or parallel.

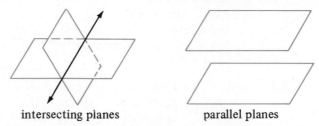

intersecting planes   parallel planes

From Postulate 4, you learned that if two planes intersect, then their intersection must be exactly one line. If they do not intersect, then the planes are parallel.

Definition:
parallel planes

Parallel planes are planes which do not intersect.

There are three possible intersections of a line and a plane.

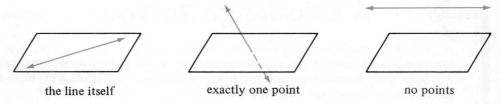

the line itself   exactly one point   no points

If a line and a plane have no points in common, they do not intersect. In this case, the line and the plane are said to be *parallel.*

Definition:
parallel line
and plane

A line and a plane are *parallel* if they do not intersect.

Segments or rays can also be parallel to a plane if the line that contains them is parallel to the plane.

$\overrightarrow{AB} \parallel P$ since $\overleftrightarrow{AB} \parallel P$ $\overline{CD} \nparallel P$ since $\overleftrightarrow{CD} \nparallel P$

Suppose that two parallel planes are intersected by a third plane. The following theorem shows that the intersection consists of two parallel lines. An indirect proof is given.

Theorem 3.8 If two parallel planes are intersected by a third plane, then the lines of intersection are parallel.

Given: plane $p \parallel$ plane q,
        p intersects r in l,
        and q intersects
        r in m.
Prove: $l \parallel m$

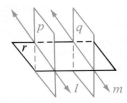

Analysis: use an indirect proof. Show l and m are coplanar and cannot intersect.

Proof

I. l and m are coplanar since both are in plane r.

II. Either l and m intersect at some point, call it A, or they do not intersect.
Suppose that they do intersect.
Since A is on l, then A is in plane p.
Since A is on m, then A is in plane q.
If A is in both planes p and q, then p and q are not parallel.
But p and q were given to be parallel.
Thus, l and m do not intersect.

    $\therefore$ $l \parallel m$, by the definition of parallel lines.

You may be able to show that some statements about parallels are not true by finding a *counterexample*. A counterexample is an example which contradicts a predicted result.

Example 1 True or false? Draw a picture to support your answer.
If two lines are parallel, then every plane containing one of the lines is parallel to every plane containing the other line.

False: $l \parallel m$, but $p \nparallel q$.

The diagram is a counterexample. ▶

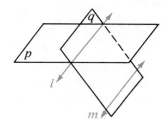

Written Exercises

True or false? Draw a picture to support your answer.

 1. Two planes parallel to the same line are parallel to each other.

2. Two lines parallel to the same plane are parallel to each other.

3. Two planes perpendicular to the same line are parallel to each other.

4. Two lines perpendicular to the same plane are parallel to each other.

5. Two planes parallel to the same plane are parallel to each other.

6. Two planes perpendicular to the same plane are parallel to each other.

7. A plane parallel to one of two intersecting planes intersects the other plane.

8. Two lines in space parallel to a third line are parallel to each other.

Find a counterexample of each of the following statements. Draw a picture to illustrate. (Ex. 9–12)

 9. A plane and a line parallel to the same line are parallel to each other.

10. A line parallel to a plane is parallel to a line contained in the plane.

11. A line in one of two parallel planes is parallel to a line in the second plane.

12. A line parallel to a second line is parallel to a plane containing the second line.

13. Given: plane $p \parallel$ plane q, and line l on q
Prove: $l \parallel p$

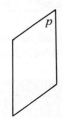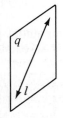

14. Given: line $l \parallel$ plane q, l on plane p, and p intersects q at line t.
Prove: $l \parallel t$

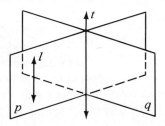

Give an indirect proof of each of the following. (Ex. 15–18)

 15. If a line intersects a plane in exactly one point, then it is not parallel to any line contained in the plane.

16. There is exactly one plane that contains a given point parallel to a second plane not containing the point.

17. If a plane intersects one of two given parallel planes, then it intersects the second of the two planes.

18. If two lines in two different planes intersect, then the planes that contain the lines intersect.

19. Skew lines were defined. Is there a need to define skew planes? why or why not?

Applications

Read → Plan → Solve → Interpret

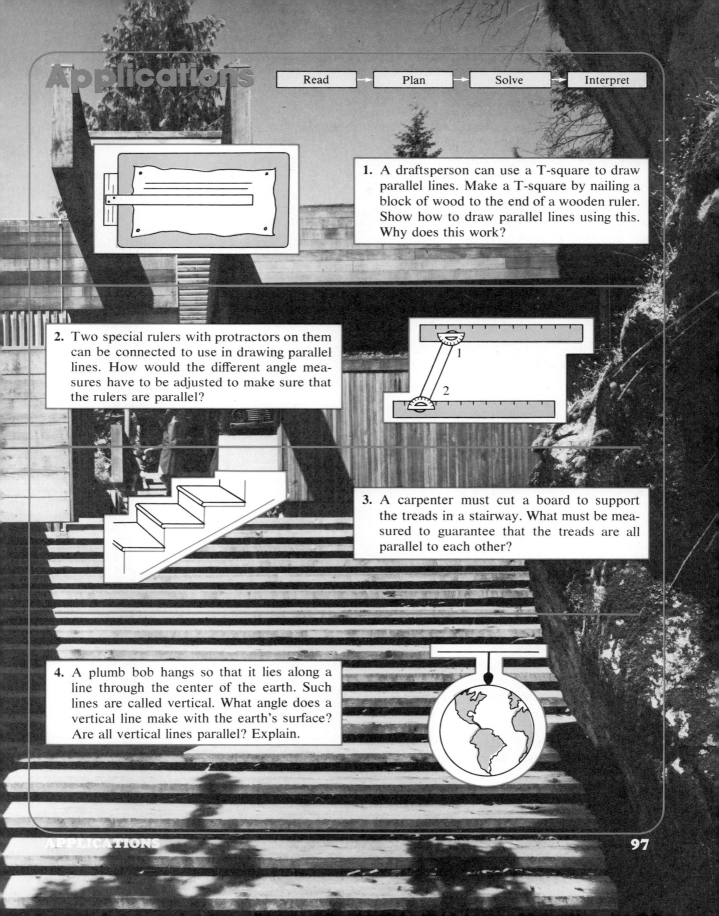

1. A draftsperson can use a T-square to draw parallel lines. Make a T-square by nailing a block of wood to the end of a wooden ruler. Show how to draw parallel lines using this. Why does this work?

2. Two special rulers with protractors on them can be connected to use in drawing parallel lines. How would the different angle measures have to be adjusted to make sure that the rulers are parallel?

3. A carpenter must cut a board to support the treads in a stairway. What must be measured to guarantee that the treads are all parallel to each other?

4. A plumb bob hangs so that it lies along a line through the center of the earth. Such lines are called vertical. What angle does a vertical line make with the earth's surface? Are all vertical lines parallel? Explain.

APPLICATIONS

97

Chapter Three Review

1. In the figure below, $l \parallel m$ and m $\angle 3 = 60$. [3.3]
   Find m $\angle 9$ and m $\angle 8$.

2. In the figure below, $l \parallel m$, m $\angle 2 = 145$, and $\angle 4 \cong \angle 6$.
   Find m $\angle 5$.

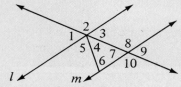

3. In the figure above, $l \parallel m$, m $\angle 1 = 5x - 5$, and m $\angle 7 = 4x + 4$.
   Find m $\angle 1$.

4. In the figure above, $l \parallel m$, m $\angle 3 = 6x + 3$, and m $\angle 10 = 10x - 15$.   Find m $\angle 8$.

Based only on the given information, which lines in the figure are parallel?   [3.4]

5. $\angle KIJ$ and $\angle JLK$ are supplementary.

6. m $\angle JIK = 120$, m $\angle IKL = 60$, m $\angle IJG = 120$.

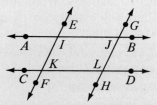

Write the converse of each statement. (Ex. 7–8)

7. If lines are parallel, then they do not intersect.   [3.4]

8. If two lines are non-coplanar, then they are skew.

9. Draw a line and a point not on the line. Construct a line through the point parallel to the given line using congruent corresponding angles.   [3.8]

10. Repeat the construction in Exercise 9, using congruent alternate interior angles.

Vocabulary

alternate exterior angle [3.2], alternate exterior angle [3.2], auxiliary line [3.6], converse [3.4], corresponding angles [3.2], indirect proof [3.7], parallel lines [3.1], skew lines [3.1], transversal [3.2]

True or false?

11. If two lines intersect so that vertical angles are congruent, then the lines are parallel. [3.1]

12. If two parallel lines are intersected by a transversal, then interior angles on the same side of the transversal are complementary. [3.3]

Complete each statement with $\parallel$, $\nparallel$, or cannot tell. (Ex. 13–14)   [3.5]

13. If $\overleftrightarrow{AD} \parallel \overleftrightarrow{EG}$ then $\overleftrightarrow{AD}$ _____ $\overleftrightarrow{HI}$.

14. If $\overleftrightarrow{AD} \perp \overleftrightarrow{CJ}$ and $\overleftrightarrow{EG} \perp \overleftrightarrow{CJ}$, then $\overleftrightarrow{AD}$ _____ $\overleftrightarrow{EG}$.

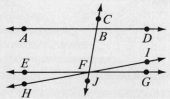

15. Give an indirect proof: A triangle cannot have both a right angle and an obtuse angle.

[3.7]

*16. Given: $\angle 2 \cong \angle 5$, $\angle 1 \cong \angle 4$
   Prove: $\overleftrightarrow{PL} \parallel \overrightarrow{ON}$

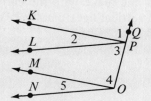

Chapter Three Test

1. In the figure below, $\overleftrightarrow{AC} \parallel \overleftrightarrow{FI}$, m $\angle FGE = 105$, and m $\angle HBC = 68$.
   Find m $\angle JBK$ and m $\angle GHB$.

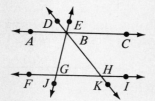

2. In the figure above, $\overleftrightarrow{AC} \parallel \overleftrightarrow{FI}$, $\overrightarrow{BK}$ bisects $\angle CBJ$, and m $\angle BGI = 80$.
   Find m $\angle CBK$ and m $\angle JBK$.

3. In the figure below, $\overleftrightarrow{AB} \parallel \overleftrightarrow{CD}$, m $\angle v = 105$, m $\angle z = 20$
   Find m $\angle y$

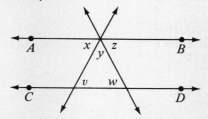

4. In the figure above, $\overleftrightarrow{AB} \parallel \overleftrightarrow{CD}$, m $\angle v = 9t - 1$, m $\angle y = 1 + 6t$, and m $\angle w = 9 + 4t$.
   Find m $\angle z$.

5. Write the converse of "If lines are coplanar, then they are parallel."

6. Draw a line and a point not on the line. Construct a line through the point parallel to the given line.

True or false? (Ex. 7–13)

7. Any two lines that are not parallel are skew lines.

8. Any two coplanar segments that do not intersect are parallel.

9. If two lines are intersected by a transveral so that alternate interior angles are congruent, then the lines are parallel.

10. The sums of the measures of the angles of two triangles are equal.

11. Any two noncoplanar lines are skew lines.

12. If two lines are not parallel to a third line, then they are not parallel to each other.

13. Through point P not on line l, there are many lines parallel to l.

14. Prove: The sum of the measures of the angles of a triangle is 180.

15. Give an indirect proof: A triangle cannot have two obtuse angles.

*16.

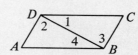

Given: $\overline{AB} \parallel \overline{CD}$, $\angle ADC \cong \angle ABC$.
Prove: $\overline{AD} \parallel \overline{BC}$

Computer Activities

Computers can be used to prove theorems. Computers cannot think! But they can be programmed to make comparisons on which decisions can be made. These decisions can be used in applying geometric proofs. You are familiar with the following theorem.

> If two lines are intersected by a transversal so that corresponding angles are congruent, then the lines are parallel.

The program below proves that the two lines shown are parallel. Notice that the program first decides if the angles are congruent (line 40) and then proves that the lines are parallel.

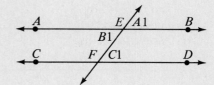

See the computer section on page 560 for more information.

PROGRAM

```
  10 PRINT "PROGRAM PROVES LINES AB AND CD ARE PARALLEL"
  20 PRINT "ENTER ANGLES A1,C1"
  30 INPUT A1, C1
  40 IF A1 = C1 THEN 70
  50 PRINT "ANGLES A1 AND C1 ARE NOT CONGRUENT"
  60 GO TO 160
  70 PRINT "ANGLES A1 AND C1 ARE CONGRUENT"
  80 PRINT "GIVEN"
  90 PRINT "ANGLES A1 AND B1 ARE CONGRUENT"
 100 PRINT "VERTICAL ANGLES ARE CONGRUENT"
 110 PRINT "ANGLES B1 AND C1 ARE CONGRUENT"
 120 PRINT "SUBSTITUTION"
 130 PRINT "LINE AB AND CD ARE PARALLEL"
 140 PRINT "IF ALTERNATE INTERIOR ANGLES ARE"
 150 PRINT "CONGRUENT, THEN LINES ARE PARALLEL"
 160 END
```

Exercises

Type in the program above and run it for the following angle measures. (Ex. 1–2)

1. m $\angle A1 = 40$ and m $\angle C1 = 30$ 2. m $\angle A1 = 30$ and m $\angle C1 = 30$

3. List other ways in which computers can be used for geometric proofs.

4. Write a program to apply the sum of the angle measures theorem for triangles. As INPUT, use the measures of three angles. Prove that the measures can be angle measures in a triangle.

College Prep Test

Directions: For each question, choose the best answer. Indicate your answer by writing the letter of this choice.

1. Parallel lines are
   - I. coplanar
   - II. noncoplanar
   - III. nonintersecting

   (A) I only
   (B) II only
   (C) III only
   (D) I and III only
   (E) II and III only

2.

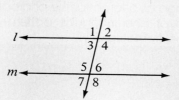

   If $l \parallel m$, then
   - I. $\angle 3 \cong \angle 6$
   - II. $\angle 1 \cong \angle 5$
   - III. $\angle 4$ and $\angle 6$ are supplementary.

   (A) I only
   (B) II only
   (C) III only
   (D) I and II only
   (E) I, II, and III.

3.

   $l \parallel m$ if
   (A) $\angle 3 \cong \angle 5$
   (B) $\angle 2$ and $\angle 6$ are supplementary.
   (C) $\angle 3$ and $\angle 5$ are complementary.
   (D) $\angle 4 \cong \angle 6$
   (E) none of these.

4.

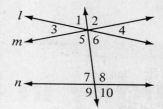

   If $l \parallel n$, then
   - I. $m \nparallel n$
   - II. $\angle 5$ and $\angle 7$ are supplementary.
   - III. $m \angle 3 + m \angle 5 = m \angle 8$

   (A) I only
   (B) II only
   (C) III only
   (D) I and II only
   (E) I and III only

5.

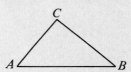

   If $m \angle A = 5x - 5$, $m \angle B = 6x - 2$, and $m \angle C = 7x + 7$, then
   (A) $m \angle A = 10$
   (B) $m \angle A = 20$
   (C) $m \angle A = 58$
   (D) $m \angle A = 77$
   (E) none of these

6. The figure shows the construction of a line through Y parallel to $\overline{XZ}$.

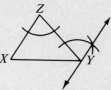

   This construction depends on
   (A) congruent corresponding angles
   (B) congruent vertical angles
   (C) congruent alternate interior angles
   (D) supplementary angles
   (E) none of these.

4 PROVING TRIANGLES CONGRUENT

Rigidity in Structural Design

The Great Pyramid, built more than four thousand years ago as a tomb for the pharoah, still stands in Egypt. The triangular pattern gave the structure extreme rigidity.

Modern buildings must be rigid in their structure. The geodesic dome uses lightweight materials to span large areas. Triangles are a basic part of the rigid framework.

4.1 Classifying Triangles

To classify triangles by the lengths of their sides
To classify triangles by the measures of their angles

A triangle is one of the basic figures studied in geometry.

Definition:
triangle

> A *triangle* is a figure consisting of three segments that have three noncollinear points as their endpoints.

The segments that form the triangle are its **sides** and the endpoints of the segments are its **vertices.**

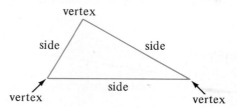

Triangles can be classified in different ways. One method of classification involves the lengths of the sides.

Definitions:
equilateral,
isosceles,
scalene
triangles

> An *equilateral triangle* is a triangle with three congruent sides.
> An *isosceles triangle* is a triangle with at least two congruent sides.
> A *scalene triangle* is a triangle with no congruent sides.

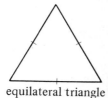 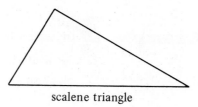

equilateral triangle   isosceles triangle   scalene triangle

Triangles can also be classified by the measures of their angles.

Definitions:
acute, right,
obtuse,
equiangular
triangles

> An *acute triangle* is a triangle with three acute angles.
> A *right triangle* is a triangle with one right angle.
> An *obtuse triangle* is a triangle with one obtuse angle.
> An *equiangular triangle* is a triangle with three congruent angles.

CLASSIFYING TRIANGLES

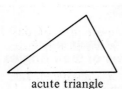
acute triangle

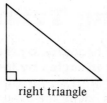
right triangle

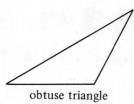
obtuse triangle

An equiangular triangle has three congruent angles. Later, you will prove that an equiangular triangle is also equilateral.

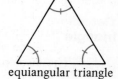
equiangular triangle

Example 1 Classify each triangle by its sides and by its angles.

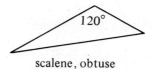
scalene, obtuse

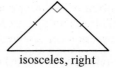
isosceles, right

A given triangle can be classified by both the lengths of its sides and the measures of its angles. However, some combinations of sides and angles are possible, while others are not.

Example 2 Draw a triangle that is both isosceles and obtuse.

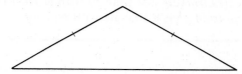

Example 3 Indicate whether the statement is always true, sometimes true, or never true.

An acute triangle is isosceles.

Sometimes true.

Example 4 True or false? Make a sketch to support your answer.

An equiangular triangle is also acute.

True.

Reading in Geometry

A word may mean one thing in geometry and something different in everyday language. Often, its meaning must be determined by analyzing the entire sentence in which it is used.

In each set of sentences below, a nonsense word is used instead of a mathematical word. The same word is used in each sentence in a different way. Find the best word to substitute for the nonsense word.

1. She had a case of *oble* appendicitis.
   His sense of hearing was *oble*.
   The measure of the angle was 96°, so he knew that it was not an *oble* angle.

2. She asked, "What's your *blark?*"
   The measure of the *blark* is 36°.
   You should consider this problem from every *blark*.

3. It was obviously a *bligle* angle.
   The directions said to make a *bligle* turn at Seventh Avenue.
   She knew that her answer was *bligle*.

4. His friends thought that he was rather *isnenck*.
   An *isnenck* triangle cannot be equilateral.
   It was an *isnenck* sound.

Oral Exercises

Classify each triangle by its sides.

1. 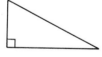 2.   3.   4.

Classify each triangle by its angles.

5.   6. 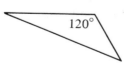 7.  8.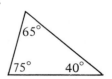

Written Exercises

Draw a triangle with the indicated properties.

 1. Both obtuse and scalene
3. Both acute and isosceles
5. Both acute and scalene

2. Both right and isosceles
4. Both right and scalene
6. Both acute and equilateral

CLASSIFYING TRIANGLES

Indicate whether each statement is always true, sometimes true, or never true.

7. An equilateral triangle is isosceles.
8. A scalene triangle is isosceles.
9. A right triangle is equiangular.
10. An equiangular triangle is equilateral.
11. An equilateral triangle is obtuse.
12. An equilateral triangle is equiangular.
13. A right triangle is scalene.
14. A right triangle is obtuse.
15. An isosceles triangle is obtuse.
16. A right triangle is isosceles.

Use the diagram to find each indicated set of triangles.

Suppose that *U* represents all triangles,
 A represents all isosceles triangles,
 B represents all equilateral triangles,
 C represents all right triangles, and
 D represents all scalene triangles.

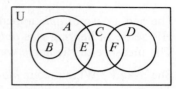

 17. If *E* includes triangles that are in both *A* and *C*, which triangles are these?

18. If *F* includes triangles that are in both *C* and *D*, which triangles are these?

19. To which set, or sets, do acute triangles belong?

20. To which set, or sets, do obtuse triangles belong?

 21. Redraw the diagram to show the set of all acute triangles.

22. Redraw the diagram to show the set of all obtuse triangles.

Prove each statement by using an indirect proof.

23. An equiangular triangle is not obtuse.
24. A scalene triangle is not isosceles.

A Challenge To You

The picture below can be drawn without lifting your pencil, retracing any part of the picture, or crossing any part of the picture already drawn. One possible way of doing this is shown at the right of the given picture.

Can each of the following pictures be drawn using the same rules?

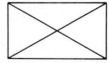   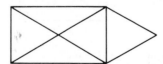   

Make several similar diagrams of your own. Can each of these be drawn under these same conditions? Is there a pattern that will enable you to look at any such picture and immediately tell whether or not it is possible to draw it under these conditions? If so, what is the pattern?

4.2 Exterior Angles and Interior Angles of Triangles

OBJECTIVE ► **To find the measures of exterior and remote interior angles of triangles**

The sides of an angle are rays. However, it often is convenient to think of two sides of a triangle as forming an angle. You will use this interpretation in many theorems about triangles. According to this interpretation, a triangle has three angles. A triangle also has *exterior angles* associated with it.

Definitions:
exterior angle and remote interior angles

An *exterior angle* of a triangle is an angle that is adjacent and supplementary to one of the angles of the triangle.

The other two angles of the triangle are called the *remote interior angles* of the exterior angle.

$\angle YZW$ is an exterior angle of $\triangle XYZ$. $\angle X$ and $\angle Y$ are the remote interior angles of $\angle YZW$.

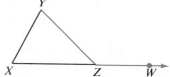

Each triangle has six exterior angles, two at each vertex, as shown in the diagram below. The two exterior angles at each vertex are vertical angles and so they are congruent.

Exterior Angle	Adjacent Angle	Remote Interior Angles
$\angle 1$	$\angle x$	$\angle y$ and $\angle z$
$\angle 2$	$\angle x$	$\angle y$ and $\angle z$
$\angle 3$	$\angle y$	$\angle z$ and $\angle x$
$\angle 4$	$\angle y$	$\angle z$ and $\angle x$
$\angle 5$	$\angle z$	$\angle x$ and $\angle y$
$\angle 6$	$\angle z$	$\angle x$ and $\angle y$

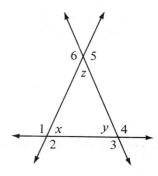

In the picture at the right, you know that m $\angle 1$ + m $\angle B$ + m $\angle A$ = 180.
  m $\angle 1$ = 180 − (124 + 20) or 36.
  m $\angle 2$ = 180 − 36 or 144.
  Thus, m $\angle 2$ = m $\angle A$ + m $\angle B$.

This leads to the following theorem.

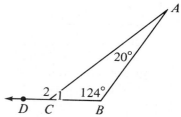

Theorem 4.1 The measure of an exterior angle of a triangle is equal to the sum of the measures of its two remote interior angles. (See Exercise 7.)

You can use this theorem to find the measures of interior and exterior angles of triangles.

Example 1 What is the measure of the exterior angle, $\angle x$?

m $\angle x = 60 + 65$ or 125.

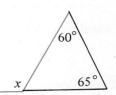

Example 2 Given: m $\angle A = x + 8$,
m $\angle B = 2x + 3$,
m $\angle BCD = 5x - 11$
Find m $\angle BCD$.

m $\angle BCD =$ m $\angle A +$ m $\angle B$
$5x - 11 = (x + 8) + (2x + 3)$ ◄ $\angle BCD$ is an exterior $\angle$.
$5x - 11 = 3x + 11$
$2x = 22$
$x = 11$

Thus, m $\angle BCD = 5(11) - 11$ or 44.

An important corollary to Theorem 4.1 is stated below.

Corollary The measure of an exterior angle of a triangle is greater than the measure of either of its remote interior angles.

Example 3 Complete the sentence with <, =, or >.

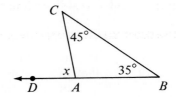

m $\angle x$ _____ 45

m $\angle x$ ___>___ 45

108   **CHAPTER FOUR**

Oral Exercises

What is the measure of each indicated exterior angle?

1.
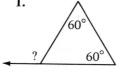

2.
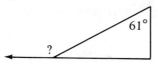

3.
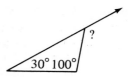

Complete each sentence with <, =, or >.

4. m ∠x _____ 60

5. m ∠y _____ 135

6. m ∠z + m ∠w _____ 45

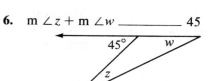

Written Exercises

Find each indicated angle measure.

Ⓐ **1.** Given: m ∠1 = 9x − 15,
m ∠3 = 4x, and
m ∠4 = 3x + 15
Find m ∠1.

3. Given: m ∠1 = 10x,
m ∠3 = 4x + 4, and
m ∠4 = 5x + 7
Find m ∠4.

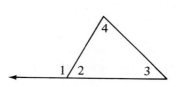

2. Given: m ∠1 = 8x − 6,
m ∠3 = 3x + 4, and
m ∠4 = 4x + 2
Find m ∠3.

4. Given: m ∠1 = 9x + 1,
m ∠3 = 4x − 2, and
m ∠4 = 6x − 7
Find m ∠1.

Prove each of the following.

Ⓑ **5.** Given: ∠A ≅ ∠D and
∠G ≅ ∠E
Prove: ∠1 ≅ ∠4

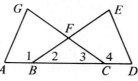

6. Given: ∠1 ≅ ∠4 and
∠G ≅ ∠E
Prove: ∠A ≅ ∠D

7. Prove Theorem 4.1.

Ⓒ **8.** Postulate 12 stated that there is exactly one line through a given point perpendicular to a given line. Using the corollary to Theorem 4.1 *but not Postulate 12,* write an indirect proof for: There is at most one line perpendicular to a given line from a given point.

CALCULATOR ACTIVITIES

1. If m ∠x = 56.493° and m ∠z = 42.398°, find m ∠w.

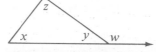

2. If m ∠w = 152.781° and m ∠z = 63.274°, find m ∠x.

4.3 Congruent Triangles

OBJECTIVES ► **To identify congruent triangles**
To find unknown measures in congruent triangles

Congruent segments have the same length, and congruent angles have the same measure. Geometric figures in general are congruent if they have the same size and shape. In triangles, the lengths of the sides determine the size, and the measures of the angles determine the shape. This leads to the following definition.

Definition:
congruent
triangles

> Two triangles are *congruent* if corresponding angles are congruent and corresponding sides are congruent.

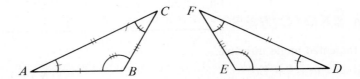

In the diagram above, the markings indicate that the corresponding angles and the corresponding sides are congruent.

Corresponding ∠'s are ≅.

$\angle A \cong \angle D$
$\angle B \cong \angle E$
$\angle C \cong \angle F$

Corresponding sides are ≅.

$\overline{AB} \cong \overline{DE}$
$\overline{BC} \cong \overline{EF}$
$\overline{CA} \cong \overline{FD}$

To indicate that triangle *ABC* is congruent to triangle *DEF*, you will write
$\triangle ABC \cong \triangle DEF$.

Example 1 Using the markings shown, complete the congruence statement.

$\triangle TJR \cong$ _____

Using the diagram,
$\angle T \cong \angle P$
$\angle J \cong \angle C$ and
$\angle R \cong \angle M$

$\overline{TJ} \cong \overline{PC}$
$\overline{JR} \cong \overline{CM}$
$\overline{RT} \cong \overline{MP}$

Thus, $\triangle TJR \cong \underline{\triangle PCM}$.

It is possible to tell from a triangle congruence statement which parts correspond. The order of the letters indicates the corresponding vertices.

$$\triangle ABC \cong \triangle DEF$$

In the statement above, $A \leftrightarrow D$, $B \leftrightarrow E$, and $C \leftrightarrow F$.

Example 2 If $\triangle BDF \cong \triangle XVT$, which angles and which sides are corresponding?

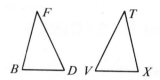

Corresponding angles: $\angle B$ and $\angle X$, $\angle D$ and $\angle V$, $\angle F$ and $\angle T$
Corresponding sides: $\overline{BD}$ and $\overline{XV}$, $\overline{DF}$ and $\overline{VT}$, $\overline{FB}$ and $\overline{TX}$

A special lettering scheme is sometimes used to name the corresponding parts of congruent triangles.

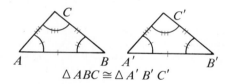

$$\triangle ABC \cong \triangle A'B'C'$$

This is read "Triangle ABC is congruent to triangle A prime B prime C prime." When this lettering scheme is used, it generally means that A corresponds to A', B to B', and C to C'.

Triangles do not have to be turned the same way to be congruent.

Example 3 Using the markings shown, complete the statement $\triangle XYZ \cong$ _____.

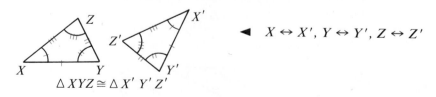

$$\triangle XYZ \cong \triangle X'Y'Z'$$

◄ $X \leftrightarrow X'$, $Y \leftrightarrow Y'$, $Z \leftrightarrow Z'$

Diagrams showing triangle congruences are not always provided. You may have to use given information to find out if two triangles are congruent.

Example 4

Complete the triangle congruence statement using the given information. Draw and label a diagram to show the correspondences.

Given: $\angle S \cong \angle M$, $\angle B \cong \angle X$, $\angle R \cong \angle T$
$\overline{SB} \cong \overline{MX}$, $\overline{BR} \cong \overline{XT}$, and $\overline{RS} \cong \overline{TM}$
$\triangle SBR \cong$ _____

Since $S \leftrightarrow M$, $B \leftrightarrow X$, and $R \leftrightarrow T$,
$\triangle SBR \cong \triangle MXT$.

Oral Exercises

1. Which triangle appears to be congruent to $\triangle ABC$?

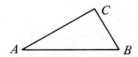 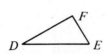 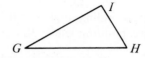 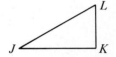

2. Which triangle appears to be congruent to $\triangle GHI$?

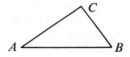 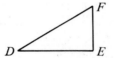  

Written Exercises

Using the markings shown, complete each congruence statement.

 1.

2.

3.

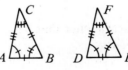

$\triangle ABC \cong$

$\triangle GHI \cong$

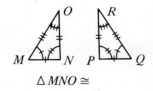

$\triangle MNO \cong$

4.

5.

6.

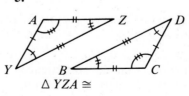

$\triangle STU \cong$

$\triangle YZA \cong$

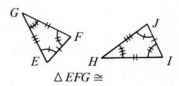

$\triangle EFG \cong$

112

CHAPTER FOUR

Complete each triangle congruence statement.
Draw and label a diagram to show the correspondences.

7. $\angle X \cong \angle X'$
    $\angle Y \cong \angle Y'$
    $\angle Z \cong \angle Z'$
    $\overline{XY} \cong \overline{X'Y'}$
    $\overline{YZ} \cong \overline{Y'Z'}$
    $\overline{ZX} \cong \overline{Z'X'}$
    $\triangle XYZ \cong$ _____

8. $\angle T \cong \angle P$
    $\angle N \cong \angle V$
    $\angle L \cong \angle C$
    $\overline{TN} \cong \overline{PV}$
    $\overline{NL} \cong \overline{VC}$
    $\angle T \cong \overline{CP}$
    $\triangle TNL \cong$ _____

9. $\angle R \cong \angle C$
    $\angle A \cong \angle H$
    $\angle Q \cong \angle W$
    $\overline{RA} \cong \overline{CH}$
    $\overline{AQ} \cong \overline{HW}$
    $\overline{QR} \cong \overline{WC}$
    _____ $\cong \triangle HCW$

Draw a labeled diagram to illustrate each of the following. (EX. 10–12)

10. $\triangle ABC \cong \triangle XYZ$
11. $\triangle EFG \cong \triangle E'F'G'$
12. $\triangle TJH \cong \triangle RXA$

Write two different congruence statements for each pair of isosceles or equilateral triangles shown.

 13.

14.

15.

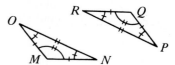

16. Given: $\triangle LVC \cong \triangle MPI$,
     $LV = 3x + 2$ and
     $MP = 5x - 8$
     Find LV.

17. Given: $\triangle LVC \cong \triangle MPI$,
     m $\angle C \cong 3x - 23$, and
     m $\angle I = 2x - 5$
     Find m $\angle I$.

Algebra Review

OBJECTIVE ►   To factor a common monomial from a polynomial

To factor out the greatest common monomial:
(1) Factor out the greatest common whole number factor other than 1.
(2) Factor out the greatest common variable factor, if any.

Example   Factor out the GCF from $10x^3 - 15x$.

$$10x^3 - 15x = 2 \cdot 5 \cdot x^3 - 3 \cdot 5 \cdot x$$
Greatest common number factor: 5   Greatest common variable factor: x
The GCF is $5x$.

Thus, $10x^3 - 15x = 5x(2x^2 - 3)$ ◄   *Distributive property*

Factor out the GCF.
1. $6x^3 - 9x$
2. $5y^4 - 15y^3 + 25y^2$
3. $8z^3 + 12z + 20$
4. $27a^5 + 36a^3 - 18a^2 + 45a$

4.4 SSS Congruence Proofs

OBJECTIVES ► **To prove triangles congruent by the side-side-side correspondence**
To construct triangles using the side-side-side pattern

You know that two triangles are congruent if the corresponding angles and the corresponding sides are congruent. However, it is not necessary to show all six of these congruences to prove that two given triangles are congruent, as you will discover in this lesson and the following lessons.

Take three sticks of different lengths. Connect the ends to form a triangle. Rearrange the three sticks to form as many triangles as possible. Each triangle that you make has the same size and shape as the first one.

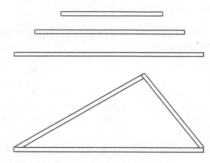

This experiment leads to the following important postulate.

┌─ **Postulate 16** **SSS for ≅ △'s** Two triangles are congruent if ─┐
the three sides of one are congruent to the corresponding sides of the other.

Postulate 16 is often called the "side-side-side" pattern.

Example 1 From the markings, which triangles do you know are congruent?

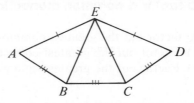

Apply Postulate 16. ► $\overline{AB} \cong \overline{DC}$, $\overline{BE} \cong \overline{CE}$, and $\overline{EA} \cong \overline{ED}$
Thus, $\triangle ABE \cong \triangle DCE$.

Example 2 Write a proper congruence statement for the triangles.
Given: $\overline{XY} \cong \overline{KL}$, $\overline{YZ} \cong \overline{LJ}$,
$\overline{ZX} \cong \overline{JK}$

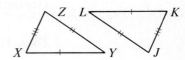

Apply Postulate 16. ► $\triangle XYZ \cong \triangle KLJ$

You can use Postulate 16 in proofs involving congruent triangles.

Example 3 Given: P bisects $\overline{AC}$
P bisects $\overline{DB}$, and
$\overline{AD} \cong \overline{CB}$
Prove: $\triangle ADP \cong \triangle CBP$

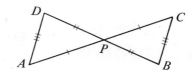

Proof

Statements		Reasons
1. P bisects $\overline{AC}$ and P bisects $\overline{DB}$.		1. Given
2. $\overline{AP} \cong \overline{CP}$	(S)	2. Definition of bisector
3. $\overline{DP} \cong \overline{BP}$	(S)	3. Definition of bisector
4. $\overline{AD} \cong \overline{CB}$	(S)	4. Given
5. $\therefore \triangle ADP \cong \triangle CBP$		5. SSS for $\cong \triangle$'s

Using Postulate 16, you can construct a triangle congruent to a given triangle. (See Exercises 9 and 10.) The construction below shows you how to construct a triangle with sides congruent to three given segments.

┌**Construction   A triangle, given segments congruent to the sides**─┐

Given: $\overline{AB}$, $\overline{CD}$, and $\overline{EF}$
Construct: $\triangle A'B'C'$ with sides
congruent to $\overline{AB}$, $\overline{CD}$, and $\overline{EF}$

A ————————— B
C ——————— D
E ——————— F

Strategy: Copy the three segments, joining each pair at a common endpoint.

Construct $\overline{A'B'} \cong \overline{AB}$.

Using center A' and radius $\cong \overline{CD}$, draw an arc.
Using center B' and radius $\cong \overline{EF}$, draw another arc.

Draw $\overline{A'C'}$ and $\overline{B'C'}$.

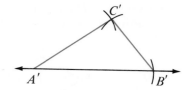

Conclusion: $\triangle A'B'C'$ is the desired triangle.

Oral Exercises _____

Using the markings shown, which of the following pairs of triangles are congruent?

1.

2.

3.

SSS CONGRUENCE PROOFS

4.   **5.**   **6.**

Written Exercises

Write a proper congruence statement for the triangles.

Ⓐ **1.** Given: $\overline{AB} \cong \overline{DE}$, $\overline{BC} \cong \overline{EF}$, and $\overline{CA} \cong \overline{FD}$

2. Given: $\overline{JK} \cong \overline{RS}$, $\overline{KL} \cong \overline{ST}$, and $\overline{LJ} \cong \overline{TR}$

3. Given: $\overline{MN} \cong \overline{HF}$, $\overline{NO} \cong \overline{FG}$, and $\overline{OM} \cong \overline{GH}$

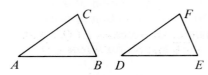 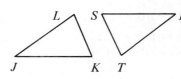 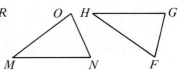

Using the given information, which of the following pairs of triangles are congruent?

4. Given: $\overline{AB} \cong \overline{DE}$, $\overline{BC} \cong \overline{EF}$, and $\overline{CA} \cong \overline{FD}$

5. Given: $\overline{GI} \cong \overline{JL}$, and $\triangle GHI$ and $\triangle JKL$ are isosceles.

6. Given: $\overline{MN} \cong \overline{QP}$, and O bisects $\overline{NQ}$ and $\overline{MP}$.

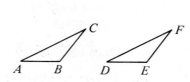   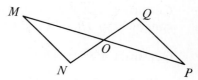

Complete the steps in each proof.

7. Given: $\overline{MP} \cong \overline{ON}$, and $\overline{OP} \cong \overline{MN}$
Prove: $\triangle MNO \cong \triangle OPM$

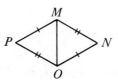

8. Given: $\overline{TR} \cong \overline{SQ}$, U bisects $\overline{TS}$, and U bisects $\overline{RQ}$.
Prove: $\triangle UTR \cong \triangle USQ$

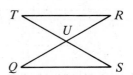

Proof

Statements	Reasons
1. $\overline{MP} \cong \overline{ON}$	1. ?
2. $\overline{OP} \cong \overline{MN}$	2. ?
3. ?	3. Reflexive prop.
4. $\therefore \triangle MNO \cong$?	4. SSS for $\cong$ △'s

Proof

Statements	Reasons
1. $\overline{TR} \cong$?	1. Given
2. ?	2. Given
3. $\overline{TU} \cong$?	3. Def. of bisector
4. $\overline{RU} \cong$?	4. Def. of bisector
5. $\therefore \triangle UTR \cong$	5. ?

Construct a triangle with sides congruent to the given segments. (Ex. 9–10)

9.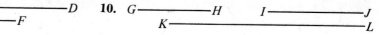

10.

11. Construct a triangle congruent to △*ABC*.

12. Construct a triangle congruent to △*XYZ*.

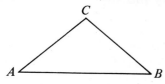

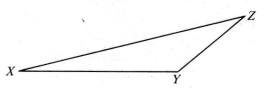

⟨B⟩ 13. Construct an equilateral triangle with sides congruent to $\overline{MN}$.

14. Construct an isosceles △*PQR* with $\overline{PQ} \cong \overline{AB}$ and $\overline{QR} \cong \overline{RP} \cong \overline{CD}$

15. Given: △*ABC* and △*DEF* are equilateral and $\overline{AB} \cong \overline{DE}$.
Prove: △*ABC* ≅ △*DEF*

16. △*GHI* is equilateral, $\overline{GI} \cong \overline{JI}$, $\overline{GH} \cong \overline{JH}$.
Prove: △*JHI* is equilateral.

17. Given: $\overline{KL} \cong \overline{NM}$, $\overline{KQ} \cong \overline{NO}$, and $\overline{QM} \cong \overline{OL}$. Prove: △*KMQ* ≅ △*NLO*

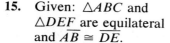

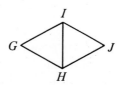

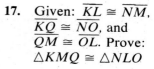

⟨C⟩ 18. Given: $\overline{AB} \cong \overline{DC}$, $\overline{AE} \cong \overline{DF}$, and $\overline{CD} \cong \overline{BF}$
Prove: △*ACE* ≅ △*DBF*

19. Given: $\overline{AD} \cong \overline{CD}$ and $\overline{DB}$ bisects $\overline{AC}$.

Prove: △*ABD* ≅ △*CBD*

20. Given: Equilateral △*XYZ* with *W* the midpoint of $\overline{XY}$
Prove: △*XWZ* ≅ △*YWZ*

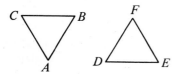

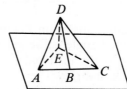

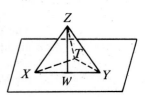

21. Given: △*XYZ*, △*XYW*, △*XWZ*, and △*YZW* are all equilateral.
Prove: △*XYZ* ≅ △*XYW* ≅ and △*XWZ* ≅ △*YZW*

22. Given: Equilateral △*XYZ* and $\overline{XW} \cong \overline{YW} \cong \overline{ZW}$
Prove: △*XWY* ≅ △*YWZ* ≅ △*ZWX*

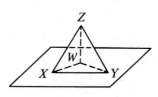

23. Can a triangle be constructed with sides congruent to any three given segments? Why or why not? Give examples to defend your answer.

SSS CONGRUENCE PROOFS

4.5 SAS and ASA Congruence Proofs

OBJECTIVES   ►To construct congruent triangles using the side-angle-side and angle-side-angle patterns
To prove triangles congruent by the side-angle-side and the angle-side-angle correspondences

Two triangles are congruent only if their corresponding angles and sides are congruent. You know, however, that it is possible to prove two triangles congruent by showing that the three corresponding pairs of sides are congruent. There are other ways of proving that two triangles are congruent without showing that all the corresponding parts are congruent.

$\triangle DEF$ below was constructed so that $\overline{DE} \cong \overline{AB}$, $\angle E \cong \angle B$, and $\overline{EF} \cong \overline{BC}$.

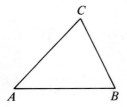
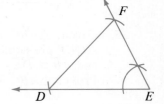

If you were to trace $\triangle DEF$ and fit it on top of $\triangle ABC$, you would see that they both have the same size and shape. This leads to the conclusion that $\triangle ABC \cong \triangle DEF$, which suggests the following postulate.

> **Postulate 17   SAS for $\cong \triangle$'s**   Two triangles are congruent if two sides and the included angle of one are congruent to the corresponding two sides and included angle of the other.

The term "included angle" in Postulate 17 refers to a specific angle of the triangle. The included angle is the angle formed by the two given sides. In the diagram below, $\angle X$ is the included angle of sides $\overline{XZ}$ and $\overline{XY}$. $\angle Q$ is the included angle of sides $\overline{QR}$ and $\overline{QP}$.

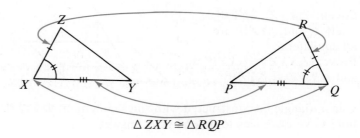

$\triangle ZXY \cong \triangle RQP$

In order to use the side-angle-side congruence postulate, you must be able to identify the appropriate sides and angles.

Example 1 To prove $\triangle ABC \cong \triangle DEF$, which side or angle of $\triangle DEF$ corresponds to the given side or angle of $\triangle ABC$?

Given	Answers
$\overline{CA}$	$\overline{FD}$
$\angle A$	$\angle D$
$\overline{AB}$	$\overline{DE}$

Example 2 Based on the markings shown, are the triangles congruent? If so, write a congruence statement.

Yes, $\triangle XYZ \cong \triangle UTV$. ◄ *Apply Postulate 17.*

A triangle can be constructed congruent to another triangle by another method. This construction involves an angle-side-angle pattern.

Example 3 Given $\triangle ABC$. Construct $\triangle A'B'C'$ so that $\angle A' \cong \angle A$, $\overline{A'B'} \cong \overline{AB}$, and $\angle B' \cong \angle B$.

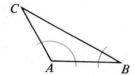

Construct $\overline{A'B'} \cong \overline{AB}$. Construct $\angle PA'B' \cong \angle CAB$. Construct $\angle A'B'C' \cong \angle ABC$.

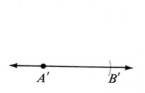 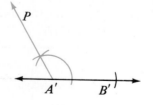 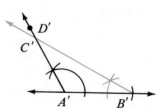

Conclusion: $\triangle A'B'C' \cong \triangle ABC$

In Example 3, if you measure all the angles and sides of $\triangle ABC$ and $\triangle A'B'C'$, you will find that the corresponding angles and sides are congruent.

SAS AND ASA CONGRUENCE PROOFS

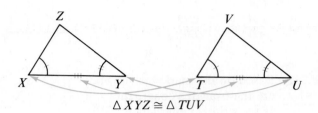

$$\triangle XYZ \cong \triangle TUV$$

The "included side" mentioned in Postulate 18 is the side whose endpoints are the vertices of the two given angles. In $\triangle XYZ$ above, $\overline{XY}$ is the included side of $\angle X$ and $\angle Y$. $\overline{TU}$ is the included side of $\angle T$ and $\angle U$.

To prove triangles congruent, you must first decide which congruence pattern must be used. Once that is determined, you can then complete the proof.

Example 4

Using the given information, mark the congruent parts on the diagram. State which congruence pattern uses the given information.

Given: $\overline{AC} \cong \overline{EC}$,
$\quad\quad\; \overline{BC} \cong \overline{DC}$
$\quad\quad\;$ *Vertical angles are* ≅ ▶

There is a SAS pattern.

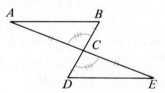

Example 5

Given: $\overline{HI}$ bisects $\angle FHG$, and
$\quad\quad\; \overline{HI} \perp \overline{FG}$.
Prove: $\triangle FIH \cong \triangle GIH$

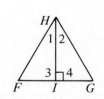

Proof

Statements		Reasons
1. $\overline{HI}$ bisects $\angle FHG$.		1. Given
2. $\angle 1 \cong \angle 2$	(A)	2. Def. of $\angle$ bisector
3. $\overline{HI} \cong \overline{HI}$	(S)	3. Reflexive property
4. $\overline{HI} \perp \overline{FG}$		4. Given
5. $\angle 3 \cong \angle 4$	(A)	5. $\perp$ forms ≅ rt. $\angle$'s.
6. ∴ $\triangle FIH \cong \triangle GIH$		6. ASA for ≅ △'s

Oral Exercises

For each pair of sides of each triangle, identify the included angle.

1.

2.

3.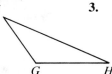

For each pair of angles of each triangle, identify the included side.

5.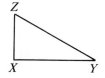

6.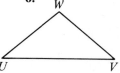

7.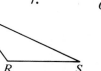

Written Exercises

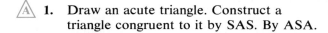

A 1. Draw an acute triangle. Construct a triangle congruent to it by SAS. By ASA.

2. Draw an obtuse triangle. Construct a triangle congruent to it by SAS. By ASA.

Complete each statement.

3. To prove that $\triangle GOP \cong \triangle ERA$ by SAS, you must show that $\overline{PO} \cong$? $\angle O \cong$? and $\overline{OG} \cong$?

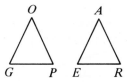

4. To prove that $\triangle OPG \cong \triangle AER$ by ASA, you must show that $\angle G \cong$? $\overline{GO} \cong$? and $\angle O \cong$?

Based on the markings shown, are the triangles congruent? If so, write a congruence statement.

5.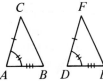

6.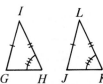

7.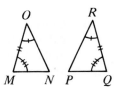

Using the given information, mark the congruent parts on the diagram. State which congruence pattern uses the given information.

8. Given: $\overline{ZY} \perp \overline{XY}$, $\overline{WV} \perp \overline{UV}$, $\angle X \cong \angle U$, and $\overline{XY} \cong \overline{UV}$

9. Given: $\angle C \cong \angle F$, $\overline{AC} \cong \overline{EF}$, and $\overline{BC} \cong \overline{DF}$

10. Given: P bisects $\overline{TR}$ and P bisects $\overline{QS}$.

 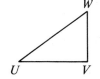 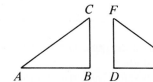

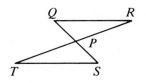

SAS AND ASA CONGRUENCE PROOFS

121

Based on the given information, are the triangles congruent? Why or why not? (Ex. 11–13)

11. Given: $\overline{AB} \cong \overline{ED}$, $\overline{AC} \cong \overline{FE}$, $\overline{CA} \perp \overline{AB}$, and $\overline{FE} \perp \overline{ED}$

12. Given: $\overline{GI} \cong \overline{JL}$, $\angle G \cong \angle J$, and $\angle H \cong \angle K$

13. Given: $\triangle MNO$ and $\triangle QPR$ are right $\triangle$'s, m $\angle m = 31$, m $\angle Q = 31$ and $\overline{MO} \cong \overline{QR}$

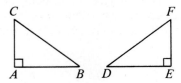 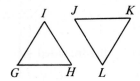 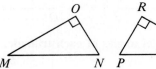 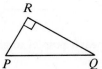

14. Given: $\overline{AE} \cong \overline{CE}$ and $\overline{DE} \cong \overline{BE}$
    Prove: $\triangle ADE \cong \triangle CBE$

15. Given: J bisects $\overline{FG}$, and $\angle F \cong \angle G$.
    Prove: $\triangle FJH \cong \triangle GJI$

16. Given: $\angle KNL \cong \angle MNL$, and $\overline{KN} \cong \overline{MN}$
    Prove: $\triangle KNL \cong \triangle MNL$

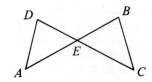 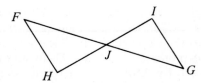 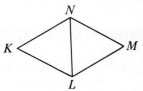

17. Given: $\overline{AC} \cong \overline{BC}$ and $\overline{CD}$ bisects $\angle ACB$.
    Prove: $\triangle ADC \cong \triangle BDC$

18. Given: $\overline{HF} \perp \overline{GE}$, and $\overline{HF}$ bisects $\overline{GE}$.
    Prove: $\triangle GFH \cong \triangle EFH$

19. Given: $\overline{LK} \parallel \overline{IJ}$, and $\overline{LI} \parallel \overline{KJ}$
    Prove: $\triangle LKI \cong \triangle JIK$

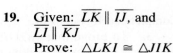 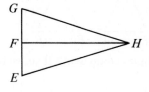 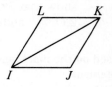

20. Construct a triangle with sides congruent to $\overline{MN}$ and $\overline{OP}$ and the included angle congruent to $\angle Q$.

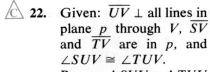 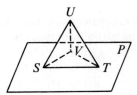

21. Construct a triangle with angles congruent to $\angle Q$ and $\angle R$, and the included side congruent to $\overline{MN}$.

22. Given: $\overline{UV} \perp$ all lines in plane p through V, $\overline{SV}$ and $\overline{TV}$ are in p, and $\angle SUV \cong \angle TUV$.
    Prove: $\triangle SVU \cong \triangle TVU$

23. Given: $\triangle STU$, $\triangle SVU$, $\triangle TVU$, and $\triangle STV$ are all equiangular.
    Prove: $\triangle STU \cong \triangle SVU \cong \triangle TVU \cong \triangle STV$.

Cumulative Review

1. If the measure of one angle of a triangle is 87° and the measure of a second angle is 49°, what is the measure of the third angle?

2. If two parallel lines are intersected by a transversal so that one angle of a pair of corresponding angles has a measure of 67°, what is the measure of the other angle in the pair?

4.6 Other Congruence Proofs

► **To recognize patterns for proving triangles congruent**
To identify congruent triangles and prove them congruent

So far you have used three different patterns to prove triangles congruent: side-side-side, side-angle-side, and angle-side-angle. There are other possibilities that should be considered. One such possibility is an angle-angle-angle pattern.

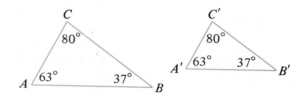

In the two triangles shown, $\angle A \cong \angle A'$, $\angle B \cong \angle B'$, and $\angle C \cong \angle C'$. But $\triangle ABC$ is not congruent to $\triangle A'B'C'$. Although the triangles are the same shape, they obviously are not the same size. The angle-angle-angle correspondence does not guarantee triangle congruence.

Another possibility is a side-side-angle pattern. You can use three sticks to find out if it works. In the diagram below, stick s and stick t form two sides of fixed length and stick t and stick r form a fixed angle. As shown, stick s can be moved so that it meets stick r in two different positions, thus forming two distinct triangles. Even though the lengths of s and t and the measure of the angle are the same in both triangles, the triangles are not congruent. Thus, the side-side-angle correspondence does not guarantee triangle congruence.

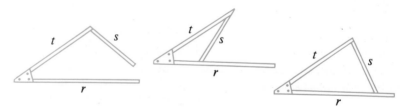

Example 1 Using the markings shown, are the triangles congruent? Why or why not?

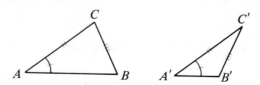

$\triangle ABC \not\cong \triangle A'B'C'$. Side-side-angle is not a triangle congruence pattern.

There is a third possible method for showing that two triangles are congruent: an angle-angle-side pattern. In the two triangles below, $\angle Z \cong \angle B$, $\angle X \cong \angle C$, and $\overline{XY} \cong \overline{CA}$. $\triangle ZXY$ appears to be congruent to $\triangle BCA$.

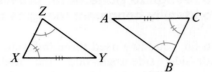

The information given does not fit any congruence pattern already used. The given congruent sides are not the included sides of the given congruent angles. However, since $\angle Z \cong \angle B$ and $\angle A \cong \angle C$, then $\angle Y \cong \angle A$. (See Theorem 3.6.) Now you have an angle-side-angle pattern, which assures you that $\triangle ZXY$ is congruent to $\triangle BCA$. So the AAS pattern does assure triangle congruence. This is stated in the next theorem.

Theorem 4.2 (AAS) Two triangles are congruent if two angles and the side opposite one of them are congruent to the corresponding two angles and side of the other. (See Exercise 19.)

Given: $\angle A \cong \angle A'$, $\angle B \cong \angle B'$, $\overline{BC} \cong \overline{B'C'}$
Prove: $\triangle ABC \cong \triangle A'B'C'$

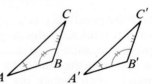

Analysis: Use ASA.

Example 2 Using the markings shown, are the triangles congruent? Why or why not?

No. AAA is not a congruence pattern.

Yes. AAS is a congruence pattern.

Example 3 Based on the given information, is there an ASA, SAS, SSS, AAA, SSA, or AAS correspondence? Are the triangles necessarily congruent?

Given: $\angle Z \cong \angle C$, $\overline{ZY} \cong \overline{CB}$, $\angle Y \cong \angle B$

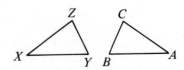

ASA. The triangles are congruent.

You *can* prove triangles congruent by:

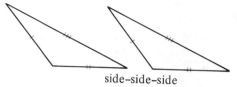

side–side–side

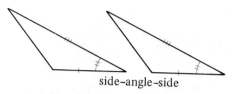

side–angle–side

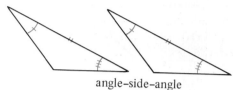

angle–side–angle

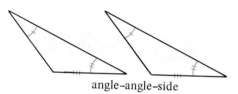

angle–angle–side

You *cannot* prove triangles congruent by:

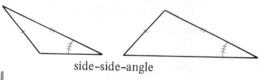

side–side–angle

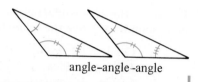

angle–angle–angle

When you are trying to prove that two triangles are congruent, you must decide which congruence pattern fits the information given. To get the necessary congruent sides or angles, you may have to recall previously learned theorems, postulates, definitions, and so forth.

Example 4 Given: $\overline{AB} \cong \overline{ED}$ and
$\overline{DE} \parallel \overline{AB}$
Prove: $\triangle ABC \cong \triangle EDC$

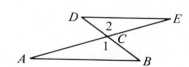

Proof

Statements		Reasons
1. $\overline{DE} \parallel \overline{AB}$		1. Given
2. $\angle A \cong \angle E$	(A)	2. Alt. int. $\angle$'s of $\parallel$ lines are $\cong$.
3. $\angle 1 \cong \angle 2$	(A)	3. Vertical $\angle$'s are $\cong$.
4. $\overline{AB} \cong \overline{ED}$	(S)	4. Given
5. $\therefore \triangle ABC \cong \triangle EDC$		5. AAS

OTHER CONGRUENCE PROOFS

Oral Exercises

Using the markings shown are the triangles congruent? Why or why not?

1.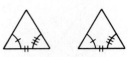

2.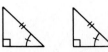

3.

4.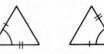

5.

6.

7.

8.

9.

Written Exercises

Based on the given information, is there an ASA, SAS, SSS, SSA, AAA, or AAS correspondence? Are the triangles necessarily congruent?

(A) 1. Given: $\overline{AB} \cong \overline{DE}$, $\overline{BC} \cong \overline{EF}$, and $\angle B \cong \angle E$

2. Given: $\angle C \cong \angle F$, $\angle A \cong \angle D$, and $\overline{BC} \cong \overline{EF}$

3. Given: $\overline{AC} \cong \overline{DF}$, $\overline{AB} \cong \overline{DE}$, and $\angle C \cong \angle F$

4. Given: $\angle A \cong \angle D$, $\angle B \cong \angle E$, and $\angle C \cong \angle F$

5. Given: $\angle A \cong \angle D$, $\overline{AC} \cong \overline{DF}$, and $\angle C \cong \angle F$

6. Given: $\overline{AC} \cong \overline{DF}$, $\overline{AB} \cong \overline{DE}$, and $\overline{BC} \cong \overline{EF}$

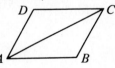

Complete the steps in each proof. (Ex. 7–8)

7. Given: $\angle B \cong \angle D$ and $\overline{DC} \parallel \overline{AB}$
   Prove: $\triangle ABC \cong \triangle CDA$.

8. Given: F is the midpoint of $\overline{EH}$ and $\overline{GI}$.
   Prove: $\triangle EFI \cong \triangle HFG$.

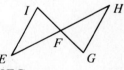

Proof

Statements		Reasons
1. $\angle B \cong \angle D$	(A)	1. ?
2. ?		2. Given
3. $\angle BAC \cong$?	(A)	3. Alt int. $\angle$'s of $\parallel$ lines are $\cong$.
4. $\overline{AC} \cong \overline{CA}$	(S)	4. ?
5. $\therefore$?		5. ?

Proof

Statements		Reasons
1. ?		1. Given
2. $\overline{EF} \cong \overline{HF}$	(S)	2. ?
3. $\angle EFI \cong$?	(A)	3. Vert. $\angle$'s are $\cong$.
4. $\overline{IF} \cong$?	(S)	4. ?
5. $\therefore$?		5. ?

9. Given: $\overline{MN} \cong \overline{KN}$ and $\angle M \cong \angle K$
   Prove: $\triangle JNM \cong \triangle LNK$

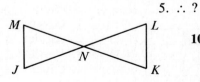

10. Given: $\angle J \cong \angle K$ and $\overline{NM} \cong \overline{NL}$
    Prove: $\triangle JNM \cong \triangle KNL$

11. Given: C is the midpoint of $\overline{EB}$ and $\angle B \cong \angle E$.
Prove: $\triangle ABC \cong \triangle DEC$

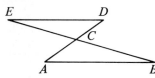

12. Given: $\overline{IG}$ bisects $\angle FIH$ and $\angle F \cong \angle H$.
Prove: $\triangle FGI \cong \triangle HGI$

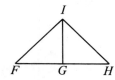

13. Given: $\overline{ML} \cong \overline{KJ}$ and $\overline{KL} \cong \overline{MJ}$
Prove: $\triangle MLK \cong \triangle KJM$

14. Given: $\overline{RO} \cong \overline{NO}$ and $\angle R \cong \angle N$
Prove: $\triangle ROQ \cong \triangle NOP$

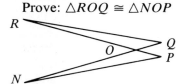

15. Given: $\overline{TV} \perp \overline{US}$ and $\overline{TV}$ bisects $\overline{US}$.
Prove: $\triangle UVT \cong \triangle SVT$

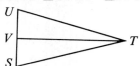

16. Given: $\overline{ZY} \parallel \overline{WX}$ and $\angle W \cong \angle Y$
Prove: $\triangle ZWX \cong \triangle XYZ$

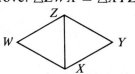

 17. Given: $\overline{FD} \parallel \overline{AC}$, $\overline{BF} \parallel \overline{CE}$, $\angle A \cong \angle D$, and $\overline{BF} \cong \overline{EC}$
Prove: $\triangle ABF \cong \triangle DEC$

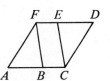

18. Given: $\overline{BF} \cong \overline{EC}$, $\overline{AB} \cong \overline{DE}$, and $\angle FBC \cong \angle CEF$
Prove: $\triangle ABF \cong \triangle DEC$

19. Prove Theorem 4.2.

 20. Given: $\overline{IH} \perp$ plane p, $\overline{GH}$ and $\overline{JH}$ are in p, and $\angle G \cong \angle J$.
Prove: $\triangle GHI \cong \triangle JHI$

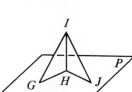

21. Given: $\overline{IH} \perp$ plane p, $\overline{GH}$ and $\overline{JH}$ are in p, $\overline{GH} \cong \overline{IH}$, and $\overline{JH} \cong \overline{IH}$.
Prove: $\triangle GHI \cong \triangle JHI$

A Challenge To You

Several different squares can be seen in this figure. There are nine different ones of size A, four of size B, and one of size C.

A   B   C

How many different squares are there in each of the following figures? Is there a formula in terms of n and m, the numbers of units in the sides?

OTHER CONGRUENCE PROOFS

1. Electric wires are to be strung across a creek between three poles. The power company needs to know how much wire is needed, but it is impossible to measure directly across the creek. How could you lay out a triangle on the ground beside the creek so that these lengths can be found?

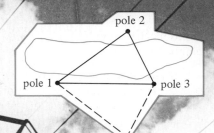

pole 2
pole 1
pole 3

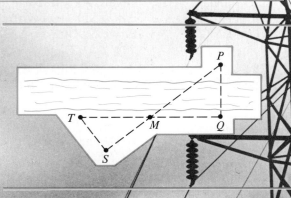

2. A surveyor must find the distance PQ across a river. He drives stakes M, S, and T on level ground so that S, M, and P are collinear and T, M, and Q are collinear. How can you find PQ?

3. An ancient device was invented for measuring the distance from the edge of the ocean to a ship at sea. The hinged rods can be adjusted to sight the ship. It can also be turned around on the post to sight a point on land. How could this device be used to find the distance from ship to shore? Why does this work?

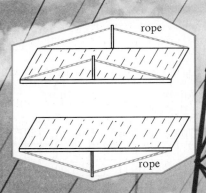

rope

rope

4. A forest ranger needs to build a small bridge over a creek. She does not have any pieces of wood long enough to reach all the way across. She decides to hinge the sides in the middle, with rope stretched to keep the bridge from sagging. Which of the two designs is the correct one to use? Why?

Computer Activities

In geometric proofs that apply exterior angle theorems, you can use a computer to compute the angle measures quickly so that the results can be accurately used in the proofs.

You will recall that every triangle has six exterior angles. An *exterior* angle of a triangle is an angle that is adjacent and supplementary to an interior angle of a triangle.

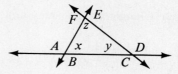

See the computer section on p. 560 for more information

PROGRAM

```
10 PRINT "PROGRAM COMPUTES EXTERIOR ANGLES OF A TRIANGLE"
20 PRINT "USING THE MEASURES OF X AND Y IN DATA STATEMENT"
30 READ X, Y
40 LET Z = 180 — {X + Y}
50 LET A = 180 — X
60 LET B = 180 — X
70 LET C = 180 — Y
80 LET D = 180 — Y
90 LET E = 180 — Z
100 LET F = 180 — Z
110 PRINT "EXTERIOR ANGLES OF TRIANGLE XYZ"
120 PRINT "A=";A, "B="; B,"C="; C, "D=";D, "E=";E,"F="; F
130 GO TO 30
140 DATA 60, 60, 72, 34, 92, 17
150 END
```

Exercises

Run the program for the following values of x and y in the DATA statement. (Ex. 1–3)

1. m $\angle X = 60$ and m $\angle Y = 60$ 2. m $\angle X = 72$ and m $\angle Y = 34$ 3. m $\angle X = 92$ and m $\angle Y = 17$

4. Write a program to find the measures of the interior angles, given the measures of Angles A, C, and F.

5. Write a program to determine if two triangles are congruent if the measures of two interior angles are given for Triangle 1 and the measures of two exterior angles are given for Triangle 2. The exterior angles must be at different vertices in Triangle 2. The measure of the included side is also given for each triangle.

ACTIVITY: ANGLE MEASURES OF TRIANGLES

Chapter Four Review

Classify each triangle by its sides and by its angles. [4.1]

1.

2.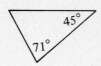

Find m ∠X in each of the following. [4.2]

3.

4.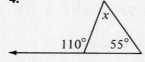

Draw each of the given triangles [4.1]
5. An obtuse scalene triangle

6. An acute isosceles triangle

Find the indicated angle measures [4.2]
7. Given: m ∠1 = 7x − 5,
   m ∠2 = 2x, and
   m ∠3 = 4x + 10
   Find m ∠1.

8. Given: m ∠1 = 3x + 4,
   m ∠2 = 4x − 4, and
   m ∠3 = 8x − 8
   Find m ∠1.

Using the markings shown, are the triangles congruent? Why or why not? [4.3]

9.

10.

Vocabulary
acute triangle [4.1], congruent triangles [4.3], equiangular [4.1], equilateral [4.1], exterior angle [4.2], included angle [4.5], included side [4.5], isosceles triangle [4.1], obtuse triangle [4.1], remote exterior angle [4.2], right triangle [4.1], scalene triangle [4.1].

Construct each of the following.
11. Draw an obtuse triangle. Construct a triangle congruent to it using a SSS pattern. [4.4]

12. Draw an acute scalene triangle. Construct a triangle congruent to it using an ASA pattern. [4.5]

Complete each statement. [4.5]
13. To prove △XYZ ≅ △RST, you must show that $\overline{XY} \cong$?, ∠Y ≅ ?, $\overline{YZ} \cong$?

14. Given: △DEF ≅ △GHI, m ∠D = 7x + 3, and m ∠G = 8x − 4
    m ∠D = ?, m ∠G = ?

Based on the given information, are the triangles congruent? Why or why not? [4.6]
15. Given: $\overline{AC} \cong \overline{EF}$, $\overline{CB} \cong \overline{FD}$, and $\overline{BA} \cong \overline{DE}$

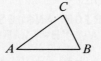 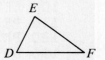

16. Given: $\overline{GH} \cong \overline{JI}$, ∠G ≅ ∠J, and $\overline{GL} \cong \overline{JK}$

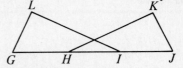

17. Given: O is the midpoint of $\overline{PN}$, and $\overline{MN} \cong \overline{QP}$.

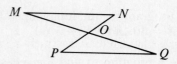

Prove each of the following. [4.6]
18. Given: T is the midpoint of $\overline{RU}$ and $\overline{SV}$.
    Prove: △STR ≅ △VTU

*19. Given: ∠R ≅ ∠U, and $\overline{ST} \cong \overline{VT}$
    Prove: △SRT ≅ △VUT

Chapter Four Test

Classify each triangle by its sides and by its angles.

1.

2.

Find m ∠x.

3.

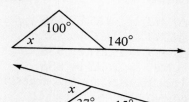

4.

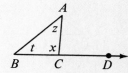

5. Given: m ∠ACD = 5y + 10, m ∠t = 40 and m ∠z = y + 30
   Find m ∠x.

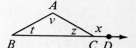

6. Given: ∠t ≅ ∠z and m ∠v = 40
   Find m ∠x.

Draw each of the following.

7. A triangle which is both obtuse and isosceles.

8. A triangle which is both right and scalene.

Construct the following:

9. Draw an obtuse triangle. Construct a triangle congruent to this triangle. Use a SAS pattern.

Based on the markings shown, are the triangles congruent? Why or why not?

10.

11.

12.

Answer each of the following.

In the figure above, ∠A ≅ ∠M and $\overline{AC} \cong \overline{MR}$. Which other parts must be congruent to prove

13. △ABC ≅ △MTR by ASA?

14. △ABC ≅ △MTR by SAS?

15. △ABC ≅ △MTR by AAS?

Prove each of the following.

16. Given: Y is the midpoint of $\overline{VZ}$ and $\overline{XW}$.
    Prove: △VYW ≅ △ZYX

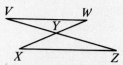

*17. Given: $\overline{UT} \parallel \overline{RS}$ and $\overline{RU} \parallel \overline{ST}$
     Prove: △RTU ≅ △TRS

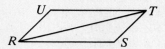

College Prep Test

Directions: For each question, choose the best answer. Indicate your answer by writing the letter of this choice.

1. **A triangle cannot be**
   I. isosceles and right
   II. equiangular and scalene
   III. equilateral and right

   (A) I only
   (B) II only
   (C) III only
   (D) I and II only
   (E) II and III only

2. If the measure of one angle of an isosceles triangle is 74°, which of these is possible?
   I. Another angle has a measure of 74°.
   II. Another angle has a measure of 32°.
   III. Another angle has a measure of 53°.

   (A) I only
   (B) II only
   (C) III only
   (D) I and II only
   (E) I, II, or III

3. m $\angle C = 64$,
   m $\angle D = 53$

   Which of these is *not* possible?

   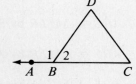

   (A) m $\angle 2 = 73$
   (B) m $\angle 1 = 117$
   (C) m $\angle 1 > 64$
   (D) m $\angle 2 > 53$
   (E) None of these

4. If $\angle X \cong \angle P$, $\angle Y \cong \angle T$, $\angle Z \cong \angle L$, $\overline{XY} \cong \overline{PT}$, $\overline{YZ} \cong \overline{TL}$, and $\overline{ZX} \cong \overline{LP}$, then

   (A) $\triangle XYZ \cong \triangle TLP$
   (B) $\triangle XYZ \cong \triangle PTL$
   (C) $\triangle XYZ \cong \triangle LPT$
   (D) $\triangle XYZ \cong \triangle LTP$
   (E) $\triangle XYZ \cong \triangle PLT$

5.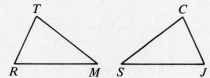

   Given: $\overline{RM} \cong \overline{JS}$, $\overline{MT} \cong \overline{SC}$, $\overline{TR} \cong \overline{CJ}$
   Conclusion:

   (A) $\triangle RMT \cong \triangle SJC$ by SSS
   (B) $\triangle RMT \cong \triangle JSC$ by SSS
   (C) $\triangle RMT \cong \triangle CSJ$ by SSS
   (D) $\triangle RMT \cong \triangle CJS$ by SSS
   (E) The triangles are not necessarily congruent.

6.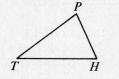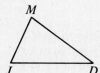

   Given: $\angle T \cong \angle D$, $\overline{TP} \cong \overline{DM}$
   To show that $\triangle THP \cong \triangle DJM$, you must show that
   I. $\angle P \cong \angle M$
   II. $\overline{PH} \cong \overline{MJ}$
   III. $\overline{TH} \cong \overline{DJ}$

   (A) I only
   (B) II only
   (C) III only
   (D) I or II only
   (E) I or III only

7. Given: $\angle A \cong \angle E$, $\angle B \cong \angle D$, $\overline{BC} \cong \overline{DF}$
   Conclusion:

   (A) $\triangle ABC \cong \triangle DEF$ by AAS
   (B) $\triangle ABC \cong \triangle DEF$ by ASA
   (C) $\triangle ABC \cong \triangle DEF$ by SAS
   (D) $\triangle ABC \cong \triangle EDF$ by AAS
   (E) $\triangle ABC \cong \triangle EFD$ by ASA

Cumulative Review (Chapters 1–4)

Write the letter that indicates the best answer.
For Items 1–5, refer to the figure below.

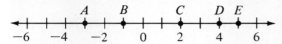

1. The coordinate of point A is
   (A) -4 (B) -3 (C) 3   (D) -2

2. The distance BC is
   (A) 2   (B) 3
   (C) -3 (D) none of these

3. All coordinates of F so that $BF = 4$ are
   (A) -4 and 4   (B) -5 and 3
   (C) -4 and 2   (D) none of these

4. Which pair of segments is congruent?
   (A) $\overline{BC}$ and $\overline{CE}$ (B) $\overline{AC}$ and $\overline{CE}$
   (C) $\overline{BC}$ and $\overline{CD}$ (D) none of these

5. The coordinate of the midpoint of AE is
   (A) C   (B) 2
   (C) 1   (D) none of these

6. If m $\angle ABC = 80$, then $\angle ABC$ is
   (A) acute   (B) right
   (C) obtuse   (D) straight

7. Which are measures of complementary angles?
   (A) 62° and 118°   (B) 40° and 60°
   (C) 26° and 65°   (D) none of these

8. The measure of an angle is 20° less than four times the measure of its complement. What is the measure of the angle?
   (A) 14°   (B) 22°
   (C) 68°   (D) none of these

9. Any two coplanar lines which do not intersect are
   (A) perpendicular   (B) parallel
   (C) skew   (D) none of these

10. If two parallel lines are intersected by a transversal, then interior angles on the same side of the transversal are
    (A) supplementary   (B) congruent
    (C) complementary   (D) none of these

11. Line l intersects both line m and line n. If $m \parallel n$, $l \perp m$, then l and n are
    (A) parallel   (B) skew
    (C) perpendicular   (D) none of these

12. It is impossible for a triangle which is scalene to also be
    (A) acute   (B) obtuse
    (C) isosceles   (D) right

13. In the figure below, the measure of $\angle x$ is
    (A) 85°   (B) 23°
    (C) 95°   (D) none of these

Find the measure of each angle. Use a protractor.
14. **15.**

Draw and label the following:
16. $\overleftrightarrow{AB}$ intersecting plane p in point C

The coordinate of point X is given. Find all possible coordinates of Y so that $\overline{XY}$ has the indicated length.
17. $X \leftrightarrow 4$; $XY = 7$

18. $X \leftrightarrow -1.6$; $XY = 3.7$

Construct each of the following:
19. Construct $\overline{CD}$ congruent to $\overline{AB}$. Then construct the midpoint of $\overline{CD}$.

20. Use a protractor to draw an angle measuring 52°. Then use a compass and straightedge to bisect the angle

True or false?
21. Any three points are contained in exactly one plane.

22. Complementary angles are congruent.

23. If an angle measures 70°, then its supplement measures 110°.

24. If two lines form congruent adjacent angles, then they are perpendicular.

25. A theorem is a statement which cannot be proved.

26. Vertical angles are supplementary.

27. The supplement of an acute angle measures 90° more than the complement of the angle.

Use the figure below to find the following:
28. If $r \parallel s$ and m $\angle 2 = 58$, find m $\angle 1$ and m $\angle 4$.

29. If m $\angle 3 = 64$ and m $\angle 8 = 49$, find m $\angle 1$ and m $\angle 10$.

30. If $r \parallel s$ and m $\angle 6 = 132$, find m $\angle 7$ and m $\angle 8$.

31. If $r \parallel s$ and m $\angle 3 = $ m $\angle 8$ and m $\angle 2 = 40$ find m $\angle 7$.

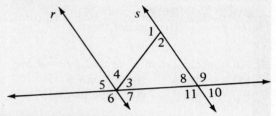

Prove each of the following:
32. Given: $\angle 1 \cong \angle 2$
Prove: $\angle 3 \cong \angle 4$

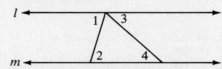

33. Given: $\angle A \cong \angle F$, $\overline{AD} \cong \overline{CF}$, and $\overline{BA} = \overline{EF}$
Prove: $\triangle ACB \cong \triangle FDE$

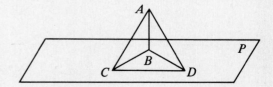

* **34.** Given: $\overline{AB} \perp$ plane p, $\overline{CB}$, $\overline{DB}$, and $\overline{CD}$ are in plane p, and $\angle ACB \cong \angle ADB$
Prove: $\triangle ABC \cong \triangle ABD$

5 APPLYING CONGRUENT TRIANGLES

Geometry in Motion

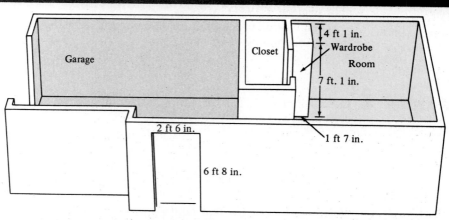

Garage

Closet

Wardrobe
Room

4 ft 1 in.

7 ft. 1 in.

2 ft 6 in.

1 ft 7 in.

6 ft 8 in.

Movers are delivering furniture to a new house. A large antique wardrobe must be placed in a certain location in a room behind the garage. How would you move the wardrobe from the truck through the garage to this room? What factors complicate the move?

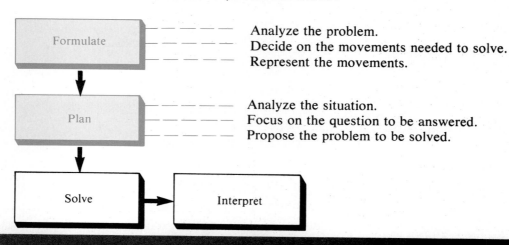

Formulate
— — — — — Analyze the problem.
— — — — — Decide on the movements needed to solve.
— — — — — Represent the movements.

Plan
— — — — — Analyze the situation.
— — — — — Focus on the question to be answered.
— — — — — Propose the problem to be solved.

Solve → Interpret

5.1 Corresponding Parts

OBJECTIVES ► **To identify corresponding parts of congruent triangles**
To use corresponding parts in proofs

If two triangles are congruent, then their corresponding sides are congruent and their corresponding angles are congruent. This statement can be simplified into the following property.

Property of corresponding parts (CPCTC)

> Corresponding parts of congruent triangles are congruent.

This property is actually a restatement of the definition of *congruent triangles*. You will use it as a reason in proofs so often that it is convenient to use the abbreviation, CPCTC.

When writing proofs that involve congruent triangles, you may need to identify the corresponding congruent parts.

Example 1 Given: $\triangle ABC \cong \triangle ZXY$. Draw a diagram to show this. Name the corresponding congruent parts.

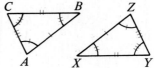

$\angle A \cong \angle Z \quad \overline{AB} \cong \overline{ZX}$
$\angle B \cong \angle X \quad \overline{BC} \cong \overline{XY}$
$\angle C \cong \angle Y \quad \overline{CA} \cong \overline{YZ}$

If you want to show that two segments or two angles are congruent, you may be able to do so by showing that they are corresponding parts of congruent triangles.

Example 2 Given: $\angle 2 \cong \angle 4$, and $\angle 3 \cong \angle 1$
Prove: $\overline{BC} \cong \overline{DA}$

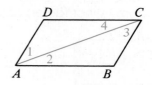

Proof

Statements		Reasons
1. $\angle 2 \cong \angle 4$	(A)	1. Given
2. $\overline{AC} \cong \overline{CA}$	(S)	2. Reflexive property
3. $\angle 3 \cong \angle 1$	(A)	3. Given
4. $\triangle ABC \cong \triangle CDA$		4. ASA
5. $\therefore \overline{BC} \cong \overline{DA}$		5. CPCTC

The property of corresponding parts can often be used to help find the measure of angles or sides of triangles or to show that lines or segments are perpendicular or parallel.

Example 3

Given: $\triangle BDA \cong \triangle CDA$, m $\angle BAD =$ 38, and $\overline{AD} \perp \overline{BC}$

Find m $\angle C$.

$CPCTC$ ▶

$$\angle C \cong \angle B$$
$$\text{m } \angle B = 180 - (90 + 38) \text{ or } 52$$
Thus, m $\angle C = 52$.

Example 4

Given: $\overline{EF} \cong \overline{GH}$, and $\overline{FG} \cong \overline{HE}$
Prove: $\overline{EF} \parallel \overline{GH}$

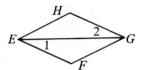

Proof

Statements		Reasons
1. $\overline{EF} \cong \overline{GH}$	(S)	1. Given
2. $\overline{FG} \cong \overline{HE}$	(S)	2. Given
3. $\overline{GE} \cong \overline{EG}$	(S)	3. Reflexive property
4. $\triangle EFG \cong \triangle GHE$		4. SSS
5. $\angle 1 \cong \angle 2$		5. CPCTC
6. $\therefore \overline{EF} \parallel \overline{GH}$		6. Lines are $\parallel$ if alt. int. $\angle$'s are $\cong$.

Oral Exercises

Name the corresponding congruent parts of each pair of congruent triangles.

1.

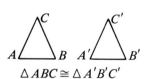

$\triangle ABC \cong \triangle A'B'C'$

2.

$\triangle DEF \cong \triangle GHI$

3.

$\triangle XYZ \cong \triangle ONM$

Complete each statement.

4.

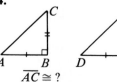

$\overline{AC} \cong ?$

5.

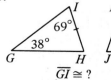

$\overline{GI} \cong ?$

6.

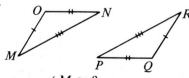

$\angle M \cong ?$

Written Exercises

Draw a diagram to show that each given pair of triangles is congruent.
Name the corresponding congruent parts.

 1. $\triangle ABC \cong \triangle DEF$ **2.** $\triangle GHI \cong \triangle XYZ$ **3.** $\triangle PTL \cong \triangle QUM$

Find the measure of the corresponding side or angle. (Ex. 4–6)

4. Given: $\triangle ABC \cong$ $\triangle DEF$, and m $\angle A = 72$

5. Given: $\triangle LMN \cong \triangle OPQ$, and $LN = 9$ cm

6. Given: $\triangle XYZ \cong \triangle HIG$, and $YZ = 42$ mm

  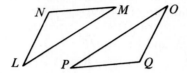

7. Given: $\overline{AD} \cong \overline{CB}$, and $\overline{CD} \cong \overline{AB}$
Prove: $\angle D \cong \angle B$

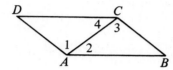

8. Given: $\overline{DC} \parallel \overline{AB}$ and $\angle 1 \cong \angle 3$
Prove: $\overline{AD} \cong \overline{CB}$

 9. Given: $\overline{AD} \cong \overline{CD}$
m $\angle ABD = 56$
$\overline{DB}$ bisects $\angle ADC$
Find m $\angle CBD$.

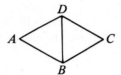

10. Given: $\overline{AD} \cong \overline{CB}$
$\overline{AD} \parallel \overline{BC}$
m $\angle ADB = 61$
m $\angle ABD = 56$
Find m $\angle C$.

11. Given: $\overline{WZ} \cong \overline{YX}$, and $\angle 2 \cong \angle 4$,
Prove: $\overline{XW} \parallel \overline{YZ}$

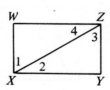

12. Given: $\overline{XW} \perp \overline{WZ}$, $\angle 1 \cong \angle 3$, and $\angle 2 \cong \angle 4$
Prove: $\overline{ZY} \perp \overline{XY}$

 13. Given: $\overline{CD} \perp \overline{AD}$, $\overline{CD} \perp \overline{BD}$, and $\overline{AD} \cong \overline{BD}$
Prove: $\triangle ABC$ is isosceles.

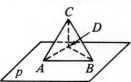

14. Given: $\overline{GH} \perp \overline{EH}$, $\overline{GH} \perp \overline{FH}$, and $\angle GEH \cong \angle GFH$
Prove: $\triangle EHF$ is isosceles.

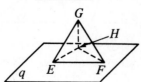

15. Given: $\overline{LK} \perp \overline{IK}$, $\overline{LK} \cong \overline{JK}$, and $\overline{LI} \cong \overline{JI}$
Prove: $\overline{JK} \perp \overline{IK}$

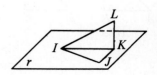

5.2 Isosceles Triangles

OBJECTIVES ► **To prove and apply theorems about isosceles triangles**
To find perimeters of isosceles triangles

An isosceles triangle has at least two congruent sides, each of which is called a *leg* of the triangle. The angle formed by the legs is called the *vertex angle*. The side opposite the vertex angle is called the *base* of the triangle and the angles opposite the legs are called *base angles*.

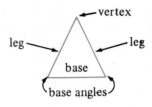

Example 1 Name the vertex angle, legs, base, and base angles of isosceles $\triangle ABC$.

vertex angle: $\angle A$ legs: $\overline{AB}, \overline{AC}$
base: $\overline{BC}$ base angles: $\angle B, \angle C$

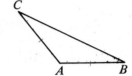

Theorem 5.1 below is proved by using corresponding parts of congruent triangles. Notice that it is necessary to draw an auxiliary line to form the two triangles. You will need to use auxiliary lines in many proofs involving isosceles triangles.

┌─ **Theorem 5.1** If two sides of a triangle are congruent, then the angles ─┐
opposite those sides are congruent.

Given: $\triangle ABC$, and
$\overline{AC} \cong \overline{BC}$
Prove: $\angle A \cong \angle B$

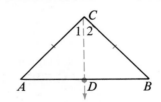

Analysis: Draw an auxiliary line to form 2 $\triangle$'s which can be proved $\cong$.

Proof

Statements		Reason
1. $\overline{AC} \cong \overline{BC}$	(S)	1. Given
2. Draw $\overrightarrow{CD}$, the bisector of $\angle ACB$ intersecting $\overline{AB}$ at D.		2. Every $\angle$, except st. $\angle$, has exactly one bisector
3. $\angle 1 \cong \angle 2$	(A)	3. Def. of $\angle$ bisector
4. $\overline{CD} \cong \overline{CD}$	(S)	4. Reflexive property
5. $\triangle ACD \cong \triangle BCD$		5. SAS
6. $\therefore \angle A \cong \angle B$		6. CPCTC

This theorem is sometimes stated, "Base angles of an isosceles triangle are congruent."

Theorem 5.1 can be used to find certain angle measures.

Example 2 Given: $\overline{AB} \cong \overline{BC}$
m $\angle B = x$, and
m $\angle A = 2x - 20$
Find m $\angle B$.

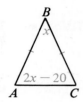

Since $\overline{AB} \cong \overline{BC}$, then $\angle A \cong \angle C$ ◄ *Use Th. 5.1*
$$m \angle C = 2x - 20$$
$$m \angle A + m \angle B + m \angle C = 180$$
$$(2x - 20) + x + (2x - 20) = 180$$
$$5x - 40 = 180$$
$$5x = 220$$
$$x = 44$$

Thus, m $\angle B = 44$.

Since an equilateral triangle is also isosceles, Theorem 5.1 applies to equilateral triangles. All three sides of an equilateral triangle are congruent. Using Theorem 5.1, it can be shown that all three angles are also congruent (Corollary 1). Since the sum of the measures of the angles of any triangle is 180°, it follows that the measure of each angle of an equilateral or equiangular triangle is 60° (Corollary 2).

Corollary 1 An equilateral triangle is also equiangular.

Corollary 2 The measure of each angle of an equilateral, or equiangular, triangle is 60°.

$\triangle ABC$ is equilateral and equiangular.
m $\angle A =$ m $\angle B =$ m $\angle C = 60$

Theorem 5.2 If two angles of a triangle are congruent, then the sides opposite those angles are congruent. (See Exercise 18.)

Given: $\triangle ABC$,
and $\angle A \cong \angle B$
Prove: $\overline{AC} \cong \overline{BC}$

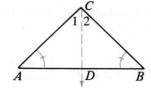

Analysis: Draw an auxiliary line to form 2△'s which can be proved ≅.

You can prove the following corollary of Theorem 5.2.

┌ **Corollary** An equiangular triangle is also equilateral. ─┐

The properties of isosceles triangles are frequently used as reasons in proofs.

Example 3 Given: $\triangle ABC$,
and $\angle 1 \cong \angle 3$
Prove: $\overline{AC} \cong \overline{BC}$

Proof

Statements	Reasons
1. $\angle 1 \cong \angle 3$	1. Given
2. $\angle 1 \cong \angle 2$	2. Vertical $\angle$'s are $\cong$.
3. $\angle 2 \cong \angle 3$	3. Substitution property
4. $\therefore \overline{AC} \cong \overline{BC}$	4. If two $\angle$'s of $\triangle$ are $\cong$, sides opp. the $\angle$'s are $\cong$.

The **perimeter** of a triangle is the sum of the lengths of the sides. You can use the properties of isosceles triangles to help find lengths of sides and perimeters.

Example 4 Find the perimeter of $\triangle ABC$.

$\angle A \cong \angle B$ ► $AC = BC = 8$ cm
Perimeter $= 8 + 8 + 12 = 28$ cm

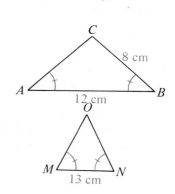

Example 5 Given: $\angle M \cong \angle N$,
$MN = 13$ cm, and
the perimeter of $\triangle MNO$ is 43 cm.
Find OM.

perimeter ► $MN + NO + OM = 43$
$13 + NO + OM = 43$
$NO + OM = 30$
$2OM = 30$ ◄ $NO = OM$ by Th. 5.2.
Thus, $OM = 15$.

Example 6 Given: $\triangle XYZ$ is equiangular, and $YZ = 10$ m.
Find the perimeter.

Use Cor. 1, Th. 5.2. ► Perimeter $= XY + YZ + ZX$
Perimeter $= 10 + 10 + 10$ or 30 m

ISOSCELES TRIANGLES **141**

Reading in Geometry

True or False? Give the page and paragraph in the lesson that support your choice.

1. The base of an isosceles triangle is one of the two congruent sides.
2. The vertex angle of an isosceles triangle is one of the two congruent angles.
3. An equilateral triangle is also equiangular.
4. Base angles of an isosceles triangle are congruent.
5. An equilateral triangle is also isosceles.
6. An isosceles triangle can have two 60° angles.

Oral Exercises

Name the vertex angle, legs, base, and base angles of each triangle.

1.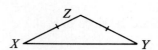
2.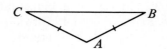
3.

Written Exercises

Find the measure of each angle.

△ 1.
2.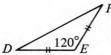
3.

4. Given: $\overline{XZ} \cong \overline{YZ}$,
   m $\angle X = 3a + 4$, and
   m $\angle Z = 2a - 4$
5. Given: $\overline{XZ} \cong \overline{YZ}$,
   m $\angle Y = 3c + 3$, and
   m $\angle Z = 4c - 16$
6. Given: $\overline{XZ} \cong \overline{YZ}$,
   m $\angle X = 4t + 4$, and
   m $\angle Y = 5t - 9$
7. Given: $\overline{XZ} \cong \overline{YZ}$,
   m $\angle X = 10e + 12$, and
   m $\angle Y = 12e - 2$

8. Given: $\overline{AB} \cong \overline{BC}$, and
   m $\angle B = 110$
   Find m $\angle A$ and m $\angle 2$.

9. Given: $\overline{FE} \perp \overline{DE}$, and
   $\overline{FE} \cong \overline{DE}$
   Find m $\angle D$ and m $\angle F$

10. Given: $\overline{GI} \cong \overline{HI}$, and
    m $\angle I = 52$
    Find m $\angle 2$, m $\angle 3$, and
    m $\angle 4$.

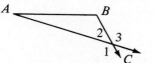
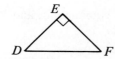
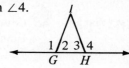

Find the perimeter of each triangle. (Ex. 11–12)

11. Given: $\overline{AB} \cong \overline{CB}$,
    $AB = 8$ cm, and
    $AC = 4$ cm

12. Given: $\angle A \cong \angle C$,
    $BC = 7$ cm, and
    $AC = 3$ cm

142

CHAPTER FIVE

13. Given: $\overline{AB} \cong \overline{AC}$
Prove: $\angle B \cong \angle 2$

14. Given: $\angle A \cong \angle 2$
Prove: $\overline{AB} \cong \overline{BC}$

Ⓑ 15. Given: $\overrightarrow{FH} \parallel \overline{DE}$ and $\overline{DF} \cong \overline{EF}$
Prove: $\angle 1 \cong \angle 2$

16. Given: $\overrightarrow{KM} \parallel \overline{IJ}$ and $\angle 1 \cong \angle 2$
Prove: $\triangle IJK$ is isosceles.

17. Given: $\angle 1 \cong \angle 2$
Prove: $\triangle OPR$ is isosceles.

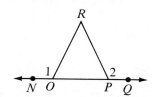

18. Prove Theorem 5.2.

19. Prove Corollary 1 of Theorem 5.2.

20. Given: $\overline{WU} \parallel \overline{ST}$ and $\overline{SV} \cong \overline{TV}$
Prove: $\overline{WV} \cong \overline{UV}$

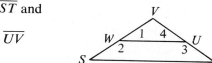

21. Given: $\overline{WU} \parallel \overline{ST}$ and $\overline{VW} \cong \overline{VU}$
Prove: $\overline{SW} \cong \overline{TU}$

22. Given: $\triangle ABC$, m $\angle A = 2x + 10$, m $\angle B = 3x - 15$, m $\angle C = 4(x - 10)$, and $\angle A \cong \angle B$
Find the perimeter of $\triangle ABC$, if possible.

23. Given: $\triangle ABC$, $AC = 4x$, $BC = 6x - 6$, $AB = 5x - 8$, and $\angle A \cong \angle B$.
Find the perimeter of $\triangle ABC$, if possible.

Ⓒ 24. Given: $\angle PXY \cong \angle PXZ$, and $\angle XYZ \cong \angle XZY$
Prove: $\triangle PYZ$ is isosceles.

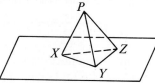

25. Given: $\angle PYZ \cong \angle PZY$, and $\angle XPY \cong \angle XPZ$
Prove: $\triangle XYZ$ is isosceles.

Algebra Review

OBJECTIVE ▶ **To simplify radicals**

To simplify a radical, factor to get a perfect square, then use

$$\sqrt{ab} = \sqrt{a} \cdot \sqrt{b}.$$

Example   Simplify $\sqrt{75}$

25 is a perfect square. ▶ $\sqrt{25 \cdot 3} = \sqrt{25} \cdot \sqrt{3} = 5\sqrt{3}$

Simplify. (All variables represent positive numbers.)

1. $\sqrt{16}$ 2. $\sqrt{32}$ 3. $\sqrt{45}$ 4. $\sqrt{147}$ 5. $\sqrt{242}$
6. $2\sqrt{25}$ 7. $3\sqrt{20}$ 8. $-4\sqrt{108}$ 9. $\sqrt{8x^2}$ 10. $\sqrt{144x^3}$

ISOSCELES TRIANGLES

Reflections

A geometric transformation is a means of relating the points of a figure with the points of a second figure, called its image, so that each point of the figure corresponds to exactly one point of the image and each point of the image corresponds to exactly one point of the figure. One such transformation is the *reflection*.

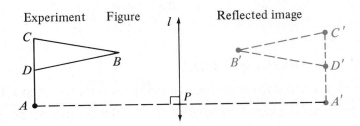

Experiment   Figure   Reflected image

1. Draw $\overline{AP} \perp l$. Extend $\overline{AP}$ to A' so that $\overline{PA'} \cong \overline{AP}$.

2. Repeat this for points B, C, and D.

3. Connect A' and D', D' and B', B' and C', and C' and D'.

4. This image is the reflection of the original figure about line l.

5. Compare the reflected image with the original figure. Are they congruent?

PROJECT

Copy each triangle and the reflection line l. Draw the reflected image using the method in the experiment above. Is each reflected image congruent to the original triangle?

1.
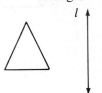

2.

3.
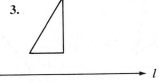

4.
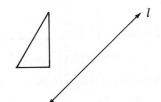

CHAPTER FIVE

The reflection line is often called the *line of symmetry*. You can find the line of symmetry using geometric constructions.

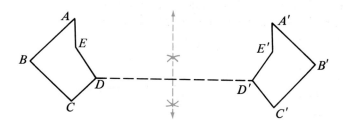

1. *A′B′C′D′E′* is the reflection of *ABCDE*.

2. Using compass and straightedge, construct the perpendicular bisector of $\overline{DD'}$.

3. Construct the perpendicular bisector of $\overline{CC'}$. What do you notice about this line?

4. The perpendicular bisector of $\overline{DD'}$ is the line of symmetry of the figure and its reflection.

PROJECT

Copy each triangle and its reflection.

5.

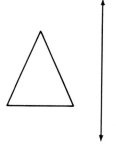

Construct the line of symmetry.

6.

7.

8.

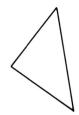

REFLECTIONS

Paper folding can be used to find the line of symmetry of a figure and its reflection, or to determine if two figures are reflections. If they are not reflections, you cannot find a line of symmetry.

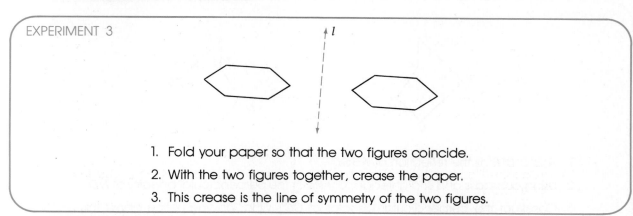

EXPERIMENT 3

l

1. Fold your paper so that the two figures coincide.
2. With the two figures together, crease the paper.
3. This crease is the line of symmetry of the two figures.

PROJECT Copy each pair of triangles on the same sheet of paper. By folding the paper, find out which triangles are reflections of each other.

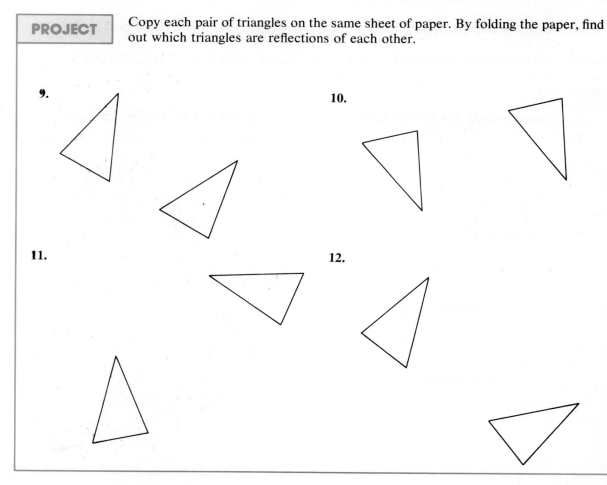

9.

10.

11.

12.

Slides

Another type of transformation is the **slide.**

EXPERIMENT 1

Figure

Slide image

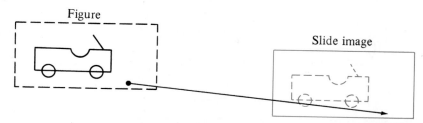

1. Trace the figure on tracing paper. Draw a dot on the tracing at the end of the slide arrow.

2. Slide the dot on the tracing along the slide arrow to the arrow head. Do not turn the paper.

3. Place carbon paper under the tracing. Trace this copy onto this sheet.

4. This figure is the slide image of the original figure with respect to the given slide arrow.

PROJECT Copy each triangle and its slide arrow. Draw the slide image with respect to the given slide arrow.

1.

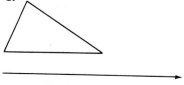

2.

3.

4.

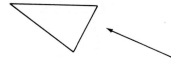

You can follow a slide with a second slide. The two slides can then be combined into a single slide.

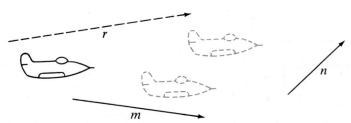

1. Draw the slide image of the original figure with respect to slide arrow *m*.

2. Draw the slide image of this image with respect to slide arrow *n*.

3. Show that this last slide image is also the slide image of the original figure with respect to slide arrow *r*.

4. Slide arrow *r* is the *resultant* of *m* and *n*.

PROJECT

Copy each figure and the two slide arrows shown. For each figure, draw the slide image with respect to slide arrow *m*. Then draw the slide image of this image with respect to slide arrow *n*. Find a single slide arrow *r* which is the resultant of *m* and *n*. This resultant arrow should give the same result in one slide that slide *m* followed by slide *n* produced.

5.

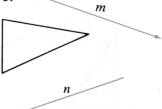

6.

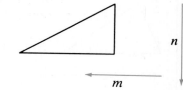

7.

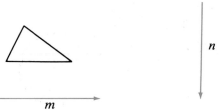

8.

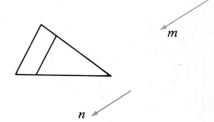

CHAPTER FIVE

Rotations

A third type of transformation is the *rotation*.

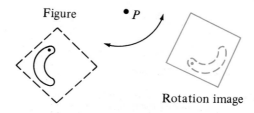

Figure   • P

Rotation image

1. Trace the figure on tracing paper. Draw a dot on the copy at the end of the rotation arrow.

2. Place a pencil, pen, or other pointed object on the copy at point P. Turn the copy around point P until the dot is at the other end of the arrow.

3. Place carbon paper under the copy and trace the copy on this sheet.

4. This figure is the rotation image of the figure with respect to P and the given rotation arrow.

PROJECT Copy each triangle and its rotation arrow. Draw the rotation image about P with respect to the given rotation arrow.

1.

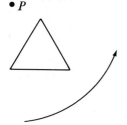

• P

2.

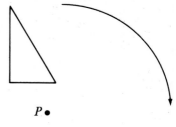

P •

3.

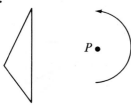

P •

4.

P •

If a figure and its rotation image are given, you can find the rotation center using geometric constructions.

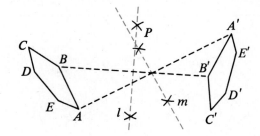
PROJECT Copy each pair of triangles. Find the rotation center using geometric constructions.

5.

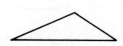

6.

7.

8.

Rotation centers can also be found by paper folding. Some pairs of figures may have more than one possible rotation center.

EXPERIMENT 3

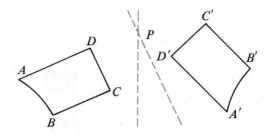

1. Fold your paper so that *A* and *A'* coincide. Crease the paper.

2. Refold your paper so that *C* and *C'* coincide. Crease the paper with these points together.

3. The point where these two creases intersect is the rotation center for the rotation of *ABCD* into *A'B'C'D'*.

PROJECT   Copy each pair of triangles. Find the rotation center by using paper folding. Check your accuracy by rotating one figure into the other. Which figures have more than one rotation center?

9.

10.

11.

12.

ROTATIONS

151

Transformations: Congruent Triangles

If two triangles are congruent, one of them can be shown to be the image of the other by a reflection, a slide, a rotation, or a combination of two of these, as shown below.

△ DEF is the image of △ ABC by a slide followed by a reflection.

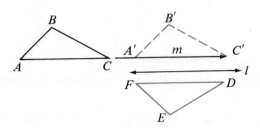

△ UVW is the image of △ RST by a rotation followed by a slide.

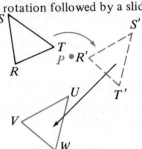

PROJECT

Copy each pair of congruent triangles. Find the transformation or pair of transformations that relates the two.

1.

2.

3.

4.

5.3 Overlapping Triangles

Sometimes a geometric figure contains two or more triangles that overlap each other. In such cases you will need to "untangle" the figure to identify the triangles involved.

Example 1 Name each triangle in the figure.

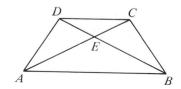

$\triangle ABC$, $\triangle ABD$, $\triangle ABE$, $\triangle ACD$,
$\triangle ADE$, $\triangle BCD$, $\triangle BCE$, $\triangle CDE$

Example 2 $\triangle FGI$ and $\triangle FGJ$ are overlapping triangles. Draw two pictures, showing each of these triangles in a different color.

$\triangle FGI$ and $\triangle FGJ$ ►
share side $\overline{FG}$.

$\triangle FGI$

$\triangle FGJ$

Below is a proof involving overlapping triangles. In proofs of this type, you may find it helpful to redraw the original diagram using two colors, or, more simply, redraw each triangle as a separate figure.

Example 3 Given: $\overline{AC} \cong \overline{AD}$ and $\angle C \cong \angle D$
Prove: $\overline{AE} \cong \overline{AB}$

Proof

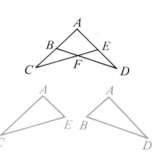

Statements		Reasons
1. $\angle C \cong \angle D$	(A)	1. Given
2. $\overline{AC} \cong \overline{AD}$	(S)	2. Given
3. $\angle A \cong \angle A$	(A)	3. Reflexive property
4. $\triangle ACE \cong \triangle ADB$		4. ASA
5. $\therefore \overline{AE} \cong \overline{AB}$		5. CPCTC

OVERLAPPING TRIANGLES

Proofs involving overlapping triangles require a careful analysis of the figure involved.

Example 4 Given: $\overline{YT} \parallel \overline{XU}$, $\overline{YT} \perp \overline{SV}$
$\overline{ST} \cong \overline{VU}$, and $\overline{RS} \cong \overline{RV}$
Prove: $\overline{XU} \cong \overline{YT}$

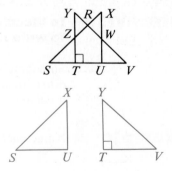

Analysis: Show $\triangle XSU \cong \triangle YVT$

Redraw each of the △'s separately. ▶

Proof

Statements	Reasons
1. $\overline{YT} \perp \overline{SV}$	1. Given
2. $\angle YTV$ is a rt. $\angle$.	2. Def. of $\perp$
3. $\overline{YT} \parallel \overline{XU}$	3. Given
4. $\angle YTV$ and $\angle XUS$ are supplementary	4. Int. $\angle$'s of $\parallel$ lines on same side of trans. are suppl.
5. $\angle XUS$ is a rt. $\angle$.	5. Subtraction (m $\angle XUS = 180 - 90$)
6. $\angle XUS \cong \angle YTV$ (A)	6. Rt. $\angle$'s are $\cong$.
7. $\overline{ST} \cong \overline{VU}$	7. Given
8. $ST = VU$	8. Def. of $\cong$ segments
9. $ST + TU = VU + TU$	9. Add. prop. of equality
10. $SU = VT$	10. Def. of between, substitution prop.
11. $\overline{SU} \cong \overline{VT}$ (S)	11. Def. of $\cong$ segments
12. $\overline{RS} \cong \overline{RV}$	12. Given
13. $\angle S \cong \angle V$ (A)	13. $\angle$'s opp. $\cong$ sides of $\triangle$ are $\cong$.
14. $\triangle XSU \cong \triangle YVT$	14. ASA
15. $\therefore \overline{XU} \cong \overline{YT}$	15. CPCTC

Oral Exercises

Name all of the different triangles in each figure

1.

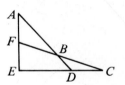

2.

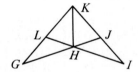

3.

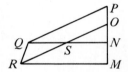

Written Exercises _____

Redraw each picture using different colors to show each of the indicated overlapping triangles. (Ex. 1–3)

A **1.** △ABD and △ABC

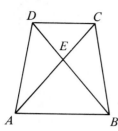

2. △FHL and △GIJ

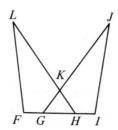

3. △MOP and △NOQ

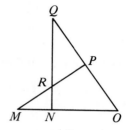

4. Given: $\overline{WT} \cong \overline{WU}$, and $\overline{SU} \cong \overline{VT}$
Prove: △SUW ≅ △VTW

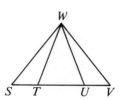

5. Given: ∠S ≅ ∠V, and $\overline{SU} \cong \overline{VT}$
Prove: △SUW ≅ △VTW

6. Given: $\overline{XZ} \cong \overline{YZ}$, and ∠ZXB ≅ ∠ZYA
Prove: $\overline{XB} \cong \overline{YA}$

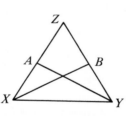

7. Given: ∠ZXY ≅ ∠ZYX, and $\overline{AX} \approx \overline{BY}$
Prove: ∠AYX ≅ ∠BXY

8. Given: $\overline{GC} \perp \overline{CD}, \overline{ED} \perp \overline{CD}$, and $\overline{CG} \cong \overline{DE}$
Prove: $\overline{DG} \cong \overline{CE}$

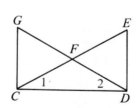

9. Given: $\overline{GC} \perp \overline{CD}$, ∠1 ≅ ∠2, and ∠G ≅ ∠E
Prove: $\overline{ED} \perp \overline{CD}$

B **10.** Given: $\overline{HI} \cong \overline{KJ}$, $\overline{HN} \cong \overline{IL}$, and $\overline{HN} \parallel \overline{IL}$
Prove: $\overline{JN} \parallel \overline{KL}$

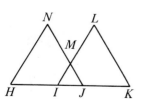

11. Given: ∠1 ≅ ∠2, ∠3 ≅ ∠4, and $\overline{OS} \cong \overline{QR}$
Prove: △OPR ≅ △QPS

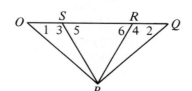

12. Given: $\overline{TX} \parallel \overline{UZ}$, $\overline{WX} \parallel \overline{VY}$, and $\overline{TV} \cong \overline{WU}$
Prove: △TVY ≅ △WUZ

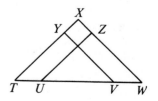

OVERLAPPING TRIANGLES

$R_{\triangle ABC}$ means the **region of** $\triangle ABC$. $R_{\triangle ABC}$ includes both $\triangle ABC$ and its interior.

Example

What is the intersection of $R_{\triangle ABC}$ and $R_{\triangle ABE}$?

$R_{\triangle ABF}$ is shaded both colors. ► $R_{\triangle ABF}$

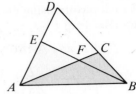

Using each of the given figures, find the intersection of the indicated regions.

 13. $R_{\triangle FBC}$ and $R_{\triangle AEC}$
14. $R_{\triangle AGF}$ and $R_{\triangle FGB}$
15. $R_{\triangle AGC}$ and $R_{\triangle DGC}$
16. $R_{\triangle ABD}$ and $R_{\triangle ABE}$
17. $R_{\triangle AFC}$ and $R_{\triangle ABG}$

18. $R_{\triangle AQE}$ and $R_{\triangle CQE}$
19. $R_{\triangle FOD}$ and $R_{\triangle COA}$
20. $R_{\triangle FAC}$ and $R_{\triangle FBC}$
21. $R_{\triangle FCE}$ and $R_{\triangle DOC}$
22. $R_{\triangle ACE}$ and $R_{\triangle BCD}$

23. $R_{\triangle ACG}$ and $R_{\triangle BCD}$
24. $R_{\triangle ABF}$ and $R_{\triangle ACG}$
25. $R_{\triangle AEF}$ and $R_{\triangle ABE}$
26. $R_{\triangle ABE}$ and $R_{\triangle BCD}$
27. R_{GCH} and $R_{\triangle BCH}$

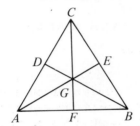

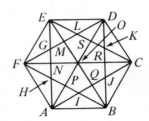

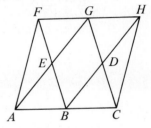

Algebra Review

OBJECTIVE ► **To factor a trinomial and the difference of two squares**

To factor a trinomial like $x^2 - 7x + 12$
1. Try factors of x^2 and 12.
2. Determine signs for correct middle terms.

Factor $x^2 - 7x + 12$

$1x \quad \square 3 \qquad (1x)(\boxminus 3) = -3x$
$1x \quad \square 4 \qquad (\boxminus 4)(1x) = -4x$
$\qquad\qquad\qquad (-3x) + (-4x) = -7x$

Thus, $x^2 - 7x + 12 = (x - 3)(x - 4)$

Factor $4x^2 - 25$

↑
Difference of squares
$(2x)^2 - (5)^2$
Thus, $4x^2 - 25 = (2x + 5)(2x - 5)$

Factor.
1. $x^2 - 6x + 8$
2. $x^2 + 2x - 15$
3. $x^2 + 9x + 20$
4. $x^2 - 1$
5. $x^2 - 81$
6. $9x^2 - 36$
7. $6x^2 - x - 2$
8. $2x^2 + 7x - 15$
9. $6x^2 - 13x + 6$

5.4 Congruent Right Triangles

OBJECTIVES ▶ **To identify the parts of a right triangle**
To apply right triangle congruence theorems

Since you often will use right triangles or parts of right triangles in your work in geometry, it will be helpful to have names for these different parts.

Definition:
hypotenuse
and leg.

> The **hypotenuse** of a right triangle is the side opposite the right angle. The **legs** are the other two sides.

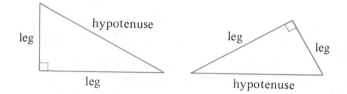

You can prove right triangles congruent by any of the methods used for other triangles. There are, however, some special methods that are used only with right triangles. Three of these special methods are actually restatements of other general congruence patterns. The first of these is proved below. It is usually called the *Leg-Leg* or *LL* pattern.

> **Theorem 5.3** **Leg-Leg (LL)** Two right triangles are congruent if the two legs of one are congruent to the corresponding legs of the other.

Given: *Rt.* △'s ABC and $A'B'C'$;
  Rt. ∠'s B and B';
  $\overline{AB} \cong \overline{A'B'}$ and $\overline{BC} \cong \overline{B'C'}$
Prove: $\triangle ABC \cong \triangle A'B'C'$

Proof

Statements		Reasons
1. Rt. △'s ABC and $A'B'C'$		1. Given
2. $\overline{AB} \cong \overline{A'B'}$	(S)	2. Given
3. ∠B and ∠B' are rt. ∠'s.		3. Given
4. ∠$B \cong ∠B'$	(A)	4. All rt. ∠'s are ≅.
5. $\overline{BC} \cong \overline{B'C'}$	(S)	5. Given
6. ∴ $\triangle ABC \cong \triangle A'B'C'$		6. SAS

Two other patterns for right triangles are special cases of other general congruence patterns. You should complete proofs of these.

┌─ **Theorem 5.4   Leg-Acute Angle (LA)**   Two right triangles ─┐
are congruent if a leg and an acute angle of one are
congruent to the corresponding leg and acute angle of
the other.

Case I

Given: Rt. △'s ABC and $A'B'C'$;
Rt. ∠'s B and B'.
$\overline{AB} \cong \overline{A'B'}$, and $\angle A \cong \angle A'$
Prove: $\triangle ABC \cong \triangle A'B'C'$

Analysis: Use ASA.

Case II

Given: Rt. △'s ABC and $A'B'C'$;
Rt. ∠'s B and B';
$\overline{AB} \cong \overline{A'B'}$, and $\angle C \cong \angle C'$
Prove: $\triangle ABC \cong A'B'C'$

Analysis: Use AAS.

┌─ **Theorem 5.5   Hypotenuse-Acute Angle (HA)**   Two ─┐
right triangles are congruent if the hypotenuse and an
acute angle of one are congruent to the hypotenuse and
the corresponding acute angle of the other.

The abbreviations LA and HA will be written when these theorems are used as reasons in proofs.

Example 1 Given: $\overline{AC} \perp \overline{BD}$ and $\overline{AB} \cong \overline{AD}$
Prove: $\triangle BCA \cong \triangle DCA$

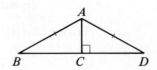

Proof

Statements		Reasons
1. $\overline{AC} \perp \overline{BD}$		1. Given
2. $\angle BCA$ and $\angle DCA$ are rt. ∠'s.		2. ⊥ forms rt. ∠'s.
3. $\triangle BCA$ and $\triangle DCA$ are rt. △'s.		3. Def. of rt. △
4. $\overline{AB} \cong \overline{AD}$	(H)	4. Given
5. $\angle B \cong \angle D$	(A)	5. ∠'s opp. ≅ sides of △ are ≅.
6. ∴ $\triangle BCA \cong \triangle DCA$		6. HA

You found earlier that side-side-angle (SSA) is not a method for proving triangles congruent. However, this pattern can be used to prove right triangles congruent. This is demonstrated in Theorem 5.6. The proof given is an outline of the complete proof. You should complete the details.

Theorem 5.6 (Hypotenuse-Leg) Two right triangles are congruent if the hypotenuse and a leg of one are congruent to the hypotenuse and corresponding leg of the other.

Given: Rt. △'s ABC and $A'B'C'$;
Rt. ∠'s B and B';
$\overline{CA} \cong \overline{C'A'}$, and $\overline{CB} \cong \overline{C'B'}$
Prove: △$ABC \cong$ △$A'B'C'$

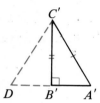

Analysis: Construct △$DC'B'$ with $\overline{B'D} \cong \overline{BA}$. Show △$ABC \cong$ △$DB'C'$. Using corresponding parts.

Outline of proof

1. Extend $\overline{A'B'}$ to D so that $\overline{B'D} \cong \overline{BA}$.
2. Draw $\overline{DC'}$.
3. m ∠$C'B'D$ + m ∠$C'B'A'$ = 180
4. m ∠$C'B'D$ = 90
5. ∠CBA is a rt. ∠.
6. ∠$CBA \cong$ ∠$C'B'D$
7. $\overline{CB} \cong \overline{C'B'}$

8. △$ABC \cong$ △$DB'C'$
9. $\overline{CA} \cong \overline{C'D}$
10. $\overline{CA} \cong \overline{C'A'}$
11. $\overline{C'D} \cong \overline{C'A'}$
12. ∠$C'A'B' \cong$ ∠$C'DB'$
13. △$DB'C' \cong$ △$A'B'C'$
14. △$ABC \cong$ △$A'B'C'$

You can use the hypotenuse-leg theorem (HL) as a reason in other proofs.

Example 2 Given: $\overline{RS} \perp \overline{PQ}$, and
$\overline{PR} \cong \overline{QR}$
Prove: $\overline{RS}$ bisects $\overline{PQ}$.

Proof

Statements		Reasons
1. $\overline{RS} \perp \overline{PQ}$		1. Given
2. ∠PSR and ∠QSR are rt. ∠'s.		2. ⊥ forms rt. ∠'s.
3. △PSR and △QSR are rt. △'s.		3. Def. of rt. △
4. $\overline{PR} \cong \overline{QR}$	(H)	4. Given
5. $\overline{RS} \cong \overline{RS}$	(L)	5. Reflexive property
6. △$PSR \cong$ △QSR		6. HL
7. $\overline{PS} \cong \overline{QS}$		7. CPCTC
8. ∴ $\overline{RS}$ bisects $\overline{PQ}$.		8. Def. of bisector

CONGRUENT RIGHT TRIANGLES

<table>
<tr><td rowspan="2">**Summary**</td><td colspan="4">**Right triangles can be proved congruent by the following:**</td></tr>
<tr><td>Leg–leg
(*LL*)</td><td>Leg–acute angle
(*LA*)</td><td>Hypotenuse–acute angle
(*HA*)</td><td>Hypotenuse–leg
(*HL*)</td></tr>
</table>

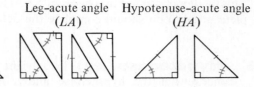 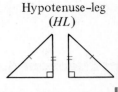

Oral Exercises

Name the hypotenuse and the legs in each right triangle.

1.   **2.**   **3.** 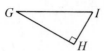 **4.**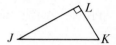

Based on the markings, which of these pairs of right triangles are congruent?

5.   **6.** 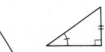 **7.**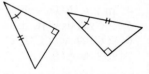

True or false?

8. The hypotenuse of a right triangle is adjacent to the right angle.

9. A leg of a right triangle is opposite an acute angle.

Using each set of given information, is rt. △*ABC* ≅ rt. △*EDF*? Give a reason for your answer.

10. $\overline{AB} \cong \overline{ED}$, and $\overline{AC} \cong \overline{EF}$

12. $\angle A \cong \angle E$, and $\angle C \cong \angle F$

14. $\overline{AC} \cong \overline{EF}$, and $\angle C \cong \angle F$

11. $\angle A \cong \angle E$, and $\overline{AB} \cong \overline{ED}$

13. $\overline{AB} \cong \overline{ED}$, and $\overline{BC} \cong \overline{DF}$

15. $\overline{AC} \cong \overline{EF}$, and $\overline{CB} \cong \overline{FD}$

Written Exercises

A **1.** Given: $\overline{ZY} \perp \overline{XY}$,
$\overline{TS} \perp \overline{RS}$
$\overline{XY} \cong \overline{RS}$, and $\overline{ZY} \cong \overline{TS}$
Prove: △*XYZ* ≅ △*RST*

3. Given: $\overline{ZY} \perp \overline{XY}$
$\overline{TS} \perp \overline{RS}$
$\overline{XY} \cong \overline{RS}$, and $\angle Z \cong \angle T$
Prove: △*XYZ* ≅ △*RST*

 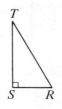

2. Given: $\overline{ZY} \perp \overline{XY}$,
$\overline{TS} \perp \overline{RS}$
$\overline{XZ} \cong \overline{RT}$, and $\angle Z \cong \angle T$
Prove: △*XYZ* ≅ △*RST*

4. Given: $\overline{ZY} \perp \overline{XY}$,
$\overline{TS} \perp \overline{RS}$
$\overline{XZ} \cong \overline{RT}$, and $\overline{XY} \cong \overline{RS}$
Prove: △*XYZ* ≅ △*RST*

5. Given: $\overline{AE} \perp \overline{BC}$, $\overline{BD} \perp \overline{AC}$ and $\overline{AD} \cong \overline{BE}$
   Prove: $\triangle ABE \cong \triangle BAD$

7. Given: $\overline{AE} \perp \overline{BC}$, $\overline{BD} \perp \overline{AC}$, and $\overline{AF} \cong \overline{BF}$
   Prove: $\triangle AFD \cong \triangle BFE$

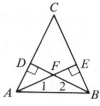

6. Given: $\overline{AE} \perp \overline{BC}$, $\overline{BD} \perp \overline{AC}$, and $\angle 1 \cong \angle 2$
   Prove: $\triangle ABE \cong \triangle BAD$

8. Given: $\overline{AE} \perp \overline{BC}$, $\overline{BD} \perp \overline{AC}$, and $\overline{FD} \cong \overline{FE}$
   Prove: $\triangle AFD \cong \triangle BFE$

 9. Given: $\overline{IJ}$ is $\perp$ bisector of $\overline{GH}$.
   Prove: $\triangle GHI$ is isosceles.

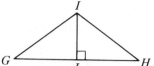

10. Given: $\overline{IJ} \perp \overline{GH}$, and $\overline{IJ}$ bisects $\angle GIH$.
    Prove: $\triangle GHI$ is isosceles.

11. Given: $\overline{LN} \perp \overline{MK}$, $\overline{MO} \perp \overline{LK}$, and $\overline{MK} \cong \overline{LK}$
    Prove: $\overline{MO} \cong \overline{LN}$

12. Given: $\overline{LN} \perp \overline{MK}$, $\overline{MO} \perp \overline{LK}$, and $\overline{NK} \cong \overline{OK}$
    Prove: $\overline{MO} \cong \overline{LK}$

13. Given: $\triangle PQR \cong \triangle UTV$, $\overline{RS} \perp \overline{PQ}$, and $\overline{VW} \perp \overline{UT}$
    Prove: $\overline{RS} \cong \overline{VW}$

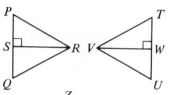

14. Given: $\triangle PQR \cong \triangle UTV$, $\overline{RS} \perp \overline{PQ}$, $\overline{VW} \perp \overline{UT}$, and $\overline{RS}$ bisects $\angle PRQ$.
    Prove: $\overline{VW}$ bisects $\angle UVT$.

 Given: $\overline{ZA} \perp$ plane P at A, $\overline{AX}$ and $\overline{AY}$ are in P, $\overline{XZ} \cong \overline{YZ}$.
15. Prove: $\triangle XAZ \cong \triangle YAZ$
16. Prove: $\angle ZXY \cong \angle ZYX$
17. Prove: $\angle AXY \cong \angle AYX$

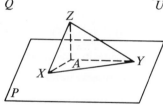

Given: $\overline{ZA} \perp$ plane P at A, $\overline{AX}$ and $\overline{AY}$ are in P, $\overline{XA} \cong \overline{YA}$.
18. Prove: $\triangle XAZ \cong \triangle YAZ$
19. Prove: $\angle ZXY \cong \angle ZYX$
20. Prove: $\angle AXY \cong \angle AYX$

Cumulative Review

1. Draw an example of overlapping triangles. Name the triangles.
2. To prove $\triangle XYZ \cong \triangle RJT$ by AAS, which congruent angles and congruent sides can you use?
3. Do perpendicular segments have to intersect? Perpendicular rays?

A Challenge To You

The floor plans of two houses are shown. Can you walk through the rooms of each house so that you go through each door exactly one time? Draw other floor plans and try them. Is there a way to predict the results without actually trying it?

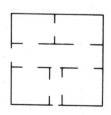
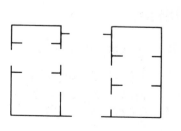

CONGRUENT RIGHT TRIANGLES

5.5 Using Corresponding Parts of Congruent Triangles

OBJECTIVE ► **To prove triangles congruent using corresponding parts of other congruent triangles**

Sometimes, when trying to prove two triangles congruent, it is impossible to show directly that a given pair of angles or sides is congruent. In such cases, however, you may be able to do the following.
  (1) Find another pair of triangles which contain the required angles or sides.
  (2) Prove that these triangles are congruent.
  (3) Use congruent corresponding parts from these triangles as the needed angles or sides.

Example 1

Given: $\overline{XZ}$ and $\overline{WY}$ bisect each other at V.
What combinations of sides and angles can be used to prove $\triangle WYZ \cong \triangle YWX$?
Which other triangles contain the needed sides and angles?

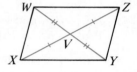

$\overline{WY} \cong \overline{WY}$ (S), $\angle YWZ \cong \angle WYX$ (A), $\overline{WZ} \cong \overline{YX}$ (S)

$\triangle VZW$ and $\triangle VXY$ contain the needed angles and sides.

Example 2 shows you how congruent corresponding parts from congruent triangles can be used to prove another triangle congruency.

Example 2

Complete the missing steps in the following proof.

Given: $\triangle AFD \cong \triangle BFE$,
       $\overline{BD} \perp \overline{AC}$ and
       $\overline{AE} \perp \overline{BC}$
Prove: $\triangle ABD \cong \triangle BAE$

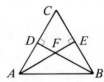

Proof

Statements		Reasons
1. $\triangle AFD \cong \triangle BFE$		1. Given
2. $\overline{AF} \cong \overline{BF}$		2. CPCTC
3. $\angle EAB \cong \angle DBA$	(A)	3. $\angle$'s opp. $\cong$ sides of $\triangle$ are $\cong$.
4. $\overline{BD} \perp \overline{AC}, \overline{AE} \perp \overline{BC}$		4. Given
5. $\angle BDA \cong \angle AEB$	(A)	5. $\perp$'s form $\cong$ rt. $\angle$'s.
6. $\overline{AB} \cong \overline{BA}$	(S)	6. Reflexive property
7. $\therefore \triangle ABD \cong \triangle BAE$		7. AAS

Example 3 Given: $\overline{AD} \cong \overline{CB}$, $\overline{DC} \cong \overline{BA}$, and
F is the midpoint of $\overline{AC}$.
Prove: $\triangle AGF \cong \triangle CEF$

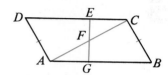

Proof

Statements		Reasons
1. $\overline{AD} \cong \overline{CB}$	(S)	1. Given
2. $\overline{DC} \cong \overline{BA}$	(S)	2. Given
3. $\overline{CA} \cong \overline{AC}$	(S)	3. Reflexive property
4. $\triangle CDA \cong \triangle ABC$		4. SSS
5. $\angle ACD \cong \angle CAB$	(A)	5. CPCTC
6. F is the midpoint of $\overline{AC}$.		6. Given
7. $\overline{AF} \cong \overline{CF}$	(S)	7. Def. of midpoint
8. $\angle AFG \cong \angle CFE$	(A)	8. Vert. $\angle$'s are $\cong$.
9. $\therefore \triangle AGF \cong \triangle CEF$		9. ASA

Written Exercises

For each figure, what combinations of sides and angles can be used to prove the indicated triangle congruency? Which other triangles contain the needed sides and angles? (Ex. 1–3)

A 1. $\triangle ABC \cong \triangle CDA$

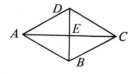

2. $\triangle FGJ \cong \triangle IHJ$

3. $\triangle KLO \cong \triangle MNO$

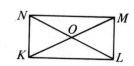

4. Given: $\overline{AD} \cong \overline{BC}$ and $\angle 1 \cong \angle 2$
   Show: $\triangle ABD \cong \triangle BAC$

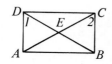

5. Given: $\overline{GI} \perp \overline{FH}$, $\overline{FJ} \perp \overline{GH}$, and $\overline{FJ} \cong \overline{GI}$
   Show: $\triangle FKI \cong \triangle GKJ$

Complete the missing steps in each proof. (Ex. 6–7)

6. Given: $\triangle JFL \cong \triangle KHL$, and $\overline{IH} \parallel \overline{FG}$
   Prove: $\triangle FIH \cong \triangle HGF$

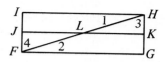

Proof

Statements		Reasons
1. ?		1. Given
2. $\angle 4 \cong \angle 3$	(A)	2. ?
3. ?	(S)	3. ?
4. ?		4. Given
5. $\angle 1 \cong \angle 2$	(A)	5. ?
6. $\therefore \triangle FIH \cong \triangle HGF$		6. ?

USING CORRESPONDING PARTS OF CONGRUENT TRIANGLES

7. Given: $\overline{AC}$ and $\overline{BD}$ bisect each other at E.
　　Prove: $\triangle ABC \cong \triangle CDA$

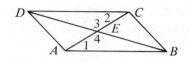

Proof

Statements		Reasons
1. ?		1. Given
2. $\overline{AE} \cong \overline{CE}$		2. ?
3. $\overline{BE} \cong$?		3. ?
4. $\angle 3 \cong \angle 4$		4. ?
5. $\triangle ABE \cong$?		5. SAS
6. $\overline{AB} \cong \overline{CD}$	(S)	6. ?
7. ?	(A)	7. CPCTC
8. $\overline{AC} \cong$?	(S)	8. ?
9. $\therefore \triangle ABC \cong \triangle CDA$		9. ?

8. Given: $\triangle FHL \cong \triangle JHK$,
　　$\overline{LG} \perp \overline{FH}$, and $\overline{KI} \perp \overline{HJ}$.
　　Prove: $\triangle LGH \cong \triangle KIH$

10. Given: $\triangle FGL \cong \triangle HIK$,
　　and $\angle FHL \cong \angle HJK$.
　　Prove: $\triangle FHL \cong \triangle HJK$

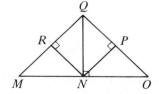

9. Given: $\triangle FHL \cong \triangle HJK$,
　　$\overline{LG} \perp \overline{FH}$, and $\overline{KI} \perp \overline{HJ}$
　　Prove: $\triangle FGL \cong \triangle HIK$

11. Given: $\triangle FGL \cong \triangle JIK$,
　　$\overline{LG} \perp \overline{FH}$, $\overline{KI} \perp \overline{HJ}$,
　　$\overline{GH} \cong \overline{HI}$
　　Prove: $\triangle FHL \cong \triangle JHK$

12. Given: $\overline{QN} \perp \overline{MO}$,
　　$\overline{NR} \perp \overline{MQ}$, $\overline{NP} \perp \overline{OQ}$,
　　and $\overline{NM} \cong \overline{NO}$.
　　Prove: $\overline{NR} \cong \overline{NP}$

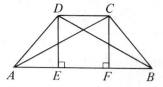

13. Given: $\overline{QN} \perp \overline{MO}$,
　　$\overline{NR} \perp \overline{MQ}$, $\overline{NP} \perp \overline{OQ}$,
　　and $\overline{NR} \cong \overline{NP}$
　　Prove: $\overline{NM} \cong \overline{NO}$

Ⓑ **14.** Given: $\overline{AD} \cong \overline{BC}$,
　　$\overline{DE} \perp \overline{AB}$, $\overline{CF} \perp \overline{AB}$,
　　and $\overline{DE} \cong \overline{CF}$
　　Prove: $\overline{AC} \cong \overline{BD}$

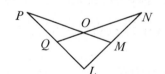

15. Given: $\overline{DE} \perp \overline{AB}$,
　　$\overline{CF} \perp \overline{AB}$, $\overline{DE} \cong \overline{CF}$,
　　and $\overline{AC} \cong \overline{DB}$
　　Prove: $\overline{AD} \cong \overline{BC}$

16. Given: $\triangle JHG \cong \triangle HJI$,
　　$\overline{JG} \perp \overline{GH}$, and
　　$m \angle JGI = 63$
　　Find $m \angle HJI$.

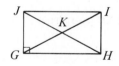

17. Given: $\triangle PLM \cong \triangle NLQ$,
　　$m \angle L = 88$, and
　　$m \angle P = 26$.
　　Find $m \angle NQL$.

18. Given: $\triangle SVW \cong RVU$,
　　$\overline{RW} \perp \overline{ST}$, and
　　$m \angle T = 60$
　　Find $\angle RVS$.

Using the given information, prove each of the following. (Ex. 19–25)

Given: $\overline{AD} \perp \overline{AB}$, $\overline{BC} \perp \overline{AB}$, and $\overline{AD} \cong \overline{BC}$

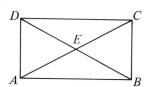

19. Prove: $\overline{AC} \cong \overline{BD}$
20. Prove: $\triangle AEB$ is isosceles.
21. Prove: $\overline{ED} \cong \overline{EC}$
22. Prove: $\overline{AB} \parallel \overline{DC}$
23. Prove: $\overline{AD} \perp \overline{DC}$ and $\overline{BC} \perp \overline{DC}$.
24. Prove: $\triangle AEB \cong \triangle CED$
25. Prove: $\overline{AE} \cong \overline{BE} \cong \overline{CE} \cong \overline{DE}$

C 26. Given: $\overline{FJ} \cong \overline{HJ}$,
$\angle 1 \cong \angle 3$, and
G is the midpoint of $\overline{FH}$
Prove: $\overline{FI} \cong \overline{HK}$

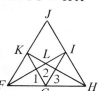

27. Given: $\overline{QR} \cong \overline{MR}$,
and $\overline{PR} \cong \overline{NR}$
Prove: $\overline{OQ} \cong \overline{OM}$

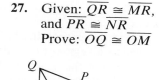
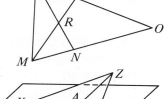

28. Given: $\overline{US} \cong \overline{TS}$, and
$\overline{UV} \cong \overline{TV}$
Prove: $\triangle UWT$ is
isosceles

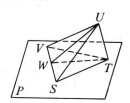

29. Given: $\overline{AZ} \cong \overline{AY}$ and
$\overline{XZ} \cong \overline{XY}$
Prove: $\overline{ZB} \cong \overline{YB}$

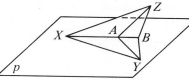

30. Given: $\angle ZXB \cong \angle YXB$
and $\angle XZA \cong \angle XYA$
Prove: $\angle XZB \cong \angle XYB$

A Challenge To You

Many different figures can be made from segments. The intersection of two or more of these segments is a *vertex*. These segments can enclose *regions*. Each figure below has a certain number of segments (S), vertices (V), and regions (R). Is there any relationship between S, V, and R?

$V = 5, S = 7, R = 3$

$V = 6, S = 7, R = 2$

$V = 9, S = 12, R = 4$

$V = 9, S = 14, R = 6$

How many regions should a figure with 8 vertices and 13 segments have? Can you draw such a figure?

How many segments should be used to connect 10 vertices to form 5 regions? Can you draw such a figure?

How many vertices are needed if 15 segments form 7 regions? Can you draw such a figure?

5.6 Bisectors

OBJECTIVE ▶ **To prove and apply theorems about bisectors**

You learned earlier that any figure which contains the midpoint of a segment is called a *bisector* of the segment. Since every segment has exactly one midpoint, it has at least one bisector. In the figure at the right, line *l* is the bisector of $\overline{AB}$.

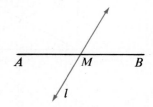

A special bisector is the perpendicular bisector. A segment, ray, or line that is both perpendicular to a segment and also a bisector of the segment is called the *perpendicular bisector* of the segment. You can use congruent triangles to prove the following theorem about perpendicular bisectors.

Theorem 5.7 Perpendicular Bisector Theorem

A point on the perpendicular bisector of a segment is equidistant from the endpoints of the segment.

Given: $\overleftrightarrow{CM}$ is ⊥ bisector of $\overline{XY}$, and
P is on $\overrightarrow{CM}$.
Prove: $PX = PY$

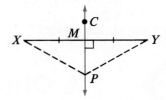

Proof

Statements		Reasons
1. $\overleftrightarrow{CM}$ is ⊥ bisector of $\overline{XY}$.		1. Given
2. P is on $\overrightarrow{CM}$.		2. Given
3. $\overline{XM} \cong \overline{YM}$	(L)	3. Def of bisector
4. $\triangle XMP$ and $\triangle YMP$ are rt. △'s.		4. ⊥ forms rt. ∠'s.
5. $\overline{PM} \cong \overline{PM}$	(L)	5. Reflexive property
6. $\triangle XMP \cong \triangle YMP$		6. LL
7. $\overline{PX} \cong \overline{PY}$		7. CPCTC
8. ∴ $\overline{PX} = \overline{PY}$		8. Def. of ≅ segments

Example 1 Based on the given information, which segments are congruent?

Given: $\overline{CP}$ is the ⊥ bisector of $\overline{AB}$.

$\overline{AP} \cong \overline{BP}$, and $\overline{AC} \cong \overline{BC}$.

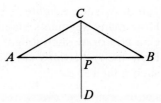

Below is another theorem about perpendicular bisectors. You should complete the details of the proof.

┌─ **Theorem 5.8** A line containing two points each equidistant from the ─┐
end points of a segment is the perpendicular bisector of
the segment. (See Exercise 13.)

Given: $AP = BP$ and
$\quad AQ = BQ$
Prove: $\overleftrightarrow{PO}$ is the ⊥ bisector
$\quad$ of $\overline{AB}$.

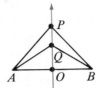

Analysis: Show $\overline{AO} \cong \overline{BO}$
and $\angle AOP \cong \angle BOP$ by
corr. parts of ≅ △'s
AOP and BOP.

Outline of Proof

1. $\overline{AP} \cong \overline{BP}$ (S)
2. $\overline{AQ} \cong \overline{BQ}$ (S)
3. $\overline{PQ} \cong \overline{PQ}$ (S)
4. $\triangle APQ \cong \triangle BPQ$
5. $\angle APQ \cong \angle BPQ$ (A)
6. $\overline{PO} \cong \overline{PO}$ (S)

7. $\triangle AOP \cong \triangle BOP$
8. $\overline{AO} \cong \overline{BO}$
9. $\angle AOP \cong \angle BOP$
10. $\angle AOP$ and $\angle BOP$ are supp.
11. $\angle AOP$ and $\angle BOP$ are rt. $\angle$'s.
12. ∴ $\overleftrightarrow{PO}$ is the ⊥ bisector of $\overleftrightarrow{AB}$

Every angle has a bisector. You can prove statements about angle bisectors using corresponding parts.

Example 2 Prove: The perpendicular bisector of a side of an equilateral triangle bisects the opposite angle.

Given: Equil. $\triangle ABC$,
$\quad \overline{CD} \perp \overline{AB}$,
$\quad$ and $\overline{CD}$ bisects $\overline{AB}$.
Prove: $\overline{CD}$ bisects $\angle C$.

Proof

Statement	Reasons
1. $\triangle ABC$ is equilateral.	1. Given
2. $\overline{CD} \perp \overline{AB}$, $\overline{CD}$ bisects $\overline{AB}$.	2. Given
3. $\triangle ADC$ and $\triangle BDC$ are rt. △'s.	3. ⊥ forms rt. $\angle$'s.
4. $\overline{AC} \cong \overline{BC}$ (H)	4. Def. of equil. △
5. $\overline{AD} \cong \overline{BD}$ (L)	5. Def. of bisector
6. $\triangle ADC \cong \triangle BDC$	6. HL
7. $\angle ACD \cong \angle BCD$	7. CPCTC
8. ∴ $\overline{CD}$ bisects $\angle C$.	8. Def. of angle bisector

Written **Exercises**

Based on the given information, which segments or angles are congruent?

A 1. Given: $\overline{ZW}$ bisects
∠XZY.

2. Given: $\overline{ZW}$ bisects
$\overline{XY}$.

3. Given: $\overline{XZ} \cong \overline{YZ}$,
and $\overline{XW} \cong \overline{YW}$

4. Given: $\overline{AC} \cong \overline{AB}$
and $\overline{DC} \cong \overline{DB}$

5. Given: $\overline{DE}$ bisects
∠BDC.

6. Given: $\overleftrightarrow{AE}$ is ⊥ bisector.
of $\overline{BC}$

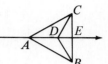

Prove each of the following.

7. The bisector of the vertex angle of an isosceles triangle bisects the base of the triangle.

8. The bisector of the base of an isosceles triangle bisects the vertex angle of the triangle.

 9. The bisector of the vertex angle of an isosceles triangle is the perpendicular bisector of the base.

10. If the perpendicular from the vertex angle of a triangle to the base bisects the vertex angle, then the triangle is isosceles.

11. All points in the bisector of an angle are equidistant from the sides of the angle. (Note: This distance is along the perpendicular from the point to the line.)

12. Perpendicular segments from the midpoints of the legs of an isosceles triangle to the base are congruent.

13. Complete the proof of Theorem 5.8.

14. Segments of the bisectors of base angles of isosceles triangles cut off by the legs of the triangle are congruent.

15. Given: $\overline{BD}$ is the ⊥ bisector of $\overline{AC}$.
Prove: ∠BAD ≅ ∠BCD

16. Given: ∠2 ≅ ∠4, and ∠FIH ≅ ∠FGH
Prove: $\overline{FH}$ is a ⊥ bisector of $\overline{GI}$

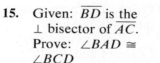

17. Given: ∠1 ≅ ∠3, and ∠FIH ≅ ∠FGH
Prove: $\overline{FH}$ is the bisector of ∠IHG.

18. Given: $\overline{ML}$ ⊥ plane p, and $\overline{MO}$ is a ⊥ bisector of $\overline{NK}$.
Prove: $\overline{LO}$ is a ⊥ bisector of $\overline{NK}$.

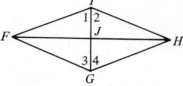

19. Given: $\overline{ML}$ ⊥ plane p, $\overline{NM} \cong \overline{KM}$, and $\overline{MO}$ bisects ∠NMK.
Prove: $\overline{LO}$ bisects ∠NLK.

Cumulative **Review**

1. List four congruence patterns for triangles.
2. List four congruence patterns for right triangles.
3. Draw an angle. Construct the bisector of the angle.

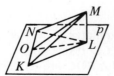

5·7 Altitudes and Medians of Triangles

OBJECTIVES ► **To identify altitudes and medians of triangles**
To prove and apply theorems about altitudes and medians of triangles

There are two special types of segments related to triangles: altitudes and medians.

Definition:
altitude of
a triangle

> An **altitude of a triangle** is a segment from a vertex of the triangle, perpendicular to the line containing the opposite side of the triangle.

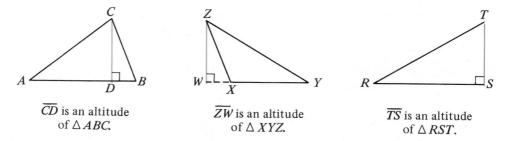

$\overline{CD}$ is an altitude
of $\triangle ABC$.

$\overline{ZW}$ is an altitude
of $\triangle XYZ$.

$\overline{TS}$ is an altitude
of $\triangle RST$.

As you can see from the figures above, altitudes (except for their endpoints) can be in the interior or exterior of the triangle or on the triangle itself. Although the endpoints of altitude $\overline{CD}$ above are not in the interior of $\triangle ABC$, all other points of the altitude are. For convenience, the statement "$\overline{CD}$ is in the interior of $\triangle ABC$" will be used. You will use a similar agreement about other segments related to triangles.

Every triangle has three altitudes, one from each vertex to the line containing the opposite side. In $\triangle ABC$ below, $\overline{CX}$, $\overline{AY}$, and $\overline{BZ}$ are all altitudes. In this case, all three altitudes are in the interior of the triangle.

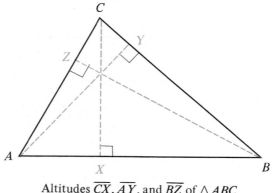

Altitudes $\overline{CX}$, $\overline{AY}$, and $\overline{BZ}$ of $\triangle ABC$

The other special segment related to a triangle is a median.

Definition:
median of
a triangle

> A **median of a triangle** is a segment from a vertex of the triangle to the midpoint of the opposite side of the triangle.

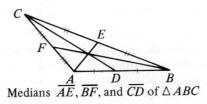

Medians $\overline{AE}, \overline{BF}$, and $\overline{CD}$ of $\triangle ABC$

Every triangle has three medians, one from each vertex. As shown in the diagram above, each median bisects the opposite side.

Example 1 Which segments are altitudes of the given triangles? Which are medians?

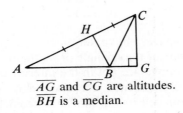

$\overline{AG}$ and $\overline{CG}$ are altitudes.
$\overline{BH}$ is a median.

$\overline{DI}$ is an altitude.
$\overline{DJ}$ is a median.

In certain cases, a median is also an altitude.

Example 2 Given: $\overline{CD}$ is a median and an altitude.
Prove: $\triangle ABC$ is isosceles.

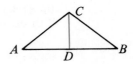

Proof

Statements		Reasons
1. $\overline{CD}$ is a median and an altitude.		1. Given
2. $\overline{CD} \perp \overline{AB}$		2. Def. of altitude
3. $\triangle ADC$ and $\triangle BDC$ are rt. $\triangle$'s.		3. $\perp$ forms rt. $\angle$'s.
4. $\overline{AD} \cong \overline{BD}$	(L)	4. Def. of median
5. $\overline{CD} \cong \overline{CD}$	(L)	5. Reflexive property
6. $\triangle ADC \cong \triangle BDC$		6. LL
7. $\overline{AC} \cong \overline{BC}$		7. CPCTC
8. $\therefore \triangle ABC$ is isosceles.		8. Def. of isosceles $\triangle$

Corresponding medians of congruent triangles are medians that are drawn to corresponding congruent sides of the triangles. You can prove that these corresponding medians are congruent.

> **Theorem 5.9** Corresponding medians of congruent triangles are congruent. (See Exercise 13.)

Given: $\triangle ABC \cong \triangle A'B'C'$, $\overline{CD}$ is a median of $\triangle ABC$, and $\overline{C'D'}$ is a median of $\triangle A'B'C'$.
Prove: $\overline{CD} \cong \overline{C'D'}$

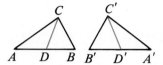

Outline of Proof

1. $\triangle ABC \cong \triangle A'B'C'$
2. $\overline{AB} \cong \overline{A'B'}$
3. $AB = A'B'$
4. $\overline{CD}$ and $\overline{C'D'}$ are medians.
5. $AD = \frac{1}{2}AB$, $A'D' = \frac{1}{2}A'B'$
6. $AD = A'D'$

7. $\overline{AD} \cong \overline{A'D'}$ (S)
8. $\angle A \cong \angle A'$ (A)
9. $\overline{CA} \cong \overline{C'A'}$ (S)
10. $\triangle CAD \cong \triangle C'A'D'$
11. $\therefore \overline{CD} \cong \overline{C'D'}$

> **Theorem 5.10** Corresponding altitudes of congruent triangles are congruent. (See Exercise 14.)

You can use Theorems 5.9 and 5.10 to find measures of corresponding altitudes or medians.

Example 3 Given: $\triangle EGH \cong \triangle KIJ$, $\overline{HF}$ and $\overline{JL}$ are corresponding altitudes, $HF = 12x - 4$, and $JL = 10x + 10$. Find HF.

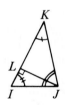

$$HF = JL \quad \blacktriangleleft Use\ Th.\ 5.10.$$
$$12x - 4 = 10x + 10$$
$$2x = 14$$
$$x = 7$$
Thus, $HF = 12(7) - 4$ or 80.

ALTITUDES AND MEDIANS OF TRIANGLES   **171**

Oral Exercises

Which segments are altitudes? Which are medians?

1.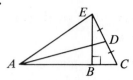

2.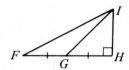

3.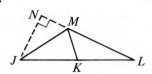

Written Exercises

Prove each of the following.

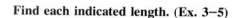

A 1. Given: $\overline{CD}$ is an altitude and $\overline{AD} \cong \overline{BD}$.
   Prove: $\triangle ADC \cong \triangle BDC$

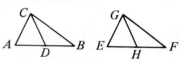

2. Given: $\overline{CD}$ is a median and $\overline{AC} \cong \overline{BC}$.
   Prove: $\triangle ADC \cong \triangle BDC$

Find each indicated length. (Ex. 3–5)

3. Given: $\triangle ABC \cong \triangle EFG$, $\overline{CD}$ and $\overline{GH}$ are corresponding medians, $CD = 6s + 2$, and $GH = 8s - 14$. Find CD.

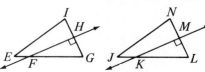

4. Given: $\triangle IJK \cong \triangle NMO$, $\overline{IL}$ and $\overline{NP}$ are corresponding altitudes, $IL = 3(t + 3)$, and $NP = 4(2t + 1)$. Find IL.

5. Given: $\triangle QRS \cong \triangle WVU$, $\overline{ST}$ and $\overline{UX}$ are corresponding medians, $ST = 9a - 2$, and $UX = 4(a + 2)$. Find ST.

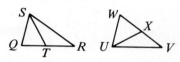

6. Given: $\overline{ZW}$ is an altitude of $\triangle XYZ$ and a bisector of $\overline{XY}$.
   Prove: $\triangle XYZ$ is isosceles.

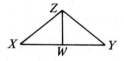

7. Given: $\overline{ZW}$ is an altitude of $\triangle XYZ$ and bisects $\angle XZY$.
   Prove: $\triangle XYZ$ is isosceles.

8. Given: $\overline{CD}$ is an altitude of $\triangle ABC$.
   Prove: m $\angle 1$ + m $\angle 2$ = m $\angle 3$ + m $\angle 4$

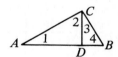

9. Given: $\overline{AC} \perp \overline{CB}$ and $\angle 1 \cong \angle 3$
   Prove: $\overline{CD}$ is an altitude of $\triangle ABC$.

B 10. Given: $\triangle EGI \cong \triangle JLN$, $\overline{FH}$ is the $\perp$ bisector of $\overline{GI}$, and $\overline{KM}$ is the $\perp$ bisector of $\overline{LN}$. Prove: $\overline{FH} \cong \overline{KM}$.

11. Given: $\triangle OPQ \cong \triangle TSV$, $\overrightarrow{PR}$ bisects $\angle OPQ$, and $\overrightarrow{SU}$ bisects $\angle VST$. Prove: $\overline{PR} \cong \overline{SU}$

12. Given: $\overline{BZ} \cong \overline{AC}$, $\overline{BZ}$ is the $\perp$ bisector of $\overline{YW}$, and $\overline{AC}$ is the $\perp$ bisector of $\overline{YX}$. Prove: $\overline{YW} \cong \overline{YX}$

 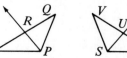

13. Complete the proof of Theorem 5.9.   **14.** Prove Theorem 5.10.

For each statement, draw a diagram and label it. State what is given and what is to be proved in terms of the diagram. Prove the statement.

15. Any two altitudes of an equilateral triangle are congruent.

16. Any two medians of an equilateral triangle are congruent.

17. The altitude to the base of an isosceles triangle is also a median.

18. If two altitudes of a triangle are congruent, then the triangle is isosceles.

19. The median to the base of an isosceles triangle is the bisector of the vertex angle.

20. The altitude to the base of an isosceles triangle is the bisector of the vertex angle.

Determine if each of the following is a true statement. If so, prove it. If not, show a counter example. (Ex. 21–24)

21. If a median of a triangle is perpendicular to the side to which it is drawn, then the triangle is isosceles.

22. If an altitude of a triangle also bisects an angle of the triangle, then the triangle is isosceles.

23. If a median of a triangle bisects the vertex angle, then the triangle is isosceles.

24. If two medians of a triangle are also angle bisectors, then the triangle is equilateral.

25. Given: $\overline{DB} \perp$ plane p, $\overline{DE}$ bisects $\angle CDA$, and $\overline{CD} \cong \overline{AD}$.
Prove: $\overline{BE}$ bisects $\angle CBA$.

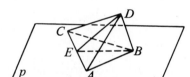

26. Given: $\overline{DB} \perp$ plane p, and $\overline{DE}$ is a median and an altitude of $\triangle CDA$.
Prove: $\overline{BE}$ is a median and an altitude of $\triangle CBA$.

27. Given: $\triangle FJG \cong \triangle FHG$, and $\overline{JI}$ is an altitude of $\triangle FJG$.
Prove: $\overline{HI}$ is an altitude of $\triangle FHG$.

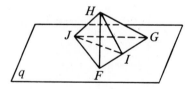

28. Given: $\triangle FJG \cong \triangle FHG$, and $\overline{HI}$ bisects $\angle FHG$.
Prove: $\overline{JI}$ bisects $\angle FJG$.

Given: $\overline{KM}$ is $\perp$ bisector of $\overline{NO}$, and $\overline{LM}$ is $\perp$ bisector of $\overline{NO}$.
29. Prove: $\triangle OLM \cong \triangle NLM$
30. Prove: $\triangle KLN \cong \triangle KLO$

Given: $\triangle KLM$ in plane r, $\overline{NO} \perp r$ at M, $\overline{NM} \cong \overline{OM}$, and $\overline{LN} \cong \overline{KN}$.
31. Prove: $\overline{LM} \cong \overline{KM}$
32. Prove: $\overline{LO} \cong \overline{KO}$

ALTITUDES AND MEDIANS OF TRIANGLES   **173**

5.8 Constructions of Altitudes and Bisectors

OBJECTIVES ► **To construct altitudes and medians of triangles**
To use constructions to determine if a statement is true or false

You have already learned several basic geometric constructions. These constructions can now be used as parts of other constructions. In Example 1, the midpoint of a segment is constructed to get a median of the triangle. In Example 2, a perpendicular is constructed to obtain an altitude of the triangle, and in Example 3, the procedure for bisecting an angle is applied three times to construct the bisector of each angle of the triangle. You may want to review these three basic constructions before studying the examples.

Example 1 Draw an obtuse △XYZ, with obtuse ∠X. Construct the median to side $\overline{YZ}$.

Construct the midpoint M of $\overline{YZ}$. Draw $\overline{XM}$. ►

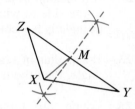

Conclusion: $\overline{XM}$ **is the required median.**

Example 2 Draw an acute △ABC. Construct the altitude to side $\overline{AB}$.

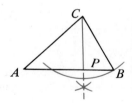

◄ *Construct a ⊥ to $\overline{AB}$ from point C.*

Conclusion: $\overline{CP}$ **is the required altitude.**

Example 3 Draw an equilateral triangle. Construct the bisectors of all three angles. Where do they meet?

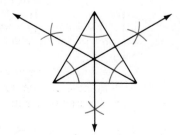

Conclusion: **All three meet in a single point in the interior of the triangle.**

A construction can sometimes be used to determine if a given statement is true or false. The construction will usually show if a statement is false, but it cannot prove conclusively that it is true.

Example 4 True or false? "The bisector of the vertex angle of an isosceles triangle bisects the base." Check by making the necessary construction.

Construct $\overrightarrow{CD}$ bisecting $\angle C$. ▶

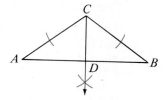

$\overline{AD}$ and $\overline{BD}$ appear to be congruent. **Thus,** the statement seems to be true.

Written Exercises _____

Copy the given triangle. Construct each of the following.

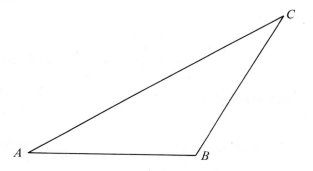

A 1. The bisector of $\angle ABC$.

2. The median to $\overline{AB}$.

3. The perpendicular bisector of $\overline{AB}$.

4. The altitude to $\overline{AC}$.

5. The altitude to $\overline{AB}$.

6. The median to $\overline{AC}$.

True or false? Check by making the necessary constructions. (Ex. 7–14)

B 7. A median of a scalene triangle can never be an altitude.

8. A median of a scalene triangle can never be an angle bisector.

9. A median of a scalene triangle can never be a perpendicular bisector of a side of the triangle.

10. An altitude of a scalene triangle can never be a perpendicular bisector of a side of the triangle.

11. A median of an isosceles triangle can never be an altitude.

12. A median of an isosceles triangle can never be an angle bisector.

13. An altitude of an isosceles triangle can never be a perpendicular bisector of a side of the triangle.

14. An angle bisector of an isosceles triangle can never be a perpendicular bisector of a side of the triangle.

15. Draw three triangles — one acute, one obtuse, and one right. Construct the three altitudes of each triangle. What conclusions can you draw about the intersections of these altitudes?

16. Repeat Exercise 14, constructing the three medians.

17. Repeat Exercise 14, constructing the three angle bisectors.

18. Repeat Exercise 14, constructing the three perpendicular bisectors of the sides.

Cumulative Review

1. Can the altitude of a triangle be located in the exterior of the triangle? If so, for what kind of triangle?

2. Can the median of a triangle be located in the exterior of the triangle? If so, for what kind of triangle?

3. Draw two parallel lines. Draw a third line intersecting one of these lines. Will this third line ever intersect the other line? Explain.

Algebra Review

OBJECTIVE ▶ To multiply and divide fractions

To multiply fractions:
1. Use $\dfrac{a}{b} \cdot \dfrac{c}{d} = \dfrac{a \cdot c}{b \cdot d}$.
2. Factor both numerator and denominator.
3. Divide out common factors.

To divide fractions:
1. Use the reciprocal of the denominator.
2. Multiply.

Example Divide $\dfrac{x^2 - 4}{x + 4} \div \dfrac{x - 2}{x^2 + x - 12}$.

Use the reciprocal of $\dfrac{x - 2}{x^2 + x - 12}$ and multiply.

$$\dfrac{x^2 - 4}{x + 4} \cdot \dfrac{x^2 + x - 12}{x - 2}$$

Use $\dfrac{a}{b} \cdot \dfrac{c}{d} = \dfrac{a \cdot c}{b \cdot d}$.

$$\dfrac{(x^2 - 4)(x^2 + x - 12)}{(x + 4)(x - 2)}$$

Factor and divide out common factors.

$$\dfrac{\overset{1}{\cancel{(x - 2)}}(x + 2)\overset{1}{\cancel{(x + 4)}}(x - 3)}{\underset{1}{\cancel{(x + 4)}}\underset{1}{\cancel{(x - 2)}}}$$

$$\dfrac{(x + 2)(x - 3)}{1}, \text{ or } x^2 - x - 6$$

Simplify.

1. $\dfrac{x^2 - 4}{4x + 12} \cdot \dfrac{2x + 6}{4x + 8}$

2. $\dfrac{9x^2 - 25}{x^2 - 16} \div \dfrac{3x - 5}{2x - 8}$

3. $\dfrac{y^2 + 3y + 2}{y^2 - 3y - 10} \div \dfrac{y^2 + 8y + 7}{y^2 - 6y + 5}$

4. $\dfrac{9 - y^2}{4 + 2y} \cdot \dfrac{8 + 4y}{9 - 3y}$

5. $\dfrac{z^2 - 4z + 3}{z^2 + 7z + 6} \cdot \dfrac{2z^2 + 6z + 4}{z^2 - z - 6}$

6. $\dfrac{6z^2 + 5z - 6}{3z^2 + 13z - 10} \div \dfrac{4z^2 - 9}{2z^2 + 7z - 15}$

176

CHAPTER FIVE

Applications

1. Electric wires are to be strung between two poles across a gulch. The power company needs to know how much wire is needed, but it is impossible to measure directly across the gulch. How could this distance be found using the given diagram? Why does this work?

2. A homemade carpenter's level has an isosceles triangular frame, with a plumb bob hanging from the vertex. The plumb bob should always hang vertically. How can this be used to show whether or not a surface is horizontal? Why does this work?

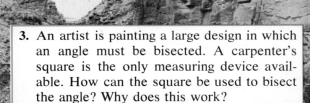

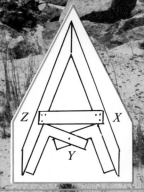

3. An artist is painting a large design in which an angle must be bisected. A carpenter's square is the only measuring device available. How can the square be used to bisect the angle? Why does this work?

4. In building an A-frame cabin, a cross brace must be fastened so that the angles it forms with the rafters are congruent. The carpenter places two carpenters squares as shown so that $YZ = YX$. Are the given angles then congruent? Why?

Chapter Five Review

Vocabulary

altitude [5.7], base angles [5.2], corresponding parts [5.1], hypotenuse [5.4], leg [5.2], median [5.7], perimeter [5.2], perpendicular bisector [5.6], vertex angle [5.2]

If $\triangle ABC \cong \triangle DFE$, name the following,

[5.1]

1. The pairs of congruent sides.

2. The pairs of congruent angles

Identify the following.

[5.4]

3. The hypotenuse of $\triangle DEF$.

4. The legs of $\triangle ABC$.

Which pairs of right triangles are congruent? What is the reason? [5.4]

5.

6.

7.

Tell whether $\overline{AX}$ is an altitude, a median, or neither. (Ex. 8–10) [5.7]

8. 9. 10.

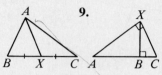

11. Given: $\overline{AD} \cong \overline{AB}$, and $\overline{AC}$ bisects $\angle DAB$
    Prove: $\overline{CD} \cong \overline{CB}$ [5.6]

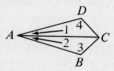

12. Given: $\overline{AC}$ bisects $\angle DCB$, [5.6]
    Prove: m $\angle 1 +$ m $\angle 4 =$ m $\angle 2 +$ m $\angle 3$

13. Given: $\triangle GHF \cong \triangle GIE$, [5.2, 5.5]
    Prove: $\overline{HE} \cong \overline{IF}$

*14. Given: $\overline{FH}$ and $\overline{EI}$ are altitudes of $\triangle GEF$, [5.7]
     and $\angle HFE \cong \angle IEF$,
     Prove: $\triangle GEF$ is isosceles

15. Given: Isosceles $\triangle LJK$, $\overline{LJ} \cong \overline{LK}$, m $\angle J =$ [5.2]
    $5x$, and m $\angle K = 6x - 11$.
    Find m $\angle J$.

16. Given: $\angle J \cong \angle K$, $JL = 2x + 7$, and $KL =$ [5.2]
    $4x + 1$
    Find KL.

*17. Draw an obtuse triangle. Construct the altitude from the vertex of one of the acute angles. [5.8]

Chapter Five Test

If $\triangle UVW \cong \triangle XYZ$, name the following.

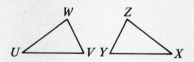

1. The pairs of congruent angles?

2. The pairs of congruent sides.

Identify the following.

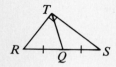

3. The hypotenuse and legs of $\triangle RST$.

4. An altitude and a median of $\triangle RST$

Which pairs of right triangles are congruent? What is the reason?

5.

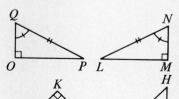

6.

True or false? (Ex. 7–8)

7. Any two altitudes of an isosceles triangle are congruent.

8. Two right triangles are congruent if a leg and hypotenuse of one are congruent to the corresponding leg and hypotenuse of the other.

9. Given: Isosceles $\triangle CED, \overline{CE} \cong \overline{DE}$, m $\angle C = 8x - 16$, and m $\angle D = 6x + 2$. Find m $\angle D$.

10. Given: $\angle C \cong \angle D$, $CE = 4y + 8$, and $DE = 6y - 2$
Find DE

11. Draw an obtuse triangle. Construct the median to the longest side.

*12. Given: $\overline{CD}$ bisects $\angle ACB$, and $\overline{CD} \perp \overline{AB}$
Prove: $\triangle ABC$ is isosceles.

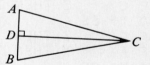

*13. Given: $\triangle EFG \cong \triangle JIK$, and $\overline{GH}$ and $\overline{KL}$ are altitudes.
Prove: $\overline{HF} \cong \overline{LI}$

14. Given: $\overline{MP}$ is an altitude of $\triangle MNO$.
Prove: m $\angle 1 +$ m $\angle 4 =$ m $\angle 2 +$ m $\angle 3$

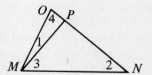

Computer Activities

The program below tests for congruent triangles by comparing two sides and the included angle of Triangle 1 to the corresponding parts of Triangle 2.

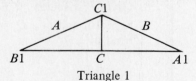

Triangle 1

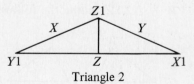

Triangle 2

See the computer section on page 560 for more information.

PROGRAM

```
  5 PRINT "PROGRAM TESTS FOR CONGRUENT TRIANGLES BY 'SAS'"
 10 PRINT "ENTER MEASURES OF CORRESPONDING SIDES"
 15 INPUT A, B, C, X, Y, Z
 20 PRINT "ENTER MEASURES OF CORRESPONDING ANGLES"
 25 INPUT A1, B1, C1, X1, Y1, Z1
 30 IF A <> X THEN 45
 35 IF B <> Y THEN 60
 40 GO TO 75
 45 IF B <> Y THEN 60
 50 IF C <> Z THEN 100
 55 GO TO 85
 60 IF C <> Z THEN 100
 65 IF A <> X THEN 100
 70 GO TO 95
 75 IF C1 = Z1 THEN 110
 80 GO TO 100
 85 IF A1 = X1 THEN 110
 90 GO TO 100
 95 IF B1 = Y1 THEN 110
100 PRINT "NOT CONGRUENT BY 'SAS'"
105 GO TO 115
110 PRINT "CONGRUENT TRIANGLES BY 'SAS'"
115 END
```

Exercises

1. Run the program for the following side and angle measures.
   $A = 3$, $B = 3$, $C = 3$, $X = 4$, $Y = 4$, $Z = 4$, $A1 = 60$, $B1 = 60$, $C1 = 60$, $X1 = 60$, $Y1 = 60$, $Z1 = 60$.
2. Make a flow chart to correspond to the statements in the program above.
   Write a program to check for congruent triangles by each of the following. (Ex. 2–3)
3. SSS   4. ASA   5. AAS

           ACTIVITY: CONGRUENT TRIANGLES

College Prep Test

For each item, choose the best answer. Indicate your answer by writing the letter of this choice.

1. In an isosceles $\triangle RST$, if m $\angle R = 38$, then which of the following cannot be true?
   (A) m $\angle S = 71$ (B) m $\angle S = 38$
   (C) m $\angle T = 71$ (D) m $\angle T = 104$
   (E) None of these

2. Given: $\triangle AFD \cong \triangle BFE$, $\overline{BD} \perp \overline{AC}$, m $\angle C =$ 50. What is m $\angle AFB$?

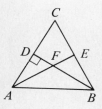

   (A) 40° (B) 50° (C) 90° (D) 100° (E) 130°

3.

How many triangles are there in the figure above?
   (A) 1 (B) 3 (C) 4 (D) 6 (E) 8

4. Right triangles cannot be proved congruent by
   (A) HL (B) SSA (C) Leg-leg
   (D) AA (E) Leg-acute angle

5. In $\triangle ABC$, $\overline{AB} \cong \overline{CB}$, m $\angle A = 2x - 10$, m $\angle B = 3x + 25$. Which of the following is true?
   (A) m $\angle A = 25$
   (B) m $\angle A = 100$
   (C) m $\angle B = 40$
   (D) m $\angle C = 25$
   (E) m $\angle C = 40$

6.

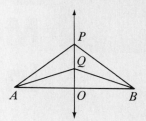

To prove that "two points each equidistant from the end points of a segment determine the perpendicular bisector of the segment," it is necessary to show that

   (A) $\triangle AOQ \cong \triangle BOQ$ by SSS
   (B) $\triangle AOP \cong \triangle BOP$ by SAS
   (C) $\triangle AOP \cong \triangle BOP$ by ASA
   (D) $\triangle AQP \cong \triangle BQP$ by SSS
   (E) $\triangle AQP \cong \triangle BQP$ by AAS

7. Which of the following cannot be true?

   (A) A median of a triangle is also an altitude.
   (B) Corresponding medians of congruent triangles are congruent.
   (C) A median of a triangle is also an angle bisector.
   (D) A median is outside the triangle.
   (E) An altitude is outside the triangle.

8. The construction of the median of a triangle involves the construction of

   (A) angle bisector
   (B) midpoint of a segment
   (C) segment congruent to a segment
   (D) angle congruent to an angle
   (E) equilateral triangle

6 EXPLORING POLYGONS

Mathematics in Surveying

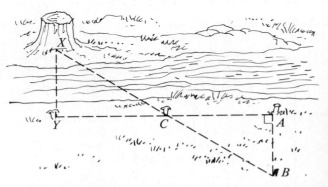

A surveyor drives a stake at *A* so that ∠*XYA* is a right angle. The stake at *C* is halfway between *Y* and *A*. The stake at *B* is on the line of sight from *C* to *X* so that ∠*YAB* is a right angle. How can the distance from *Y* to *X* be determined without crossing the river?

Mathematics helps surveyors make accurate measurements of the earth. This surveyor is sighting through an instrument called a transit.

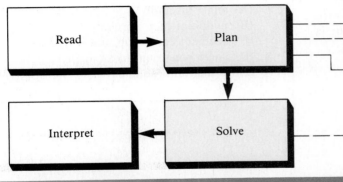

Read → Plan

- Analyze the information
- Decide on the property that can be used to solve **CPCTC**
- Write a mathematical sentence $\overline{XY} \cong \overline{AB}$

Plan → Solve

Interpret ← Solve

- Solve the sentence by measuring
  Measure the distance from A to B.

6.1 Convex and Concave Polygons

OBJECTIVES ► **To identify and name polygons and their parts**
To identify convex and concave polygons

In this lesson you will work with a special type of geometric figure called a *polygon*. You have already studied one type of polygon—the triangle. All properties that are true for polygons in general apply to triangles.

Definition: polygon

> A *polygon* is the union of three or more coplanar segments which intersect only at each endpoint, with each endpoint shared by exactly two segments.

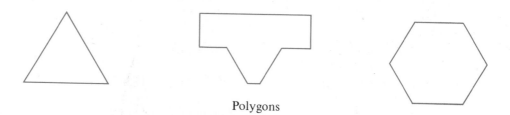

Polygons

Some coplanar figures which are the union of segments are not polygons; the segments may not intersect in the proper way.

Example 1 Which of the following figures are polygons? Indicate why the others are not.

Not a polygon. Two of the segments intersect at a point that is not an end point.

Not a polygon. The end points of some of the segments are shared by three segments.

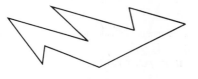

A polygon

Not a polygon. Two end points are not shared by a second segment.

The segments which make up a polygon are called the *sides* of the polygon and the endpoints of the segments are called the *vertices* of the polygon. The number of sides is always equal to the number of vertices. Polygons are classified according to the number of sides they contain. A polygon with five sides is called a 5-gon; a polygon with 17 sides is called a 17-gon. However, certain polygons have special names.

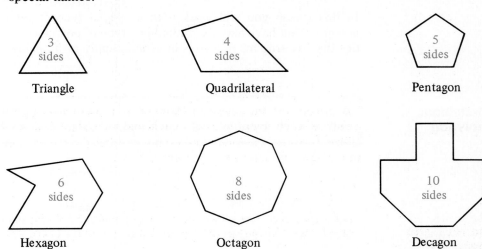

A specific polygon is often named by listing its vertices in order. The polygon below is polygon ABCDEF. The segment, $\overline{EB}$, is a *diagonal* of polygon *ABCDEF*.

Definition:
diagonal of a polygon

A *diagonal* of a polygon is a segment which connects any two nonconsecutive vertices.

Example 2 For each polygon, list the sides and vertices and classify the polygon. How many diagonals can be drawn for each polygon?

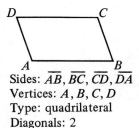

Sides: $\overline{AB}, \overline{BC}, \overline{CD}, \overline{DA}$
Vertices: A, B, C, D
Type: quadrilateral
Diagonals: 2

Sides: $\overline{PQ}, \overline{QR}, \overline{RS}, \overline{ST}, \overline{TU}, \overline{UP}$
Vertices: P, Q, R, S, T, U
Type: hexagon
Diagonals: 9

In Chapter 1 you learned that an angle separates the plane that contains it into three sets of points: the angle itself, the interior of the angle, and the exterior of the angle. A polygon separates the plane that contains it in a similar manner. In the diagram below, point P is in the interior of the polygon and point Q is in the exterior. The exterior of a polygon can contain lines but the interior cannot.

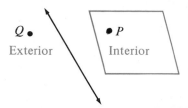

The union of a polygon and its interior is called a polygonal region. Some polygonal regions "bend inward" while others do not. Those that bend inward are called *concave* and those that do not are called *convex*. A more formal definition of convex and concave is presented below.

Definition: convex and concave regions

> A polygonal region is *convex* if the segment $\overline{XY}$ joining any two points X and Y of the region is part of the region. If the region is not convex, then it is *concave*.

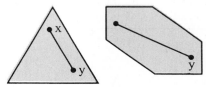

Convex polygonal regions

Concave polygonal regions

A polygon that determines a convex region is called a *convex polygon*. A polygon which determines a concave region is called a *concave polygon*. Most of the polygons that you will study will be convex. In this book, when *polygon* is used it will mean *convex polygon*.

Example 3

Which of the following are convex polygonal regions? Show why or why not.

Which of the following are convex polygons?

Convex

Concave

Concave

Convex

CONVEX AND CONCAVE POLYGONS

185

Example **4** Draw each of the following.

A convex pentagon   A concave hexagon

                    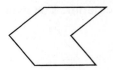

Reading in Geometry _____

Many words used in geometry are derived from Latin or Greek root words. The word *polygon* has two root words: *poly*, meaning *many;* and *gon* meaning *angle*.

Look up each of the following words in a dictionary. Write the root words and their meanings.

1. triangle	**2.** quadrilateral	**3.** pentagon
4. hexagon	**5.** octagon	**6.** decagon
7. bisector	**8.** perpendicular	**9.** transversal
10. hypotenuse	**11.** congruent	**12.** isosceles

Oral Exercises _____

Which of the following are polygons?

1.   **2.**   **3.**   **4.**

Which of the following are convex polygons?

5.   **6.**   **7.**   **8.**

Name each of the following polygons.

9.   **10.**   **11.**   **12.**

Written Exercises

Which of the following are polygons? Indicate why the others are not.

A 1. 　　2. 　　3. 　　4.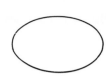

5. 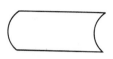　　6. 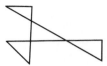　　7. 　　8.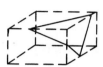

For each polygon, list the sides and vertices and classify the polygon. How many diagonals can be drawn for each polygon?

9. 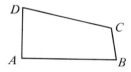　　10. 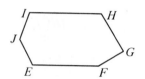　　11.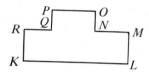

Which of the following are convex polygonal regions? Show why or why not.

12.　　　　13.　　　　14.　　　　15.

Draw each of the following.

16. A convex quadrilateral　　17. A convex hexagon　　18. A concave decagon
19. A concave pentagon　　20. A concave octagon　　21. A concave quadrilateral

How many sides does each type of polygon have? (Use a dictionary, if necessary.) Draw a picture of each type.

B 22. Heptagon　　23. Undecagon　　24. Nonagon　　25. Dodecagon

Cumulative Review

1. Prove that the base angles of an isosceles triangle are congruent.
2. Draw three different angles. Estimate their measures, check the measures with a protractor.
3. Construct a 45° angle.

6.2 Angles of Convex Polygons

OBJECTIVES ► **To prove and apply the theorem about the sum of the angle measures of a convex quadrilateral**
To develop and apply a formula for the sum of the angle measures of any convex polygon

The sum of the measures of the angles of a triangle is 180°. If you draw diagonal $\overline{AC}$ in quadrilateral $ABCD$, two triangles are formed. The sum of the angle measures of the quadrilateral should be that of the two triangles, or 360°. This is proved in the following theorem.

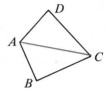

┌ Theorem 6.1   The sum of the measures of the angles of a convex ┐
quadrilateral is 360°.

Given: Convex quad. $ABCD$
Prove: m $\angle A$ + m $\angle B$ + m $\angle C$ + m $\angle D = 360$

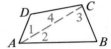

Proof

Statements	Reasons
1. Convex quad. $ABCD$	1. Given
2. Draw $\overline{AC}$.	2. Two points are contained in exactly one line.
3. m $\angle A$ = m $\angle 1$ + m $\angle 2$	3. Angle addition postulate
4. m $\angle C$ = m $\angle 3$ + m $\angle 4$	4. Angle addition postulate
5. m $\angle A$ + m $\angle B$ + m $\angle C$ + m $\angle D$ = m $\angle 1$ + m $\angle 2$ + m $\angle B$ + m $\angle 3$ + m $\angle 4$ + m $\angle D$	5. Substitution property
6. m $\angle 2$ + m $\angle B$ + m $\angle 3$ = 180	6. Sum of meas. of $\angle$'s of a $\triangle$ = 180°.
7. m $\angle 1$ + m $\angle D$ + m $\angle 4$ = 180	7. Sum of meas. of $\angle$'s of a $\triangle$ = 180°.
8. m $\angle 1$ + m $\angle 2$ + m $\angle B$ + m $\angle 3$ + m $\angle 4$ + m $\angle D$ = 360	8. Addition prop. of equality and substitution property
9. ∴ m $\angle A$ + m $\angle B$ + m $\angle C$ + m $\angle D$ = 360	9. Substitution property

Example 1   Given: m $\angle x = 142$,
m $\angle Y = 63$, and
m $\angle Z = 134$
Find m $\angle W$.

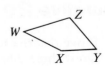

$142 + 63 + 134 + \text{m} \angle W = 360$
m $\angle W = 360 - 339$, or 21

Example 2 Given: m $\angle A = 5x + 10$
m $\angle B = 6x - 2$,
m $\angle C = 4x + 17$, and
m $\angle D = 4x + 12$.
Find m $\angle A$ and m $\angle C$.

$(5x + 10) + (6x - 2) + (4x + 17) + (4x + 12) = 360$
$19x + 37 = 360$
$19x = 323$
$x = 17$
Thus, m $\angle A = 5(17) + 10$, or 95
and m $\angle C = 4(17) + 17$, or 85.

If all possible diagonals of a given polygon are drawn from a single vertex, triangles are formed. The number of triangles formed is two less than the number of sides. If the polygon has n sides, then there will be $n - 2$ triangles.

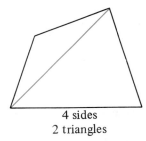

4 sides
2 triangles

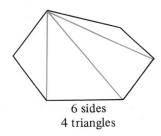

6 sides
4 triangles

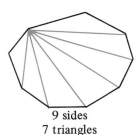

9 sides
7 triangles

The following theorem is based on this pattern.

Theorem 6.2 The sum of the measures of the angles of a convex polygon with n sides is $(n - 2)$ 180.

Theorem 6.2 can be proved for any particular integer n, where $n \geq 3$. You can use it to find the sum of the angle measures of any convex polygon.

Example 3 Find the sum of the measures of the angles of a convex hexagon.

A hexagon has 6 sides. ▶ $(6 - 2)$ $180 = 720$

Thus, the sum of the angle measures is 720.

You can also use Theorem 6.2 to determine the number of sides in a polygon and to find the measure of one of the angles.

Example 4 How many sides does a convex polygon have if the sum of the measures of its angles is 1980°?

$$(n - 2)\ 180 = 1980$$
$$180n - 360 = 1980$$
$$180n = 2340$$
$$n = 13$$

Thus, the polygon has 13 sides.

Example 5 The measure of the second angle of a pentagon is twice the measure of the first angle. The measure of each of the other three angles is three times the measure of the first. What is the measure of each angle?

$$\text{Sum} = (5 - 2)\ 180 \text{ or } 540$$
$$x + 2x + 3x + 3x + 3x = 540$$
$$12x = 540$$
$$x = 45$$

Thus, The measure of the first angle is 45°.
The measure of the second angle is 2(45) or 90°.
The measure of each of the other angles is 3(45) or 135°.

Oral **Exercises** _____

How many triangles are formed by drawing all of the diagonals from a single vertex of each of the following polygons?

1.   2.   3.   4.

How many triangles are formed by drawing all of the diagonals from a single vertex of a polygon with each given number of sides?

5. 7	**6.** 10	**7.** 14	**8.** 20	**9.** 42	**10.** 134

Written **Exercises** _____

For each of the following convex quadrilaterals, the measures of three angles are given. Find the measure of the fourth angle.

 1. 42°, 88°, 112°   **2.** 87°, 123°, 131°   **3.** 90°, 90°, 90°
4. 8°, 52°, 203°   **5.** 59°, 60°, 161°,   **6.** 120°, 60°, 30°

Find the measure of each angle of convex quadrilateral ABCD.

7. m $\angle A = 8x$, m $\angle B = 7x + 10$, m $\angle C = 11x - 10$, and m $\angle D = 10x$

8. m $\angle A = 9x + 5$, m $\angle B = 11x + 5$, m $\angle C = 7x - 8$, and m $\angle D = 14x - 11$

9. m $\angle A = 8x + 1$, m $\angle B = 9x + 1$, m $\angle C = 15x - 7$, and m $\angle D = 13x + 5$

Find the sum of the measures of the angles of each convex polygon.

10. A pentagon
13. A forty-gon

11. An octagon
14. A 52-gon

12. A dodecagon
15. A hundred-gon

Draw a picture of each of the following convex polygons. Using a protractor, measure each angle. Add these to determine the sum of the angle measures of the polygon. Compare this with the sum found by the formula of Theorem 6.2.

16. A pentagon

17. A heptagon

18. An octagon

The sum of the measures of the angles of a convex polygon is given. Find the number of sides of the polygon.

19. 540°
23. 2340°

20. 1080°
24. 3600°

21. 1800°
25. 2880°

22. 1620°
26. 7560°

Which of the following cannot be the sum of the angle measures of a convex polygon? (Ex. 27–30)

27. 1530°

28. 3420°

29. 6480°

30. 4500°

 31. If all of the angles of a hexagon are congruent, then what is the measure of each angle?

32. If all of the angles of an octagon are congruent, then what is the measure of each angle?

33. Three angles of a hexagon are congruent. The other angles are also congruent, each with a measure twice that of the first three. What is the measure of each angle?

34. The measure of one angle of an octagon is twice that of the first. All of the other angles are congruent, each with a measure three times that of the first. What is the measure of each angle?

Prove each of the following.

35. Prove Theorem 6.2 for convex pentagons.

36. Prove Theorem 6.2 for convex hexagons.

Another approach can be used to prove Theorem 6.2. Prove each of the following, based on the diagram shown.

37. Prove Theorem 6.1, using the diagram.

38. Prove Theorem 6.2 for convex pentagons, using the diagram.

39. Prove Theorem 6.2 for convex hexagons, using the diagram.

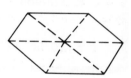

ANGLES OF CONVEX POLYGONS

Using a protractor, measure each angle of each concave quadrilateral. Add these to determine the sum of the angle measures. Does the formula of Theorem 6.1 apply? What relationship exists between these angle measures?

40.
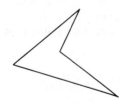

41.
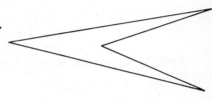

42.

Using a protractor, measure each angle of each concave polygon. Add these to determine the sum of the angle measures. Does the formula of Theorem 6.2 apply? What relationship exists between these angle measures?

43.

44.

45.
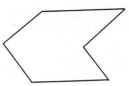

CALCULATOR ACTIVITIES

Example 1 Find the sum of the measures of the angles of a convex 792-gon.

Press 792 ⊟ 2 ⊟ ⊠ 180 ⊟ .
Display is 142200.

The answer is 142200°.

Example 2 Can a convex polygon have an angle measure sum of 29810°?

Press 29810 ⊡ 180 ⊟ ⊞ 2 ⊟ .
Display is 167.61111.
If the display is a whole number, the answer is "yes."
Since 167.61111 is not a whole number, the answer is "No."

Find the sum of the measures of the angles of each convex polygon.
1. 313-gon 　　　 2. 477-gon 　　　 3. 1029-gon 　　　 4. 1346-gon

Can a convex polygon have an angle measure sum of each of the following?
5. 10380° 　　　 6. 97000° 　　　 7. 18000° 　　　 8. 18180°

6.3 Exterior Angles of Convex Polygons

OBJECTIVES ► **To identify the exterior angles of a convex polygon**
To develop and apply a formula for the sum of the measures of the exterior angles of a convex polygon

Every convex polygon has two congruent *exterior angles* at each vertex. Quadrilateral *ABCD* has eight exterior angles, angles 1 through 8. The two exterior angles at each vertex are congruent, since they are vertical angles.

You can easily find the sum of the measures of the exterior angles, one at each vertex, by measuring with a protractor.

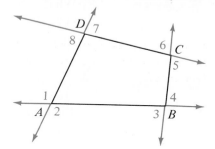

Example 1

Measure each exterior angle shown, using a protractor. What is the sum of the measures?

m ∠1 = 98, m ∠2 = 113,
m ∠3 = 81, m ∠4 = 68
Thus, m ∠1 + m ∠2 + m ∠3 + m ∠4 = 360

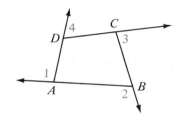

The result of Example 1 can be shown to be true for any convex quadrilateral. An outline of the proof is given.

Theorem 6.3 The sum of the measures of the exterior angles, one at each vertex, of any convex quadrilateral is 360°.

Given: Convex quad. *ABCD*, and
exterior ∠'s 1, 2, 3, and 4.
Prove: m ∠1 + m ∠2 + m ∠3 +
m ∠4 = 360

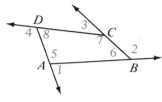

Outline of Proof

1. m ∠1 + m ∠5 = 180
2. m ∠2 + m ∠6 = 180
3. m ∠3 + m ∠7 = 180
4. m ∠4 + m ∠8 = 180
5. m ∠1 + m ∠2 + m ∠3 + m ∠4 + m ∠5 +
   m ∠6 + m ∠7 + m ∠8 = 720
6. m ∠5 + m ∠6 + m ∠7 + m ∠ 8 = 360
7. ∴ m ∠1 + m ∠2 + m ∠3 + m ∠4 = 360

Theorem 6.3 can be shown to be true for any convex polygon.

> **Theorem 6.4** The sum of the measures of the exterior angles, one at each vertex, of any convex polygon is 360°. (See Exercises 6 and 7.)

Example 2 What is the sum of the measures of the exterior angles, one at each vertex, of a convex 138-gon?

The sum is 360°.

Example 3 The measures of the exterior angles, one at each vertex, of a convex quadrilateral are m $\angle x = a + 2$, m $\angle y = a + 4$, m $\angle z = a + 6$, and m $\angle w = a + 8$. Find the measure of each angle.

$$\text{m } \angle x + \text{m } \angle y + \text{m } \angle z + \text{m } \angle w = 360$$
$$(a + 2) + (a + 4) + (a + 6) + (a + 8) = 360$$
$$4a + 20 = 360$$
$$4a = 340$$
$$a = 85$$

Thus, m $\angle x = 85 + 2$ or 87, m $\angle y = 85 + 4$ or 89, m $\angle z = 85 + 6$ or 91, m $\angle z = 85 + 8$ or 93.

Oral Exercises

Which of the angles shown in each figure are exterior angles?

1.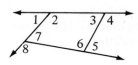

2.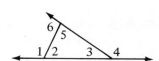

3.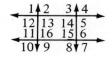

What is the sum of the measures of the exterior angles shown in each figure?

4.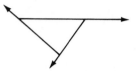

5.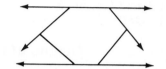

6.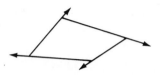

What is the sum of the measures of the exterior angles, one at each vertex, of each of the given convex polygons?

7. An octagon
8. A nonagon
9. A dodecagon
10. A 21-gon
11. A 312-gon
12. A 978-gon

Written Exercises

Copy each polygon. Draw an exterior angle at each vertex. Use a protractor to measure each exterior angle drawn. What is the sum of these measures? Does the result agree with Theorem 6.4?

 1.

2.

3.

4. The measures of the exterior angles of a convex pentagon, one at each vertex, are m $\angle p = x$, m $\angle q = 2x$, m $\angle r = 3x$, m $\angle S = 4x$, and m $\angle t = 5x$. Find the measure of each exterior angle.

5. The measures of the exterior angles of a convex hexagon, one at each vertex, are m $\angle 1 = 6x - 1$, m $\angle 2 = 10x + 2$, m $\angle 3 = 8x + 2$, m $\angle 4 = 9x - 3$, m $\angle 5 = 5x + 4$, and m $\angle 6 = 12x + 6$.
Find the measure of each exterior angle.

B **6.** Prove Theorem 6.4 for triangles.

7. Prove Theorem 6.4 for convex pentagons.

For each convex polygon, compute the sum of the measures of all pairs of interior angles of the polygon and their corresponding exterior angles, one at each vertex. Compute the sum of the measures of the interior angles of the polygon. Using these sums, compute the sum of the measures of the exterior angles, one at each vertex.

8. A triangle

9. A heptagon

10. A 30-gon

Algebra Review

OBJECTIVE ▶ **To solve fractional equations of the form $\dfrac{ax + b}{cx} = d$**

To solve a fractional equation of the form $\dfrac{ax + b}{cx} = b$:

1. Multiply both sides of the equation by cx.
2. Solve for x, using appropriate equation properties.

Example Solve $\dfrac{7x + 9}{2x} = 5$

$$7x + 9 = 10x \quad \blacktriangleleft \quad \textit{Mult. by } 2x.$$
$$-3x = -9 \quad \blacktriangleleft \quad \textit{Add } -10 \textit{ to both sides.}$$
$$x = 3$$

Solve.

1. $\dfrac{5x + 32}{3x} = 7$

2. $\dfrac{4x - 8}{3x} = 2$

3. $\dfrac{9x - 7}{5x} = 2$

4. $\dfrac{8x + 7}{5x} = 3$

5. $\dfrac{2x - 31}{4x} = 7$

6. $\dfrac{2x - 9}{3x} = 8$

EXTERIOR ANGLES OF CONVEX POLYGONS

6.4 Regular Polygons

OBJECTIVES ► To identify regular polygons
To determine angle measures and the number of sides of regular polygons.

A polygon is *equilateral* if all of its sides are congruent. If all of its angles are congruent, then the polygon is *equiangular*.

Equilateral polygons   Equiangular polygons

Some polygons are both equilateral and equiangular.

Definition:
regular polygon

A *regular polygon* is a convex polygon which is both equilateral and equiangular.

  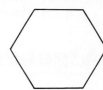

Some regular polygons

You can find the measure of an angle of a regular polygon if you know how many sides it has.

Example 1 Find the measure of each angle of a regular hexagon.

Use Theorem 6.2. ► The sum of the measures is $(6 - 2)(180)$ or 720.

Thus, the measure of each angle is $\frac{720}{6}$ or 120°.

Example 1 can be generalized in the following corollary to Theorem 6.2.

Corollary The measure of an angle of a regular polygon with n sides is $\frac{(n-2)\,180°}{n}$.

CHAPTER SIX

A similar corollary of Theorem 6.4 can be used to find the measure of an exterior angle of a regular polygon.

> **Corollary** The measure of an exterior angle of a regular polygon with n sides is $\dfrac{360°}{n}$.

Example 2 Find the measure of each exterior angle of a regular octagon.

$$\text{Measure} = \frac{360}{8} \text{ or } 45°$$

If you know the measure of one angle or one exterior angle of a regular polygon, you can find the number of sides of the polygon.

Example 3 How many sides does a regular polygon have if the measure of each angle is 144°?

$$144 = \frac{(n-2)\ 180}{n}$$ ◄ *The measure of each $\angle$ is $\dfrac{(n-2)\ 180}{n}$.*

$$144n = (n-2)\ 180$$
$$144n = 180n - 360$$
$$-36n = -360$$
$$n = 10$$

A 10-sided polygon is a decagon. ► **Thus,** the polygon has 10 sides.

Example 4 How many sides does a regular polygon have if the measure of each exterior angle is 72°?

$$72 = \frac{360}{n}$$ ◄ *The measure of each exterior $\angle$ is $\dfrac{360}{n}$.*

$$72n = 360$$
$$n = 5$$

Thus, the polygon has 5 sides.

Written Exercises

Draw each indicated type of regular polygon and label the congruent parts.

A 1. Triangle   2. Quadrilateral   3. Hexagon   4. Octagon

Find the measure of an angle of each of the following regular polygons.

5. Triangle   6. Quadrilateral   7. Pentagon   8. Octagon
9. Nonagon   10. Decagon   11. 30-gon   12. 100-gon

REGULAR POLYGONS

Find the measure of an exterior angle of each of the following regular polygons.

   13. Triangle   14. Quadrilateral   15. Pentagon   16. Octagon
   17. Decagon   18. 30-gon   19. 50-gon   20. 100-gon

Find the number of sides in each regular polygon with angles of the given measure.

   21. 60°   22. 135°   23. 150°   24. 171°

Find the number of sides in each regular polygon with exterior angles of the given measure.

   25. 72°   26. 36°   27. 30°   28. 15°

Which of the following are possible measures of the interior angles of a regular polygon? If the measures are possible, how many sides does the polygon have?

Ⓑ 29. 90°   30. 100°   31. 110°   32. 125°   33. 150°   34. 175°

Which of the following are possible measures of exterior angles of a regular polygon? If the measures are possible, how many sides does the polygon have?

   35. 180°   36. 150°   37. 120°   38. 100°   39. 50°   40. 30°

True or false? Draw pictures to illustrate. (Ex. 41–42)

Ⓒ 41. An angle of a regular polygon cannot be congruent to an exterior angle.   42. For no value of *n* is an equilateral *n*-gon equiangular.

   43. A regular polygon was defined to be a convex polygon. Are there any concave polygons which have all angles and all sides congruent? Sketch and investigate.

CALCULATOR ACTIVITIES

You can use a calculator to find the measure of each angle of a regular polygon with a large number of sides, such as a 213-gon. The process is shown below.

Press 213 ⊟ 2 ⊟ ⊠ 180 ⊟ ⊞ 213 ⊟ .
The answer is 178.30986°.

Find the measure of an angle of each regular polygon.

   1. 814-gon   **2.** 697-gon   **3.** 1024-gon
   4. 613-gon   **5.** 4213-gon   **6.** 9027-gon

Find the measure of an exterior angle of each regular polygon.

   7. 896-gon   **8.** 211-gon   **9.** 45-gon
   10. 102-gon   **11.** 379-gon   **12.** 2135-gon

6.5 Constructing Regular Polygons

OBJECTIVES ▶ **To construct regular polygons with 3, 4, or 6 sides**
To construct angles with certain specified measures

A regular polygon with three sides is an equilateral triangle. You can construct an equilateral triangle as shown below.

┌─ **Construction** An equilateral triangle ──────────────────┐

Given: $\overline{AB}$

A ———————— B

Construct: An equilateral triangle with sides ≅ $\overline{AB}$.

Open the compass to length AB. Draw an arc with center A.	Keep the same compass opening. Draw an arc with center B, intersecting the first arc at C.	Draw $\overline{AC}$ and $\overline{BC}$.

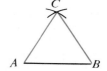

Conclusion: △*ABC* is equilateral.

└──┘

Each angle of an equilateral triangle has a measure of 60°. Therefore, you can construct a 30° angle by first constructing an equilateral triangle and then bisecting one of its angles.

Example 1 Construct a 30° angle.

Construct equil. △ABC. ▶
Bisect ∠CAB.

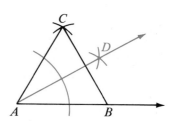

Conclusion: m ∠*BAD* = 30

A regular hexagon can be formed by joining six equilateral triangles as shown. This is the basis for the following construction.

Construction A regular hexagon

Given: $\overline{AB}$

A ——— B

Construct: A regular hexagon with sides $\cong \overline{AB}$

Open the compass to length AB. Draw a circle with center P.

Keep the same compass opening. Starting with any point A on the circle, draw a series of arcs on the circle.

Draw the segments.

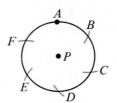

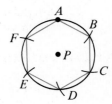

Conclusion: *ABCDEF* is a regular hexagon.

Using procedures similar to the above for constructing a regular hexagon, many other types of regular polygons can be constructed. Also, by bisecting angles of various measures, angles of other measures can be constructed. The example below shows two such constructions.

Example 2 Construct each of the following.
A square with sides $\cong \overline{AB}$ A 150° angle

Construst ⊥'s at A and B. ▶

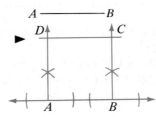

Bisect ∠CAB of equil. △ABC. ◀

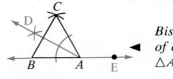

Conclusion: *ABCD* is a square.

Conclusion: m ∠*DAE* = 150

Written Exercises _____

Draw a segment. Construct the following with sides congruent to the segment.

△A 1. An equilateral triangle   2. A square   3. A regular hexagon

Construct an angle with each given measure.

    4. 60°   5. 90°   6. 120°   7. 30°   8. 45°   9. 150°

△B 10. 15°   11. 75°   12. 105°   13. $37\frac{1}{2}°$ 14. 165°   15. $157\frac{1}{2}°$

Construct each of the following.

16. An equilateral triangle with sides twice as long as a given segment

17. A regular hexagon with sides half as long as a given segment.

△C 18. A regular octagon with sides congruent to a given segment.

19. A regular dodecagon with sides congruent to a given segment.

20. A square with a diagonal congruent to a given segment.

21. A regular 16-gon with sides congruent to a given segment.

22. A regular hexagon with an 11-cm perimeter.

23. An equilateral triangle with a 14-cm perimeter

A regular pentagon can also be constructed.

Draw diameter $\overline{AB}$ in circle O. Construct $\overline{CO}$, the ⊥ bisector of $\overline{AB}$. Construct D, the midpoint $\overline{OB}$.

With D as center and $\overline{CD}$ as a radius, draw arc $\overarc{CE}$. Draw $\overline{CE}$.

Open compass to length CE. Starting at C, draw a series of arcs on the circle. Draw the segments.

24. Construct a five-pointed star.   25. Construct a regular decagon.

Cumulative Review _____

1. If the coordinate of p is -12 and the coordinate of M, the midpoint of $\overline{PQ}$, is 3, what is the coordinate of Q?

2. What is the sum of the measures of a regular heptagon?

3. What congruence pattern for right triangles is not true for triangles in general?

CONSTRUCTING REGULAR POLYGONS

Applications

1. Square carpet tiles can be used to cover a floor. The tiles will fit together with no gaps or overlapping. What geometric properties insure that this is true?

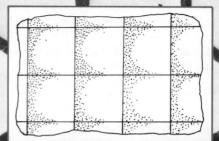

2. Triangular tiles are used for the floor on the left. They are all arranged in rows. Why can this be done? Can all types of triangles be used as patterns? Why?

3. Which of the quadrilaterals on the right can be used as a pattern for carpet tiles to cover a floor? Why? Make paper cutouts to test your answer.

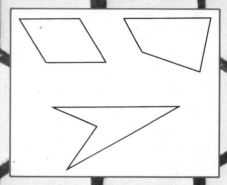

4. Many bathroom floors are made out of ceramic tiles in the shape of regular hexagons. Can regular pentagons or regular octagons be used for such a floor? Why? Make paper cutouts to test your answers. What other types of regular polygons can be used for such floor tiles?

Computer Activities

Formulas can be used in computer programs to make rapid and accurate computations. The formula for the degree measure of an angle of a regular polygon with n sides is

$$m \angle A = \frac{(n-2)\,180}{n}$$

From this formula, you can derive a formula to determine the number of sides of a regular polygon, as shown on the right

See the computer section on page 560 for more information.

$$n = \frac{360}{180 - m \angle A}$$

PROGRAM

```
10 PRINT "PROGRAM COMPUTES THE MEASURE OF AN ANGLE OR"
20 PRINT "THE NUMBER OF SIDES OF A REGULAR POLYGON"
30 PRINT "DO YOU WANT TO ENTER AN ANGLE MEASURE OF A POLYGON?"
40 PRINT "ANSWER 1 FOR 'YES' OR 2 FOR 'NO'"
50 INPUT A
60 IF A = 1 THEN 120
70 PRINT "DO YOU WANT TO ENTER THE NUMBER OF SIDES IN A POLYGON?"
80 PRINT "ANSWER 1 FOR 'YES' OR 2 FOR 'NO'"
90 INPUT N
100 IF N = 1 THEN 170
110 GO TO 220
120 PRINT "ENTER ANGLE MEASURE OF A REGULAR POLYGON"
130 INPUT A
140 LET N = 360/{180 - A}
150 PRINT "NUMBER OF SIDES IS"; N
160 GO TO 30
170 PRINT "ENTER THE NUMBER OF SIDES IN A REGULAR POLYGON"
180 INPUT N
190 LET A = {{N - 2} * 180}/N
200 PRINT "MEASURE OF ANGLE IS"; A; "DEGREES"
210 GO TO 30
220 END
```

Exercises

Run the program above for the following values. (Ex 1–2)
1. a 150° angle   2. 8 sides
3. Alter the program to compute (1) the measure of an exterior angle, given the number of sides or (2) the number of sides, given the measure of an exterior angle.
4. Write a program to determine if a given angle measure can be a possible measure of an interior angle of a regular polygon. If so, determine the number of sides.

ACTIVITY: REGULAR POLYGONS

Chapter Six Review

Which of the figures below are polygons? Why are the others not polygons? [6.1]

1.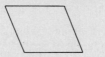

3.   4.

Which polygons are convex? Which are concave? [6.1]

5.   6.

7.   8.

Find each indicated angle measure. [6.2]

9. Find the sum of the measures of the angles of a pentagon.

10. Find the sum of the measures of the angles of a 20-gon.

11. Find the sum of the measures of the exterior angles, one at each vertex, of a dodecagon. [6.3]

12. Find the sum of the measures of the exterior angles, one at each vertex, of a 29-gon.

13. Find the measure of each angle of a regular pentagon. [6.4]

14. Find the measure of each exterior angle of a regular dodecagon.

*15. Prove: The sum of the measures of the angles of a pentagon is 540°. [6.2]

True or false?

16. Two sides of a polygon always intersect at a vertex. [6.1]

17. If each exterior angle of a regular polygon has a measure of 90°, then the polygon is a square. [6.4]

*18. All the sides of an equiangular polygon are congruent. [6.4]

19. A dodecagon has ten sides. [6.1]

20. The sum of the measures of the angles of a regular polygon is 360°. [6.2]

21. A polygon must be coplanar. [6.1]

Find each indicated angle measure.

22. In quadrilateral $ABCD$, m $\angle A = 4x + 9$, m $\angle B = 5x + 2$, m $\angle C = 9x - 1$, and m $\angle D = 7x$. Find the measure of each angle. [6.2]

23. The measures of the exterior angles, one at each vertex, of a pentagon are m $\angle a = 3t + 7$, m $\angle b = 4t + 4$, m $\angle c = 6t - 2$, m $\angle d = 5t + 4$, and m $\angle e = 6t - 13$. Find the measure of each exterior angle. [6.3]

Find each of the following.

24. Find the number of sides in a regular polygon each of whose angles measures 144°. [6.4]

25. Find the number of sides in a regular polygon, each of whose exterior angles measures 14.4°. [6.4]

Construct each of the following.

26. Draw a segment 5 cm long. Construct a regular hexagon with sides congruent to the segment. [6.5]

27. Construct a 60° angle.

28. Construct a 45° angle.

29. Construct a 15° angle.

Vocabulary
concave [6.1], convex [6.1], decagon [6.1], diagonal [6.1], exterior angle [6.3], hexagon [6.1], octagon [6.1], pentagon [6.1], polygon [6.1], regular polygon [6.4]

Chapter Six Test

Which of the figures below are polygons? Why are the others not polygons?

1.

2.

3.

4.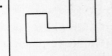

Which polygons are convex? Which are concave?

5.

6.

7.

8.

Find each indicated angle measure.

9. Find the sum of the measures of the angles of a 32-gon.

10. Find the sum of the measures of the exterior angles, one at each vertex, of a 27-gon.

11. Find the measure at each angle of a regular hexagon.

12. Find the measure of each exterior angle of a regular 30-gon.

13. In quadrilateral $ABCD$, m $\angle A = 7x - 4$, m $\angle B = 8x - 1$, m $\angle C = 8x + 4$, and m $\angle D = 7x + 1$. Find the measure of each angle.

14. The measures of the exterior angles, one at each vertex, of a triangle are m $\angle 1 = 2y + 10$, m $\angle 2 = 3y - 30$, m $\angle 3 = y + 80$. Find the measure of each angle.

Find each of the following.

15. Find the number of sides in a regular polygon each of whose angles measures 140°.

16. Find the number of sides in a regular polygon each of whose exterior angles measures 18°.

True or false?

17. A decagon is a polygon with 12 sides.

18. If each angle of a regular polygon has a measure of 60°, then the polygon is a triangle.

*19. An equilateral polygon is also equiangular.

20. A regular polygon cannot have an angle whose measure is 150°.

21. A concave polygon cannot be equilateral.

Construct each of the following.

22. A regular hexagon with sides congruent to $\overline{AB}$.

$A \overline{\hspace{4cm}} B$

23. A 30° angle.

24. A 135° angle.

Prove the following.

*25. The sum of the measures of the exterior angles of a triangle is 360°.

College Prep Test

For each item, choose the best answer. Indicate your answer by writing the letter of this choice.

1. Which of the following is a polygon?

I   II   III

(A) I only
(B) II only
(C) III only
(D) I and III only
(E) None of these

2. Which of the following is a convex polygon?

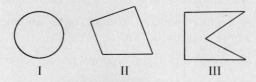

I   II   III

(A) I only
(B) II only
(C) III only
(D) I and II only
(E) II and III only

3. The sum of the measures of the angles of a convex 10-gon is

(A) 360   (B) 1440
(C) 1800   (D) 2160
(E) None of these

4. The sum of the measures of the exterior angles of a convex 20-gon is

(A) 360   (B) 3240
(C) 3600   (D) 3960
(E) None of these

5. Each angle of a regular pentagon has a measure of
(A) 72   (B) 90
(C) 108   (D) 135
(E) None of these

6. If an angle of a regular polygon has a measure of 156°, then the polygon has
(A) 13 sides   (B) 15 sides
(C) 16 sides   (D) 17 sides
(E) None of these

7. The angles of a quadrilateral have measures of $5x$, $3x + 20$, $4x + 5$, and $5x - 5$. The measure of one of the angles is
(A) 20   (B) 50
(C) 90   (D) 95
(E) 105

8. Which of the following is not necessary for a figure to be a polygon?
   I. Contains 3 or more segments
  II. Is convex
 III. Is coplanar

(A) I only
(B) II only
(C) III only
(D) I and II only
(E) I and III only

9. To construct a 30° angle, you must first construct a
(A) Right triangle
(B) An equilateral triangle
(C) A square
(D) An octagon
(E) A perpendicular bisector

Famous Mathemeticians: Amalie Noether

Amalie Noether was well known as a teacher and mathematician. Born in Germany in 1882, she began her advanced education studying French and English. Her interests soon turned to mathematics, and she became one of the most famous abstract algebraists in the world.

Opposition to women in University positions prevented her from receiving a position at the University of Göttingen for which she was sponsored. She did, however, give lectures, which were announced under the name of another famous mathematician, David Hilbert.

Because of oppression in her native Germany, Noether came to the United States in 1933. She taught at Bryn Mawr College. At the peak of her career, she died on April 14, 1935.

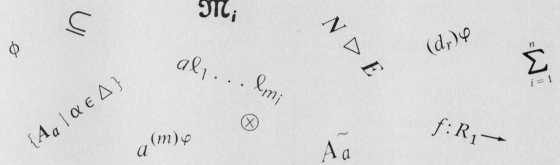

7.1 Finding Properties of Quadrilaterals

OBJECTIVES ▶ **To identify diagonals and consecutive and opposite sides and angles of quadrilaterals**
To investigate properties of quadrilaterals

As you learned in the last chapter, some polygons are given special names according to the number of sides they have. A *quadrilateral* is a polygon with four sides. The *sides* of a quadrilateral are segments, and each endpoint of each segment is a *vertex* of the quadrilateral.

Quadrilaterals have *opposite* and *consecutive sides* and *opposite* and *consecutive angles*. The consecutive sides of a quadrilateral intersect to share a common vertex, while opposite sides do not intersect. The vertices of consecutive angles are endpoints of the same side of the quadrilateral. Vertices of opposite angles are not endpoints of the same side.

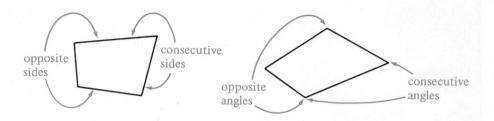

Example 1 List the pairs of consecutive sides and consecutive angles of quadrilateral *ABCD*.

Consecutive sides	Consecutive angles
$\overline{AB}$ and $\overline{BC}$	$\angle A$ and $\angle B$
$\overline{BC}$ and $\overline{CD}$	$\angle B$ and $\angle C$
$\overline{CD}$ and $\overline{DA}$	$\angle C$ and $\angle D$
$\overline{DA}$ and $\overline{AB}$	$\angle D$ and $\angle A$

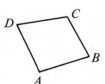

Example 2 Which side is opposite each given side? Which angle is opposite each given angle?

$\overline{XY}, \overline{YZ}, \angle X, \angle W$

$\overline{WZ}$ is opposite $\overline{XY}$.
$\overline{WX}$ is opposite $\overline{YZ}$.
$\angle Z$ is opposite $\angle X$.
$\angle Y$ is opposite $\angle W$.

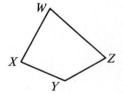

Quadrilaterals, like other polygons, have diagonals. A *diagonal* of a quadrilateral always connects opposite vertices. The diagonals of some quadrilaterals are congruent while others are not. The diagonals, $\overline{AC}$ and $\overline{BD}$, of quadrilateral $ABCD$ below are congruent, but the diagonals, $\overline{EG}$ and $\overline{FH}$, of quadrilateral $EFGH$ are not.

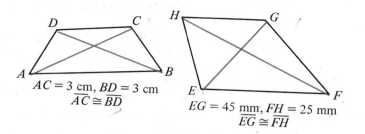

$AC = 3$ cm, $BD = 3$ cm
$\overline{AC} \cong \overline{BD}$

$EG = 45$ mm, $FH = 25$ mm
$\overline{EG} \cong \overline{FH}$

You should make drawings to investigate other statements of the properties of quadrilaterals, including statements about sides, angles, and diagonals.

Example 3 Do the diagonals of a quadrilateral bisect each other? Draw pictures to defend your answer.

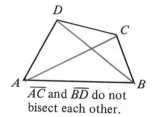

$\overline{AC}$ and $\overline{BD}$ do not bisect each other.

$\overline{EG}$ and $\overline{FH}$ seem to bisect each other.

Thus, the diagonals of a quadrilateral do not necessarily bisect each other.

Example 4 Are opposite angles of a quadrilateral congruent? Draw pictures to defend your answer.

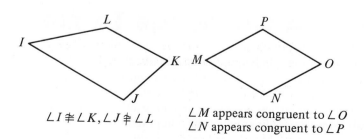

$\angle I \not\cong \angle K, \angle J \not\cong \angle L$

$\angle M$ appears congruent to $\angle O$
$\angle N$ appears congruent to $\angle P$

Thus, the opposite angles of a quadrilateral are not necessarily congruent.

FINDING PROPERTIES OF QUADRILATERALS

Oral Exercises

Name the pairs of consecutive sides and opposite sides of each quadrilateral.

Name the pairs of consecutive angles and opposite angles of each quadrilateral.

1.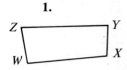

2.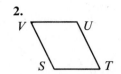

3.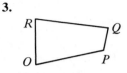

4.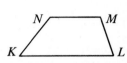

Written Exercises

Name the diagonals of each quadrilateral. Do the diagonals intersect?

 1.

2.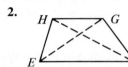

3.

4.

For each of the following, draw a quadrilateral to fit the description.

   5. Congruent opposite sides

   6. Congruent consecutive sides

   7. No congruent sides

   8. No congruent angles

Draw pictures to defend your answer to each of the following.

   9. Can a quadrilateral have exactly two congruent consecutive sides?

   10. Can a quadrilateral have exactly two congruent consecutive angles?

B **11.** Are any sides of a quadrilateral necessarily congruent?

   12. Do the diagonals of a quadrilateral bisect its angles?

   13. Are congruent triangles formed by the diagonals of a quadrilateral?

   14. Are opposite sides of a quadrilateral parallel?

C **15.** Do the segments that join the midpoints of consecutive sides of a quadrilateral have any special properties?

   16. Do the segments that join the midpoints of opposite sides of a quadrilateral have any special properties?

A Challenge To You

A triangle has three sides, but no diagonals. A quadrilateral has four sides with two diagonals. A pentagon has five sides and five diagonals. A hexagon has six sides and nine diagonals. How many diagonals does a heptagon have? An octagon? How many diagonals does an n-gon have? Can you write a formula for this?

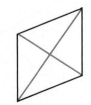

4 sides –2 diagonals

5 sides – 5 diagonals

7.2 Finding Properties of Parallelograms

To prove and apply theorems about parallelograms

Some quadrilaterals have special properties and special names. One of these is the *parallelogram*.

Definition:
parallelogram

> A *parallelogram* is a quadrilateral in which both pairs of opposite sides are parallel. (Parallelogram *ABCD* is written □*ABCD*.)

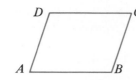

ABCD is a parallelogram.

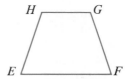

EFGH is not a parallelogram
(*FG* and *EH* are not parallel)

The following theorem will help you prove other properties of parallelograms.

> **Theorem 7.1** A diagonal of a parallelogram forms two congruent triangles.

Given: □*ABCD* with
     diagonal $\overline{BD}$
Prove: △*DAB* ≅
     △*BCD*

Analysis: Use ASA.
Alt. int. ∠'s of ‖ lines
are ≅.

Proof

Statements		Reasons
1. □*ABCD*, with diagonal $\overline{BD}$		1. Given
2. $\overline{AB} \parallel \overline{DC}$ and $\overline{AD} \parallel \overline{BC}$		2. Def. of □.
3. ∠1 ≅ ∠4	(A)	3. Alt. int. ∠'s of ‖ lines are ≅.
4. $\overline{BD} \cong \overline{DB}$	(S)	4. Reflexive property
5. ∠3 ≅ ∠2	(A)	5. Alt. int. ∠'s of ‖ lines are ≅.
6. ∴ △*DAB* ≅ △*BCD*		6. ASA

The definition tells you that the opposite sides of a parallelogram are parallel. Since corresponding parts of congruent triangles are congruent, you can easily show that opposite sides and opposite angles of parallelograms are congruent. These properties are stated in Corollaries 1 and 2.

You can use Theorem 7.1 and its corollaries to find unknown lengths of sides and measures of angles of parallelograms.

Example 1 Given: $\square ABCD$, m $\angle A = 120$
Find the measure of each
of the other angles.

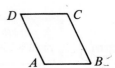

m $\angle C = 120$ ◄ *Use Corollary 2.*
m $\angle B =\ \ 60$ ◄ *Interior $\angle$'s of $\parallel$ lines on the same*
m $\angle D =\ \ 60$ *side of transversal are supplementary.*

Example 2 Given: $\square EFGH$, $EF = 3x - 4$, and
$GH = 2x + 2$
Find EF.

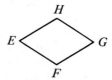

$EF = GH$ ◄ *Use Corollary 1.*
$3x - 4 = 2x + 2$
$x = 6$
Thus, $EF = 3 \cdot 6 - 4$, or 14.

─────────────────◆━◆━◆─────────────────

You can use corresponding parts of congruent triangles to prove a theorem about the diagonals of a parallelogram.

┌ **Theorem 7.2** The diagonals of a parallelogram bisect each other. ──┐

Given: $\square WXYZ$
    with Diagonals
    $\overline{XZ}$ and $\overline{WY}$
Prove: $\overline{XO} \cong \overline{ZO}$ and
    $\overline{YO} \cong \overline{WO}$

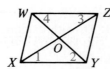

Analysis: Show that
$\overline{XO}$ and $\overline{ZO}$, $\overline{WO}$ and
$\overline{YO}$ are corresponding
sides of $\cong \triangle$'s.

Outline of proof

1. $\overline{WZ} \parallel \overline{XY}$
2. $\angle 1 \cong \angle 3, \angle 2 \cong \angle 4$
3. $\overline{XY} \cong \overline{ZW}$

4. $\triangle XYO \cong \triangle ZWO$
5. $\therefore\ \overline{XO} \cong \overline{ZO}$ and $\overline{YO} \cong \overline{WO}$

(See Exercise 16.)
└   ┘

Example 3 Given: $\square ABCD$, $AC = 16$, and $BD = 12$
Find AO and BO.

Apply Th. 7.2. ▶ $AO = \frac{1}{2}(AC)$ or 8

$BO = \frac{1}{2}(BD)$ or 6

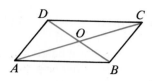

Example 4 $EFGH$ is a parallelogram. Which of the following
pairs of triangles are congruent? Why?

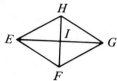

$\triangle EFG$ and $\triangle GHE$
Congruent by Th. 7.1.

$\triangle EIF$ and $\triangle GIF$
Not necessarily congruent

You have proved several important theorems and corollaries about a parallelogram. These, along with the definition, provide you with the basic properties of a parallelogram, as summarized below.

Properties of a Parallelogram

Opposite sides
are parallel.

Opposite sides
are congruent.

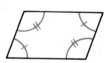

Opposite angles
are congruent.

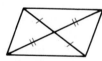

Diagonals bisect
each other.

Oral Exercises

Which of the following polygons are parallelograms? (Ex. 1–4)

1.
2.
3.
4.

5. Which sides of $\square ABCD$ are parallel?

6. Which sides of $\square ABCD$ are congruent?

7. Which angles of $\square ABCD$ are congruent?

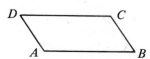

8. Which angles of $\square ABCD$ are supplementary?

FINDING PROPERTIES OF PARALLELOGRAMS

Written Exercises

1. Given: $\square ABCD$, and
   $m \angle A = 120$
   Find the measure of each
   of the other angles.

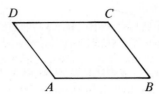

3. Given: $\square ABCD$, and
   $m \angle A = 3 \, m \angle B$
   Find $m \angle A$ and $m \angle B$.

2. Given: $\square ABCD$, and
   $m \angle B = 53$
   Find the measure of each
   of the other angles.

4. Given: $\square ABCD$
   $m \angle B = 4x - 5$, and
   $m \angle D = 3x + 10$
   Find $m \angle B$ and $m \angle C$.

5. Given: $\square EFGH$,
   $EF = 5x - 7$, and
   $GH = 3x + 1$
   Find GH.

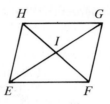

7. Given: $\square EFGH$,
   $EI = 7x - 4$, and
   $GI = 5x + 2$
   Find EI.

6. Given: $\square EFGH$,
   $EH = 3x - 5$, and
   $FG = 2x + 2$
   Find EH.

8. Given: $\square EFGH$,
   $FI = 4x - 6$, and
   $HI = 3x + 1$
   Find HI.

JKLM is a parallelogram. Which of the following pairs of triangles are congruent?
Why? (Ex. 9–14)

9. $\triangle MNJ$ and $\triangle KNL$

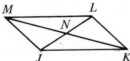

10. $\triangle MJK$ and $\triangle LKJ$

11. $\triangle MNL$ and $\triangle KNJ$

12. $\triangle MJK$ and $\triangle KLM$

13. $\triangle MNJ$ and $\triangle KNJ$

14. $\triangle JKL$ and $\triangle LMJ$

15. Prove: Consecutive angles of a parallelo-
    gram are supplementary.

16. Complete the proof of Theorem 7.2.

17. Prove Corollaries 1 and 2.

18. Given: $\square ABCD$; diagonals $\overline{AC}$ and $\overline{BD}$
    intersect at G.
    Prove: G is the midpoint of $\overline{EF}$.

19. Given: $\square XYZW$; T is the midpoint of
    $\overline{WZ}$; and U is the midpoint of $\overline{XY}$.
    Prove: V is the midpoint of $\overline{TU}$ and $\overline{XZ}$.

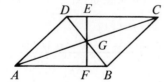

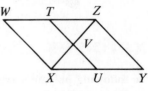

20. Given: $\square ABCD \parallel \square EFGH$; $\square ADHE \parallel \square BCGF$;
    $\square ABFE \parallel \square DCGH$; and I, J, K, and L are coplanar.
    Prove: $\overline{LK} \cong \overline{IJ}$, and $\angle ILK \cong \angle IJK$

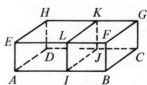

Cumulative Review

1. What is the measure of each exterior angle of a regular hexagon?

2. What is the measure of each angle of a regular dodecagon?

3. Is a regular pentagon a convex or a concave polygon?

7·3 Proving Parallelograms

OBJECTIVE ► **To prove that some quadrilaterals are parallelograms**

You already know that certain quadrilaterals are also parallelograms. One way to prove that a quadrilateral is a parallelogram is to show that the definition of a parallelogram is satisfied. In other words, you must show that each pair of opposite sides of the quadrilateral is parallel.

For example, if you show that $\overline{AB} \parallel \overline{DC}$ and $\overline{AD} \parallel \overline{BC}$, then you have proved that quadrilateral $ABCD$ is a parallelogram.

Two additional ways of proving that a quadrilateral is a parallelogram follow.

Theorem 7.3 If both pairs of opposite sides of a quadrilateral are congruent, then the quadrilateral is a parallelogram.

Given: $\overline{AB} \cong \overline{CD}$ and $\overline{AD} \cong \overline{CB}$
Prove: $ABCD$ is a ▱

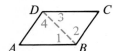

Analysis: Draw $\overline{BD}$. Show opposite sides ∥ by using ≅ alt. int. ∠'s.

Proof

Statements		Reasons
1. Draw $\overline{BD}$.		1. Two points are contained in exactly one line.
2. $\overline{AB} \cong \overline{CD}$	(S)	2. Given
3. $\overline{AD} \cong \overline{CB}$	(S)	3. Given
4. $\overline{BD} \cong \overline{DB}$	(S)	4. Reflexive property
5. $\triangle ABD \cong \triangle CDB$		5. SSS
6. $\angle 1 \cong \angle 3$ and $\angle 2 \cong \angle 4$		6. CPCTC
7. $\overline{AB} \parallel \overline{DC}$ and $\overline{AD} \parallel \overline{BC}$		7. If alt. int. ∠'s are ≅, then lines are ∥.
8. ∴ $ABCD$ is a ▱.		8. Def. of ▱

Theorem 7.4 If both pairs of opposite angles of a quadrilateral are congruent, then the quadrilateral is a parallelogram.

Given: $\angle A \cong \angle C$, and $\angle B \cong \angle D$
Prove: $ABCD$ is a parallelogram

Analysis: Show opposite sides ∥ by proving that the adj. ∠'s are supplementary.

(See Exercise 17.)

PROVING PARALLELOGRAMS

A fourth way to prove that a quadrilateral is a parallelogram is to show that two sides are both parallel and congruent.

Theorem 7.5 If two sides of a quadrilateral are parallel and congruent, then the quadrilateral is a parallelogram.

Given: $\overline{AB} \parallel \overline{CD}$ and
$\overline{AB} \cong \overline{CD}$

Prove: $ABCD$ is a parallelogram.

Analysis: Show that $\overline{BC} \cong \overline{DA}$ by proving $\triangle ABC \cong \triangle CDA$. Apply Th. 7.3.

Proof

Statements		Reasons
1. Draw $\overline{AC}$.		1. Two points are contained in exactly one line.
2. $\overline{AB} \cong \overline{CD}$	(S)	2. Given
3. $\overline{AB} \parallel \overline{CD}$		3. Given
4. $\angle 1 \cong \angle 2$	(A)	4. Alt. int. $\angle$'s of $\parallel$ lines are $\cong$.
5. $\overline{AC} \cong \overline{CA}$	(S)	5. Reflexive property
6. $\triangle ABC \cong \triangle CDA$		6. SAS
7. $\overline{BC} \cong \overline{DA}$		7. CPCTC
8. $\therefore ABCD$ is a $\square$.		8. If both pairs of opp. sides are $\cong$, then quad. is a $\square$.

You can also prove that a quadrilateral is a parallelogram by showing that the diagonals bisect each other. You should complete the proof of this theorem as an exercise.

Theorem 7.6 If the diagonals of a quadrilateral bisect each other, then the quadrilateral is a parallelogram.
(See Exercise 18.)

Summarized below are five ways to prove that a quadrilateral is a parallelogram. Each of these is a *sufficient condition* for proving that a given quadrilateral is a parallelogram; a quadrilateral that satisfies any one of these five conditions is a parallelogram.

Summary

To prove that a quadrilateral is a parallelogram:

1. Show that both pairs of opposite sides are parallel.
2. Show that both pairs of opposite sides are congruent.
3. Show that both pairs of opposite angles are congruent.
4. Show that two sides are congruent and parallel.
5. Show that the diagonals bisect each other.

You can now use the methods just summarized to determine if a given quadrilateral is a parallelogram.

Example 1 If a diagonal of a quadrilateral forms two congruent triangles, is the quadrilateral a parallelogram?

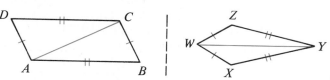

$\triangle ABC \cong \triangle CDA$
ABCD is a parallelogram.
Thus, the quadrilateral is not necessarily a parallelogram.

$\triangle WXY \cong \triangle WZY$
WXYZ is not a parallelogram.

◄ *WXYZ is called a kite.*

Example 2 In quadrilateral *ABCD*, $AO = CO = 8$ and $BO = DO = 7$. Is *ABCD* a parallelogram? Why?

Since $AO = CO$ and $BO = DO$, the diagonals bisect each other.
Thus, *ABCD* is a parallelogram. ◄ *Use Th. 7.6.*

Reading in Geometry

You learned that the converse of a statement is formed by interchanging the "if" and the "then" clauses. Write the converse of each of the seven statements below. Pick out the statements and converses that were proved as theorems. Give the theorem numbers of each.

1. If the diagonals of a quadrilateral bisect each other, then the quadrilateral is a parallelogram.

2. If both pairs of opposite angles of a quadrilateral are congruent, then the quadrilateral is a parallelogram.

3. If a diagonal of a quadrilateral forms two congruent triangles, then the quadrilateral is a parallelogram.

4. If both pairs of opposite sides of a quadrilateral are congruent, then the quadrilateral is a parallelogram.

5. If the diagonals of a quadrilateral are perpendicular, then the quadrilateral is a parallelogram.

6. If two sides of a quadrilateral are congruent and parallel, then the quadrilateral is a parallelogram.

7. If the diagonals of a quadrilateral are congruent, then the quadrilateral is a parallelogram.

PROVING PARALLELOGRAMS

Written Exercises

Based only on the markings shown which of these quadrilaterals are parallelograms?

 1.

2.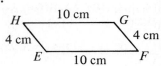

3.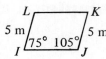

4.

5.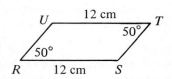

6.

Based on the information given in each case, is *ABCD* a parallelogram? Give a reason for your answer. (Ex. 7–16)

7. m $\angle DAB = 120$ and
   m $\angle BCD = 120$

8. $AB = 12$, $DC = 12$, $\overline{AB} \parallel \overline{DC}$

9. $\overline{AB} \cong \overline{DC}$ and $\overline{AB} \parallel \overline{DC}$

10. $\angle 1 \cong \angle 5$ and $\angle 2 \cong \angle 6$

11. $\angle 4 \cong \angle 8$ and $\angle 1 \cong \angle 5$

12. $\triangle ABD \cong \triangle ADC$

13. $\overline{AB} \parallel \overline{DC}$ and $\overline{AD} \parallel \overline{BC}$

14. $\overline{AB} \cong \overline{DC}$ and $\overline{AD} \cong \overline{BC}$

15. $\overline{AE} \cong \overline{EC}$ and $\overline{BE} \cong \overline{ED}$

16. $\triangle AEB \cong \triangle CED$

B 17. Prove Theorem 7.4.

18. Prove Theorem 7.6.

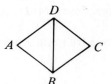

19. Given: $\overline{UZ} \cong \overline{XV}$ and
    $\triangle XUW \cong \triangle ZVY$
    Prove: $UXVZ$ is a $\square$

20. Given: $\square XYZW$ and
    $\overline{WU} \cong \overline{YV}$
    Prove: $UXVZ$ is a $\square$

21. Given: $\triangle ABD$ is equilateral
    and $\triangle CDB$ is equilateral
    Prove: $ABCD$ is a $\square$

22. Given: $\triangle ABD$ is equiangular
    and $\triangle CDB$ is equiangular
    Prove: $ABCD$ is a $\square$

Give a proof or counterexample to defend your answer.

23. If consecutive angles of a quadrilateral are supplementary, is the quadrilateral a parallelogram?

24. If the diagonals of a quadrilateral are perpendicular, is the quadrilateral a parallelogram?

25. If the diagonals of a quadrilateral are congruent, is the quadrilateral a parallelogram?

26. If the diagonals of a quadrilateral bisect its angles, is the quadrilateral a parallelogram?

C 27. If the bisectors of a pair of opposite angles of a quadrilateral form a parallelogram with two sides of the quadrilateral, is the quadrilateral a parallelogram?

28. If the segments joining the midpoints of consecutive sides of a quadrilateral form a parallelogram, is the quadrilateral a parallelogram?

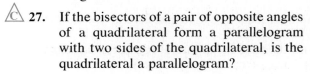

7.4 A Special Segment

OBJECTIVE ▶ **To prove and apply the theorem about the segment joining the mid-points of two sides of a triangle**

You can use the properties of parallelograms to prove a theorem about a special segment in a triangle.

⌐ **Theorem 7.7** The segment joining the midpoints of two sides of a tri- ⌐
angle is parallel to the third side, and its length is half
the length of the third side.

Given: $\triangle ABC$, D is the
midpoint of $\overline{AC}$, and
E is the midpoint of $\overline{BC}$.
Prove: $\overline{DE} \parallel \overline{AB}$,

$$DE = \frac{1}{2}AB$$

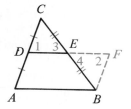

Analysis: Form □ and
use properties of □'s.

Proof

Statements		Reasons
1. $\triangle ABC$		1. Given
2. Draw $\overline{EF} \cong \overline{DE}$ so E is between D and F		2. ≅ segment postulate
3. Draw $\overline{BF}$	(S)	3. Two pt. are contained in exactly 1 line.
4. $\angle 4 \cong \angle 3$		4. Vertical $\angle$'s are $\cong$.
5. E is the midpoint of $\overline{BC}$	(A)	5. Given
6. $\overline{BE} \cong \overline{CE}$		6. Def. of midpoint
7. $\triangle FEB \cong \triangle DEC$	(S)	7. SAS
8. $\angle 1 \cong \angle 2$ and $\overline{CD} \cong \overline{BF}$		8. CPCTC
9. D is the midpoint of $\overline{AC}$		9. Given
10. $\overline{CD} \cong \overline{DA}$		10. Def. of midpoint
11. $\overline{BF} \cong \overline{DA}$		11. Substitution
12. $\overline{BF} \parallel \overline{DA}$		12. Lines are $\parallel$ if alt. int. $\angle$'s are $\cong$.
13. $ABFD$ is a □		13. Quad. is □ if 2 sides $\parallel$ and $\cong$.
14. $\overline{DF} \parallel \overline{AB}$ and $\therefore \overline{DE} \parallel \overline{AB}$		14. Def. of □
15. $\overline{DF} \cong \overline{AB}$ and $DF = AB$		15. Opp. sides of □ are $\cong$; def. of $\cong$ seg.
16. $DF = DE + EF$		16. Def. of *between*
17. $DE = \frac{1}{2}DF$		17. Step 2, step 16, algebraic properties
18. $\therefore DE = \frac{1}{2}AB$		18. Substitution

You can now use Theorem 7.7 to find the lengths of segments associated with triangles. Examples 1 and 2 illustrate two such applications.

Example 1

Given: E is the midpoint of $\overline{AB}$, D is the midpoint of $\overline{AC}$, and $ED = 6$.
Find BC.

Use Th. 7.7. ▶ $6 = \frac{1}{2}(BC)$ **Thus, $BC = 12$.**

Example 2

Given: $\overline{AD} \cong \overline{DB}$, $\overline{AE} \cong \overline{EC}$, $DE = 2x + 3$, and $BC = 5x + 4$
Find DE and BC.

Use Th. 7.7. ▶ $2x + 3 = \frac{1}{2}(5x + 4)$

$$2(2x + 3) = 5x + 4$$
$$4x + 6 = 5x + 4$$
$$2 = x \qquad \textbf{Thus, } DE = 7 \text{ and } BC = 14.$$

Theorem 7.7 can also be used in proofs that involve parallel lines.

Example 3

Prove: The segments joining the midpoints of consecutive sides of a quadrilateral form a parallelogram.

Given: Quad. $ABCD$ with E, F, G, H the midpoints of $\overline{AB}$, $\overline{BC}$, $\overline{CD}$, and $\overline{DA}$, respectively
Prove: $EFGH$ is a $\square$.

Proof

Statements	Reasons
1. Draw $\overline{AC}$, forming $\triangle ABC$ and $\triangle ADC$	1. Two pts. are contained in exactly one line; Def. of $\triangle$
2. Quad, $ABCD$ with E, F, G, H the midpoints of $\overline{AB}$, $\overline{BC}$, $\overline{CD}$, and $\overline{DA}$, resp.	2. Given
3. $\overline{HG} \parallel \overline{AC}$, $\overline{EF} \parallel \overline{AC}$	3. Seg. joining midpts. of 2 sides of $\triangle$ is $\parallel$ to 3rd side.
4. $\overline{HG} \parallel \overline{EF}$	4. Lines $\parallel$ to same line are $\parallel$.
5. $HG = \frac{1}{2} AC$, $EF = \frac{1}{2} AC$	5. Seg. joining midpts. of 2 sides of $\triangle$ has length $\frac{1}{2}$ length of 3rd side.
6. $HG = EF$ and $\overline{HG} \cong \overline{EF}$	6. Substitution and def. of $\cong$ seg.
7. $\therefore EFGH$ is a $\square$.	7. Quad. is $\square$ if two sides are $\parallel$ and $\cong$.

Oral **Exercises**

Find each indicated length if V is the midpoint of $\overline{XZ}$ and W is the midpoint of $\overline{YZ}$.

1. If $VW = 8$, then $XY = $?
3. If $VW = 3$, then $XY = $?
5. If $VW = 2\frac{1}{2}$ then $XY = $?

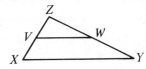

2. If $XY = 18$, then $VW = $?
4. If $XY = 4$, then $VW = $?
6. If $XY = 9$, then $VW = $?

Written Exercises _____

If *W*, *V*, and *U* are the midpoints of the sides of △*XYZ*, then complete each statement. (Ex. 1–6)

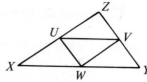

A
1. If *XZ* = 10, then *WV* = ?
3. $\overline{VW}$ ∥ ?
5. If *XW* = 2, then *UV* = ?

2. If *UW* = *t*, then *YZ* = ?
4. $\overline{XY}$ ∥ ?
6. If *ZV* = *t*, then *UW* = ?

7. Given: *M* and *N* are the midpoints of $\overline{JL}$ and $\overline{KL}$. *JK* = 6*x* − 4, and *MN* = 2*x* + 1
Find *MN*.

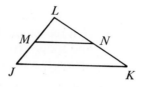

8. Given: *M* and *N* are the midpoints of $\overline{JL}$ and $\overline{KL}$, *JK* = 3*x* − 8, and *MN* = *x* + 4
Find *JK*.

9. Given: *S*, *T*, and *U* are the midpoints of $\overline{RP}$, $\overline{PQ}$, and $\overline{QR}$ respectively.
Prove: *RSTU* is a ▱.

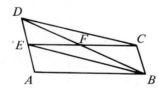

10. Given: *S*, *T*, and *U* are the midpoints of $\overline{RP}$, $\overline{PQ}$, and $\overline{QR}$ respectively.
Prove: △*SPT* ≅ △*UTQ*.

B
11. Given: *E* and *F* are the midpoints of $\overline{DA}$ and $\overline{DB}$, respectively. $\overline{FC}$ ≅ $\overline{EF}$.
Prove: *EABC* is a ▱.

12. Given: *E* and *F* are the midpoints of $\overline{DA}$ and $\overline{DB}$ respectively. $\overline{EC}$ ≅ $\overline{AB}$.
Prove: *DEBC* is a ▱.

13. Given: *K* and *M* are the midpoints of $\overline{JG}$ and $\overline{IH}$ respectively. *L* is the midpoint of $\overline{KM}$ and $\overline{JH}$.
Prove: *GHIJ* is a ▱.

14. Given: ▱*GHIJ*, *K* and *L* are the midpoints of $\overline{JG}$ and $\overline{JH}$ respectively.
Prove: *GHMK* is a ▱.

C
15. Prove: The segments joining the midpoints of the opposite sides of a quadrilateral bisect each other.

16. Prove: The opposite angles of the quadrilateral formed by the bisectors of the angles of a convex quadrilateral are supplementary.

17. Given: $\overline{QP}$ ∥ $\overline{NO}$, *R*, *S*, and *T* are midpoints of $\overline{QN}$, $\overline{QO}$, and $\overline{PO}$, respectively.
Prove: $RT = \frac{1}{2}(QP + NO)$

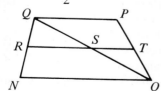

18. Given: $\overline{AD}$ ∥ $\overline{BE}$ ∥ $\overline{CF}$, $\overline{AD}$ ≅ $\overline{BE}$ ≅ $\overline{CF}$
Prove: ∠*EDF* ≅ ∠*BAC*

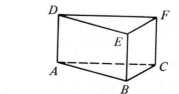

A SPECIAL SEGMENT

7.5 Parallel Lines and Congruent Segments

OBJECTIVES ▶ **To use properties of parallelograms to prove theorems about parallel lines**
To divide a segment into a given number of congruent segments

You can use some properties of parallelograms to prove theorems about parallel lines.

Theorem 7.8   If three parallel lines cut off congruent segments on one transversal, then they cut off congruent segments on every transversal.

Given: $l \parallel m \parallel n$, transversals $\overleftrightarrow{AC}$ and $\overleftrightarrow{DF}$, and $\overline{CB} \cong \overline{BA}$
Prove: $\overline{EF} \cong \overline{DE}$

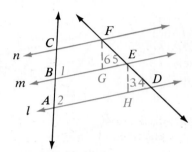

Analysis: Make $\square$'s by drawing $\overline{FG} \parallel \overline{CB}$ and $\overline{EH} \parallel \overline{BA}$.
Show $\triangle FGE \cong \triangle EHD$.

Proof

Statements		Reasons
1. $l \parallel m \parallel n$, trans. $\overleftrightarrow{AC}$, $\overleftrightarrow{DF}$		1. Given
2. Draw $\overline{FG} \parallel \overline{CB}$ and $\overline{EH} \parallel \overline{BA}$		2. Through a given pt., there is exactly one line $\parallel$ to a given line.
3. $AHEB$ and $BGFC$ are $\square$'s		3. Def. of $\square$
4. $\overline{FG} \cong \overline{CB}$ and $\overline{EH} \cong \overline{BA}$		4. Opp. sides of a $\square$ are $\cong$.
5. $\overline{CB} \cong \overline{BA}$		5. Given
6. $\overline{EH} \cong \overline{FG}$	(S)	6. Substitution property
7. $\angle 6 \cong \angle 1$, $\angle 3 \cong \angle 2$		7. Corr. $\angle$'s of $\parallel$ lines are $\cong$.
8. $\angle 1 \cong \angle 2$		8. Corr. $\angle$'s of $\parallel$ lines are $\cong$.
9. $\angle 6 \cong \angle 3$	(A)	9. Substitution property
10. $\angle 5 \cong \angle 4$	(A)	10. Corr. $\angle$'s of $\parallel$ lines are $\cong$.
11. $\triangle FGE \cong \triangle EHD$		11. AAS
12. $\therefore \overline{EF} \cong \overline{DE}$		12. CPCTC

A corollary of Theorem 7.8 extends the theorem to more than three parallel lines.

Corollary   If any given number of parallel lines cut off congruent segments on one transversal, then they cut off congruent segments on every transversal.

One application of Theorem 7.8 and its corollary is to find unknown lengths of segments cut off by parallel lines.

Example 1
Given: $\overleftrightarrow{AD} \parallel \overleftrightarrow{BE} \parallel \overleftrightarrow{CF}$, $AB = 8$
$BC = 8$, and $DE = 7$
Find DF

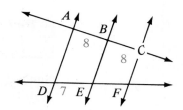

$EF = DE = 7$ ◄ *Use Th. 7.8.*
Thus, $DF = 7 + 7$ or 14.

Example 2
Given: $\overleftrightarrow{GJ} \parallel \overleftrightarrow{HK} \parallel \overleftrightarrow{IL}$, $GH = 15$,
$HI = 15$, $JK = 3x - 9$, and $KL = 2x - 2$
Find JL

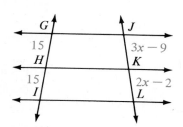

Use Th. 7.8. ► $3x - 9 = 2x - 2$
$x = 7$

$JK = 3 \cdot 7 - 9$, or 12
$KL = 2 \cdot 7 - 2$ or 12
Thus, $JL = 12 + 12$ or 24.

Another application of Theorem 7.8 and its corollary is a construction in which a given segment can be divided into any specified number of congruent segments.

┌ **Construction**   To divide $\overline{AB}$ into three congruent segments. ─────┐

Given: $\overline{AB}$
Construct: Points P and Q on $\overline{AB}$ so that $\overline{AP} \cong \overline{PQ} \cong \overline{QB}$.

Strategy: Apply corollary to Th. 7.8 by constructing parallel lines.

Draw $\overrightarrow{AX}$.

Set compass at any convenient opening. On $\overrightarrow{AX}$, construct $\overline{AC} \cong \overline{CD} \cong \overline{DE}$.

Draw $\overline{BE}$. Construct $\overline{CP} \parallel \overline{BE}$ and $\overline{DQ} \parallel BE$.

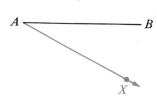

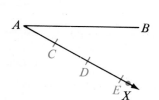

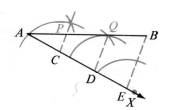

Conclusion: $\overline{AP} \cong \overline{PQ} \cong \overline{QB}$

PARALLEL LINES AND CONGRUENT SEGMENTS

If you were asked to find the shortest path between points A and B, you probably would select the straight one.

Postulate 19 The shortest path joining two points is a segment.

Similarly, if you were asked to find the shortest segment from point P to line l, you would choose $\overline{PQ}$.

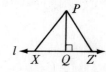

Postulate 20 The shortest segment joining a point and a line is the segment perpendicular to the line.

The length of this shortest segment is called the *distance* from a point to a line. This can be used to define the distance between two parallel lines.

Definition:
distance between parallel lines

The **distance between two parallel lines** is the distance from a point on one line to the other line.

You should complete the proof of the following theorem.

Theorem 7.9 Parallel lines are equidistant at all *points*.

Given: $l \parallel m$, $\overline{PX} \perp m$
and $\overline{QY} \perp m$
Prove: $PX = QY$

Analysis: $\overline{PX}$ and $\overline{QY}$ are opp. sides of a $\square$

(See Exercise 25.)

Oral **Exercises**

Find each indicated length if $l \parallel m \parallel n$, $AD = 6$, and $DG = 6$.

1. If $CF = 5$, then $FI = ?$
3. If $BE = 4$, then $BH = ?$
5. If $FI = 9$, then $CF = ?$
7. If $CI = 12$, then $CF = ?$

2. If $BE = 6$, then $EH = ?$
4. If $CF = 7$, then $CI = ?$
6. If $EH = 3$, then $BH = ?$
8. If $BH = 9$, then $BE = ?$

Written Exercises

Find each indicated length if $l \parallel m \parallel n \parallel r \parallel s \parallel t$, **and** $\overline{LK} \cong \overline{KJ} \cong \overline{JI} \cong \overline{IH} \cong \overline{HG}$. (Ex. 1–10)

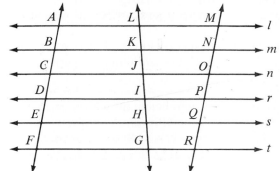

1. If $AB = 4$, then $CD = ?$
2. If $OP = 9$, then $QR = ?$
3. If $NO = 6$, then $NP = ?$
4. If $EF = 8$, then $CF = ?$
5. If $CD = 3$, then $BF = ?$
6. If $PQ = 5$, then $MR = ?$
7. If $BF = 36$, then $CD = ?$
8. If $NQ = 15$, then $OQ = ?$
9. If $CE = 5$, then $AD = ?$
10. If $MP = 8$, then $NR = ?$

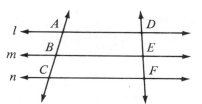

11. Given: $l \parallel m \parallel n$, $\overline{AB} \cong \overline{BC}$, $DE = 4x - 7$, and $EF = 2x + 1$. Find DE.
12. Given: $l \parallel m \parallel n$, $\overline{AB} \cong \overline{BC}$, $DE = 2x + 13$, and $EF = 5x + 1$. Find DF.
13. Given: $l \parallel m \parallel n$, $\overline{DE} \cong \overline{EF}$, $AC = 7x - 2$, and $BC = 3x + 4$. Find AB.
14. Given: $l \parallel m \parallel n$, $\overline{DE} \cong \overline{EF}$, $AB = 2x - 1$, and $AC = 7x - 8$. Find AC.

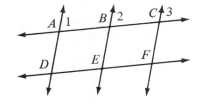

15. Given: $\angle 1 \cong \angle 2 \cong \angle 3$ and $\overline{AB} \cong \overline{BC}$
    Prove: $\overline{DE} \cong \overline{EF}$.
16. Given: $\overline{AB} \parallel \overline{DE}$, $\overline{BE} \parallel \overline{CF}$, $\overline{AB} \cong \overline{DE}$, and $\overline{AB} \cong \overline{BC}$
    Prove: $\overline{DE} \cong \overline{EF}$
17. Given: $\angle 1 \cong \angle 2$, $\overleftrightarrow{BE} \parallel \overleftrightarrow{CF}$, and $\overline{DE} \cong \overline{EF}$
    Prove: $\overline{AB} \cong \overline{BC}$.
18. Given: $\overleftrightarrow{AD} \parallel \overleftrightarrow{BE} \parallel \overleftrightarrow{CF}$, $\overline{AB} \cong \overline{BC}$, and $\overline{AB} \cong \overline{DE}$
    Prove: $\overline{AB} \cong \overline{EF}$.

19. Draw a segment 10 cm long. Divide it into three congruent segments.
20. Draw a segment 10 cm long. Divide it into four congruent segments.
21. Draw a segment 10 cm long. Divide it into five congruent segments.

22. Draw a segment 8 cm long. Construct a segment two-thirds as long.
23. Draw a segment 12 cm long. Construct a segment four-fifths as long.
24. Draw a segment 8 cm long. Construct a segment four-thirds as long.
25. Prove Theorem 7.9.
26. Prove Corollary 7.8 for four parallel lines.

True or false? If true, prove the statement. If false, show a counterexample.

27. If three lines cut off congruent segments on each of two transversals, then the lines are parallel.
28. If a segment is parallel to one side of a triangle and bisects a second side, then it bisects the third side.
29. If two lines are equidistant at all points, then the lines are parallel.
30. If a segment joining a point on each of two sides of a triangle is half as long as the third side, then it is parallel to the third side.

PARALLEL LINES AND CONGRUENT SEGMENTS

7.6 Rhombi, Rectangles, and Squares

OBJECTIVES ▶ **To identify rhombi, rectangles, and squares**
To prove and apply properties of rhombi, rectangles, and squares

There are three special kinds of parallelograms. While all three have parallel opposite sides, each has additional properties which distinguish it from the others.

Definition:
rhombus,
rectangle,
and square

> A *rhombus* is a parallelogram with four congruent sides.
> A *rectangle* is a parallelogram with four right angles.
> A *square* is a rectangle with four congruent sides.

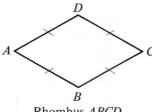

Rhombus *ABCD*

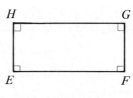

Rectangle *EFGH*

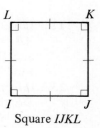

Square *IJKL*

You should be able to use the properties of a rhombus (plural: *rhombi*), a rectangle, and a square to identify each of them.

Example 1 True or false?

Statements	Answers
Some rhombi are squares.	True
Some rhombi are parallelograms.	True
A square is both a rhombus and a rectangle.	True
All rhombi are rectangles.	False

Example 2 True or false? If true, prove the statement. If false, give a counterexample.

Consecutive angles of a rhombus are congruent.

False.
m $\angle A = 60$
m $\angle B = 120$
m $\angle C = 60$
m $\angle D = 120$

In the examples that follow, you will examine certain properties involving the diagonals of parallelograms, rhombi, rectangles, and squares.

Example 3 Which of the following figures have congruent diagonals: a parallelogram, a rhombus, a rectangle, a square? Draw pictures to show this.

Thus, the rectangle and square appear to have congruent diagonals.

Example 4 Given: Rect. $ABCD$ with diagonals $\overline{AC}$ and $\overline{BD}$.
Prove: $\overline{BD} \cong \overline{AC}$

Proof

Statements		Reasons
1. Rect. $ABCD$, diagonals $\overline{AC}$ and $\overline{BD}$		1. Given
2. $\overline{AD} \cong \overline{BC}$	(S)	2. Opp. sides of $\square$ are $\cong$.
3. $\angle DAB \cong \angle CBA$	(A)	3. A rect. has four $\cong$ rt. $\angle$'s.
4. $\overline{AB} \cong \overline{BA}$	(S)	4. Reflexive property
5. $\triangle DAB \cong \triangle CBA$		5. SAS
6. $\therefore \overline{BD} \cong \overline{AC}$		6. CPCTC

Example 4 shows that the diagonals of a rectangle are congruent. A square is a rectangle by definition, so the diagonals of a square are also congruent.

Example 5 Prove: The diagonals of a rhombus are perpendicular.

Given: Rhombus $XYZW$ with diagonals $\overline{XZ}$ and $\overline{WY}$
Prove: $\overline{WY} \perp \overline{XZ}$.

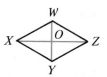

Proof

Statements	Reasons
1. Rhombus $XYZW$, diagonals $\overline{XZ}$ and $\overline{WY}$	1. Given
2. $\overline{XW} \cong \overline{ZW}$ and $\overline{XY} \cong \overline{ZY}$	2. Def. of rhombus
3. $\therefore \overline{WY} \perp \overline{XZ}$	3. Two pt. each equidistant from the end pt. of a seg. determine the $\perp$ bisector of the seg.

RHOMBI, RECTANGLES, AND SQUARES

Property	Rhombus	Rectangle	Square
All sides ≅	X		X
4 ≅ rt. ∠'s		X	X
≅ diagonals		X	X
⊥ diagonals	X		X

Summary — Special properties of rhombi, rectangles, and squares.

From this summary, you should observe that a square has all the special properties of both a rhombus and a rectangle.

Example 6

Given: Rectangle $ABCD$, $AC = 3x + 2$, and $BD = 5x - 8$
Find BD.

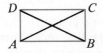

$$5x - 8 = 3x + 2$$
$$2x = 10 \quad \blacktriangleleft \quad \textit{The diagonals of a rect. are} \cong.$$
$$x = 5$$

Thus, $BD = 5(5) - 8$ **or** 17

Reading in Geometry

Copy each sentence. Underline once the words that are part of the "Given." Underline twice the words that are part of the "Prove."

1. If all four sides of a quadrilateral are congruent, then the quadrilateral is a rhombus.
2. If all four angles of a quadrilateral are congruent, then the quadrilateral is a rectangle.
3. If the diagonals of a parallelogram are perpendicular, then the parallelogram is a rhombus.
4. The opposite sides of a parallelogram are congruent.
5. The adjacent sides of a square are congruent.
6. The diagonals of a rhombus are perpendicular.

Oral Exercises

Tell whether each figure appears to be a rhombus, a rectangle, a square, or none of these. Some figures can correctly be identified in more than one way.

1.

2.

3.
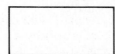

4.

Based only on the markings shown, identify each figure as a rhombus, a rectangle, a square, or none of these. Some figures may correctly be identified in more than one way.

5.   **6.**   **7.**   **8.**

Written Exercises

True or false?

 1. All squares are rectangles.
3. Some rectangles are rhombi.
5. All rhombi are squares.

2. All squares are parallelograms.
4. Some rhombi are rectangles.
6. Some parallelograms are rectangles.

For each given property, determine which of the following figures have that property: a parallelogram, a rhombus, a rectangle, or a square. (Ex. 7–16)

7. Opposite sides are parallel.
9. Opposite angles are congruent.
11. Diagonals are congruent.
13. Diagonals bisect each other.
15. Consecutive angles are congruent.

8. Opposite sides are congruent.
10. Opposite angles are supplements.
12. Diagonals are perpendicular.
14. Consecutive sides are congruent.
16. Consecutive angles are supplements.

17. Given: Rhombus $ABCD$, and m $\angle A = 75$
Find m $\angle B$ and m $\angle C$.

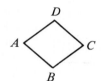

18. Given: Rhombus $ABCD$, and $BC = 12$
Find AB and CD.

19. Given: Square $EFGH$, $EG = 8x$, and $FH = 12x - 4$
Find EG.

20. Given: Square $EFGH$, $EI = 5x - 1$, and $IG = 4x + 1$
Find EI.

True or false? If true, prove the statement. If false, give a counterexample.

 21. The diagonals of a rectangle are congruent.
23. The diagonals of a rhombus bisect the vertex angles.
25. The diagonals of a square are congruent.

22. The diagonals of a rectangle are perpendicular.
24. The diagonals of a rectangle bisect the vertex angles.
26. The diagonals of a square bisect each other.

Cumulative Review

1. Find the distance between two points with coordinates −8 and 17.
2. Can two triangles be proved congruent by a side-side-angle correspondence?
3. What is the median of a triangle?

RHOMBI, RECTANGLES, AND SQUARES

7.7 Proving Rhombi, Rectangles, and Squares

OBJECTIVE ► **To prove that a quadrilateral is a rhombus, a rectangle, or a square**

Although a rhombus was defined to be a parallelogram with four congruent sides, you can prove that a figure is a rhombus based on other properties. Similarly, you can prove that a figure is a rectangle without showing that it has four right angles.

Example 1 Prove: A parallelogram with perpendicular diagonals is a rhombus.

Given: $\square ABCD$ and $\overline{AC} \perp \overline{BD}$
Prove: $ABCD$ is a rhombus.

Proof

Statements		Reasons
1. $\overline{DE} \cong \overline{BE}$	(S)	1. Diag. of a $\square$ bisect each other.
2. $\overline{AC} \perp \overline{BD}$		2. Given
3. $\angle DEA \cong \angle BEA$	(A)	3. $\perp$ lines form $\cong$ rt. $\angle$'s.
4. $\overline{AE} \cong \overline{AE}$	(S)	4. Reflexive property
5. $\triangle AED \cong \triangle AEB$		5. SAS
6. $\overline{AD} \cong \overline{AB}$		6. CPCTC
7. $\overline{AD} \cong \overline{CB}$ and $\overline{AB} \cong \overline{CD}$		7. Opp. sides of a $\square$ are $\cong$.
8. $\overline{AB} \cong \overline{CB} \cong \overline{CD} \cong \overline{AD}$		8. Substitution
9. $\therefore ABCD$ is a rhombus.		9. Def. of rhombus

Example 2 Prove: A parallelogram with at least one right angle is a rectangle.

Given: $\square FGHI$ and rt. $\angle F$
Prove: $FGHI$ is a rectangle.

Proof

Statements	Reasons
1. $\square FGHI$, rt. $\angle F$	1. Given
2. $\angle H \cong \angle F$	2. Opp. $\angle$'s of a $\square$ are $\cong$.
3. $\overline{IF} \parallel \overline{HG}$	3. Def. of $\square$
4. $\angle F$ and $\angle G$ are supplementary	4. Int. $\angle$'s of $\parallel$ lines on same side of trans. are supplementary.
5. m $\angle F = 90$	5. Def. of rt. $\angle$.
6. m $\angle G = 90$	6. Def. of supp. $\angle$'s, subst., subtraction
7. m $\angle H = 90$	7. Steps 2, 5 and def. of $\cong \angle$'s
8. $\angle I \cong \angle G$	8. Opp. $\angle$'s of a $\square$ are $\cong$.
9. m $\angle I = 90$	9. Steps 6, 8 and def. of $\cong \angle$'s
10. $\therefore FGHI$ is a rectangle	10. Def. of rectangle

Example 3 Prove: A parallelogram with congruent diagonals is a rectangle

Given: $\square PQRS$ and $\overline{PR} \cong \overline{SQ}$
Prove: $PQRS$ is a rectangle

Proof

Statements		Reasons
1. $\square PQRS$, $\overline{PR} \cong \overline{SQ}$	(S)	1. Given
2. $\overline{RQ} \cong \overline{SP}$	(S)	2. Opp. sides of a $\square$ are $\cong$.
3. $\overline{PQ} \cong \overline{QP}$	(S)	3. Reflexive property
4. $\triangle PQR \cong \triangle QPS$		4. SSS
5. $\angle PQR \cong \angle QPS$		5. CPCTC
6. $\overline{RQ} \parallel \overline{SP}$		6. Def. of $\square$
7. $\angle PQR$ and $\angle QPS$ are supplementary		7. Int. $\angle$'s of $\parallel$ lines on same side of trans. are supp.
8. $\angle PQR$ is a rt. $\angle$.		8. $\cong$ supp $\angle$'s are rt $\angle$'s.
9. $\therefore$ $PQRS$ is a rectangle.		9. $\square$ with 1 rt. $\angle$ is a rectangle.

Summarized below are methods for proving that a parallelogram is a rhombus, a rectangle, or a square.

Summary	To show $\square ABCD$ is a rectangle, show that it has a rt. $\angle$, or $\cong$ diagonals.	To show $\square ABCD$ is a rhombus, show that 2 adj. sides are $\cong$, or the diag. are $\perp$.	To show $\square ABCD$ is a square, show that it is a rect. with 2 $\cong$ adj. sides, or a rhombus with a rt. $\angle$.
	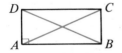		

It is also possible to determine whether a quadrilateral not specifically identified as a parallelogram is a rhombus, a rectangle, or a square.

Example 4 True or False? Draw a picture to defend your answer. A quadrilateral with four congruent sides is a rhombus.

True. The quadrilateral is a parallelogram, since both pairs of opposite sides are $\cong$.

Example 5 For the given property, tell whether quadrilateral $EFGH$ is a rhombus, a rectangle, a square, or cannot tell.

Given: $\overline{EG} \cong \overline{FH}$

Cannot tell.

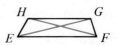

Oral Exercises

Tell whether each figure is a rhombus, a rectangle, a square, or cannot tell.

1.

2.

3.
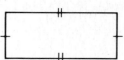

4.

5.
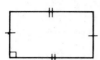

6.

7.

8.

Written Exercises

True or false? Draw a picture to defend your answer.

1. A parallelogram with two right angles is a rectangle.

2. A rhombus with at least one right angle is a square.

3. A quadrilateral with perpendicular diagonals is a rhombus.

4. A quadrilateral with congruent diagonals is a rectangle.

For each given set of properties, tell whether quadrilateral WXYZ is a rhombus, a rectangle, a square, or cannot tell. (Ex. 5–14)

5. $\square WXYZ$ and $\overline{WX} \perp \overline{XY}$
7. $\square WXYZ$ and $\overline{XZ} \cong \overline{WY}$
9. $\overline{WX} \perp \overline{XY}$ and $\overline{XY} \perp \overline{YZ}$
11. $\overline{WV} \cong \overline{XV} \cong \overline{YV} \cong \overline{ZV}$

13. $\square WXYZ$ and $\overline{WX} \cong \overline{XY}$

6. $\overline{XZ} \cong \overline{WY}$
8. $\overline{XV} \cong \overline{VZ}$ and $\overline{WV} \cong \overline{VY}$
10. $\square WXYZ$ and $\overline{XZ} \perp \overline{WY}$
12. $\square WXYZ$, $\overline{XV} \cong \overline{VZ}$, and $\overline{WV} \cong \overline{VY}$
14. $\square WXYZ$, $\overline{WX} \perp \overline{XY}$, and $\overline{XY} \perp \overline{YZ}$

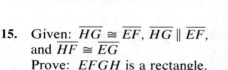

15. Given: $\overline{HG} \cong \overline{EF}$, $\overline{HG} \parallel \overline{EF}$, and $\overline{HF} \cong \overline{EG}$
Prove: $EFGH$ is a rectangle.

16. Given: $\overline{EF} \cong \overline{FG} \cong \overline{GH} \cong \overline{HE}$
Prove: $EFGH$ is a rhombus.

17. Prove: A parallelogram with two consec- congruent sides is a rhombus.

18. Prove: If the diagonals of a rhombus are congruent, then the rhombus is a square.

19. Prove: The segments connecting the mid-points of consecutive sides of a rhombus form a rectangle.

20. Prove: If the diagonals of a rectangle are perpendicular, then the rectangle is a square.

True or false? If true, prove the statement. If false, give a counterexample.

21. If all sides of a quadrilateral are congru- ent, then the quadrilateral is a rhombus.

22. If all angles of a quadrilateral are congru- ent, then the quadrilateral is a rectangle.

23. If the diagonals of a quadrilateral bisect each other, then the quadrilateral is a rectangle.

24. If the diagonals of a quadrilateral are per- pendicular bisectors of each other, then the quadrilateral is a rhombus.

CHAPTER SEVEN

Applications

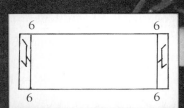

1. The yard lines on a football field must be marked off for the first game of the season. A permanent marker is at the end of each goal line. There are no other markers on the field. How can the coach lay off the yard lines so that they are parallel to the goal line and parallel to each other? Why does this work?

2. Parallel rulers are useful instruments for drawing parallel lines. Why do the two rulers stay parallel in all positions?

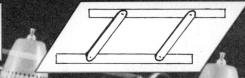

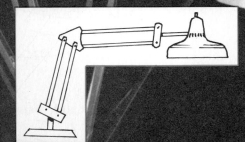

3. The lamp shown can be raised or lowered using the center or base hinges. Why will the light always point in the same direction when raised or lowered by the center or base hinges?

4. Two tall poles are on opposite sides of a house. A wire is to be strung between them as a short wave radio antenna. The distance between the poles cannot be measured directly. How can this length be found using the triangle suggested in the picture?

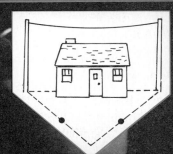

Chapter Seven Review

Based only on the markings shown, tell whether each figure is a parallelogram, a rhombus, a rectangle, a square, or none of these. [7.6]

1.

2.

3.

4.

For each given set of properties, tell whether quadrilateral $ABCD$ is a parallelogram, a rhombus, a rectangle, a square, or cannot tell.

5. $\overline{AC} \cong \overline{BD}$

6. $\overline{AB} \cong \overline{DC}, \overline{AB} \parallel \overline{DC}$

7. $\angle A \cong \angle B \cong \angle C \cong \angle D$

8. $\overline{AE} \cong \overline{CE}, \overline{BE} \cong \overline{DE}$

9. $\triangle ABC \cong \triangle ADC$

10. $\overline{AB} \cong \overline{BC} \cong \overline{CD} \cong \overline{DA}$, and $\overline{DA} \perp \overline{AB}$

True or false?

11. A quadrilateral can have no congruent sides. [7.1]

12. A parallelogram can have no congruent sides. [7.2]

13. A quadrilateral can have no congruent angles. [7.1]

14. A parallelogram can have no congruent angles. [7.2]

15. A square is a rhombus. [7.6]

16. A rhombus is a rectangle.

17. No rectangles are rhombi.

Vocabulary
consecutive angles [7.1] consecutive sides [7.1] diagonals [7.1] opposite angles [7.1] opposite sides [7.1] parallelogram [7.2] quadrilateral [7.1] rectangle [7.6] rhombus [7.6] square [7.6]

Construct each of the following. (Ex. 18–19)

18. Draw a segment 10 cm long. Divide it into three congruent segments. [7.5]

19. Draw a segment 12 cm long. Construct a segment three-fifths as long.

20. Given: $l \parallel m \parallel n$, $AB = 5$, $AC = 10$, $DE = 4$
Find EF.

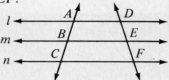

21. Given: $l \parallel m \parallel n$, $AB = 7$, $BC = 7$, $DE = 5x - 3$, $EF = 3x + 1$
Find DE.

22. Given: K is the midpoint of $\overline{GJ}$, I is the midpoint of $\overline{JH}$, $KI = 7$ [7.4]
Find GH.

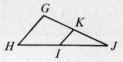

23. Given: $\overline{GK} \cong \overline{KJ}$, $\overline{HI} \cong \overline{IJ}$, $GH = 3x + 3$, $KI = 2x - 2$
Find KI.

24. Given: $\overline{EA} \cong \overline{EC}$; B, D, and F are midpoints of $\overline{AC}$, $\overline{CE}$, and $\overline{EA}$. [7.7]
Prove: $BDEF$ is a rhombus.

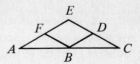

25. Prove: Consecutive angles of a parallelogram are supplementary. [7.2]

*26. Prove: The diagonals of a square bisect each other. [7.4]

Chapter Seven Test

Based only on the markings shown, tell whether each figure is a parallelogram, a rhombus, a rectangle, a square, or none of these.

1.
2.

3.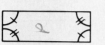
4.

For each given set of properties, tell whether quadrilateral $ABCD$ is a parallelogram, a rhombus, a rectangle, a square, or cannot tell.

5. $\overline{AB} \parallel \overline{DC}, \overline{AD} \parallel \overline{BC}$
6. $\overline{AB} \cong \overline{BC}, \overline{CD} \cong \overline{DA}$
7. $\triangle ABD \cong \triangle CDB$
8. $\overline{AB} \cong \overline{DC}, \overline{BC} \cong \overline{AD}, \overline{AC} \cong \overline{BD}$
9. $\overline{AE} \cong \overline{EC}, \overline{BE} \cong \overline{DE}, \overline{AC} \perp \overline{BD}$ at E
10. $\overline{AB} \cong \overline{BC} \cong \overline{CD}, \overline{CB} \perp \overline{AB}$

True or false?
11. The diagonals of a parallelogram are congruent.
12. The opposite angles of a rhombus are congruent.
13. A square is a rectangle.
14. A rectangle is a parallelogram.
15. A quadrilateral whose diagonals are perpendicular bisectors of each other is a rhombus.
16. A quadrilateral whose diagonals are congruent is a rectangle.
17. No rhombi are rectangles.

Construct each of the following. (Ex. 18–19)
18. Copy $\overline{XY}$. Divide $\overline{XY}$ into three congruent segments.

$X \longrightarrow Y$

19. Copy $\overline{PQ}$. Construct a segment three-fifths as long as $\overline{PQ}$.

$P \longrightarrow Q$

20. Given: $t \parallel r \parallel s$. $PQ = 9$, $QR = 9$, $ST = 8$
Find SU.

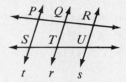

21. Given: $t \parallel r \parallel s$, $PQ = 7$, $PR = 14$, $ST = 4x - 3$, $TU = x + 6$
Find TU.

22. Given: K and I are the midpoints of $\overline{GJ}$ and $\overline{HJ}$. $KI = 9$
Find GH.

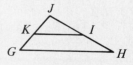

23. Given: $\overline{GK} \cong \overline{KJ}, \overline{HI} \cong \overline{IJ}, KI = 2x - 1$, $GH = 3x + 3$
Find KI.

*24. Prove: The diagonals of a square are congruent.

25. Given: $\square WXYZ, \overline{WU} \cong \overline{YV}$
Prove: $UXVZ$ is a $\square$.

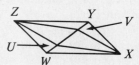

Computer Activities

You can use the following program to determine which kind a parallelogram is. From the measures of two adjacent sides and of the diagonals you can show whether a figure is a rectangle, rhombus, or square.

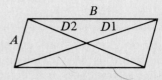

Computer logic permits a sequence of preliminary decisions to be made before a final decision is printed. Drop through logic follows a main path through a program without any branches. In the program below, if the figure is a square, you will follow drop through logic.

See the computer section on page 560 for more information.

PROGRAM

```
 5 PRINT "PROGRAM DETERMINES TYPE OF PARALLELOGRAM"
10 PRINT "ENTER MEASURES OF SIDES A, B"
15 INPUT A, B
20 PRINT "ENTER MEASURES OF DIAGONALS D1, D2"
25 INPUT D1, D2
30 IF A < > B THEN 60
35 IF D1 < > D2 THEN 50
40 PRINT "PARALLELOGRAM IS A SQUARE"
45 GO TO 80
50 PRINT "PARALLELOGRAM IS A RHOMBUS"
55 GO TO 80
60 IF D1 < > D2 THEN 75
65 PRINT "PARALLELOGRAM IS A RECTANGLE"
70 GO TO 80
75 PRINT "FIGURE IS NOT A RECTANGLE, SQUARE OR RHOMBUS"
80 END
```

Exercises

Run the program for the following values. (Ex. 1–2)

1. $A = 8$, $B = 4$, $D1 = 3$, $D2 = 5$
2. $A = 2$, $B = 2$, $D1 = 2.8$, $D2 = 2.8$

3. Rewrite the program to identify a particular parallelogram by right angles and by the measures of two adjacent sides.

4. Write a program to prove that two quadrilaterals are congruent, given the measures of the corresponding sides and the corresponding angles.

College Prep Test

For each item, choose the best answer. Indicate your answer by writing the letter of this choice.

1. For quadrilateral $GHDQ$, a pair of consecutive sides is

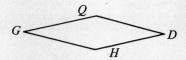

   I $\overline{GH}$ and $\overline{HD}$
   II $\overline{GH}$ and $\overline{DQ}$
  III $\overline{GH}$ and $\overline{QG}$

  (A) I only
  (B) II only
  (C) III only
  (D) I and II only
  (E) I and III only

2. Which of the following is not true about a parallelogram?
  (A) Opposite sides are congruent.
  (B) Adjacent sides are congruent.
  (C) Opposite angles are congruent.
  (D) Opposite sides are parallel.
  (E) Diagonals bisect each other.

3. A quadrilateral is a parallelogram if
  (A) Diagonals are perpendicular.
  (B) Diagonals are congruent.
  (C) Two adjacent sides are congruent.
  (D) Adjacent angles are supplementary.
  (E) A diagonal forms two congruent triangles.

4. If $\overline{AD} \cong \overline{DC}$ and $\overline{BE} \cong \overline{EC}$, which of the following is true?
  I   If $AB = 10$, then $DE = 5$
  II $\overline{DE} \parallel \overline{AB}$
  III If $BC = 16$, then $BE = 8$

  (A) I only
  (B) II only
  (C) III only
  (D) I, II, and III
  (E) I and II only

5. If $l \parallel m \parallel n$, $AB = 5$, $AC = 10$, $DE = 3x + 4$, and $DF = 10x - 4$, then

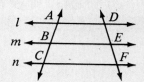

  (A) $DE = 5$ and $DF = 10$
  (B) $DE = 7\frac{3}{7}$
  (C) $DE = 6\frac{2}{7}$
  (D) $DE = 3$
  (E) None of these

6. Which of the following is *not* true about a rectangle?
  (A) The diagonals are congruent.
  (B) All angles are congruent.
  (C) The diagonals bisect each other.
  (D) The diagonals are perpendicular.
  (E) Adjacent angles are supplementary.

7. Which of the following is *not* sufficient to prove that a parallelogram is a rectangle?
  (A) The diagonals are congruent.
  (B) The diagonals are perpendicular.
  (C) Two adjacent angles are congruent.
  (D) One angle is a right angle.
  (E) All angles are congruent.

8. Which of the following is sufficient to prove that a quadrilateral is a rhombus?
  (A) The diagonals are perpendicular.
  (B) The diagonals are congruent.
  (C) The diagonals bisect each other.
  (D) Each diagonal is a perpendicular bisector of the other.
  (E) Two adjacent sides are congruent.

Constant Width Curves

When a circular roller is turned between two parallel surfaces, it will always maintain contact with both surfaces.

A circle is a closed curve of constant width.

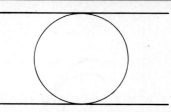

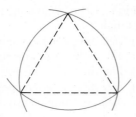

Another curve of constant width is the Reuleau triangle. It is constructed by connecting the vertices of an equilateral triangle with arc centered at the third vertex.

A constant width curve can be constructed using a regular polygon with an odd number of sides. Connect the vertices of the regular polygon with arcs.

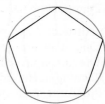

Formulate	⟶	Analyze the situation.
		Focus on the question to be answered.
		Identify what information is needed.
		Propose the problem to be solved.

Plan

Solve ⟶ Interpret

8.1 Trapezoids

OBJECTIVES ► **To identify trapezoids**
To investigate and prove properties of trapezoids

You have learned that a parallelogram is a quadrilateral with both pairs of opposite sides parallel. Another special kind of quadrilateral, a *trapezoid,* is defined below.

Definition:
trapezoid

> A **trapezoid** is a quadrilateral with exactly one pair of parallel sides. (Trapezoid *ABCD* is written trap. *ABCD*.)

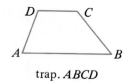

trap. *ABCD*

Example 1 Does the figure appear to be a trapezoid?

You can investigate some of the properties of trapezoids by making careful drawings.

Example 2 Make drawings to determine whether or not the diagonals of a trapezoid are congruent.

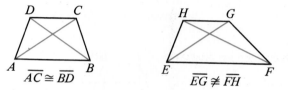

Thus, the diagonals of a trapezoid are not necessarily congruent.

TRAPEZOIDS

The definition of trapezoid is used in the proof in Example 3.

Example 3

Given: Trap. $ABCD$, $\overline{AD} \cong \overline{BC}$, $\overline{DE} \perp \overline{AB}$, and $\overline{CF} \perp \overline{AB}$

Prove: $\angle 1 \cong \angle 2$

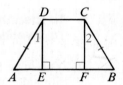

Proof

Statements		Reasons
1. Trap. $ABCD$		1. Given
2. $\overline{AB} \parallel \overline{DC}$		2. Def. of trapezoid
3. $\overline{DE} \perp \overline{AB}$, $\overline{CF} \perp \overline{AB}$		3. Given
4. $\overline{DE} \cong \overline{CF}$	(L)	4. $\parallel$ lines are equidistant.
5. $\overline{AD} \cong \overline{BC}$	(H)	5. Given
6. $\triangle DEA$ and $\triangle CFB$ are rt. $\triangle$'s		6. $\perp$'s form rt. $\angle$'s; def. of rt. $\triangle$.
7. $\triangle DEA \cong \triangle CFB$		7. HL
8. $\therefore \angle 1 \cong \angle 2$		8. CPCTC

Oral Exercises

Which of the following appear to be trapezoids?

1.
2.
3.
4.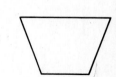

5.
6.
7.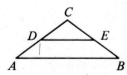
8.

Written Exercises

A 1. Given: D is midpoint of $\overline{AC}$, and E is midpoint of $\overline{BC}$

Prove: $ABED$ is a trapezoid.

2. Given: Trap. $FGHI$, $\overline{FI} \cong \overline{GH}$, $\overline{IJ} \perp \overline{FG}$, and $\overline{HK} \perp \overline{FG}$

Prove: $\angle F \cong \angle G$

3. Given: Trap. $ONML$, $\overline{LO} \cong \overline{LN}$, $\overline{LP} \perp \overline{ON}$, and $\overline{MQ} \perp \overline{ON}$

Prove: $\overline{LO} \cong \overline{MN}$

Make drawings to determine each of the following

4. Can a trapezoid have two congruent sides?
5. Can a trapezoid have two congruent angles?
6. Can a trapezoid have congruent diagonals?
7. Can a trapezoid have diagonals which bisect each other?
8. Can a trapezoid have two right angles?
9. Can a trapezoid have diagonals which are perpendicular?
10. Can a trapezoid have three congruent sides?
11. Can a trapezoid have three congruent angles?

True or false? If the statement is true, prove it. If false, show a counterexample.

 12. Opposite angles of a trapezoid are congruent.
13. Opposite angles of a trapezoid are supplementary.
14. Consecutive angles of a trapezoid are supplementary.
15. Diagonals of a trapezoid bisect the angles of the trapezoid.
16. The segments joining the midpoints of adjacent sides of a trapezoid form a trapezoid.
17. The segments joining the midpoints of opposite sides of a trapezoid bisect each other.
18. If the diagonals of a quadrilateral bisect each other, then the quadrilateral is a trapezoid.
19. If the diagonals of a quadrilateral are congruent, then the quadrilateral is a trapezoid.

Cumulative Review _____ Trapezoids

1. Draw an isosceles triangle which is also a right triangle.
2. What is the difference between a postulate and a theorem?
3. In using the angle-side-angle congruence pattern for triangles, what is meant by the included side?

Algebra Review

OBJECTIVE ▶ To add and subtract algebraic fractions.

Example   Simplify $\dfrac{4x}{x^2 - 9} - \dfrac{5}{x + 3}$

$$\dfrac{4x}{(x-3)(x+3)} + \dfrac{-1\,(5)(x-3)}{(x-3)(x+3)} \blacktriangleleft \quad \dfrac{G}{b} - \dfrac{C}{d} \; means \; \dfrac{C}{b} + \dfrac{-1\,(c)}{d}$$

$$LCD = (x - 3)(x + 3) \quad \blacktriangleright \quad \dfrac{4x - 5\,(x - 3)}{(x - 3)(x + 3)}, \; or \; \dfrac{-x + 15}{x^2 - 9}$$

Simplify

1. $\dfrac{3}{a - 3} + \dfrac{6a + 1}{a^2 - 9}$

2. $\dfrac{3x + 1}{x^2 - 4} - \dfrac{4}{x - 2}$

3. $\dfrac{3}{y} - \dfrac{2}{y + 6}$

4. $4 + \dfrac{6c - 2}{3}$

5. $4 - \dfrac{3z - 5}{5z + 3}$

6. $\dfrac{4f + 3}{2f + 1} + \dfrac{2f + 4}{2f - 1}$

7. $\dfrac{w + 1}{w + 2} + 3w$

8. $\dfrac{3b - 2}{2b^2 - b} - \dfrac{2b}{4b^2 - 1}$

8.2 Altitudes and Medians of Trapezoids

OBJECTIVES ► **To identify sides of trapezoids**
To prove and apply theorems about the median and an altitude of a trapezoid

The sides of a trapezoid are usually given specific names.

Definitions:
bases and legs of trapezoid

> The **bases** of a trapezoid are the two parallel sides.
> The **legs** of a trapezoid are the two nonparallel sides.

Example 1 Which sides of each trapezoid are the bases?

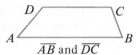 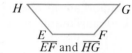 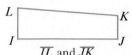

A special segment of a trapezoid which is frequently used is the *altitude*.

Definition:
altitude of trapezoid

> An **altitude** of a trapezoid is any segment from a point on one base perpendicular to the line containing the other base.

A triangle can have exactly three altitudes. However, a trapezoid can have many. $\overline{DE}$, $\overline{JF}$, $\overline{IG}$, and $\overline{HB}$ are all altitudes of trap. *ABCD*.

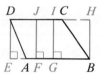

Example 2 Prove: All altitudes of a trapezoid are congruent.

Given: Trap. *ABCD* with altitudes $\overline{EH}$ and $\overline{FG}$
Prove: $\overline{EH} \cong \overline{FG}$

Proof

Statements	Reasons
1. Trap. *ABCD*, altitudes $\overline{EH}$ and $\overline{FG}$	1. Given
2. $\overline{DC} \parallel \overline{AB}$	2. Def. of trapezoid
3. $\overline{EH} \perp \overline{AB}$, $\overline{FG} \perp \overline{AB}$	3. Def. of altitude
4. $\therefore EH = FG$ and $\overline{EH} \cong \overline{FG}$	4. $\parallel$ lines are equidistant.; Def. of $\cong$ seg.

Another special segment in a trapezoid is the *median*.

Definition:
median of trapezoid

The **median** of a trapezoid is the segment that joins the midpoints of the legs.

Median *EF*

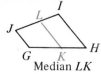

Median *LK*

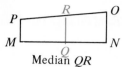

Median *QR*

The following theorem is about the median of a trapezoid. You should complete the details of the proof.

Theorem 8.1 The median of a trapezoid is parallel to its bases, and its length is half the sum of the lengths of the bases.

Given: Trap. $ABCD$,
$\overline{AB} \parallel \overline{DC}$,
and median
$\overline{XY}$,

Prove: $\overline{XY} \parallel \overline{DC} \parallel$
$\overline{AB}$, and
$XY = \frac{1}{2}(DC + AB)$

Analysis: Through X draw $\overline{RS} \parallel \overline{CB}$. Show $RSBC$, $RXYC$, and $XYBS$ are $\square$'s.

Outline of Proof

I. Prove $\overline{XY} \parallel \overline{DC} \parallel \overline{AB}$

1. Trap. $ABCD$, $\overline{AB} \parallel \overline{DC}$, median $\overline{XY}$
2. Draw $\overrightarrow{CD}$.
3. Draw $\overline{RS} \parallel \overline{CB}$ through X.
4. $\overline{SB} \parallel \overline{RC}$
5. $RSBC$ is a $\square$.
6. $\angle 1 \cong \angle 2$ and $\angle 3 \cong \angle 4$
7. $\overline{DX} \cong \overline{XA}$
8. $\triangle RXD \cong \triangle SXA$
9. $RX = SX$ and $RX = \frac{1}{2}(RS)$
10. $CY = YB$ and $CY = \frac{1}{2}(CB)$
11. $RS = CB$
12. $RX = CY$
13. $RXYC$ is a $\square$.
14. $\therefore \overline{XY} \parallel \overline{DC}$
15. Similarly, $XYBS$ is a $\square$.
16. $\overline{XY} \parallel \overline{AB}$
17. $\therefore \overline{XY} \parallel \overline{DC} \parallel AB$.

II. Prove $XY = \frac{1}{2}(DC + AB)$

18. $XY = RC$
19. $RC = DC + RD$
20. $XY = DC + RD$
21. $RD = SA$
22. $XY = DC + SA$
23. $XY = SB$
24. $XY + XY = DC + SA + SB$
25. $2(XY) = DC + AB$
26. $\therefore XY = \frac{1}{2}(DC + AB)$

(See Exercise 20.)

ALTITUDES AND MEDIANS OF TRAPEZOIDS

Example 3 Given: *ABCD* is a trapezoid.
Find the length of median $\overline{EF}$.

$EF = \frac{1}{2}(8 + 12)$ or 10.

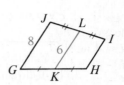

Example 4 Given: trap. *GHIJ*, median $\overline{KL}$,
GJ = 8, and *KL* = 6.
Find *HI*.

$6 = \frac{1}{2}(8 + HI)$

$12 = 8 + HI$

Thus, *HI* = 4.

Example 5 Given: trap. *MNOP*, median $\overline{QR}$
PO = 2*x* + 2, *MN* = 7*x* − 2, and *QR* = 4*x* + 1
Find *QR*.

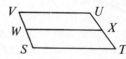

$4x + 1 = \frac{1}{2}[(2x + 2) + (7x - 2)]$

$8x + 2 = (2x + 2) + (7x - 2)$

$8x + 2 = 9x$

$x = 2$

Thus, *QR* = 4(2) + 1, or 9.

When you are planning a proof involving trapezoids, there frequently are several possible conclusions that can be drawn from the given data. You may need to determine these to help you select the plan for the proof.

Example 6 Write two possible conclusions that can be drawn from the given data.

Given: $\overline{VU} \parallel \overline{ST}$, $\overline{VW} \cong \overline{WS}$, and
$\overline{UX} \cong \overline{XT}$

Possible conclusions: $WX = \frac{1}{2}(VU + ST)$ ◄ *Other conclusions are possible*

$\overline{WX} \parallel \overline{VU}$

Written **Exercises**

Find the length of the median of each trapezoid.

Ⓐ **1.**   6 cm

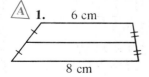

8 cm

2.   8 cm

10 cm

3.   20 cm

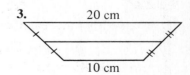

10 cm

Using each given set of measurements for trap. *ABCD*, find the length of median $\overline{EF}$.

4. $DC = 8$ and $AB = 12$.
6. $DC = 13$ and $AB = 21$.
8. $DC = 2x - 1$, $AB = 5x + 1$, and $EF = 3x + 2$.

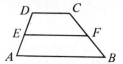

5. $DC = 9$ and $AB = 11$.
7. $DC = 10$ and $AB = 13$.
9. $DC = x + 3$, $AB = 3x - 5$, and $EF = x + 7$.

Using each given set of measurements for trap. *GHIJ* and median *KL*, find the indicated base length.

10. $JI = 4$ and $KL = 6$. $GH = ?$
12. $JI = 9$, $KL = 14$. $GH = ?$
14. $JI = x + 5$, $KL = 3x$, and $GH = 4x - 3$. Find GH.

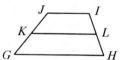

11. $JI = ?$ $KL = 9$ and $GH = 10$.
13. $JI = ?$ $KL = 13$ and $GH = 19$.
15. $JI = x + 5$, $KL = 3x - 7$, and $GH = 3x - 1$. Find JI.

Write two possible conclusions that can be drawn from the given data. (Ex. 16–17)

B 16. Given: trap. *MNOP*, Q is the midpoint of $\overline{PM}$, and R is the midpoint of $\overline{NO}$.

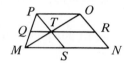

17. Given: trap *MNOP* with median $\overline{QR}$ and diagonal $\overline{MO}$.

18. Prove: The median of a trapezoid bisects both diagonals of the trapezoid.
20. Complete the proof of Theorem 8.1

19. Prove: The median of a trapezoid bisects each altitude of the trapezoid that intersects it.

Prove each conclusion, or disprove it by giving a counterexample. (Ex. 21–24)

Given: trap. *UVWX* with median $\overline{YZ}$ and diagonal $\overline{UW}$ intersecting both $\overline{YZ}$ and $\overline{XA}$ at B.

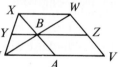

C 21. Conclusion: *AVWX* is a trapezoid.
23. Conclusion: $\triangle UAX$ is isosceles.

Given: trap. *UVWX*, median $\overline{YZ}$, diagonal $\overline{UW}$ intersecting both $\overline{YZ}$ and $\overline{XA}$ at B, and $\overline{XB} \perp \overline{UW}$

22. Conclusion: $\triangle UBY$ is isosceles.
24. Conclusion: $\triangle BWZ$ is isosceles.

25. Is there any relationship between the lengths of the legs, the bases, and the altitudes of a trapezoid? Give a reason for your answer.
27. Does Theorem 8.1 apply to parallelograms? Give a reason for your answer.

26. Is there any relationship between the length of the median of a trapezoid and the length of an altitude? Give a reason for your answer.

CALCULATOR ACTIVITIES

Find the length of the median m of each trapezoid with bases $\overline{AB}$ and $\overline{CD}$.

1. $AB = 9.25$, $CD = 12.47$
3. $AB = 1.125$, $CD = 3.375$

2. $AB = 26.23$, $CD = 43.67$
4. $AB = 16.124$, $CD = 24.252$

ALTITUDES AND MEDIANS OF TRAPEZOIDS

8.3 Isosceles Trapezoids

► **To identify isosceles trapezoids**
To prove and apply theorems about isosceles trapezoids

You have learned earlier that an isosceles triangle has at least two congruent sides. Similarly, an isosceles trapezoid has two congruent legs.

Definition:
isosceles
trapezoid

> An **isosceles trapezoid** is a trapezoid with congruent legs.

You should be able to identify isosceles trapezoids.

Example 1 Which of the following trapezoids appear to be isosceles?

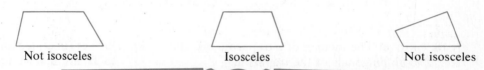

Not isosceles   Isosceles   Not isosceles

Each isosceles trapezoid has two sets of base angles. The definition of isosceles trapezoid tells you that the legs are congruent. The following theorem shows that the base angles are also congruent.

Theorem 8.2 The base angles of an isosceles trapezoid are congruent.

Given: Trap. $ABCD$,
$\overline{AB} \parallel \overline{DC}$, and
$\overline{AD} \cong \overline{BC}$
Prove: $\angle A \cong \angle B$

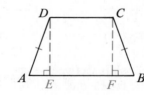

Analysis: Draw $\overline{DE} \perp$ $\overline{AB}$, $\overline{CF} \perp \overline{AB}$. Show $\angle A$ and $\angle B$ are corr. parts of $\cong \triangle$'s.

Proof

Statements	Reasons
1. Trap. $ABCD$, $\overline{AB} \parallel \overline{DC}$	1. Given
2. Draw $\overline{DE} \perp \overline{AB}$, $\overline{CF} \perp \overline{AB}$	2. There is exactly one $\perp$ from a pt. to a line.
3. $\angle DEA$ and $\angle CFB$ are rt. $\angle$'s	3. Def. of $\perp$
4. $\triangle AED$ and $\triangle BFC$ are rt. $\triangle$'s.	4. Def. of rt. $\triangle$.
5. $\overline{AD} \cong \overline{BC}$	5. Given
6. $\overline{DE} \cong \overline{CF}$	6. $\parallel$ lines are equidistant.
7. $\triangle AED \cong \triangle BFC$	7. *HL*
8. $\therefore \angle A \cong \angle B$	8. CPCTC

Example 2   Given: Isosceles trap. *STUV* and $\overline{VU} \parallel \overline{ST}$
Find m $\angle S$ and m $\angle U$.

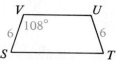

$VU \parallel ST$ ▶   m $\angle S$ + m $\angle V$ = 180
m $\angle S$ = 180 − 108 or 72.
m $\angle U$ = m $\angle V$ ◀   *Apply. Th. 8.2*
m $\angle U$ = 108
Thus, m $\angle S$ = 72 and m $\angle U$ = 108.

The converse of Theorem 8.2 is also true and is stated below. You should complete the proof of this theorem.

Theorem 8.3   If the base angles of a trapezoid are congruent, then the trapezoid is isosceles.
(See Exercise 15.)

Theorem 8.4 presents another property of isosceles trapezoids.

Theorem 8.4   The diagonals of an isosceles trapezoid are congruent.

Given: Isosceles trap. *WXYZ*,
$\overline{WX} \cong \overline{ZY}$, and $\overline{WZ} \parallel \overline{XY}$
Prove: $\overline{XZ} \cong \overline{YW}$

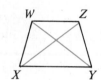

Analysis: show that $\overline{XZ}$ and $\overline{YW}$ are $\cong$ corresponding parts of $\cong$ △'s *XYZ* and *YXW*.

(See Exercise 16.)

Although the diagonals of an isosceles trapezoid are congruent, this does not necessarily mean that every quadrilateral with congruent diagonals is an isosceles trapezoid. The figures below show this. However, any trapezoid with congruent diagonals is isosceles and this is proved as the next theorem.

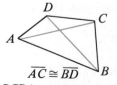

$\overline{AC} \cong \overline{BD}$
ABCD is not a trapezoid.

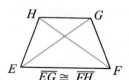

$\overline{EG} \cong \overline{FH}$
EFGH is an isosceles trapezoid.

┌─ **Theorem 8.5** If the diagonals of a trapezoid are congruent, then the ─┐
trapezoid is isosceles.

Given: Trap. $ABCD$, $\overline{AB} \parallel DC$, and
$\overline{AC} \cong \overline{BD}$
Prove: $\overline{BC} \cong \overline{AD}$

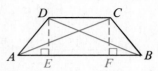

Proof

Statements	Reasons
1. Trap. $ABCD$, $\overline{AB} \parallel \overline{DC}$	1. Given
2. Draw $\overline{CF} \perp \overline{AB}$, $\overline{DE} \perp \overline{AB}$.	2. There is exactly one $\perp$ from a pt. to a line.
3. $\angle AFC$ and $\angle BED$ are rt. $\angle$'s.	3. Def. of $\perp$
4. $\triangle DFC$ and $\triangle BED$ are rt. $\triangle$'s.	4. Def. of rt. $\triangle$
5. $\overline{CF} \cong \overline{DE}$	5. $\parallel$ lines are equidistant.
6. $\overline{AC} \cong \overline{BD}$	6. Given
7. $\triangle AFC \cong \triangle BED$	7. HL
8. $\angle BAC \cong \angle ABD$	8. CPCTC
9. $\overline{AB} \cong \overline{BA}$	9. Reflexive property
10. $\triangle BAC \cong \triangle ABD$	10. SAS
11. $\therefore \overline{BC} \cong \overline{AD}$	11. CPCTC

Summary	To prove that a trapezoid is isosceles:

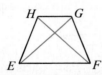

1. Show that the legs are congruent: $\overline{EH} \cong \overline{FG}$
2. Show that a pair of base angles are congruent: $\angle E \cong \angle F$ or $\angle G \cong \angle H$
3. Show that the diagonals are congruent: $\overline{EG} \cong \overline{FH}$

Oral Exercises

Which of the following trapezoids appear to be isosceles?

1.

2.

3.

4.

Written Exercises

Find the unknown angle measures in each isosceles trapezoid. (Ex. 1−6)

[A] 1.

2.

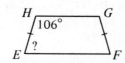

3.

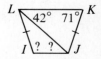

4.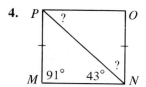

5.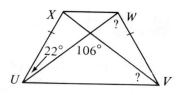

6.

7. Given: $\overline{AB} \cong \overline{AC}$, and
$\overline{DE} \parallel \overline{BC}$
Prove: $BCDE$ is an isosceles
trapezoid.

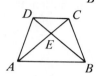

8. Given: $BCDE$ is an isosceles
trapezoid with $\overline{EB} \cong \overline{DC}$
Prove: $\triangle ABC$ is isosceles.

9. Given: Isos. trap. $ABCD$, and
$\overline{DC} \parallel \overline{AB}$
Prove: $\triangle ABD \cong \triangle BAC$

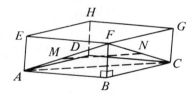

10. Given: Isos. trap. $ABCD$, and
$\overline{DC} \parallel \overline{AB}$
Prove: $\triangle AED \cong \triangle BEC$

True or false? If the statement is true, prove it. If false, give a counterexample.
(Ex. 11−14)

11. If a trapezoid is isosceles, then opposite
angles are supplementary.

12. If a trapezoid is isosceles, then the diagonals bisect each other.

13. If opposite angles of a trapezoid are
supplementary, then the trapezoid is
isosceles.

14. If the opposite angles of a quadrilateral
are supplementary, then the quadrilateral
is an isosceles trapezoid.

15. Prove Theorem 8.3.

16. Prove Theorem 8.4.

17. Given: $\overline{FB} \perp \overline{AB}$,
$\overline{FB} \perp \overline{BC}$, $\overline{AB} \cong \overline{BC}$,
M is midpoint of $\overline{AF}$,
and N is midpoint of
$\overline{FC}$
Prove: $ACNM$ is an
isos. trap.

18. Given: $\square ABCD \parallel$
$\square EFGH$, $\overline{FB} \perp \overline{AB}$,
$\overline{FB} \perp \overline{BC}$, M is midpoint of $\overline{AF}$, N is midpoint of $\overline{FC}$, and
$\triangle AFE \cong \triangle CFG$
Prove: $ACNM$ is an
isos. trap.

Cumulative Review

1. Give an example to show that angle-angle-angle is not a congruence pattern.
2. Why are adjacent angles of a parallelogram supplementary?
3. Draw an acute angle. Construct its bisector.

A Challenge To You

A fly is walking from a spot A on the ceiling of a room to a spot B on the
floor. What is the shortest path the fly can take? How can you show that
it is the shortest possible path?

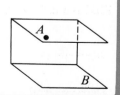

8.4 Congruent Quadrilaterals

► **To identify congruent quadrilaterals**
To prove theorems about congruent quadrilaterals

Parallelograms, squares, rectangles, rhombi, and trapezoids are specific types of quadrilaterals. In order to prove certain theorems about them, additional properties of quadrilaterals are needed.

Congruent quadrilaterals have the same size and shape. The size of a quadrilateral depends upon the lengths of the sides while the shape depends upon the angle measures.

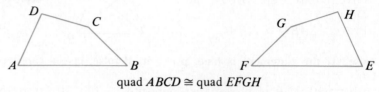

quad $ABCD \cong$ quad $EFGH$

Definition:
congruent
quadrilaterals

> Two quadrilaterals are **congruent** if their corresponding sides are congruent and their corresponding angles are congruent.

The congruence statement specifies which sides and angles correspond.

quad $ABCD \cong$ quad $EFGH$

Example 1 Quad. $JKLM \cong$ quad. $NOPQ$
Name the pairs of congruent sides.
Name the pairs of congruent angles

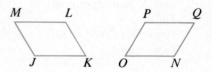

Congruent sides: $\overline{JK} \cong \overline{NO}$, $\overline{KL} \cong \overline{OP}$, $\overline{LM} \cong \overline{PQ}$, $\overline{MJ} \cong \overline{QN}$
Congruent angles: $\angle J \cong \angle N$, $\angle K \cong \angle O$, $\angle L \cong \angle P$, $\angle M \cong \angle Q$

Example 2 According to the markings shown, what is a correct congruence statement for the two trapezoids?

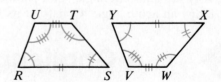

Trap. $RSTU \cong$ Trap. $YXWV$

You can prove that two quadrilaterals are congruent without showing that all four pairs of sides and all four pairs of angles are congruent. The following theorem shows one of several possible congruence patterns.

Theorem 8.6

SASAS for ≅ quadrilaterals Two quadrilaterals are congruent if any three sides and the included angles of one are congruent, respectively, to three sides and the included angles of the *other*.

Given: quad. *ABCD* and
quad. *EFGH*
$\overline{DA} \cong \overline{HE}$, $\angle A \cong \angle E$,
$\overline{AB} \cong \overline{EF}$, $\angle B \cong \angle F$,
and $\overline{BC} \cong \overline{FG}$
Prove: quad *ABCD* ≅ quad *EFGH*

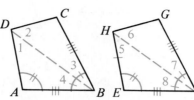

Analysis: Draw diagonals.
Show that corr. sides and
∠'s are corr. parts of ≅ △'s

Outline of proof

1. Draw diagonals $\overline{DB}$ and $\overline{HF}$
2. $\triangle DAB \cong \triangle HEF$
3. $\angle 1 \cong \angle 5$, $\overline{DB} \cong \overline{HF}$, $\angle 4 \cong \angle 8$
4. $\angle ABC \cong \angle EFG$
5. $\angle 3 \cong \angle 7$
6. $\triangle DBC \cong \triangle HFG$
7. $\overline{DC} \cong \overline{HG}$
8. $\angle C \cong \angle G$, $\angle 2 \cong \angle 6$
9. $\angle ADC \cong \angle EHG$
10. ∴ quad *ABCD* ≅ quad *EFGH*

In a similar manner, you can prove an angle-side-angle-side-angle congruence pattern.

Theorem 8.7

ASASA for ≅ quadrilaterals Two quadrilaterals are congruent if any three angles and the included sides of one are congruent, respectively, to three angles and the included sides of the other. (See Exercise 16.)

Theorems 8.6 and 8.7 can now be used to prove quadrilaterals congruent.

Example 3

Given: Square *ABEF* and Square *BCDE*
Prove: Square *ABEF* ≅ Square *BCDE*

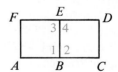

Proof

Statements	Reasons
1. Square *ABEF* and Square *BCDE*	1. Given
2. $\overline{AB} \cong \overline{BE} \cong \overline{EF}$ and $\overline{CB} \cong \overline{BE} \cong \overline{ED}$	2. Def. of square and rectangle
3. $\overline{AB} \cong \overline{CB}$ and $\overline{ED} \cong \overline{EF}$	3. Substitution property.
4. $\overline{BE} \cong \overline{BE}$	4. Reflexive property
5. $\angle 1, \angle 2, \angle 3, \angle 4$ are rt. ∠'s	5. Def. of square
6. $\angle 1 \cong \angle 2$, $\angle 3 \cong \angle 4$	6. All rt. ∠'s are ≅
7. ∴ Square ABEF ≅ Square *BCDE*	7. SASAS for ≅ quad.

CONGRUENT QUADRILATERALS

Oral Exercises

Which of the following quadrilaterals appear to be congruent?

1.

  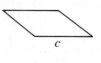

a *b* *c*

2.

 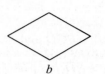

a *b* *c*

3.

a *b* *c*

4.

a *b* *c*

Written Exercises

For each pair of congruent quadrilaterals, name the pairs of congruent sides and the pairs of congruent angles.

1. quad ABCD ≅ quad *JKLM*

2. quad *EFGH* ≅ quad *NOPQ*

According to the markings shown, what is a correct congruence statement? (Ex. 3–5)

Ⓐ **3.**

4.

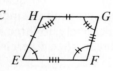

5.

6. Given: $\overline{FE}$ is the ⊥ bisector of $\overline{AB}$, $\overline{AD} \cong \overline{BC}$, and $\angle A \cong \angle B$.
Prove: quad *AEFD* ≅ quad *BEFC*.

7. Given: $\overline{EF}$ bisects $\angle DFC$, $\overline{DF} \cong \overline{CF}$, and $\overline{FE}$ is the ⊥ bisector of $\overline{AB}$
Prove: quad *AEFD* ≅ quad *BEFC*.

Ⓑ **8.** Given: Rhombus *ABEF* and Rhombus *CBED*; $\angle 1 \cong \angle 2$
Prove: Rhombus *ABEF* ≅ Rhombus *CBED*.

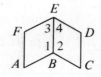

9. Given: Rhombus *ABEF* and Rhombus *CBED*; $\angle 1$ and $\angle 4$ are supplementary
Prove: Rhombus *ABEF* ≅ Rhombus *CBED*.

10. Given: $\overline{DA} \cong \overline{CB}$, $\overline{EA} \cong \overline{FB}$, and $\angle A \cong \angle B$
Prove: quad *EABC* ≅ quad *FBAD*

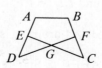

11. Given: $\triangle DEG \cong \triangle CFG$, and $\overline{EA} \cong \overline{FB}$
Prove: quad *EABC* ≅ quad *FBAD*

252

CHAPTER EIGHT

12. Given: Trap. *HILM* and
Trap. *JILK*, $\angle 1 \cong \angle 2$,
$\overline{HI} \cong \overline{JI}$, and
$\angle MHI \cong \angle KJI$
Prove: Trap. *HILM* $\cong$
Trap. *JILK*

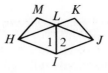

13. Given: Isos trap. *HILM* and
Isos. Trap. *JILK*;
$\triangle HLM \cong \triangle JLK$
Prove: Trap. *HILM* $\cong$
JILK

14. Given: $\overline{AE} \cong \overline{BD}$, and
$\triangle FEG \cong \triangle CBG$
Prove: quad *ABGF* $\cong$
quad *DEGC*

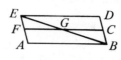

15. Given: $\triangle ABE \cong \triangle DEB$,
$\overline{EF} \cong \overline{AF}$, $\overline{DC} \cong \overline{BC}$, and
$\overline{EG} \cong \overline{GB}$
Prove: quad *ABGF* $\cong$
quad *DEGC*

16. Give a complete proof of step 2 in the proof of Theorem 8.6.

17. Give a complete proof of steps 5 and 9 in the proof of Theorem 8.6.

18. Prove Theorem 8.7.

19. A SSS congruence correspondence is sufficient to show that two triangles are congruent. Is a similar (SSSS) pattern sufficient to show that two quadrilaterals are congruent? Give an argument in defense of your answer.

20. Which of the following congruence patterns is sufficient to show that two quadrilaterals are congruent: SSASS, AASAA, SSAAS, AASSA, ASSAS? Give an argument in defense of your answer.

Algebra Review

OBJECTIVE ▶ **To solve fractional equations**

To solve a fractional equation:
(1) Multiply each side by the LCD.
(2) Solve the resulting equation.

Example Solve $\dfrac{3x - 5}{4} = \dfrac{2x + 3}{3}$.

$$LCD = 6 \quad \blacktriangleright \quad 12\left(\frac{3x - 5}{4}\right) = 12\left(\frac{2x + 3}{3}\right)$$
$$3(3x - 5) = 4(2x + 3)$$
$$9x - 15 = 8x + 12$$
$$x = 27$$

Solve.

1. $\dfrac{4x - 2}{3} = \dfrac{5x + 1}{4}$

2. $\dfrac{2y - 5}{3} = \dfrac{3y + 2}{4}$

3. $\dfrac{z + 2}{3} = \dfrac{4z - 3}{6} - \dfrac{z}{2}$

4. $\dfrac{2w - 3}{6} - \dfrac{w + 5}{9} = \dfrac{w - 1}{2}$

5. $\dfrac{4}{t} + \dfrac{3}{5} = 3$

6. $\dfrac{3}{4v} = \dfrac{5}{6} - \dfrac{2}{3v}$

8.5 Constructing Quadrilaterals

OBJECTIVE ► **To construct quadrilaterals with given properties**

You can use the unique properties of each type of quadrilateral to construct a given quadrilateral.

Example 1 Construct a parallelogram with adjacent sides congruent to two given segments and the included angle congruent to a given angle. Describe your strategy.

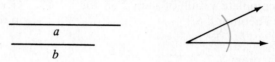

Strategy: Construct congruent opposite sides.

Construct ∠A ≅ given ∠. Construct $\overline{AB}$ so AB = a and $\overline{AD}$ so AD = b.   Construct $\overline{DC}$ and $\overline{BC}$ so DC = a and BC = b.

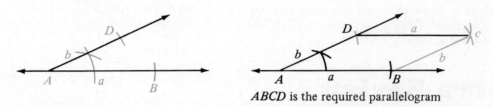

ABCD is the required parallelogram

Example 2 Construct a rhombus with diagonals congruent to two given segments. Describe your strategy.

Strategy: Construct diagonals that are perpendicular bisectors of each other.

Bisect segment of length *b*.
Construct $\overline{AB}$ so AB = a.
Construct ⊥ bisector of AB.

On ⊥ bisector of $\overline{AB}$, mark off segments of length $\frac{1}{2}b$. Connect end points.

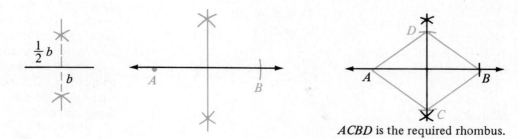

ACBD is the required rhombus.

Written Exercises

Construct each of the following. Describe your strategy. (Ex. 1–14)

1. Draw a segment 7 cm long. Construct a square with sides congruent to the segment.

2. Draw two segments with different lengths. Construct a rectangle with sides congruent to these segments.

3. Construct a parallelogram with sides congruent to the given segments and an angle congruent to the given angle.

4. Construct a rhombus with sides congruent to the given segment and an angle congruent to the given angle.

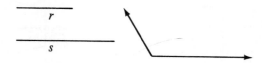

 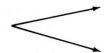

5. Draw a segment. Construct a square with diagonals congruent to this segment.

6. Draw two segments. Construct a rhombus with diagonals congruent to these segments.

7. Draw a segment 10 cm long. Construct a rectangle with diagonals congruent to this segment and a side with half the length of a diagonal.

8. Draw a segment 12 cm long. Construct a parallelogram with one side congruent to this segment, a side half as long, and a 60° angle.

9. Construct an isosceles trapezoid with three sides of length s and diagonal of length d.

10. Construct a rhombus with sides and one diagonal congruent to the given segment.

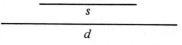

11. Construct a trapezoid with bases and a leg congruent to the given segments and a base angle measuring 45°.

12. Construct an isosceles trapezoid with three sides of length s and diagonal of length d.

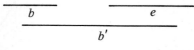

13. Construct a quadrilateral congruent to quad. *ABCD* using an angle-side-angle-side-angle pattern.

15. Is it possible to construct a quadrilateral congruent to quad. *ABCD* using a side-side-side-side pattern?

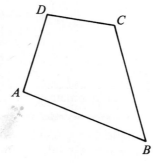

14. Construct a quadrilateral congruent to quad. *ABCD* using a side-angle-side-angle-side pattern.

16. Is it possible to construct a quadrilateral congruent to quad. *ABCD* using a side-side-side-side-angle pattern?

CONSTRUCTING QUADRILATERALS

8.6 Symmetric Polygons

OBJECTIVES ▶ To identify symmetric polygons
To determine and apply congruence properties of symmetric polygons.

Some polygons are their own reflections. If the polygon were drawn on a piece of paper, you could fold it along a line so that the two halves would coincide. Such a polygon is called a *symmetric polygon*. The line is called a *line of symmetry*. Each of the following figures is a symmetric polygon.

> **Postulate 21**   A line of symmetry of a symmetric polygon is the perpendicular bisector of any segment joining a pair of corresponding points of the polygon.

In quadrilateral *ABCD*, $\overleftrightarrow{AC}$ is the line of symmetry. Points *B* and *D* are corresponding points. $\overline{CD}$ and $\overline{CB}$ are corresponding sides, as are $\overline{AD}$ and $\overline{AB}$. According to Postulate 21 the line of symmetry, $\overleftrightarrow{AC}$, bisects $\overline{DB}$ and is perpendicular to it.

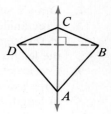

Some polygons have more than one line of symmetry.

Example 1   Draw all lines of symmetry of the symmetric polygon. How many are there?

There are six lines of symmetry.

The figure in Example 1 is a regular hexagon. Notice that there are six lines of symmetry for this regular six-sided figure.

The following theorems state two important properties of symmetric polygons. You should complete the proofs, as indicated.

┌ Theorem 8.8 Corresponding sides of a symmetric polygon are congruent. ┐

Given: polygon $ABCDEF$,
with line of sym-
metry $\overleftrightarrow{AD}$

Prove: $\overline{AB} \cong \overline{AF}$, $\overline{BC} \cong$
$\overline{FE}$, and $\overline{CD} \cong \overline{ED}$

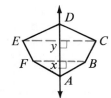

Analysis: Use congruent quadrilaterals and △'s.

Outline of proof

1. Draw diagonals $\overline{EC}$ and $\overline{FB}$, intersecting $\overleftrightarrow{AD}$ at Y and X
2. $\overleftrightarrow{AD}$ is the $\perp$ bisector of $\overline{FB}$, $\overleftrightarrow{AD}$ is the $\perp$ bisector of $\overline{EC}$.
3. $\therefore \overline{AB} \cong \overline{AF}$ and $\overline{CD} \cong \overline{ED}$
4. $\overline{BX} \cong \overline{FX}$ (S)

5. $\angle BXY \cong \angle FXY$ (A)
6. $\overline{XY} \cong \overline{XY}$ (S)
7. $\angle XYC \cong \angle XYE$ (A)
8. $\overline{CY} \cong \overline{EY}$ (S)
9. Quad $BXYC \cong$ quad $FXYE$
10. $\therefore \overline{BC} \cong \overline{FE}$

(See Exercise 20.)

┌ Theorem 8.9 Corresponding angles of a symmetric polygon are congruent. (See Exercises 18 and 19.) ┐

Using these theorems, it is possible to identify which sides and which angles of a symmetric polygon are congruent.

Example 2 If $ABCDE$ is symmetric about $\overleftrightarrow{AX}$, which sides and which angles are congruent?

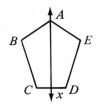

Sides: $\overline{AB} \cong \overline{AE}$, $\overline{BC} \cong \overline{ED}$
Angles: $\angle B \cong \angle E$, $\angle C \cong \angle D$

Oral Exercises

Which of the following polygons appear to be symmetric?

1.

2.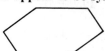

3.

4.

SYMMETRIC POLYGONS

Written Exercises _____

Copy each figure. Draw all the lines of symmetry of each polygon. How many are there?

 1.

2.

3.

4.

Each polygon is symmetric about the line of symmetry shown. Which sides and which angles are congruent?

5.

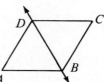

6.

7.

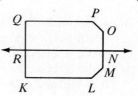

8.

Copy each figure and find the perpendicular bisector of the segment joining each pair of corresponding points. Based on your results, is the figure symmetric? (Ex. 9–11)

B **9.**

10.

11.

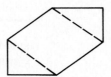

12. Is it possible for a quadrilateral to have exactly one line of symmetry? Exactly two? Exactly three? More than three? Draw pictures to defend your answer.

13. Is it possible for a pentagon to have exactly one line of symmetry? Exactly two? Exactly three? Exactly four? More than four? Draw pictures to defend your answer.

14. Is there any relationship between the number of sides of a regular polygon and the number of lines of symmetry? If so, what is it?

15. Can a decagon be drawn with exactly one line of symmetry? Exactly two? Draw pictures to defend your answer.

C **16.** If corresponding sides of a polygon are congruent, then is the polygon necessarily symmetric?

17. If corresponding angles of a polygon are congruent, then is the polygon necessarily symmetric?

18. Prove Theorem 8.9 using a hexagon.

19. Prove Theorem 8.9 using an octagon.

20. Complete the proof of Theorem 8.8.

21. Theorem 8.8 was proved using a hexagon. Prove it using a heptagon.

8.7 Congruence and Reflections

OBJECTIVES ► **To identify reflections**
To prove and apply theorems relating reflections and congruence

When you place an object before a mirror, you see the reflected image of that object in the mirror. In geometry, the concept of reflection is similar except that the mirror is replaced by a line of symmetry.

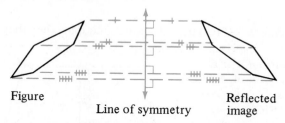

Figure   Reflected
Line of symmetry   image

Definition:
reflection.

> Two polygons are **reflections** of each other if all segments joining pairs of corresponding points have the same perpendicular bisector.

You can use this definition to draw reflections and to determine if two polygons are reflections of each other.

Example 1 Draw the reflection of the given figure about the given line of symmetry.

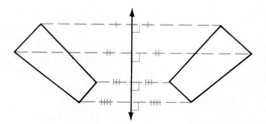

Example 2 Show that the two figures below are *not* reflections of each other.

Use the construction for a ⊥ bisector. ►

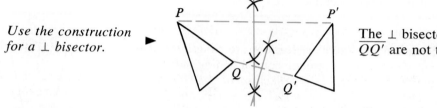

The ⊥ bisectors of $\overline{PP'}$ and $\overline{QQ'}$ are not the same.

CONGRUENCE AND REFLECTIONS

259

If two figures are drawn on a sheet of paper and the paper can be folded so that the figures coincide, then the two figures are reflections of each other. The fold is the line of symmetry. If the paper cannot be folded so that they coincide, then the figures are not reflections of each other.

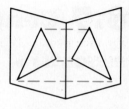

Since reflections drawn on paper can be made to coincide, they must have the same size and shape. This leads to the following theorem and corollary.

Theorem 8.10 If two triangles are reflections, then they are congruent.

Given; $\triangle A'B'C'$ is a *reflection* of $\triangle ABC$.
Prove: $\triangle ABC \cong \triangle A'B'C'$

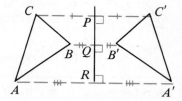

Analysis: Use $\cong$ quadrilaterals to show $\cong$ sides.

Outline of proof

1. $\overline{CP} \cong \overline{C'P}$	(S)		8. $\overline{BQ} \cong \overline{B'Q'}$	(S)
2. $\angle CPQ \cong \angle C'PQ$	(A)		9. $\angle BQR \cong \angle B'QR$	(A)
3. $\overline{PQ} \cong \overline{PQ}$	(S)		10. $\overline{QR} \cong \overline{QR}$	(S)
4. $\angle PQB \cong \angle PQB'$	(A)		11. $\angle ARQ \cong \angle A'RQ$	(A)
5. $\overline{BQ} \cong \overline{B'Q}$	(S)		12. $\overline{AR} \cong \overline{A'R}$	(S)

6. Quad. $CBQP \cong$ Quad. $C'B'QP$
7. $\overline{CB} \cong \overline{C'B'}$; $\angle CBQ \cong \angle C'B'Q$

13. Quad. $ARQB \cong$ Quad. $A'RQB'$
14. $\overline{AB} \cong \overline{A'B'}$; $\angle ABQ \cong \angle A'B'Q$

15. m $\angle CBQ =$ m $\angle C'B'Q$; m $\angle QBA =$ m $\angle QB'A'$
16. m $\angle ABC +$ m $\angle CBQ +$ m $\angle QBA = 360$; m $\angle A'B'C +$ m $\angle C'B'Q +$ m $\angle QB'A' = 360$
17. m $\angle ABC +$ m $\angle CBQ +$ m $\angle QBA =$ m $\angle A'B'C' +$ m $\angle C'B'Q +$ m $\angle QB'A'$
18. m $\angle ABC =$ m $\angle A'B'C$; $\angle ABC \cong \angle A'B'C'$
19. $\therefore \triangle ABC \cong \triangle A'B'C'$

Corollary If two quadrilaterals are reflections, then they are congruent. (See Exercise 17.)

Since a figure and its reflections are congruent, you can determine congruent corresponding sides and angles. If $\triangle ABC$ is a reflection of $\triangle EDG$, then $\triangle ABC \cong \triangle EDF$. $\overline{AB} \cong \overline{ED}$, $\overline{BC} \cong \overline{DF}$, and $\overline{CA} \cong \overline{FE}$. $\angle A \cong \angle E$, $\angle B \cong \angle D$, and $\angle C \cong \angle F$.

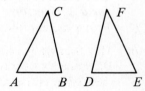

Written Exercises _____

Copy each picture. Draw the reflection of the given figure about the given line of symmetry.

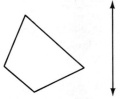
A   **1.**

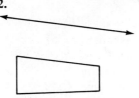
2.

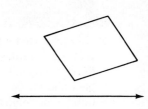
3.

Copy each picture. Determine which are reflections by constructing the line of symmetry. Check your work by folding the paper along the line of symmetry.

4.

5.

6.

In each pair of reflections list the corresponding congruent sides and angles. (Ex. 7–9)

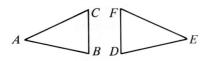
7.

8.

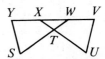
9.

B   **10.** △*ABC* is a reflection of △*DEF*. Is △*ABC* ≅ △*DEF*? Why?

11. Trap. *GHIJ* is a reflection of trap. *LKNM*. Describe the line of symmetry.

12. *l* is the perpendicular bisector of $\overline{OS}$, $\overline{PT}$, $\overline{QU}$, and $\overline{RV}$. Is *OPQR* ≅ *STUV*? Why?

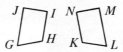

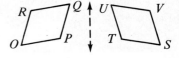

True or false?

13. Reflected triangles are congruent.

14. Reflected polygons are congruent.

15. Congruent triangles are reflections.

16. Congruent polygons are reflections.

C   **17.** Prove the corollary to Theorem 8.10.

18. If a triangle is reflected about a line and the image is then reflected about the same line, what is the result?

19. Describe a construction for finding the line of symmetry of reflections.

CONGRUENCE AND REFLECTIONS

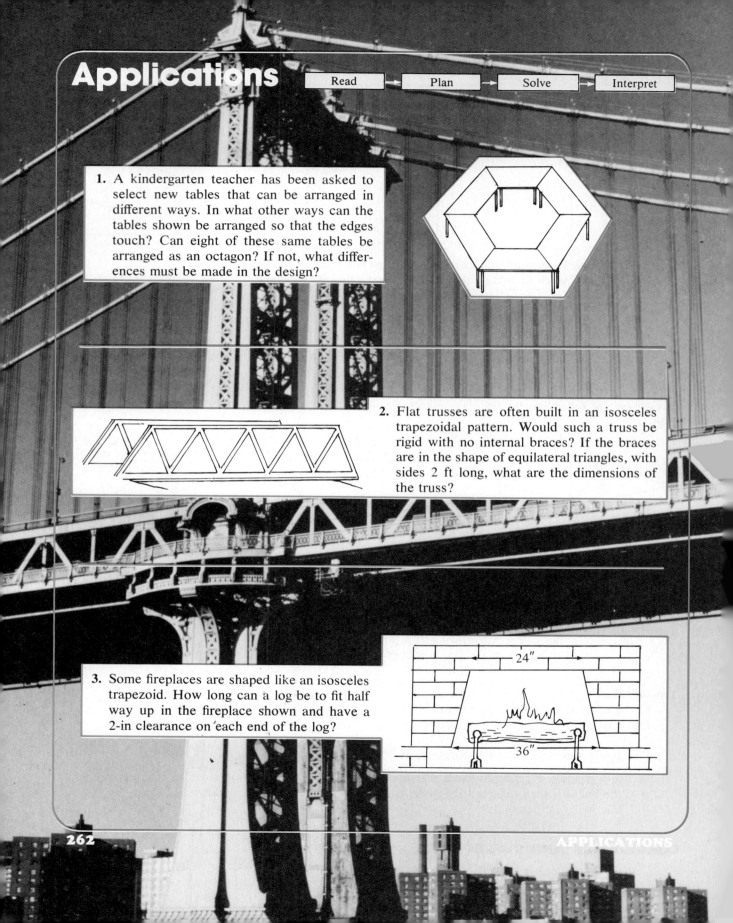

1. A kindergarten teacher has been asked to select new tables that can be arranged in different ways. In what other ways can the tables shown be arranged so that the edges touch? Can eight of these same tables be arranged as an octagon? If not, what differences must be made in the design?

2. Flat trusses are often built in an isosceles trapezoidal pattern. Would such a truss be rigid with no internal braces? If the braces are in the shape of equilateral triangles, with sides 2 ft long, what are the dimensions of the truss?

3. Some fireplaces are shaped like an isosceles trapezoid. How long can a log be to fit half way up in the fireplace shown and have a 2-in clearance on each end of the log?

Computer Activities

An isosceles trapezoid is symmetric about a line through the midpoints of its bases. This symmetric property can be used to determine the measures of missing parts. With a Cathode Ray Tube (CRT), part of the figure can actually be rotated and placed "on top of" the other part.

If graphic capabilities are not available, you can use the following program to find three missing angles of an isosceles trapezoid, given one angle.

See the computer section on page 560 for more information.

PROGRAM

```
10 PRINT "PROGRAM FINDS THREE MISSING ANGLE MEASURES"
20 PRINT "ENTER ANGLE G"
30 INPUT G
40 LET A = 180 - G
50 PRINT "ANGLE A = "; A; "ANGLES A AND G ARE SUPPLEMENTARY"
60 PRINT "ANGLE B = "; A; "ANGLES A AND B ARE CONGRUENT"
70 PRINT "ANGLE C = "; G; "ANGLES C AND G ARE CONGRUENT"
80 END
```

Exercises

Run the program for the following values for angle G. (EX. 1-3)

1. 91   **2.** 73   **3.** 22

4. Write a program to find the missing measures $G1$ and $G2$ in the isosceles trapezoid.

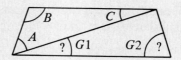

ACTIVITY: MISSING PARTS IN A TRAPEZOID

Chapter Eight Review

Identify each of the following. [8.2]
1. The median of trap. *ABCD*

2. An altitude of trap. *ABCD*

3. Bases of trap. *ABCD*

4. Legs of trap. *ABCD*

Which of the following appear to be isosceles trapezoids? [8.3]

5.   6.

True or false? Draw pictures to defend your answers.

7. Two sides of a trapezoid are congruent. [8.1]

8. An isosceles trapezoid is a symmetric quadrilateral. [8.3]

9. Consecutive angles of a trapezoid are supplementary.

10. The median of a trapezoid is parallel to a base. [8.2]

11. Quadrilaterals can be proved congruent by an *ASASA* correspondence. [8.4]

12. All congruent quadrilaterals are reflections of each other. [8.7]

13. If a quadrilateral has congruent diagonals, then the quadrilateral is a trapezoid. [8.1]

14. Diagonals of an isosceles trapezoid are congruent. [8.3]

15. A line of symmetry is the perpendicular bisector of the segment connecting corresponding points of a figure and its reflection. [8.6]

Vocabulary
altitude [8.2], isosceles trapezoid [8.3], line of symmetry [8.6], median [8.2] symmetric polygon [8.6], trapezoid [8.1]

Construct each of the following. (Ex. 16–18)
16. An isosceles trapezoid with a base of length *a*, a leg of length *b*, and a base angle congruent to the given angle. [8.5]

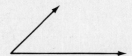

17. An isosceles trapezoid with a base of length *a*, an altitude of length *b*, and a leg of length *c*.

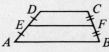

18. Copy the reflections below. Construct their line of symmetry. [8.6]

19. Given: $AB = 13$, and $CD = 9$ [8.2]
Find *EF*.

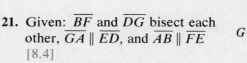

20. Given: $AB = 7x - 5$, $EF = 3x + 1$, and $DC = 2x + 1$
Find *EF*.

21. Given: $\overline{BF}$ and $\overline{DG}$ bisect each other, $\overline{GA} \parallel \overline{ED}$, and $\overline{AB} \parallel \overline{FE}$ [8.4]
Prove; $CGAB \cong CDEF$

*22. Given: isos. trap. *HIJK*, $\overline{HK} \cong \overline{IJ}$, and $\overline{KJ} \parallel \overline{HI}$ [8.3]
Prove: $\triangle HIK \cong \triangle IHJ$

Chapter Eight Test

Identify each of the following.

1. A median of trap. *HJLM*.

2. An altitude of trap. *PQRS*.

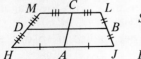

Which of the following appear to be isosceles trapezoids?

3.
4.

True or false. Draw pictures to defend your answers.

5. A trapezoid has one pair of parallel sides.

6. The diagonals of a trapezoid are congruent.

7. If a trapezoid has congruent diagonals, then it is isosceles.

8. Opposite angles of an isosceles trapezoid are supplementary.

9. Quadrilaterals can be proved congruent by a *SSSS* correspondence.

10. A reflection of a figure has the same shape as the figure.

11. A symmetric quadrilateral may have exactly two lines of symmetry.

12. The reflection of an isosceles trapezoid is an isosceles trapezoid.

13. A line of symmetry of a symmetric polygon is the perpendicular bisector of the segment connecting corresponding points of the polygon.

Construct each of the following. [Ex. 14–15]

14. An isosceles trapezoid with one base of length *a*, a second base of length *b*, and an altitude of length *c*.

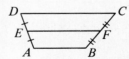

15. Copy the figures below. Show by constructing the perpendicular bisectors of the segments joining two sets of corresponding points that the polygons are not reflections of each other.

16. Given: $AB = 12$, and $CD = 18$
Find *EF*.

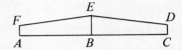

17. Given: $AB = x + 3$, $CD = 4x - 3$, and $EF = 3x - 1$
Find *EF*.

18. Prove: The diagonals of an isosceles trapezoid are congruent.

*19. Given: $\overline{EB}$ is the $\perp$ bisector of $\overline{AC}$, $\overline{EB}$ bisects $\angle FED$, and $\overline{FE} \cong \overline{DE}$.
Prove: quad $ABEF \cong$ quad $CBED$

College Prep Test

For each item choose the best answer. Indicate your answer by writing the letter of this choice.

1. Which of these is not a property of all trapezoids?
   (A) Two sides are parallel
   (B) Diagonals intersect
   (C) Two pairs of angles are supplementary
   (D) Diagonals are congruent
   (E) None of these.

2. Given: Trap. $ABCD$, median $\overline{EF}$, $DC = 20x + 2$, $EF = 26x$, and $AB = 24x + 4$. Which of the statements are true?

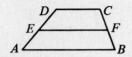

   I $AB = 22$
   II $EF = 19\frac{1}{2}$
   III $DC = 17$

   (A) I only
   (B) II only
   (C) III only
   (D) I and III only
   (E) I, II, and III

3. Which of these is sufficient to prove that a quadrilateral is an isosceles trapezoid?
   (A) Diagonals are congruent
   (B) Diagonals are perpendicular
   (C) Opposite angles are supplementary
   (D) Two angles are congruent
   (E) None of these

4. You can prove two quadrilaterals congruent by
   (A) $SSSS$
   (B) $AAAA$
   (C) $SASAS$
   (D) $SAAAA$
   (E) $SSASS$

5. To construct a rhombus given the two diagonals, you must
   (A) Construct a triangle with the diagonals as two of the sides
   (B) Construct a perpendicular to one segment
   (C) Bisect one segment
   (D) Construct a perpendicular bisector of one segment.
   (E) Bisect an angle.

6. Which of the following are true?
   I A symmetric triangle can have exactly two lines of symmetry
   II A symmetric quadrilateral can have exactly two lines of symmetry
   III A symmetric quadrilateral can have exactly four lines of symmetry.

   (A) I only
   (B) II only
   (C) III only
   (D) I and II only
   (E) II and III only

7. Which of the following is *not* true?
   (A) A reflection is congruent to the original figure.
   (B) Corresponding sides of a figure and its reflection are parallel.
   (C) Corresponding sides of a figure and its reflection are congruent.
   (D) The line of symmetry bisects a segment connecting corresponding points of a figure and its reflection.
   (E) The line of symmetry is perpendicular to a segment connecting corresponding points of a figure and its reflection.

Write the letter that indicates the best answer.

1. Which are measures of supplementary angles?
   (A) 40° and 50°   **(B)** 32° and 68°
   (C) 95° and 85°   **(D)** none of these

2. If two coplanar lines are perpendicular to the same line, then they are _____ to each other.
   (A) perpendicular   **(B)** parallel
   (C) supplementary   **(D)** none of these

3. It is impossible for a triangle to be
   (A) both scalene and right
   (B) both obtuse and isosceles
   (C) both equilateral and obtuse
   (D) both acute and isosceles

4. Two of the medians of an isosceles triangle are
   (A) congruent   **(B)** altitudes
   (C) perpendicular   **(D)** angle bisectors

5. The legs of an isosceles right triangle are
   (A) perpendicular   **(B)** altitudes
   (C) congruent   **(D)** all of these

6. In $\triangle ABC$, $\overline{AC} \cong \overline{BC}$, m $\angle A = 4x - 19$, and m $\angle B = 2x + 17$. Then m $\angle A$ is equal to

   (A) 18   **(B)** 36
   (C) 53   **(D)** 74

7. A polygon with seven sides is a
   (A) hexagon   **(B)** octagon
   (C) nonagon   **(D)** none of these

8. An angle of a regular polygon cannot measure
   (A) 90°   **(B)** 108°
   (C) 120°   **(D)** none of these

9. The sum of the measures of the exterior angles of a hexagon is
   (A) 360°   **(B)** 720°
   (C) 1080°   **(D)** none of these

10. If a parallelogram has a pair of congruent adjacent sides, then it is a
   (A) rectangle   **(B)** rhombus
   (C) square   **(D)** none of these

11. In $\triangle ABC$, D is the midpoint of $\overline{AB}$, E is the midpoint of $\overline{AC}$, and $CB = 12$. Then $ED =$ _____.

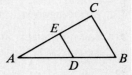

   (A) 3   **(B)** 6
   (C) 9   **(D)** none of these

12. The length of the median of a trapezoid is the _____ of the lengths of the bases.
   (A) average   **(B)** sum
   (C) difference   **(D)** none of these

13. In isosceles trapezoid $ABCD$, $\overline{AD} \cong \overline{BC}$. If $\overline{DE} \perp \overline{AB}$ and E is between A and B, then
   (A) $AB = 2(DC)$ **(B)** $\overline{AD} \cong \overline{DC}$
   (C) $AB = DC + 2(AE)$ **(D)** none of these

Give all other names for each figure named below.

14. $\overline{BC}$

15. $\overrightarrow{AB}$

True or false?

16. Complementary angles are adjacent.

17. Two congruent supplementary angles are right angles.

18. If two lines are parallel to the same line, then they are perpendicular to each other.

19. Adjacent sides of a parallelogram are congruent.

20. An octagon is a polygon with eight sides.

21. Each exterior angle of a regular hexagon measures 120°.

22. The sum of the measures of the interior angles of a pentagon is 540°.

23. If one of the base angles of an isosceles triangle measures 40° then the triangle is obtuse.

24. The bases of an isosceles trapezoid cannot be congruent.

25. If a median of a triangle is also an altitude, then the triangle is isosceles.

26. If the diagonals of a parallelogram are congruent, then the parallelogram is a square.

27. A regular hexagon has exactly three lines of symmetry.

Find each indicated measure.

28. Given: $l \parallel m$,
m $\angle 1 = x + 17$,
and m $\angle 2 = 2x - 11$.
Find m $\angle 1$ and
m $\angle 2$.

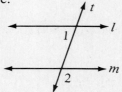

29. Given: $\triangle PQR$ with
$\overline{ST} \parallel \overline{PQ}$, $PS = 6$,
$SR = 6$, and $ST = 6$.
Find PQ.

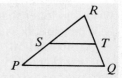

30. Given: $\square ABCD$ with
$\overline{AB} \parallel \overline{CD}$, median
$\overline{EF}$, $DC = 9$, and
$EF = 12$
Find AB.

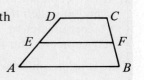

Construct each of the following:

31. A 45° angle.

32. Draw a segment. Divide it into three congruent segments.

33. Draw an acute triangle. Construct an altitude to one of the sides.

Prove each of the following:

34. Given: $\overline{AB} \cong \overline{AC}$ and
$\angle B \cong \angle C$
Prove: $\overline{EB} \cong \overline{DC}$

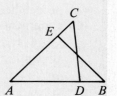

35. Given: $\square RSTU$
with $\angle RVU \cong$
$\angle RSW$
Prove: $VSWU$ is
a parallelogram.

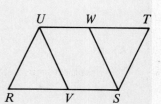

36. Given: Quadrilateral $ABCD$
with E the midpoint of $\overline{AB}$, F the
midpoint of $\overline{BC}$, G
the midpoint of $\overline{DC}$,
and H the midpoint
of $\overline{AD}$. Prove: $\overline{EG}$
and $\overline{HF}$ bisect each other.

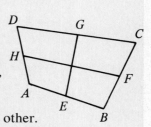

SIMILARITY

Shadows

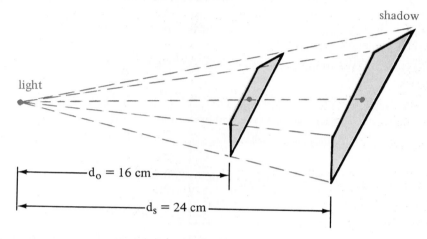

shadow

light

$d_o = 16$ cm

$d_s = 24$ cm

A shadow can involve measurements that form a true proportion. If the shadow is parallel to the object, then it will have the same shape as the object. The lengths of corresponding sides form equal ratios:

$$\frac{\text{HEIGHT OF SHADOW } (h_s)}{\text{HEIGHT OF OBJECT } (h_o)} = \frac{\text{DISTANCE OF SHADOW FROM LIGHT } (d_s)}{\text{DISTANCE OF OBJECT FROM LIGHT } (d_o)}$$

If the measure of h_s is 12 cm, what is the measure of h_o?

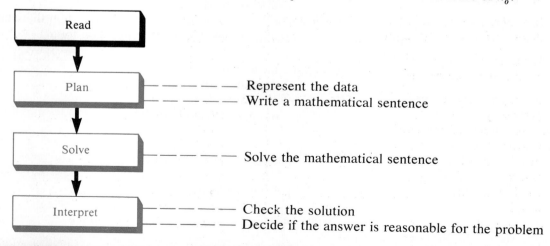

Read

Plan — — — — — — — Represent the data
— — — — — — — Write a mathematical sentence

Solve — — — — — — — Solve the mathematical sentence

Interpret — — — — — — — Check the solution
— — — — — — — Decide if the answer is reasonable for the problem

9.1 Using Proportions

OBJECTIVES ► **To identify, write, and solve proportions**
To find the geometric mean of two numbers

The boy at the right is 5 feet tall. The man is 6 feet tall. The boy is $\frac{5}{6}$ as tall as the man. The man is $\frac{6}{5}$ or $1\frac{1}{5}$ times as tall as the boy. The ratio of the boy's height to the man's height is $\frac{5}{6}$ or 5 to 6. The ratio of the man's height to the boy's height is $\frac{6}{5}$ or 6 to 5.

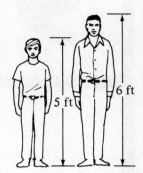

5 ft   6 ft

Definition:
ratio

> The *ratio* of two numbers a and b is the number $\frac{a}{b}$ $(b \neq 0)$.

To compare two measures, you may use a ratio. To solve some types of problems, you may need to use two ratios to form a proportion.

Definitions:
proportion
extremes
means

> A *proportion* is an equation of the form $\frac{a}{b} = \frac{c}{d}$ $(b \neq 0, d \neq 0)$; a and d are the *extremes* of the proportion; b and c are the *means* of the proportion.

The example below shows you how to write a true proportion and how to find its solution.

Example 1

The numbers 2 and x have the ratio 6 to 9. Write a proportion that states this. Identify the means and the extremes. Solve the proportion for x.

$$\frac{2}{x} = \frac{6}{9} \qquad \begin{array}{l} \text{The means are } x \text{ and } 6. \\ \text{The extremes are 2 and 9.} \end{array}$$

$$(9x)\left(\frac{2}{x}\right) = (9x)\left(\frac{6}{9}\right) \quad \blacktriangleleft \quad \textit{Multiply by the LCD, 9x.}$$

$$18 = 6x$$
$$x = 3$$

Thus, the solution is 3.

In a true proportion, the product of the extremes equals the product of the means. If $\frac{a}{b} = \frac{c}{d}$ ($b \neq 0$, $d \neq 0$), then $ad = bc$.

You will be asked to prove this property of proportions in Exercise 61.

Example 2 Which is a true proportion?

$$\frac{3}{7} = \frac{9}{21} \qquad\qquad\qquad \frac{5}{7} = \frac{7}{9}$$

$3 \times 21 = 7 \times 9$ ◄ *Use the proportion property* ► $5 \times 9 \neq 7 \times 7$
$63 = 63$ $\qquad\qquad\qquad\qquad\qquad\qquad\qquad\qquad 45 \neq 49$

Thus, $\frac{3}{7} = \frac{9}{21}$ is a true proportion; $\frac{5}{7} = \frac{7}{9}$ is not a true proportion.

Example 3 Solve the proportion $\frac{2}{3} = \frac{x}{12}$ for x.

The product of the extremes equals ► $24 = 3x$
the product of the means. $\qquad\qquad\qquad x = 8$

Thus, the solution is 8.

The converse of the Proportion Property is also true: If $ad = bc$, then $\frac{a}{b} = \frac{c}{d}$ ($b \neq 0$, $d \neq 0$). You can also show that $\frac{a}{c} = \frac{b}{d}$, $\frac{b}{a} = \frac{d}{c}$, and $\frac{c}{a} = \frac{d}{b}$.

Example 4 If $4x = 5y$, write three different proportions.

Arrange the numbers so that the property of proportions is true. ► $\frac{4}{5} = \frac{y}{x}$, $\frac{5}{4} = \frac{x}{y}$, $\frac{x}{5} = \frac{y}{4}$

In the proportion $\frac{3}{m} = \frac{m}{12}$, both means are represented by the variable m.

You can solve for m. $\qquad \frac{3}{m} = \frac{m}{12}$
$\qquad\qquad\qquad\qquad\qquad 36 = m^2$
$\qquad\qquad\qquad\qquad m = 6$ or $m = -6$

The number 6 is called the **geometric mean** of 3 and 12.

The positive number m is the *geometric mean* of two positive numbers a and b if $\frac{a}{m} = \frac{m}{b}$.

To find the geometric mean of two numbers, you must set up the proportion and then solve for the mean.

Example 5 Find the geometric mean of 2 and 7.

$$\frac{2}{m} = \frac{m}{7}$$
$$14 = m^2$$
$$m = \sqrt{14} \text{ or } m = -\sqrt{14}$$

Thus, the geometric mean of 2 and 7 is $\sqrt{14}$.

You can write and solve proportions involving geometric properties.

Example 6 The measures of two complementary angles have the ratio 1 to 5. What is the measure of each angle?

Let $x =$ measure of one angle
$90 - x =$ measure of its complement
$$\frac{x}{90 - x} = \frac{1}{5}$$
$$5x = 1(90 - x)$$
$$5x = 90 - x$$
$$6x = 90$$
$$x = 15$$
$$90 - x = 75$$

Thus, the measures are 15° and 75°.

Oral Exercises

Which of the following are ratios?

1. $\frac{3}{5}$

2. $4x$

3. $2 + 7$

4. $\frac{p}{q}$

5. $x = 7$

6. $\frac{y}{5}$

7. mn

8. $\frac{2c}{d}$

Which of the following are proportions? For each proportion, identify the means and the extremes.

9. $\frac{3}{5}$

10. $\frac{x}{6} = \frac{2}{3}$

11. $\frac{2}{9} + \frac{3}{18}$

12. $\frac{5x}{7y}$

13. $\frac{x}{9} - \frac{3}{12}$

14. $\frac{a}{b} = \frac{m}{n}$

15. $\frac{2}{5} = \frac{x}{10} + \frac{y}{5}$

16. $\frac{3}{m} = \frac{m}{12}$

True or false?

17. A proportion is the sum of two ratios.

18. The ratio 5 to 8 is the same as the ratio 8 to 5.

Written Exercises _____

Which of the following are true proportions?

(A) 1. $\dfrac{3}{4} = \dfrac{9}{12}$

2. $\dfrac{5}{6} = \dfrac{3}{4}$

3. $\dfrac{2}{3} = \dfrac{10}{15}$

4. $\dfrac{6}{8} = \dfrac{39}{52}$

5. $\dfrac{1}{2} = \dfrac{1+3}{2+3}$

6. $\dfrac{3}{4} = \dfrac{4}{3+4}$

7. $\dfrac{5}{6} = \dfrac{4 \cdot 5}{4 \cdot 6}$

8. $\dfrac{3}{4} = \dfrac{3+3}{4+3}$

Identify the means and the extremes of each proportion. Solve for x.

9. $\dfrac{2}{3} = \dfrac{10}{x}$

10. $\dfrac{4}{6} = \dfrac{x}{15}$

11. $\dfrac{x}{9} = \dfrac{4}{12}$

12. $\dfrac{6}{x} = \dfrac{10}{15}$

13. $\dfrac{12}{8} = \dfrac{9}{x}$

14. $\dfrac{3}{5} = \dfrac{7}{x}$

15. $\dfrac{4}{9} = \dfrac{6}{x}$

16. $\dfrac{x}{3} = \dfrac{7}{12}$

Write three different proportions for each equation.

17. $3 \cdot 4 = 2 \cdot 6$

18. $5 \cdot 9 = 3 \cdot 15$

19. $2 \cdot 8 = 4 \cdot 4$

20. $6 \cdot 6 = 4 \cdot 9$

21. $5x = 10 \cdot 3$

22. $4n = 7m$

23. $3x = yz$

24. $ab = cd$

Find the geometric mean of each pair of numbers.

25. 1 and 4

26. 9 and 16

27. 5 and 20

28. 3 and 12

29. 3 and 7

30. 5 and 4

31. 7 and 11

32. x and y

Which of the following are true proportions for all replacements of the variables?

(B) 33. $\dfrac{am}{bn} = \dfrac{ar}{bg}$

34. $\dfrac{ab}{ad} = \dfrac{cd}{cb}$

35. $\dfrac{ab}{ac} = \dfrac{bd}{cd}$

36. $\dfrac{a+b}{c+b} = \dfrac{a-b}{c-b}$

Find the ratio of x to y for each of the following.

37. $7x = 9y$

38. $13x = 12y$

39. $5y = 7x$

40. $4y = 6x$

41. $14x = 21y$

42. $35y = 25x$

43. $ax = by$

44. $y = cx$

Use proportions to solve each of the following problems.

45. The measures of two complementary angles have the ratio 2 to 3. What is the measure of each angle?

46. The measures of two supplementary angles have the ratio 4 to 5. What is the measure of each angle?

47. The sum of the lengths of two segments is 242. The ratio of the lengths is 5 to 6. What is the length of each segment?

48. The difference between the lengths of two segments is 6. The ratio of the lengths is 3 to 5. What is the length of each segment?

49. The length and the width of a rectangle have the ratio 3 to 2 The perimeter is 20 cm. Find the length and the width.

50. The length and the width of a rectangle have the ratio 5 to 3. The perimeter is 48 m. Find the length and the width.

(C) 51. The length and the width of a rectangle have the ratio 5 to 6. Their product is 120. Find the length and the width.

52. The length and the width of a rectangle have the ratio 3 to 2. Their product is 54. Find the length and the width.

USING PROPORTIONS

True or false? If true, give a proof using algebraic properties. If false, give a numerical counterexample. (Assume each denominator $\neq 0$.)

Example If $\dfrac{a}{b} = \dfrac{c}{d}$, then $\dfrac{d}{c} = \dfrac{b}{a}$.

$$\text{True:} \qquad \frac{a}{b} = \frac{c}{d} \qquad\qquad \text{Given}$$

$$(bd)\left(\frac{a}{b}\right) = (bd)\left(\frac{c}{d}\right) \qquad \text{Mult. prop. of equality}$$

$$ad = bc$$

$$\frac{ad}{ac} = \frac{bc}{ac} \qquad\qquad \text{Div. prop. of equality}$$

$$\frac{d}{c} = \frac{b}{a}$$

53. If $\dfrac{a}{b} = \dfrac{c}{d}$, then $\dfrac{a}{c} = \dfrac{b}{d}$.

54. If $\dfrac{a}{b} = \dfrac{c}{d}$, then $\dfrac{a+n}{b+n} = \dfrac{c}{d}$.

55. If $\dfrac{a}{b} = \dfrac{c}{d}$, then $\dfrac{a+b}{b} = \dfrac{c+d}{d}$.

56. If $\dfrac{a}{b} = \dfrac{c}{d}$, then $\dfrac{a-b}{b} = \dfrac{c-d}{d}$.

57. If $\dfrac{a}{b} = \dfrac{c}{d}$, then $\dfrac{a}{a+b} = \dfrac{c}{c+d}$.

58. If $\dfrac{a}{b} = \dfrac{c}{d}$, then $\dfrac{a+b}{c+d} = \dfrac{a+d}{c+b}$.

59. If $\dfrac{a}{b} = \dfrac{c}{d}$, then $\dfrac{an}{bn} = \dfrac{cm}{dm}$.

60. If $\dfrac{a}{b} = \dfrac{c}{d}$, then $\dfrac{a^n}{b^n} = \dfrac{c^n}{d^n}$.

61. Prove: If $\dfrac{a}{b} = \dfrac{c}{d}$, and $b \neq 0$, $d \neq 0$, then $ad = bc$.

62. Prove: If $ad = bc$, and $b \neq 0$, $d \neq 0$, then $\dfrac{a}{b} = \dfrac{c}{d}$.

CALCULATOR ACTIVITIES

A calculator can help you to solve proportions.

For example, in $\dfrac{24}{42} = \dfrac{37}{x}$, $x = \dfrac{42 \cdot 37}{24}$. You can now proceed as shown.

Press $\quad 42 \otimes 37 \ominus$
Display 1554
Press $\quad \oslash 24 \ominus$
Display 64.75

Thus, $x = 64.8$ to the nearest tenth.

Find x to the nearest tenth.

1. $\dfrac{46}{59} = \dfrac{28}{x}$

2. $\dfrac{37}{89} = \dfrac{x}{52}$

3. $\dfrac{x}{123} = \dfrac{57}{65}$

4. $\dfrac{59}{x} = \dfrac{129}{107}$

9.2 Similar Polygons

To identify similar polygons
To find the measures of sides and angles of similar polygons

Congruent polygons have the same size and shape, quadrilateral $ABCD$ is congruent to quadrilateral $EFGH$.

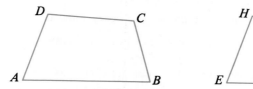

Similar polygons have the same shape, but not necessarily the same size.

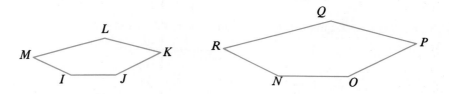

Polygon $IJKLM$ is similar to polygon $NOPQR$.

Definition:
similar polygons

> Two polygons are *similar* if corresponding angles are congruent and the lengths of corresponding sides are proportional.

If Polygon $IJKLM$ is similar to Polygon $NOPQR$, then you will write $IJKLM \sim NOPQR$. The symbol $\sim$ means *is similar to*. In this case, $\angle I \cong \angle N$, $\angle J \cong \angle O$, $\angle K \cong \angle P$, $\angle L \cong \angle Q$, and $\angle M \cong \angle R$.

Also $\dfrac{IJ}{NO} = \dfrac{JK}{OP} = \dfrac{KL}{PQ} = \dfrac{LM}{QR} = \dfrac{MI}{RN}$. If the lengths of corresponding sides are proportional, you may simply say that the sides are proportional.

Example 1 For Similar Triangles ABC and DEF, which angles are congruent? Which sides are proportional?

$\angle A \cong \angle D$, $\angle B \cong \angle E$, $\angle C \cong \angle F$ ◀ *Corresponding $\angle$'s are $\cong$.*

$\dfrac{AB}{DE} = \dfrac{BC}{EF} = \dfrac{CA}{FD}$. ◀ *Corresponding sides are proportional.*

To determine if two polygons are similar, you must check both the corresponding angles and the corresponding sides.

Example 2 Is Square *ABCD* similar to Rectangle *EFGH*? Why or why not?

 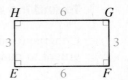

All corresponding angles are congruent. They are right angles.

All corresponding sides are not proportional. $\frac{4}{6} \neq \frac{4}{3}$.

Thus, square *ABCD* $\not\sim$ rect. *EFGH*.   ◄ $\not\sim$ *means is not similar to.*

Using the property of proportions, you can find the lengths of sides of similar polygons.

Example 3 Quad, *QRST* ~ Quad. *UVWX*. Find the unknown lengths.

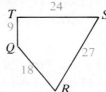

$$\frac{QR}{UV} = \frac{18}{12} \text{ or } \frac{3}{2} \qquad \frac{27}{p} = \frac{3}{2} \qquad \frac{24}{n} = \frac{3}{2} \qquad \frac{9}{m} = \frac{3}{2}$$
$$3p = 54 \qquad 3n = 48 \qquad 3m = 18$$
$$p = 18 \qquad n = 16 \qquad m = 6$$

Thus, *VW* = 18, *WX* = 16, and *XU* = 6.

Written Exercises

Are the pairs of polygons similar? Why or why not?

△ **1.**

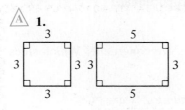

2.

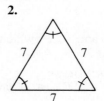

3.

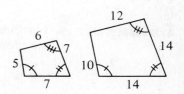

Which angles are congruent? Which sides are proportional?

4. △*XYZ* ~ △*MNO*   **5.** rect. *ABCD* ~ rect. *EFGH*   **6.** *VWXYZ* ~ *ABCDE*

Find the unknown lengths in each of the following.

7. △ABC ~ △DEF

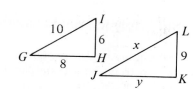

8. △GHI ~ △JKL

9. Quad. *MNOP* ~ Quad. *QRST*

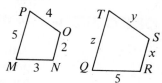

Ⓑ 10. ▱RSTU ~ ▱PONM

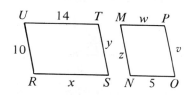

11. Quad. *ABCD* ~ quad. *EFGH*

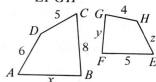

12. *DEFGH* ~ *IJKLM*

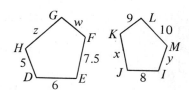

13. Given: trap. *ABCD* ~ trap. *LMNO*, *AB* = 4, *BC* = 6, *CD* = 4, *DA* = 2, *LM* = 2. Find *NO* and *OL*.

14. Given: ▱*RSTU* ~ ▱*HJKL*, *RS* = 12, *UR* = 8, *JK* = 6. Find *HJ* and *KL*.

15. Given: rhombus *ABCD* ~ rhombus *EFGH*, *AB* = 8, *FG* = 12. Find *BC* and *GH*.

16. Given: Quad. *ABCD* ~ Quad. *EFGH*, m ∠*A* = 47, m ∠*B* = 39, m ∠*C* = 112. Find m ∠*F* and m ∠*H*.

17. Given: Pent. *QRSTU* ~ Pent. *VWXYZ*, m ∠*Q* = 68, m ∠*R* = 110, m ∠*S* = 91, m ∠*T* = 94. Find m ∠*X*, m ∠*V*, and m ∠*Z*.

18. Given: ▱*EFGH* ~ ▱*IJKL*, m ∠*E* = 70. Find m ∠*J* and m ∠*L*.

Ⓒ 19. If two polygons are similar, are they necessarily congruent? Why?

20. If two polygons are congruent, are they necessarily similar? Why?

21. Prove: All squares are similar.

CALCULATOR ACTIVITIES

For the similar △'s, find the indicated length.

1. *a* = 7.2, *b* = 5.8, *e* = 6.9. Find *d*.
2. *b* = 9.36, *e* = 12.47, *f* = 16.59. Find *c*.
3. *d* = 17.32, *f* = 19.56, *c* = 14.92. Find *a*.
4. *e* = 4.536, *f* = 6.738, *c* = 4.291. Find *b*.

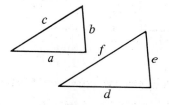

9.3 Angle-Angle Similarity

OBJECTIVE ► **To recognize and apply the angle-angle similarity pattern**

Although all corresponding angles are congruent and all corresponding sides are proportional when two triangles are similar, there are simpler patterns that can be used to prove triangles similar. If you are given $\triangle ABC$, you can construct $\triangle DEF$ so that $\angle D \cong \angle A$ and $\angle E \cong \angle B$.

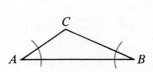 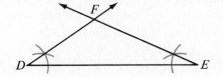

It appears that $\triangle ABC \sim \triangle DEF$. This leads to the following postulate.

┌ **Postulate 22** AA for $\sim \triangle$'s If two angles of a triangle are congru- ┐
ent to two angles of a second triangle, then the two tri-
angles are similar.

You can use this postulate in problems that involve similar triangles.

Example 1 Are the triangles similar? Give a reason for your answer.

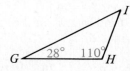 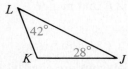

m $\angle I = 180 - (28 + 110) = 180 - 138$ or 42, $\angle G \cong \angle J$, $\angle I \cong \angle L$

Thus, $\triangle GHI \sim \triangle JKL$ by AA for $\sim \triangle$'s.

Example 2 Given: $\overline{PQ} \parallel \overline{MN}$
Prove: $\triangle MNO \sim \triangle PQO$

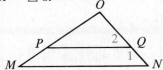

Proof

Statements	Reasons
1. $\overline{PQ} \parallel \overline{MN}$	1. Given
2. $\angle 1 \cong \angle 2$	2. Corr. $\angle$'s of $\parallel$ lines are $\cong$.
3. $\angle O \cong \angle O$	3. Reflexive property
4. $\therefore \triangle MNO \sim \triangle PQO$	4. AA for $\sim \triangle$'s

You can find unknown lengths using the proportions that exist between the sides of similar triangles. You can also use similar triangles to prove that lengths of segments are proportional.

Example 3 Given: $\overline{AB} \perp \overline{BC}$, $\overline{DE} \perp \overline{BC}$
Find AD.

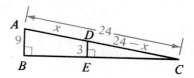

$\angle C \cong \angle C$
$\angle B \cong \angle DEC$ ◄ $\perp$'s form $\cong$ rt. $\angle$'s.
$\triangle ABC \sim \triangle DEC$
$\dfrac{9}{3} = \dfrac{24}{24-x}$ ◄ *Corresponding sides of $\sim \triangle$'s are proportional.*
$9(24 - x) = 24 \cdot 3$
$216 - 9x = 72$
$-9x = -144$
$x = 16$ **Thus, $AD = 16$.**

Example 4 Given: $\overline{DE} \parallel \overline{AB}$
Prove: $\dfrac{AC}{DC} = \dfrac{BC}{EC}$

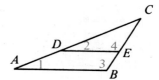

Proof

Statements	Reasons
1. $\overline{DE} \parallel \overline{AB}$	1. Given
2. $\angle 1 \cong \angle 2$, $\angle 3 \cong \angle 4$	2. Corr. $\angle$'s of $\parallel$ lines are $\cong$.
3. $\triangle ABC \sim \triangle DEC$	3. AA for $\sim \triangle$'s
4. $\therefore \dfrac{AC}{DC} = \dfrac{BC}{EC}$	4. Corr. sides of $\sim \triangle$'s are proportional.

Reading in Geometry

Without looking up these words in your book or in a dictionary, indicate which is the correct spelling for each word.

1.	simalar	similur	similar	similiar	similer
2.	proportionul	perportional	preportional	proportional	proportionial
3.	congruent	congruant	congerant	congruunt	congrunt
4.	extreems	extrimes	exterms	extrims	extremes
5.	ratuo	ratio	rasho	rashio	rashuo
6.	altutude	altitude	altatude	altitud	altatood
7.	quaderlateral	quadrulateral	quadralateral	quadriliaterial	quadrilateral
8.	paralel	paruhlel	paralell	parallel	parillel

ANGLE-ANGLE SIMILARITY

Written Exercises _____

Are the triangles similar? Give a reason for your answer. (Ex. 1-6)

 1.

2.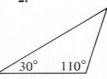

3.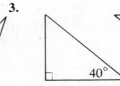

4.

5.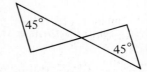

6.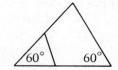

7. Given: $\angle 1 \cong \angle 2$
Prove: $\triangle ABD \sim$
$\triangle CED$

8. Given: $\angle J \cong \angle G$
Prove: $\triangle HFG \sim$
$\triangle HIJ$

9. Given: $\overline{OK} \parallel \overline{MN}$
Prove: $\triangle OKL \sim$
$\triangle MNL$

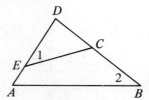

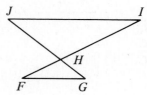

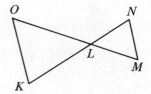

10. Given: $\overline{TQ} \perp \overline{PR}$, $\overline{SR} \perp$
$\overline{PR}$, $TQ = 4$, $SR = 6$,
$PS = 15$
Find PT.

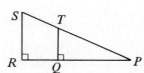

11. Given: $\overline{TQ} \perp \overline{PR}$, $\overline{SR} \perp$
$\overline{PR}$, $PQ = 9$, $QR = 6$,
$TQ = 6$
Find SR.

Based on the information given in each case, is $\triangle ABC \sim \triangle DEF$? (Ex. 12-13)

12. m $\angle A = 47$, m $\angle B = 85$,
m $\angle C = x + 4$, m $\angle E =$
$2x - 1$, m $\angle F = x + 5$

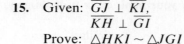

13. m $\angle A = 55$, m $\angle C = 75$,
m $\angle D = 2x + 3$, m $\angle F =$
$3x - 1$, m $\angle E = x + 22$

14. Given: $\overline{CF} \perp \overline{AB}$,
$\overline{BD} \perp \overline{AC}$
Prove: $\triangle FBE \sim \triangle DCE$

15. Given: $\overline{GJ} \perp \overline{KI}$,
$\overline{KH} \perp \overline{GI}$
Prove: $\triangle HKI \sim \triangle JGI$

16. Given: $\overline{MN} \parallel \overline{PO}$
Prove: $\triangle MNQ \sim \triangle OPQ$

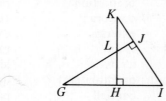

17. Given: $\square RSTU$
Prove: $\triangle RSV \sim \triangle WTV$

18. Given: $\overline{CA} \perp \overline{AB}, \overline{DE} \perp \overline{AB}$
Prove: $\dfrac{CB}{DB} = \dfrac{AB}{EB}$

19. Given: $\overline{ML} \parallel \overline{JK}$
Prove: $\dfrac{MN}{NK} = \dfrac{LN}{NJ}$

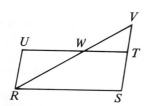
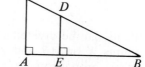
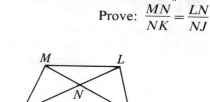

True or false? (Ex. 20–23)

20. All equiangular triangles are similar.

21. All isosceles triangles are similar.

22. An obtuse triangle cannot be similar to an acute triangle.

23. All isosceles triangles with à 40° angle angle are similar.

24. Given: $\overline{CM} \perp \overline{TX}$,
$\overline{PQ} \perp \overline{TN}, \overline{JL} \perp \overline{XN}$
Prove: $\triangle JCP \sim \triangle XTN$

25. Given: $\overline{WZ} \cong \overline{XY}$,
$\overline{WX} \cong \overline{ZY}$
Prove: $\triangle WTZ \sim \triangle VWX$

26. Given: $\angle 1 \cong \angle 2$
Prove: $\dfrac{SQ}{TS} = \dfrac{PQ}{PR}$

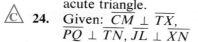
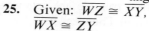
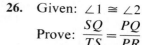

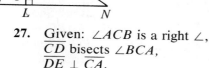

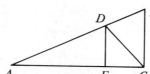
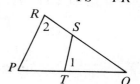

27. Given: $\angle ACB$ is a right $\angle$,
$\overline{CD}$ bisects $\angle BCA$,
$\overline{DE} \perp \overline{CA}$.
Prove: $\dfrac{AD}{AB} = \dfrac{CE}{BC}$

28. Given: $\overline{BC} \perp \overline{AC}$,
$\overline{DE} \perp \overline{AC}$,
$\angle EDC \cong \angle DCE$.
Prove: $\dfrac{1}{BC} + \dfrac{1}{AC} = \dfrac{1}{DE}$

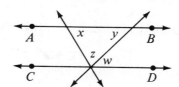

Cumulative Review

1. Given: $\overleftrightarrow{AB} \parallel \overleftrightarrow{CD}$,
m $\angle x = 70$, m $\angle w = 40$.
Find m $\angle z$.

2. Given: $\overleftrightarrow{AB} \parallel \overleftrightarrow{CD}$,
m $\angle x = 2r + 23$,
m $\angle z = 6r + 14$,
m $\angle y = 12r - 17$
Find m $\angle W$.

A Challenge To You

Copy the three sets of dots on your paper. For each set, how many different sizes of squares can be drawn by connecting four dots? One example is shown for each set of dots.

ANGLE-ANGLE SIMILARITY

9.4 Proportionality in Triangles

OBJECTIVE ► **To write and solve proportions when a line is parallel to a side of a triangle**

Two different segments can be divided so that the lengths of the resulting parts are proportional. Points X on $\overline{AB}$ and Y on $\overline{CD}$ divide the segments proportionally, since $\frac{2}{4} = \frac{3}{6}$. In general, if $\frac{AX}{XB} = \frac{CY}{YD}$, then $\overline{AB}$ and $\overline{CD}$ are divided proportionally.

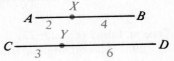

Since the sides of a triangle are segments, you can divide them proportionally. One way is shown in Theorem 9.1.

Theorem 9.1 If a line is parallel to one side of a triangle and intersects the other two sides, then it divides the two sides proportionally.

Given: $\triangle ABC$, $\overleftrightarrow{DE} \parallel \overline{AB}$

Prove: $\dfrac{AD}{DC} = \dfrac{BE}{EC}$

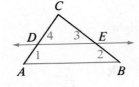

Analysis: Show that $\triangle ABC \sim \triangle DEC$. Then use properties of algebra.

Proof

Statements	Reasons
1. $\triangle ABC, \overleftrightarrow{DE} \parallel \overline{AB}$	1. Given
2. $\angle 1 \cong \angle 4, \angle 2 \cong \angle 3$	2. Corr. $\angle$'s of $\parallel$ lines are $\cong$.
3. $\triangle ABC \sim \triangle DEC$	3. AA for $\sim \triangle$'s
4. $\dfrac{AC}{DC} = \dfrac{BC}{EC}$	4. Def. of $\sim \triangle$'s
5. $\dfrac{AC}{DC} - 1 = \dfrac{BC}{EC} - 1$	5. Subtraction property
6. $\dfrac{DC}{DC} = 1, \dfrac{EC}{EC} = 1$	6. Algebraic fact $\left(\dfrac{a}{a} = 1, a \neq 0\right)$
7. $\dfrac{AC}{DC} - \dfrac{DC}{DC} = \dfrac{BC}{EC} - \dfrac{EC}{EC}$	7. Substitution property
8. $\dfrac{AC - DC}{DC} = \dfrac{BC - EC}{EC}$	8. Algebraic fact $\left(\dfrac{a}{b} - \dfrac{c}{b} = \dfrac{a-c}{b}, \ b \neq 0\right)$
9. $AC - DC = AD, BC - EC = BE$	9. Def. of between; subtraction prop.
10. $\therefore \dfrac{AD}{DC} = \dfrac{BE}{EC}$	10. Substitution property

Using the definition of similar triangles or Theorem 9.1, you can show that the following proportions are true: if $\overleftrightarrow{DE} \parallel \overline{AB}$ in $\triangle ABC$ $\dfrac{AD}{DC} = \dfrac{BE}{EC}$, $\dfrac{DC}{AC} = \dfrac{EC}{BC}$, and $\dfrac{AD}{AC} = \dfrac{BE}{BC}$. You may use these triangle proportionality properties as reasons in proofs or in finding lengths.

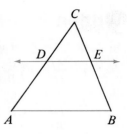

Example 1 Given: $\overline{UV} \parallel \overline{RS}$, $UR = 6$, $TV = 5$, and $VS = 10$
Find TU.

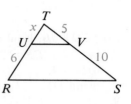

$$\dfrac{x}{6} = \dfrac{5}{10} \quad \blacktriangleleft \quad \dfrac{TU}{UR} = \dfrac{TV}{VS}$$

$$10x = 30$$
$$x = 3$$
Thus, $TU = 3$.

Example 2 Given: $\overline{JK} \parallel \overline{GH}$, $IG = 12$, $IK = 6$, and $KH = 9$
Find IJ and JG.

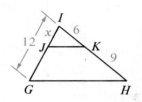

$$\dfrac{x}{12} = \dfrac{6}{15} \quad \blacktriangleleft \quad \dfrac{IJ}{IG} = \dfrac{IK}{IH}, \ IH = 6 + 9$$

$$15x = 72$$

$$x = 4\dfrac{12}{15} \text{ or } 4\dfrac{4}{5}$$

Thus, $IJ = 4\dfrac{4}{5}$, $JG = 12 - 4\dfrac{4}{5}$ or $7\dfrac{1}{5}$.

You can prove the converse of Theorem 9.1, using properties of similar triangles.

┌ **Theorem 9.2** If a line divides two sides of a triangle proportionally, ┐
└ then it is parallel to the third side of the triangle. ┘

Oral Exercises

In $\triangle PQR$, $\overline{ST} \parallel \overline{PQ}$. Complete each proportion.

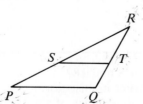

1. $\dfrac{RS}{SP} = \dfrac{RT}{?}$

2. $\dfrac{RP}{SP} = \dfrac{RQ}{?}$

3. $\dfrac{TQ}{RQ} = \dfrac{?}{RP}$

4. $\dfrac{QT}{TR} = \dfrac{?}{SR}$

5. $\dfrac{RP}{RS} = \dfrac{RQ}{?}$

6. $\dfrac{RQ}{TQ} = \dfrac{RP}{?}$

Written Exercises

In $\triangle ABC$, $\overline{DE} \parallel \overline{CB}$ which of the following proportions are always true?

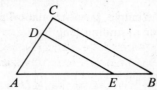

Ⓐ 1. $\dfrac{AD}{DC} = \dfrac{AE}{EB}$ 2. $\dfrac{AD}{DC} = \dfrac{DE}{CB}$

3. $\dfrac{AD}{DE} = \dfrac{AC}{CB}$ 4. $\dfrac{AD}{AC} = \dfrac{AE}{AB}$

5. $\dfrac{BE}{EA} = \dfrac{AD}{DC}$ 6. $\dfrac{AD}{DC} = \dfrac{AB}{AE}$

In $\triangle ABE$, $\overleftrightarrow{CD} \parallel \overline{AB}$. Find each indicated length. (Ex. 7−16)

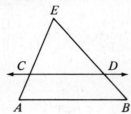

7. $AC = 3$, $CE = 2$, $BD = 4$. Find DE.

8. $AE = 6$, $CE = 4$, $BE = 9$ Find BD.

9. $AC = 4$, $CE = 7$, $BD = 5$ Find DE.

10. $EA = 9$, $EC = 5$, $ED = 12$ Find EB.

11. $EB = 10$, $ED = 4$, $EA = 14$ Find EC.

12. $AC = 12$, $AE = 20$, $ED = 10$ Find BD.

13. $AC = 9$, $AE = 13$, $DE = 8$ Find BE.

14. $AE = 16$, $EB = 12$, $DB = 9$ Find EC.

15. $EC = 4$, $CA = 8$, $EB = 18$ Find DB.

16. $ED = 5$, $DB = 3$, $AE = 10$ Find AC and CE.

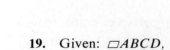

Ⓑ 17. Given: $\angle 1 \cong \angle 2$
Prove: $\dfrac{BD}{DC} = \dfrac{BE}{EA}$

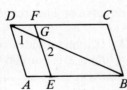

18. Given: $\overline{CA} \perp \overline{AB}$, $\overline{DE} \perp \overline{AB}$
Prove: $\dfrac{AE}{EB} = \dfrac{CD}{DB}$

Ⓒ 19. Given: $\square ABCD$, $\overline{EF} \parallel \overline{DA}$
Prove: $\dfrac{AE}{EB} = \dfrac{DF}{FC}$

20. Given: $\square ABCD$, $\angle 1 \cong \angle 2$
Prove: $\dfrac{DC}{DF} = \dfrac{AB}{AE}$

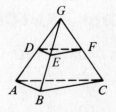

21. Prove: If three parallel lines intersect two transversals, then the segments determined are proportional.

22. Given: $\overline{AB} \parallel \overline{DE}$, $\overline{BC} \parallel \overline{EF}$
Prove: $\triangle DFG \sim \triangle ACG$

Cumulative Review

1. What is the geometric mean of 8 and 18?
2. Draw an obtuse angle. Construct its bisector.
3. What is true about corresponding angles of similar polygons? about corresponding sides?

9.5 SAS and SSS Similarity

OBJECTIVE ►

To recognize and apply the SAS and SSS similarity patterns

In addition to the angle-angle pattern, you can prove two other methods for show-ing that triangles are similar. One of these methods involves two pairs of corre-sponding sides and the angles included by these sides.

$\triangle DEF$ below was constructed so that $\angle D \cong \angle A$ and $\dfrac{DE}{AB} = \dfrac{DF}{AC} = \dfrac{3}{2}$.

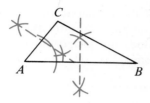 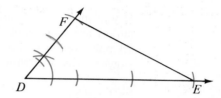

If you measure the other parts of the triangles, you will find that $\angle F \cong \angle C$, $\angle E \cong \angle B$, and $\dfrac{FE}{CB} = \dfrac{3}{2}$. Since all pairs of corresponding angles are congruent and all pairs of corresponding sides are proportional, then $\triangle DEF \sim \triangle ABC$. This suggests the following theorem.

┌ **Theorem 9.3**   SAS for $\sim \triangle$'s   If an angle of one triangle is congruent ┐
to an angle of another triangle and the corresponding
sides that include these angles are proportional, then
the triangles are similar. (See Exercise 36.)

Given: $\angle Z \cong \angle V, \dfrac{ZX}{VT} = \dfrac{YZ}{UV}$

Prove: $\triangle XYZ \sim \triangle TUV$

 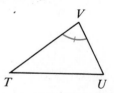

Example 1   Are the two triangles similar?

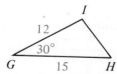 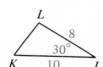

$\dfrac{GI}{JL} = \dfrac{12}{8}$ $\dfrac{GH}{JK} = \dfrac{15}{10}$ ◄   *Two pairs of corresponding sides are proportional.*

$\dfrac{12}{8} = \dfrac{15}{10}$

$m \angle G = 30$ $m \angle J = 30$ ◄   *The included $\angle$'s are $\cong$.*

     Thus, $\triangle GHI \sim \triangle JKL$, by SAS for $\sim \triangle$'s.

Another method of proving triangles similar involves the ratios of the lengths of corresponding sides of the triangles, $\triangle RST$ below was constructed so that each side is twice as long as the corresponding side of $\triangle XYZ$.

$$\frac{ST}{YZ} = \frac{RS}{XY} = \frac{RT}{XZ} = \frac{2}{1}$$

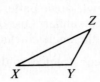
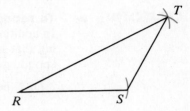

If you measure the angles of the triangles, you will find that the corresponding angles are congruent. Since all pairs of corresponding angles are congruent and all pairs of corresponding sides are proportional, then $\triangle XYZ \sim \triangle RST$. This suggests the following theorem.

Theorem 9.4   SSS for $\sim$ $\triangle$'s   If the corresponding sides of two triangles are proportional, then the triangles are similar. (See Exercise 37.)

Given: $\dfrac{AB}{DE} = \dfrac{BC}{EF} = \dfrac{CA}{FD}$

Prove: $\triangle ABC \sim \triangle DEF$

Example 2 Are the two given triangles similar?

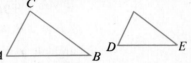

$$\frac{8}{12} = \frac{10}{15} = \frac{12}{18} \text{ or } \frac{QR}{TU} = \frac{PQ}{ST} = \frac{RP}{US} \quad \blacktriangleleft \quad \textit{Corresponding sides are proportional.}$$

Thus, $\triangle PQR \sim \triangle STU$ by SSS for $\sim$ $\triangle$'s.

You now have three methods for proving triangles similar.

Summary		AA for $\sim$ $\triangle$'s	SAS for $\sim$ $\triangle$'s	SSS for $\sim$ $\triangle$'s
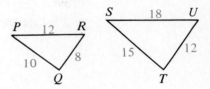		If $\angle A \cong \angle D$ and $\angle B \cong \angle E$, then $\triangle ABC \sim \triangle DEF$.	If $\angle A \cong \angle D$ and $\dfrac{AC}{DF} = \dfrac{AB}{DE}$, then $\triangle ABC \sim \triangle DEF$.	If $\dfrac{AB}{DE} = \dfrac{BC}{EF} = \dfrac{CA}{FD}$, then $\triangle ABC \sim \triangle DEF$.

       CHAPTER NINE

You will use either angle-angle, side-angle-side, or side-side-side in proofs that triangles are similar.

Example 3 Prove: All equilateral triangles are similar.

Given: Equilateral △'s *ABC* and *DEF*
Prove: △*ABC* ~ △*DEF*

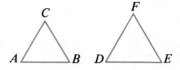

Proof

Statements	Reasons
1. △*ABC* and △*DEF* are equilateral	1. Given
2. $AB = BC = CA$ $DE = EF = FD$	2. Def. of equilat. △
3. $\dfrac{AB}{DE} = \dfrac{BC}{EF} = \dfrac{CA}{FD}$	3. Division prop. of equality; subst.
4. ∴ △*ABC* ~ △*DEF*	4. SSS for ~ △'s

Example 4 Given: $\dfrac{RT}{ST} = \dfrac{PT}{QT}$

Prove: $\dfrac{RT}{ST} = \dfrac{RP}{SQ}$

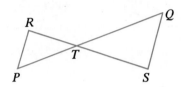

Proof

Statements	Reasons
1. $\dfrac{RT}{ST} = \dfrac{PT}{QT}$	1. Given
2. ∠*PTR* ≅ ∠*QTS*	2. Vertical ∠'s are ≅
3. △*PTR* ~ △*QTS*	3. SAS for ~ △'s
4. ∴ $\dfrac{RT}{ST} = \dfrac{RP}{SQ}$	4. Corr. sides of ~ △'s are proportional

Reading in Geometry

The statement, △*ABC* ~ △*DEF*, implies other statements. If △*ABC* ~ △*DEF*, which of the following statements must also be true?
1. The ratio of *AC* to *AB* is equal to the ratio of *DF* to *DE*.
2. Angle *C* is congruent to angle *E*.
3. Segment *CB* is congruent to segment *FE*.
4. If the measure of angle *A* is 80 degrees, then the measure of angle *D* is 80 degrees.
5. *DF* is to *FE* as *AC* is to *CB*.
6. Triangle *ABC* is congruent to triangle *DEF*.
7. If the ratio of *AC* to *DF* is 2 to 3, then the ratio of *AB* to *DE* is 2 to 3.
8. The ratio of the measure of angle *C* to the measure of angle *F* is 1 to 1.

Written Exercises

Are the triangles similar? Give a reason for your answer.

 1.

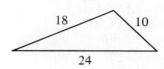

2.

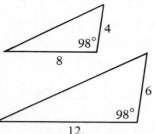

3.

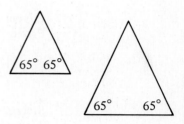

4.

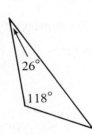

5.

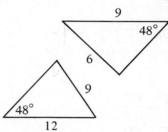

6.

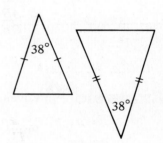

7.

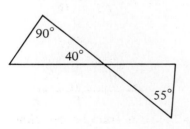

8.

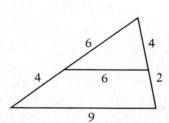

9.

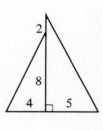

Which of the following are the lengths of sides of similar triangles?

10. 3, 4, 5 and 6, 8, 10

11. 9, 15, 18 and 6, 10, 12

12. $\frac{4}{5}, \frac{6}{5}, \frac{8}{5}$ and $\frac{2}{8}, \frac{3}{8}, \frac{4}{8}$

13. $\frac{3}{4}$, 1, $\frac{5}{4}$ and $\frac{4}{5}$, 1, $\frac{6}{5}$

14. 3.6, 12, 12.6 and 3, 10, 10.5

15. 3.5, 4.6, 5.7 and 2.1, 3.3, 4.6

In which of the following cases is $\triangle ABC \sim \triangle DEF$?

16. $\dfrac{AB}{DE} = \dfrac{BC}{EF} = \dfrac{CA}{FD}$

17. $\dfrac{AB}{BC} = \dfrac{DE}{EF}$, $\angle B \cong \angle E$

18. $\dfrac{AB}{DE} = \dfrac{BC}{EF}$, $\angle C \cong \angle F$

19. $\angle A \cong \angle D$, $\angle C \cong \angle E$

20. $\dfrac{BC}{EF} = \dfrac{AC}{DF}$, $\angle B \cong \angle D$

21. $\dfrac{AB}{BC} = \dfrac{BC}{DE} = \dfrac{DE}{EF}$

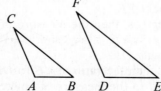

22. Given: $\triangle TZS \sim \triangle XTR$
    Prove: $\triangle TZS \sim \triangle XZY$

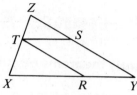

23. Given: $\square TSYR$
    Prove: $\triangle XRT \sim \triangle TSZ$

24. Given: $\overline{LR} \perp \overline{NM}$,
    $\overline{NP} \perp \overline{LM}$
    Prove: $\triangle LPQ \sim \triangle NRQ$

26. Given: Altitudes $\overline{LR}$ and
    $\overline{NP}$ of $\triangle LMN$
    Prove: $\triangle LMR \sim \triangle NMP$

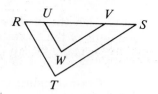

25. Given: $\overline{LR} \perp \overline{NM}$,
    $\overline{NP} \perp \overline{LM}$
    Prove: $\triangle NQR \sim \triangle NMP$

27. Given: $\overline{LR} \perp \overline{NM}$
    $\angle LNR \cong \angle LMR$
    Prove: $\triangle LNR \sim \triangle LMR$

B 28. Given: $\square ABCD$
    Prove: $\triangle BCE \sim \triangle FAB$

29. Given: $\overline{RT} \parallel \overline{UW}$,
    $\overline{TS} \parallel \overline{WV}$
    Prove: $\triangle RST \sim \triangle UVW$

30. Given: $\overline{AD} \cong \overline{DB}$,
    $\overline{BE} \cong \overline{EC}$
    Prove: $\triangle ABC \sim \triangle DBE$

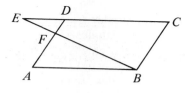

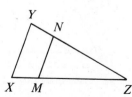

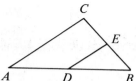

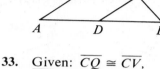

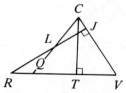

31. Given: $\triangle RVT \cong \triangle SUT$
    Prove: $\dfrac{TU}{TR} = \dfrac{TV}{TS}$

32. Given: $\dfrac{XZ}{MZ} = \dfrac{YZ}{NZ}$
    Prove: $\dfrac{XZ}{MZ} = \dfrac{XY}{MN}$

33. Given: $\overline{CQ} \cong \overline{CV}$,
    $\overline{CT} \perp \overline{RV}, \overline{RJ} \perp \overline{CV}$
    Prove: $\dfrac{CQ}{RV} = \dfrac{QT}{JV}$

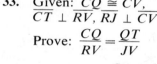

34. Prove: Any two isosceles right triangles are similar.

35. Prove: Two isosceles triangles are similar if an angle of one is congruent to the corresponding angle of the other.

C 36. Prove Theorem 9.3. Use the following pictures and analysis.
    Given: $\angle Z \cong \angle V$
    $\dfrac{ZX}{VT} = \dfrac{YZ}{UV}$
    Prove: $\triangle XYZ \sim \triangle TUV$

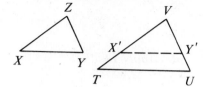

    Analysis: Construct $\triangle X'Y'V$ so that $\overline{VX'} \cong \overline{ZX}$, and $\overline{VY'} \cong \overline{ZY}$. Show $\triangle XYZ \sim \triangle TUV$ by AA.

37. Prove Theorem 9.4.

For each of the following, draw pictures. Which triangles are similar? Which triangles are congruent? State and prove appropriate theorems.

38. Connect the midpoints of the sides of a triangle.

39. Form a triangle from the perpendiculars to the sides of a triangle.

SAS AND SSS SIMILARITY

9.6 Other Proportional Segments

OBJECTIVE ▶ **To prove and apply theorems about proportional segments in triangles**

There are special segments related to a triangle. Three that you have already studied are the medians, the angle bisectors, and the altitudes.

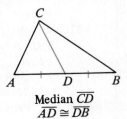

Median $\overline{CD}$
$\overline{AD} \cong \overline{DB}$

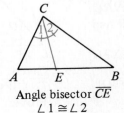

Angle bisector $\overline{CE}$
$\angle 1 \cong \angle 2$

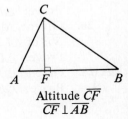

Altitude $\overline{CF}$
$\overline{CF} \perp \overline{AB}$

You can prove that the lengths of these segments within similar triangles are proportional to the lengths of the corresponding sides of the triangles.

Theorem 9.5 Corresponding medians of similar triangles are proportional to corresponding sides. (See Exercise 16.)

Given: $\triangle ABC \sim \triangle EFG$; $\overline{CD}$ is a median to $\overline{AB}$; $\overline{GH}$ is a median to $\overline{EF}$.

Prove: $\dfrac{CD}{GH} = \dfrac{CB}{GF}$

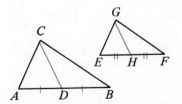

Analysis: show $\triangle CDB \sim \triangle GHF$. Corresponding sides of $\sim \triangle$'s are proportional.

Theorem 9.5 can sometimes be used to find unknown lengths of segments.

Example 1 Given: $\triangle STU \sim \triangle WXY$, medians $\overline{TV}$ and $\overline{XZ}$
Find XZ.

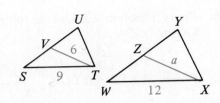

$\dfrac{TV}{XZ} = \dfrac{ST}{WX}$ ◀ *Apply Th. 9.5*

Let $a = XZ$

$\dfrac{6}{a} = \dfrac{9}{12}$

$9a = 72$

$a = 8$.

Thus, $XZ = 8$.

Theorem 9.6 Corresponding altitudes of similar triangles are proportional to corresponding sides. (See Exercise 17.)

Theorem 9.6 can also be used to find unknown lengths of segments.

Example 2 Given: $\triangle ABC \sim \triangle TUV$, altitudes $\overline{AD}$ and $\overline{TW}$ Find AB.

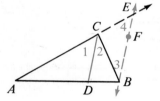

$$\frac{AD}{TW} = \frac{AB}{TU} \qquad \blacktriangleleft \quad Apply\ Th.\ 9.6.$$

$$\frac{4}{3} = \frac{x+1}{x-1}$$

$$4(x-1) = 3(x+1)$$

$$4x-4 = 3x+3$$

$$x = 7$$

Thus, $AB = 7 + 1$ or 8.

Angle bisectors form proportional segments in a triangle. You should complete the proof of the following theorem.

Theorem 9.7 The bisector of an angle of a triangle divides the opposite side into segments proportional to the other sides of the triangle.

Given: $\triangle ABC$, $\overline{CD}$ bisects $\angle ACB$.

Prove: $\dfrac{AD}{DB} = \dfrac{AC}{BC}$

Analysis: use ∥ auxiliary lines to form proportional segments. Substitute in the resulting proportion.

Outline of proof

1. Draw $\overleftrightarrow{BF} \parallel \overline{DC}$ through B.
2. Draw $\overrightarrow{AC}$ intersecting $\overleftrightarrow{BF}$ at E.
3. $\dfrac{AD}{DB} = \dfrac{AC}{CE}$
4. $\angle 2 \cong \angle 3$
5. $\angle 1 \cong \angle 4$
6. $\overline{CD}$ bisects $\angle ACB$
7. $\angle 1 \cong \angle 2$
8. $\angle 3 \cong \angle 4$
9. $BC = CE$
10. $\therefore \dfrac{AD}{DB} = \dfrac{AC}{BC}$

OTHER PROPORTIONAL SEGMENTS

Example 3

Given: $\angle Y \cong \angle Z$, $RT = 9$
$QT = 12$, $RQ = 14$.
Find RN and NQ.

$$\frac{RN}{NQ} = \frac{RT}{TQ} \quad \blacktriangleright \quad \frac{x}{14-x} = \frac{9}{12}$$

$$12x = 9(14-x)$$
$$12x = 126 - 9x$$
$$21x = 126$$
$$x = 6$$

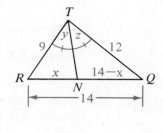

Thus, $RN = 6$ and $NQ = 14 - 6$ or 8.

You can divide a segment into two segments whose lengths have a given ratio by a construction based on Theorem 9.7.

Construction To divide $\overline{AB}$ into two segments whose lengths have the ratio $\frac{2}{3}$.

Given: Segment $\overline{AB}$
Construct: R on $\overline{AB}$
so that $\dfrac{AR}{RB} = \dfrac{2}{3}$.

$$A \rule{3cm}{0.4pt} B$$

Strategy: Apply Th. 9.7.
Construct $\triangle ABC$ so that
$\dfrac{AC}{BC} = \dfrac{2}{3}$.

Draw a segment PQ.
Construct segments with
lengths $2\,PQ$ and $3\,PQ$.

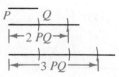

Construct $\triangle ABC$ so that
$AC = 2\,PQ$ and $BC = 3\,PQ$.

Bisect $\angle ACB$. Draw
bisector intersecting
$\overline{AB}$ at R.

Conclusion: $\dfrac{AR}{RB} = \dfrac{AC}{BC} = \dfrac{2}{3}$

Oral Exercises

In $\triangle MNO$, $\overline{OP}$ bisects $\angle MON$. Complete each proportion.

1. If $\dfrac{MO}{NO} = \dfrac{5}{6}$, then $\dfrac{MP}{PN} = ?$

2. If $\dfrac{MP}{PN} = \dfrac{1}{2}$, then $\dfrac{MO}{NO} = ?$

3. If $\dfrac{MO}{NO} = \dfrac{2}{3}$, then $\dfrac{MP}{PN} = ?$

4. If $\dfrac{MP}{PN} = \dfrac{3}{4}$, then $\dfrac{MO}{NO} = ?$

Written Exercises

1. Given: $\overline{CD}$ bisects $\angle ACB$; $AC = 7$; $AD = 5$; $DB = 6$. Find CB.

2. Given: $\overline{CD}$ bisects $\angle ACB$; $AC = 5$; $CB = 8$; $DB = 6$. Find AD.

3. Given: $\overline{CD}$ bisects $\angle ACB$; $AC = 5$; $CB = 10$; $AB = 12$. Find AD and DB.

4. Given: $\overline{CD}$ bisects $\angle ACB$; $AC = 6$; $CB = 10$; $AB = 12$. Find AD and DB.

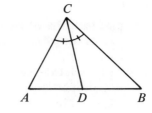

5. Given: $\triangle EGH \sim \triangle IKL$; $\overline{HF}$ and $\overline{LJ}$ are medians; $HE = 9$, $LI = 6$; $HF = x + 2$; $LJ = 2x - 4$. Find HF.

6. Given: $\triangle EGH \sim \triangle IKL$; $\overline{HF}$ and $\overline{LJ}$ are medians; $EF = 9$; $IJ = 6$; $HF = 2x + 1$; $LJ = x + 3$. Find LJ.

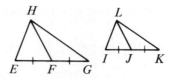

7. Given: $\triangle MOP \sim \triangle QST$; $\overline{PN}$ and $\overline{TR}$ are altitudes; $MP = 15$; $PN = 10$; $QT = 2x + 2$; $TR = x + 3$. Find QT and TR.

8. Given: $\triangle MOP \sim \triangle QST$; $\overline{PN}$ and $\overline{TR}$ are altitudes; $TR = 3$; $TS = 5$; $PN = 2x + 1$; $PO = 4x - 5$. Find PN and PO.

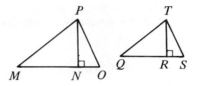

9. Given: $\overline{YZ}$ bisects $\angle WYX$; $WZ = 3$; $ZX = 4$; the perimeter of $\triangle WXY$ is 21. Find YX.

10. Given: $\overline{YZ}$ bisects $\angle WYZ$; $WZ = 4$; $ZX = 5$; the perimeter of $\triangle WXY$ is 27. Find YW.

11. Given: $\triangle ABD$ and $\triangle DBC$, $\overline{AE}$ and $\overline{CE}$ are angle bisectors

    Prove: $\dfrac{AD}{AB} = \dfrac{DC}{CB}$

12. Given: $\triangle ABC \sim \triangle EFG$, $\overline{CD}$ and $\overline{GH}$ are medians.

    Prove: $\dfrac{CD}{GH} = \dfrac{AD}{EH}$

13. Given: $\triangle RST \sim \triangle VWX$, $\overline{TU}$ and $\overline{XY}$ are altitudes.

    Prove: $\dfrac{TU}{XY} = \dfrac{US}{YW}$

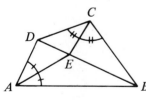

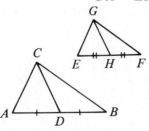

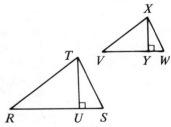

14. Draw $\overline{AB}$. Construct P so that $\dfrac{AP}{PB} = \dfrac{3}{4}$.

15. Draw $\overline{XY}$. Construct Q so that $\dfrac{XQ}{QY} = \dfrac{2}{5}$.

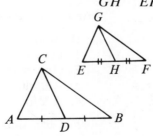

16. Prove Theorem 9.5.

17. Prove Theorem 9.6.

18. Complete the proof of Theorem 9.7.

19. Prove: If two triangles are similar, then corresponding altitudes are proportional to corresponding medians.

20. Prove: The diagonals of a trapezoid divide each other into proportional segments.

OTHER PROPORTIONAL SEGMENTS

9.7 Products of Lengths

OBJECTIVES ► **To find products of lengths of sides of triangles.**
To prove products of lengths equal using proportions.

Every proportion has a related pair of cross-products. Given the cross-products, you can write several proportions.

Example 1 Write two proportions that give the product $PQ \cdot QR = FE \cdot EG$.

$$\frac{PQ}{EG} = \frac{FE}{QR} \text{ or } \frac{FE}{PQ} = \frac{QR}{EG} \quad \blacktriangleleft \text{ Make one pair of factors the means; the other pair, the extremes.}$$

You can use similar triangles to obtain true proportions. These proportions can then be used to find the products of lengths of sides of the triangles.

Example 2 Given: $\triangle ABC \sim \triangle DEF$, $AB = 6$,
$DF = 9$
Find $AC \cdot DE$.

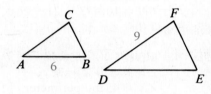

Corr. sides of $\sim \triangle$'s. ► $\dfrac{AC}{DF} = \dfrac{AB}{DE}$

$$AC \cdot DE = DF \cdot AB \qquad \textbf{Thus, } AC \cdot DE = 9 \cdot 6 \text{ or } 54.$$

Example 3 Given: $ABCD$
Prove: $AG \cdot EG = FG \cdot CG$

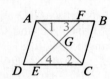

Proof

Statements	Reasons
1. $\square ABCD$	1. Given
2. $\overline{AB} \parallel \overline{CD}$	2. Opp. sides of a $\square$ are $\parallel$.
3. $\angle 1 \cong \angle 2, \angle 3 \cong \angle 4$	3. Alt. int. $\angle$'s of $\parallel$ lines are $\cong$.
4. $\triangle AGF \sim \triangle CGE$	4. AA for $\sim \triangle$'s
5. $\dfrac{AG}{CG} = \dfrac{FG}{EG}$	5. Corr. sides of $\sim \triangle$'s are proportional.
6. $\therefore AG \cdot EG = FG \cdot CG$	6. Property of proportions

Example 4 In Example 3, if $AG = 7$ and $EG = 4$, find $FG \cdot CG$.

$$FG \cdot CG = AG \cdot EG \qquad \textbf{Thus, } FG \cdot CG = 7 \cdot 4 \text{ or } 28.$$

Sometimes you can use similar triangles to find the square of the length of a segment. This is illustrated below.

Example 5 Given: $\overline{AC} \perp \overline{BC}$, altitude $\overline{CD}$
Prove: $AD \cdot DB = (CD)^2$

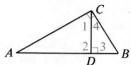

Proof

Statements	Reasons
1. $\overline{AC} \perp \overline{BC}$, altitude $\overline{CD}$	1. Given
2. $\angle 2 \cong \angle 3$	2. Def. of altitude; $\perp$ forms $\cong$ rt. $\angle$'s
3. $\triangle ACB$, $\triangle ADC$, and $\triangle CDB$ are rt. $\triangle$'s	3. $\perp$'s form rt. $\angle$'s; def. of rt. $\triangle$.
4. $\angle 1$ is a complement of $\angle A$	4. Acute $\angle$'s of a rt. $\triangle$ are compl.
5. $\angle B$ is a complement of $\angle A$	5. Same as 4
6. $\angle 1 \cong \angle B$	6. Compl. of same $\angle$ are $\cong$.
7. $\triangle ADC \sim \triangle CDB$	7. AA for $\sim$ $\triangle$'s
8. $\dfrac{AD}{CD} = \dfrac{CD}{DB}$	8. Corr. sides of $\sim$ $\triangle$'s are proportional.
9. $\therefore AD \cdot DB = (CD)^2$	9. Property of proportions

Written Exercises

Write two proportions that give each product. (Ex. 1–3)

A **1.** $XY \cdot ZW = AB \cdot CD$

2. $RJ \cdot TK = SP \cdot AD$

3. $(RP)^2 = AJ \cdot WF$

4. Given: $\triangle JQT \sim \triangle CPK$, $CP = 8$, $QT = 12$ Find $JQ \cdot PK$.

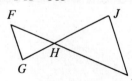

5. Given: $\triangle JQT \sim \triangle CPK$, $JQ = 31$, $PK = 18$ Find $CP \cdot QT$.

6. Given: $\overline{CA} \perp \overline{AE}$, $\overline{BD} \perp \overline{EC}$ Prove: $BC \cdot AE = BD \cdot EC$

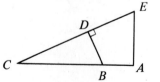

7. Given: $\overline{FG} \parallel \overline{JI}$ Prove: $GH \cdot IH = FH \cdot JH$

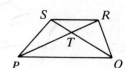

8. Given: $\overline{KL} \perp \overline{LN}$, $\overline{KO} \perp \overline{ON}$ Prove: $LM \cdot NM = OM \cdot KM$

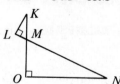

9. Given: $\overline{UY} \perp \overline{YW}$, $\overline{WX} \perp \overline{UX}$ Prove: $VY \cdot VW = VX \cdot VU$

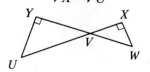

10. Given: $\overline{PQ} \parallel \overline{SR}$ Prove: $ST \cdot PQ = TQ \cdot SR$

11. Given: $\angle 1 \cong \angle 2$ Prove: $ZA \cdot BC = AB \cdot ZC$

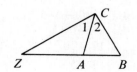

PRODUCTS OF LENGTHS

295

Indicate which information is unnecessary. Then find the product. [Ex. 12–14]

B **12.** Given: $\triangle XYZ \sim \triangle RST$
Find $RT \cdot YZ$.

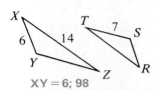

XY = 6; 98

13. Given: $\overline{FD} \perp \overline{CD}$,
$\overline{EB} \perp \overline{FC}$
Find $FB \cdot FC$.

CD = 6; 63

14. Given: $\triangle JNM \sim \triangle MLK$
Find $ML \cdot NM$.

JK = 5, KM = 12; 80

15. Given: $\overrightarrow{TR} \perp \overrightarrow{PQ}$,
$\angle 1 \cong \angle 4$
Prove: $ST \cdot RU = SR \cdot TU$

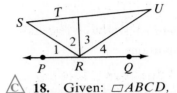

16. Given: $\square RQXZ$
Prove: $ZF \cdot FR = FP \cdot FX$

17. Given: $\angle a \cong \angle b$,
$\overline{JK} \parallel \overline{YZ}$
Prove: $XK \cdot JK = KZ \cdot XJ$

C **18.** Given: $\square ABCD$,
$\angle X \cong \angle Y$
Prove: $BF \cdot BE = BF \cdot BC$

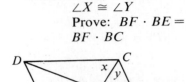

19. Given: $\overline{AB} \parallel \overline{CD}$,
$\angle X \cong \angle Y$
Prove: $ED \cdot CB = DA \cdot EF$

20. Given: $\angle 1 \cong \angle 4$,
$\angle 5 \cong \angle J$
Prove: $LM \cdot NM = LN \cdot MJ$

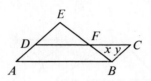

Algebra Review

OBJECTIVE ▶ **To perform operations with radicals**

Example Simplify.

$$5\sqrt{3} + 4\sqrt{12} - 2\sqrt{75}$$
$$5\sqrt{3} + 4\sqrt{4 \cdot 3} - 2\sqrt{25 \cdot 3}$$
$$5\sqrt{3} + 8\sqrt{3} - 10\sqrt{3}$$
$$3\sqrt{3}$$

$$3\sqrt{2} \cdot \sqrt{2}$$
$$3\sqrt{2 \cdot 2}$$
$$3 \cdot 2$$
$$6$$

$$\frac{12\sqrt{75}}{4\sqrt{3}}$$
$$\frac{12}{4} \cdot \sqrt{\frac{75}{3}}$$
$$3\sqrt{25} = 15$$

Simplify.

1. $\sqrt{2} + \sqrt{50}$
2. $\sqrt{27} + \sqrt{75}$
3. $\sqrt{72} - \sqrt{50}$
4. $\sqrt{80} - \sqrt{5}$
5. $\sqrt{12} - \sqrt{48} + \sqrt{3}$
6. $\sqrt{98} - 4\sqrt{8} + 3\sqrt{128}$
7. $\sqrt{5} \cdot \sqrt{5}$
8. $\sqrt{32} \cdot \sqrt{2}$
9. $5\sqrt{8} \cdot 7\sqrt{3}$
10. $\dfrac{12\sqrt{20}}{3\sqrt{5}}$
11. $\dfrac{4\sqrt{48}}{8\sqrt{3}}$
12. $\dfrac{14\sqrt{150}}{7\sqrt{2}}$

9.8 Similarity in Space

OBJECTIVE ▶ To prove and apply theorems about proportions and similarity in space

Remember that two planes are parallel if they do not intersect. Plane $m \parallel$ plane n.

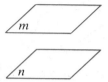

You can often apply properties of similar triangles to figures in space. In many cases, parallel planes are comparable to parallel lines.

Example 1

Prove: If two lines are intersected by three parallel planes, then the corresponding segments that are formed are proportional.

Given: Lines t and q intersected by planes l, m, and n at A, C, F, and B, E, G respectively; $l \parallel m \parallel n$

Prove: $\dfrac{AC}{CF} = \dfrac{BE}{EG}$

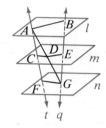

Analysis: A line $\parallel$ to a side of a $\triangle$ divides the other 2 sides proportionally.

Proof

Statements	Reasons
1. $l \parallel m \parallel n$	1. Given
2. Draw $\overline{AG}$, intersecting m at D.	2. Two points are contained in exactly one line.
3. Draw $\overline{AB}$, $\overline{FG}$, $\overline{CD}$, $\overline{DE}$.	3. Same as 2
4. $\overline{AB} \parallel \overline{DE}$	4. $\parallel$ planes intersected by 3rd plane form $\parallel$ lines of intersection.
5. $\dfrac{AD}{DG} = \dfrac{BE}{EG}$	5. A line $\parallel$ to a side of a $\triangle$ divides the other 2 sides proportionally.
6. $\overline{CD} \parallel \overline{FG}$	6. Same as 4
7. $\dfrac{AC}{CF} = \dfrac{AD}{DG}$	7. Same as 5
8. $\therefore \dfrac{AC}{CF} = \dfrac{BE}{EG}$	8. Substitution property

The example above is comparable to Theorem 9.1, which involved a line parallel to a side of a triangle. In each case, proportional segments were determined by the parallel lines or planes.

You can use the results of Example 1 to find unknown lengths.

Example 2 Given: $p \parallel q \parallel r$, $AB = 6$, $BC = 7$, $DE = 9$
Find EF.

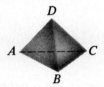

$$\frac{AB}{BC} = \frac{DE}{EF} \quad \blacktriangleleft \quad \textit{Apply Example 1.}$$

$$\frac{6}{7} = \frac{9}{EF}$$

$$6 \cdot EF = 63$$

Thus, $EF = 10\frac{1}{2}$.

$ABCD$ is a solid figure called a **tetrahedron.**
$\triangle ABC$ is its **base.** $\triangle ABD$, $\triangle BCD$,
and $\triangle CAD$ are its **faces.**

Theorem 9.8 If a tetrahedron is intersected by a plane parallel to its base, then the triangle formed by the intersection is similar to the base.

Given: Tetrahedron $ABCD$
intersected by plane p in
$\triangle EFG$, $p \parallel \triangle ABC$
Prove: $\triangle EFG \sim \triangle ABC$

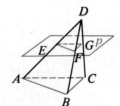

Analysis: Each face of the tetrahedron contains similar triangles. Sides of similar triangles are proportional.

Outline of proof

$\overline{EF} \parallel \overline{AB}$
$\triangle EFD \sim \triangle ABD$
$\dfrac{EF}{AB} = \dfrac{DF}{DB} = \dfrac{DE}{DA}$

$\overline{GE} \parallel \overline{CA}$
$\triangle GED \sim \triangle CAD$
$\dfrac{GE}{CA} = \dfrac{DG}{DC} = \dfrac{DE}{DA}$

$\dfrac{EF}{AB} = \dfrac{FG}{BC} = \dfrac{GE}{CA}$
$\therefore \triangle EFG \sim \triangle ABC$

Example 3 If $p \parallel \triangle ABC$, find XY.

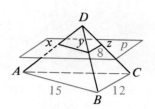

$$\frac{XY}{15} = \frac{8}{12}$$

$$12 \cdot XY = 120$$

Thus, $XY = 10$.

Written Exercises

1. Given: $p \parallel q \parallel r$,
$AB = 7$, $BC = 9$, and
$DE = 8$.
Find EF.

3. Given: $p \parallel q \parallel r$,
$AB = 6$, $BC = 9$,
$DE = 2x + 1$, and
$EF = 4x - 1$.
Find DE and EF.

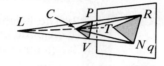

2. Given: $p \parallel q \parallel r$,
$AB = 8$, $AC = 18$, and
$DE = 10$.
Find EF.

4. $p \parallel q \parallel r$, $AB = 6$,
$AC = 14$, $DE = 3x + 1$,
$EF = 5x - 1$.
Find DE and EF.

5. Given: $q \parallel \triangle PCV$, the
distance from L to
$\triangle PCV = 12$, $\frac{VP}{NR} = \frac{2}{3}$.

Find the distance from
L to q.

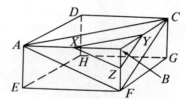

6. Given: $q \parallel \triangle PCV$; the
distance from q to
$\triangle PCV = 2x + 6$; the
distance from L to
$\triangle PCV = 4x - 2$; and
$\frac{VC}{NT} = \frac{3}{5}$. Find the
distance from L to q.

7. Given: $\triangle XBZ \sim$
$\triangle ABF$ and $\triangle YBZ \sim$
$\triangle CBF$
Prove: $\triangle XBY \sim$
$\triangle ABC$

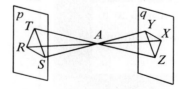

8. Given: $\triangle XBZ \sim$
$\triangle YBZ$ and $\triangle ABF \sim$
$\triangle CBF$
Prove: $\triangle XBY \sim$
$\triangle ABC$

9. Given: $p \parallel q$,
$\frac{AR}{AX} = \frac{AS}{AY} = \frac{AT}{AZ}$
Prove: $\triangle ATS \sim$
$\triangle AZY$

10. Given: $p \parallel q$,
$\frac{AR}{AX} = \frac{AS}{AY} = \frac{AT}{AZ}$
Prove: $\triangle RST \sim$
$\triangle XYZ$

11. Write a complete proof of Theorem 9.8.

12. Given: $\overline{AF} \parallel \overline{BG}$, $\overline{FE} \parallel \overline{GD}$
Prove: $\frac{ED}{DC} = \frac{AB}{BC}$

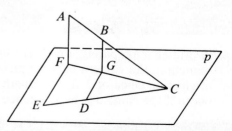

Applications

1. A tax assessor needed a quick estimate of the height of a building. Her helper stands in the doorway of the building. Holding a pencil in her hand with her arm outstretched, the assessor backed off until her helper appeared as tall as the pencil. How will she estimate the height of the building? Why does this work?

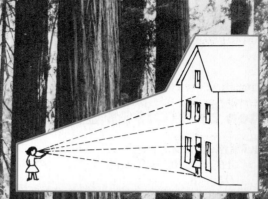

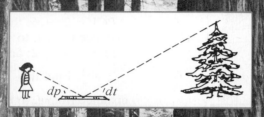

2. The height of a tall object can also be estimated with the help of a mirror placed horizontally on the ground. Suppose that a person's eyes are 5 ft above the ground. Standing 8 ft from the mirror, she can see the top of the tree in the mirror. If the mirror is 48 ft from the foot of the tree, how tall is the tree? Why does it work?

3. The plans for a small cabin are drawn to a scale of $\frac{1}{8}$ in to a foot. What are the dimensions of the cabin?

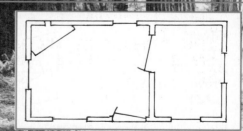

4. A printer is preparing a negative of a photo for a print plate. If specifications call for a reduction, the camera must be placed closer than the original distance. At the camera's original distance of 3 ft, the length of the photo is 10 in. What will be the length of the photo if the camera is at a distance of 2.1 ft?

Computer Activities

A proportion is an equation of the form $\frac{a}{b} = \frac{c}{d}$. In BASIC, you write this proportion with only one variable on the left side of the equation: $A = (C * B)/D$. BASIC allows only one equality to be checked at a time.

The program below uses proportions to prove triangles similar. In this program, you will see that in BASIC $\frac{A}{X} = \frac{B}{Y} = \frac{C}{Z}$ becomes $P1 = P2$ and $P2 = P3$ where $P1 = A/X$, $P2 = B/Y$, $P3 = C/Z$.

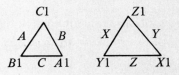

See the computer section on p. 560 for more information.

PROGRAM

```
 10 PRINT "PROGRAM DETERMINES IF TWO TRIANGLES ARE SIMILAR"
 20 PRINT "USING MEASURES OF SIDES AND ANGLES IN DATA STATEMENT"
 30 REM A AND X, B AND Y, C AND Z ARE CORRESPONDING SIDES
 40 READ A, B, C, X, Y, Z
 50 REM A1 AND X1, B1 and Y1 ARE CORRESPONDING ANGLES
 60 READ A1, B1, X1, Y1
 70 LET C1 = 180 - {A1 + B1}
 80 LET Z1 = 180 - {X1 + Y1}
 90 LET P1 = A/X
100 LET P2 = B/Y
110 LET P3 = C/Z
120 IF P1 < > P2 THEN 190
130 IF P2 < > P3 THEN 190
140 IF A1 < > X1 THEN 190
150 IF B1 < > Y1 THEN 190
160 IF C1 < > Z1 THEN 190
170 PRINT "TRIANGLE ABC IS SIMILAR TO TRIANGLE XYZ"
180 GO TO 999
190 PRINT "TRIANGLES ARE NOT SIMILAR"
900 DATA 3, 4, 5, 6, 8, 10, 30, 60, 30, 60
999 END
```

Exercises

1. Run the program for the values given in the DATA statement.

2. Change statement 900 in the program to test other values for triangles.

3. Write a program to find the geometric mean of two positive numbers A and B using the formula in BASIC $M = SQR(A * B)$. SQR is the BASIC function for finding the square root of a number.

Chapter Nine Review

Solve each proportion for x. [9.1]

1. $\dfrac{8}{12} = \dfrac{x}{15}$ **2.** $\dfrac{x}{9} = \dfrac{5}{4}$

Find the ratio of x to y for each of the following.

3. $3x = 8y$ **4.** $ay = bx$

Find the geometric mean of each pair of numbers.

5. 9 and 16 **6.** 2 and 5

Use a proportion to solve the following problem.

*7. The length and the width of a rectangle have the ratio 7 to 4. The area of the rectangle is 252. Find the length and the width.

Are the triangles similar? Give a reason for your answer. (Ex. 8–10) [9.2]

8.

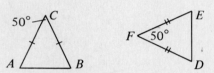

9.

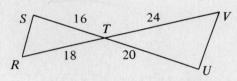

10. Given: $\overline{DE}$ ∥ $\overline{AB}$, $CE = 8$, $DE = 12$, and $CB = 15$
Find AB. [9.4]

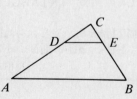

Vocabulary
ratio [9.1]
proportion [9.1]
geometric mean [9.1]
similar polygons [9.2]

11. Given: $\overline{TU}$ bisects ∠RTS, $RU = 4$, $US = 6$, and $TR = 12$. Find TS. [9.6]

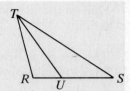

12. Given: $\overline{GH} \perp \overline{DE}$, $\overline{EF} \perp \overline{DF}$, $DH = 8$, $DF = 12$, $DG = 3x - 1$, and $DE = 4x + 2$
Find DG and DE.
[9.3]

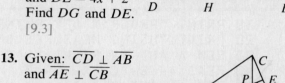

13. Given: $\overline{CD} \perp \overline{AB}$ and $\overline{AE} \perp \overline{CB}$
Prove: $\triangle CPE \sim \triangle CBD$
[9.5]

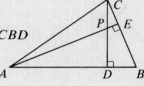

14. Given: Rhombus $ABCD$
Prove: $DP \cdot CR = DC \cdot PR$
[9.5, 9.7]

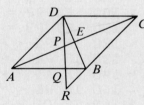

15. Given: D is the midpoint of $\overline{AC}$, E is the midpoint of $\overline{CB}$, and F is the midpoint of $\overline{AB}$.
Prove: $DE \cdot CB = DF \cdot AB$
[9.7]

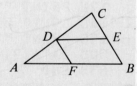

Solve each proportion for x.

1. $\dfrac{3}{5} = \dfrac{7}{x}$ **2.** $\dfrac{12}{x} = \dfrac{16}{20}$

Find the ratio of x to y.

3. $5x = 4y$

Find the geometric mean of the given pair of numbers.

4. 9 and 36

Use a proportion to solve the following problem.

* **5.** The length and the width of a rectangle have the ratio 4 to 3. Their area is 300. Find the length and the width.

Are the triangles similar? Give a reason for your answer. (Ex. 6–7)

6.

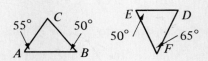

7.

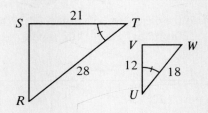

8. Given: $\overline{DE} \parallel \overline{AB}$,
$AD = 6$, $DC = 10$,
and $BC = 12$
Find EC.

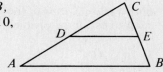

9. Given: $\triangle ABC \sim$
$\triangle DEF$, $AB = 15$,
$AC = 12$, $DE =$
$2x - 4$, and
$DF = x + 1$
Find DE.

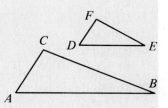

10. Given: $\overline{ED} \parallel \overline{AB}$
Prove: $\triangle ABG \sim$
$\triangle DEG$

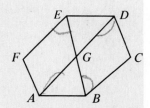

11. Given: $ABDE$ is
a square.
Prove: $AE \cdot CF$
$= CE \cdot AF$

* **12.** Prove that a triangle whose vertices are the midpoints of the sides of a given triangle is similar to the given triangle.

College Prep Test

Directions: Choose the one best answer to each question or problem.

1. In $\triangle ABC$
$\overline{DE} \parallel \overline{AC}$
$BE = 2$
$CE = 4$
$DE = 3$
Find AC.

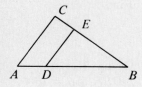

(A) 5.4   (B) 6   (C) 7.2   (D) 7.6   (E) 9

2. In the figure below,
$MQ = 6$
$MS = 4$
$SN = 14$
$\overline{PN} \perp \overline{PM}$
$\overline{QS} \perp \overline{MS}$
Find QP.

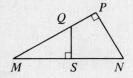

(A) 6   (B) 7   (C) 9   (D) 10   (E) 12

3. If it takes 30 minutes for Jane to type three pages, how many hours will it take her to type 63 pages at the same rate?

(A) 6.3   (B) 630   (C) 15   (D) $10\frac{1}{2}$

(E) none of these

4. If k pencils cost c cents, how many pencils can be bought for d dollars?

(A) $\dfrac{kd}{c}$ (B) $\dfrac{kd}{100\,c}$ (C) $\dfrac{100\,kd}{c}$

(D) $\dfrac{100\,cd}{k}$ (E) $\dfrac{cd}{100\,k}$

5. A vertical pole 6 feet high casts a shadow 4 feet long at the same time a tree casts a shadow 64 feet long. How many feet high is the tree?
(A) 44   (B) 96   (C) 72   (D) 192   (E) 256

6.

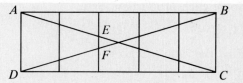

In the figure above, rectangle $ABCD$ is made up of 5 rectangles of equal area. $AD = 45$. Find EF.
(A) 9   (B) 15   (C) 12   (D) 10   (E) 18

7. In the figure,
$PL = 2KP$
$OL = 2MO$
$OP = 14$
Find KM.

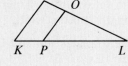

(A) 7   (B) 18   (C) 21   (D) 24   (E) 28

8. On a map drawn to a scale $\frac{1}{2}$ inch $= 200$ miles, what is the distance between two cities which are $3\frac{1}{2}$ inches apart?

(A) 300 miles   (B) 350 miles   (C) 700 miles
(D) 1200 miles   (E) 1400 miles

9.

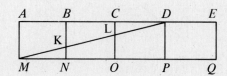

In the figure, $ABNM$, $BCON$, $CDPO$ and $DEQP$ are congruent rectangles.
$AM = 21$
Find KN.
(A) 3   (B) 5.25   (C) 10.5   (D) 7   (E) 14

APPLYING SIMILAR TRIANGLES

The Golden Rectangle

Read

↓

Plan

↓

Solve

↓

Interpret

This attractive drawing shows the golden rectangle as part of its design. A golden rectangle is said to have the most pleasing proportions of a rectangle.

In a golden rectangle, the width divided by the length will always equal about 0.618, the *golden ratio*. We can find this ratio by setting up a proportion.

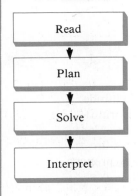

$$\frac{AP}{PB} = \frac{AB}{AP}$$
$$(AP)^2 = (PB)(AB)$$
$$x^2 = (1-x)(1)$$
$$x^2 = 1-x$$
$$x^2 + x - 1 = 0$$

By the quadratic formula
$$x = \frac{-1 \pm \sqrt{5}}{2}, \text{ or } 0.618$$

$AB = 1$, $AP = x$, $PB = 1 - x$

This system of rectangles was constructed using a specific pattern.

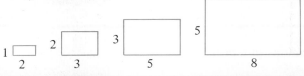

1. Give the dimensions of the next three rectangles in the sequence.

2. Find the value of the ratio of the width to the length of each. What value are these ratios approaching?

10.1 Similarity in Right Triangles

OBJECTIVE ► **To find the lengths of sides and altitudes of right triangles**

When the altitude to the hypotenuse of a right triangle is drawn, three pairs of similar triangles are formed.

Theorem 10.1 In a right triangle, the altitude to the hypotenuse forms two triangles, each similar to the original triangle, and each similar to the other.

Given: Rt. $\triangle ABC$, rt. $\angle ACB$, alt. $\overline{CD}$
Prove: $\triangle ADC \sim \triangle ACB$; $\triangle CDB \sim \triangle ACB$;
$\quad\quad\;\; \triangle ADC \sim \triangle CDB$

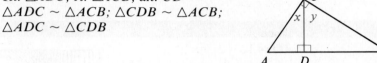

Proof

Statements	Reasons
1. Rt. $\triangle ABC$, rt. $\angle ACB$, alt. $\overline{CD}$	1. Given
2. $\overline{CD} \perp \overline{AB}$	2. Def. of altitude
3. $\angle ADC$ and $\angle CDB$ are rt. $\angle$'s.	3. $\perp$ lines form rt. $\angle$'s.
4. $\triangle ADC$ and $\triangle CDB$ are rt. $\triangle$'s.	4. Def. of rt. $\triangle$'s.
5. $\angle ACB \cong \angle ADC \cong \angle CDB$	5. All rt. $\angle$'s are $\cong$.
6. $\angle A \cong \angle A$, $\angle B \cong \angle B$	6. Reflexive property
7. $\triangle ADC \sim \triangle ACB$	7. AA for $\sim$ $\triangle$'s
8. $\triangle CDB \sim \triangle ACB$	8. AA for $\sim$ $\triangle$'s
9. $\angle A \cong \angle y$, $\angle B$, $\cong \angle x$	9. Def. of $\sim$ $\triangle$'s
10. $\therefore$ $\triangle ADC \sim \triangle CDB$	10. AA for $\sim$ $\triangle$'s

In the figure for Theorem 10.1, since $\triangle ADC \sim \triangle CDB$, it follows that $\dfrac{AD}{CD} = \dfrac{CD}{DB}$.

Thus, CD is the geometric mean of AD and DB. This is stated in Corollary 1.

Corollary 1 In a right triangle, the length of the altitude to hypotenuse is the geometric mean of the lengths of the segments of the hypotenuse that are formed. (See Exercise 19.)

$$\frac{a}{h} = \frac{h}{b}$$

Examples 1 and 2 are applications of Corollary 1.

Example 1

Given: rt. $\triangle RST$ with altitude $\overline{SU}$,
$RU = 10$, and $SU = 8$.
Find TU.

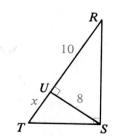

Let $x = TU$
$$\dfrac{RU}{SU} = \dfrac{SU}{TU} \quad \blacktriangleright \quad \dfrac{10}{8} = \dfrac{8}{x}, \text{ by Corollary 1.}$$
$$10x = 64$$
$$x = 6.4, \text{ or } TU = 6.4$$

Example 2

Given: rt. $\triangle ABC$ with altitude $\overline{CD}$,
$AB = 18$, and $DB = 6$.
Find CD.

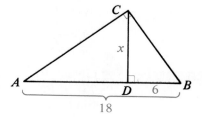

Since $AD = AB - DB$,
$AD = 18 - 6$, or 12.
Let $x = CD$.
$$\dfrac{AD}{CD} = \dfrac{CD}{DB} \quad \blacktriangleright \quad \dfrac{12}{x} = \dfrac{x}{6}$$
$$x^2 = 72$$
$$x = \sqrt{72}, \text{ or } 6\sqrt{2}, \text{ so } CD = 6\sqrt{2}.$$

The altitude to the hypotenuse of right triangle ABC
divides the hypotenuse into two segments, $\overline{AD}$ and
$\overline{DB}$. $\overline{AD}$ is adjacent to leg $\overline{AC}$.

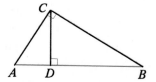

Corollary 2

If the altitude is drawn to the hypotenuse of a right triangle, then the length of either leg is the geometric mean
of the length of the hypotenuse and the length of the
segment of the hypotenuse adjacent to that leg.

Given: Rt. $\triangle ABC$ with rt. $\angle ACB$ and altitude $\overline{CD}$

Prove: $\dfrac{AB}{AC} = \dfrac{AC}{AD}; \dfrac{AB}{CB} = \dfrac{CB}{DB}$

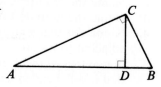

Proof

Statements	Reasons
1. Rt. $\triangle ABC$, rt. $\angle ACB$, alt. $\overline{CD}$	1. Given
2. $\triangle ADC \sim \triangle ACB$	2. Alt. to hyp. forms $\sim$ rt. $\triangle$'s.
3. $\therefore \dfrac{AB}{AC} = \dfrac{AC}{AD}$	3. Def. of $\sim \triangle$'s

(See Exercise 20 for 2nd part of proof.)

SIMILARITY IN RIGHT TRIANGLES

You can use Corollary 2 to find the length of the hypotenuse or the length of either of the legs of a right triangle. You can use Corollary 2 to find the length of the segment of the hypotenuse adjacent to either leg.

Example 3 Given: Rt. $\triangle ABC$ with rt. $\angle ACB$ and altitude $\overline{CD}$, $CA = 7$ and $BA = 9$. Find DA.

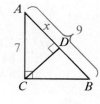

Let $x = DA$.
$$\frac{AB}{AC} = \frac{AC}{AD} \quad \blacktriangleright \quad \frac{9}{7} = \frac{7}{x} \text{ by Corollary 2.}$$
$$9x = 49$$
$$x = \frac{49}{9} \quad \text{Thus, } DA = \frac{49}{9}, \text{ or } 5\frac{4}{9}.$$

Example 4 Given: Rt. $\triangle RST$ with rt. $\angle RTS$, $\overline{TU} \perp \overline{RS}$, $RU = 6$, and $US = 3$. Find TS.

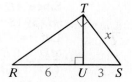

$RS = 6 + 3$, or 9
Let $x = TS$.
$$\frac{RS}{TS} = \frac{TS}{US} \quad \blacktriangleright \quad \frac{9}{x} = \frac{x}{3}$$
$$x^2 = 27$$
$$x = \sqrt{27}, \text{ or } 3\sqrt{3}$$
Thus, $TS = 3\sqrt{3}$.

Reading in Geometry

For Exercises 1–13 $\triangle ABC$ is a rt. $\triangle$ with rt. $\angle ACB$ and $\overline{CD} \perp \overline{AB}$.

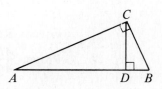

1. Name the legs of rt. $\triangle ABC$.
2. Name the hypotenuse of rt. $\triangle ABC$.
3. Name the altitude to the hypotenuse of rt. $\triangle ABC$.
4. Name the segment of the hypotenuse that is adjacent to leg $\overline{AC}$.
5. Name the segment of the hypotenuse that is adjacent to leg $\overline{CB}$.
6. Name the hypotenuse of rt. $\triangle ADC$.
7. Name the legs of rt. $\triangle CDB$.
8. Name three triangles that are similar to each other.
9. Name an angle that has the same measure as $\angle A$.
10. Name an angle that has the same measure as $\angle B$.
11. CD is the geometric mean of _____ and _____.
12. AC is the geometric mean of _____ and _____.
13. CB is the geometric mean of _____ and _____.

Written Exercises

In rt. △RST, ∠RTS is a rt. ∠ and $\overline{TU}$ is an altitude. Find the indicated lengths.

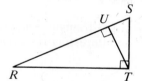

  1. $RU = 8$, $TU = 4$, $US = ?$
  3. $RU = 27$, $TU = ?$ $US = 3$
  5. $RU = ?$, $TU = 2$, $US = 1$
  7. $RU = 12$, $TU = 6$, $US = ?$

  2. $RS = 32$, $RT = 24$, $RU = ?$
  4. $RS = ?$, $US = 4$, $TS = 6$
  6. $RS = 16$, $RU = 8$, $RT = ?$
  8. $RS = 25$, $US = 5$, $TS = ?$

In rt. △JKL, ∠JKL is a rt. ∠ and $\overline{KM}$ is an altitude. Find the indicated lengths. (Ex. 9–16)

  9. $JL = 20$, $ML = 4$, $KM = ?$
  11. $JL = ?$, $JM = 4$, $JK = 6$
  13. $JL = 16$, $ML = 8$, $KL = ?$
  15. $JL = 25$, $JM = 5$, $KM = ?$

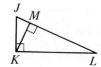

  10. $JL = 18$, $KL = 12$, $ML = ?$
  12. $JL = 8$, $JK = ?$, $JM = 2$
  14. $JL = ?$, $JK = 24$, $JM = 18$
  16. $JL = 20$, $KL = ?$, $ML = 15$

  17. Given: $\overline{BC} \perp \overline{AC}$, $\overline{CE} \perp \overline{AB}$, $\overline{ED} \perp \overline{AC}$
    Prove: △BEC ~ △CED

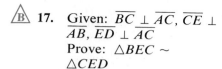

  18. Given: $\overline{BC} \perp \overline{AC}$, $\overline{CE} \perp \overline{AB}$, $\overline{ED} \perp \overline{AC}$
    Prove: $BE \cdot AD = ED \cdot CE$
    (Hint: First prove △BEC ~ △EDA.)

  19. Prove Corollary 1.

  20. Complete the proof of Corollary 2.

∠XZY is a right angle, $\overline{ZH} \perp \overline{XY}$, $\overline{HM} \perp \overline{XZ}$. Can the length of each indicated segment be found by methods in this lesson? If so, find the length. (Ex. 21–26)

  21. Given: $HY = 4$ and $XH = 16$. Find XZ.
  23. Given: $XH = 9$ and $ZH = 6$. Find HY and ZY.
  25. Given: $XZ = 12$ and $ZH = 7$. Find ZY and HY.

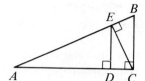

  22. Given: $XM = 16$ and $MZ = 4$. Find MH and ZH.
  24. Given: $MZ = 4$ and $MX = 6$. Find ZH and XH.
  26. Given: $XZ = 9$ and $XY = 12$. Find XH and MH.

  27. Prove or disprove: In a right triangle, the ratios of the length of each leg to the length of the segment of the hypotenuse determined by the altitude and adjacent to that same leg are equal.

  28. Prove or disprove: In a right triangle, the product of the lengths of the hypotenuse and the altitude to the hypotenuse is equal to the product of the lengths of the legs.

∠ACB is a rt. ∠, $\overline{CD} \perp \overline{AB}$, and $\overline{DE} \perp \overline{AC}$. Prove each of the following.

  29. $r \cdot s = u(u + v)$
  31. $h^2 + s^2 = s(r + s)$

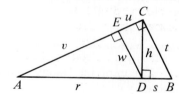

  30. $w^2 + h^2 = u \cdot v + r \cdot s$
  32. $h^2 = u(v + u)$

SIMILARITY IN RIGHT TRIANGLES

10.2 The Pythagorean Theorem

OBJECTIVE ▶ **To apply the Pythagorean Theorem**

Consider the two right triangles shown below. If the length of each of the three sides is squared, an interesting relationship may be seen for each triangle.

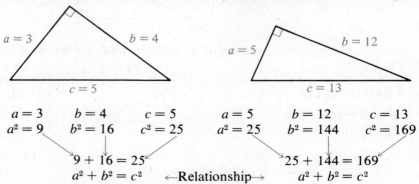

$$
\begin{array}{ccc}
a = 3 & b = 4 & c = 5 \\
a^2 = 9 & b^2 = 16 & c^2 = 25
\end{array}
\qquad
\begin{array}{ccc}
a = 5 & b = 12 & c = 13 \\
a^2 = 25 & b^2 = 144 & c^2 = 169
\end{array}
$$

$$9 + 16 = 25 \qquad\qquad 25 + 144 = 169$$

$$a^2 + b^2 = c^2 \quad \leftarrow\text{Relationship}\rightarrow \quad a^2 + b^2 = c^2$$

It can be proved that the relationship shown above is true for all right triangles. Pythagoras, a famous Greek mathematician and philosopher, is given credit for the first proof of the relationship. Hence, the theorem is called the Pythagorean Theorem. The outline of a more recent proof is given below. You may wish to complete this proof as Exercise 32.

Theorem 10.2 Pythagorean Theorem   In any right triangle, the square of the length of the hypotenuse is equal to the sum of the squares of the lengths of the two legs.

Given: Rt. $\triangle ABC$ with rt. $\angle ACB$
Prove: $a^2 + b^2 = c^2$

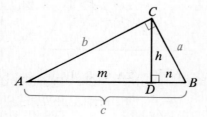

Analysis: Use Th. 10.1 and its corollaries to write proportions. Then use algebra.

Outline of proof

1. $\dfrac{c}{a} = \dfrac{a}{n}$ and $\dfrac{c}{b} = \dfrac{b}{m}$
2. $a^2 = cn$ and $b^2 = cm$
3. $a^2 + b^2 = cn + cm$
4. $a^2 + b^2 = c(n + m)$
5. But $m + n = c$
6. $\therefore a^2 + b^2 = c \cdot c$, or $a^2 + b^2 = c^2$

The Pythagorean Theorem has many applications. Several are given in the examples that follow.

Example 1 Given: Rt. $\angle C$, $BC = 12$, and $AC = 16$
Find AB.

$C^2 = a^2 + b^2$ by the Pythagorean Th.
$C^2 = 12^2 + 16^2$
$C^2 = 144 + 256$
$C^2 = 400$
$C = \sqrt{400}$, or 20
Thus, $AB = 20$.

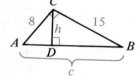

Example 2 Find the length of a base of a rectangle if an altitude drawn to the base is 10 m long and a diagonal is 26 m long.

$b^2 + 10^2 = 26^2$
$b^2 + 100 = 676$
$b^2 = 576$
$b = \sqrt{576}$, or 24
Thus, the base is 24 m long.

Example 3 Find the length of the altitude to the hypotenuse of a right triangle if the lengths of the legs are 8 and 15.

$C^2 = 8^2 + 15^2$
$C^2 = 64 + 225$
$C^2 = 289$
$C = \sqrt{289}$, or 17

Since $\triangle ABC \sim \triangle CBD$, $\dfrac{AC}{AB} = \dfrac{CD}{CB}$

$\dfrac{8}{17} = \dfrac{h}{15}$

$17h = 120$

$h = 7\dfrac{1}{17}$

Thus, the length of the altitude to the hypotenuse is $7\dfrac{1}{17}$.

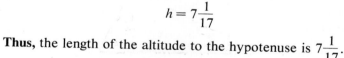

Since the diagonals of a rhombus are perpendicular bisectors of each other, you can apply the Pythagorean Theorem to the right triangles that are formed by the diagonals.

Example 4 The diagonals of a rhombus are 20 cm and 16 cm long. Find the length of a side.

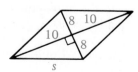

$S^2 = 10^2 + 8^2$
$S^2 = 100 + 64$
$S^2 = 164$
$S = \sqrt{164}$, or $2\sqrt{41}$
Thus, a side is $2\sqrt{41}$ cm long.

THE PYTHAGOREAN THEOREM

Written Exercises _____

For each right triangle, find the indicated length.

△ **1.**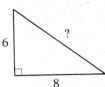

2.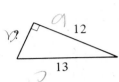

3.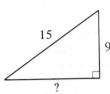

4.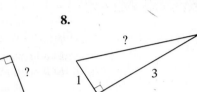

5.

6.

7.

8.

In each of the following sets of numbers, the first two are the lengths of legs of a right triangle and the third is the length of a hypotenuse. Find each missing number.

9. 3, 4, _____   **10.** 5, _____, 13   **11.** _____, 40, 41   **12.** 3, 5, _____

13. _____, 24, 25   **14.** 5, 5, _____   **15.** $\sqrt{3}$, _____, $\sqrt{5}$ **16.** $\sqrt{7}$, _____, 7

Solve each problem.

17. Find the length of each side of a rhombus with diagonals 12 mm and 16 mm long

18. A diagonal of a rhombus is 20 m long. A side is 26 m long. Find the length of the other diagonal.

19. Find the length of a base of a rectangle if an altitude drawn to the base is 15 cm long and a diagonal is 39 cm long.

20. Find the length of a diagonal of a square if a side is 7 cm long.

△ **21.** If the length of a side of a square is s, and the length of a diagonal is d, write a formula for d in terms of s.

22. If the length of a diagonal of a square is d, and the length of a side is s, write a formula for s in terms of d.

23. Find the length of the altitude to the hypotenuse of a right triangle if the lengths of the legs are 10 and 24.

24. Find the length of the altitude to the hypotenuse of a right triangle if the lengths of the legs are 8 and 15.

25. Find the length of the hypotenuse of a right triangle if the length of the altitude to the hypotenuse is 6 and the length of a leg is 10.

26. Find the length of a leg of a right triangle if the length of the other leg is 5 and the length of the altitude to the hypotenuse is 4.

27. Given: Equilateral △ABC with $\overline{CD} \perp \overline{AB}$ and $AC = 10$. Find CD.

28. Given: Equilateral △ABC with $\overline{CD} \perp \overline{AB}$ and $DB = 4$. Find CD.

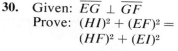

29. Given: $\overline{DB} \perp \overline{AC}$
Prove: $(AD)^2 + (BC)^2 = (AB)^2 + (DC)^2$

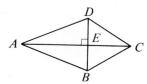

30. Given: $\overline{EG} \perp \overline{GF}$
Prove: $(HI)^2 + (EF)^2 = (HF)^2 + (EI)^2$

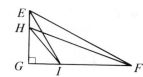

31. Given: $\overline{RT} \perp \overline{TU}$ and $\overline{RT} \perp \overline{RS}$
Prove: $(RU)^2 - (TU)^2 = (TS)^2 - (RS)^2$

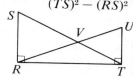

32. Prove Theorem 10.2.

Solve each problem.

Example   Each face of a *rectangular solid* is a rectangle. For the one shown, the lengths of the edges are, a, b, and c. Find d, the length of diagonal $\overline{HB}$.

In rt. $\triangle HEB$, $d^2 = c^2 + y^2$.
In rt. $\triangle EAB$, $y^2 = a^2 + b^2$.
So, $d^2 = a^2 + b^2 + c^2$.
Thus, $d = \sqrt{a^2 + b^2 + c^2}$.

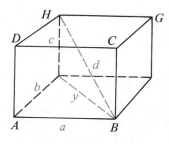

33. If the edges of a rectangular solid are 6 cm, 8 cm, and 24 cm long, find the length of a diagonal of the solid.

34. A cube is a rectangular solid with congruent edges. Find the length of a diagonal of a cube if the length of an edge is 7.

35. Find a formula for the length of a diagonal of a cube if the length of each edge is s.

Example   In $\triangle RST$, $RS = 6$, $RT = 5$, $ST = 4$. Find the length of altitude $\overline{TU}$.

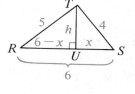

In rt. $\triangle STU$, $x^2 + h^2 = 16$
In rt. $\triangle RUT$, $(6 - x)^2 + h^2 = 25$
$\quad\quad 36 - 12x + x^2 + h^2 = 25$
$\quad\quad 36 - 12x \quad\ + 16\ = 25$
$\quad\quad\quad\quad\quad -12x = -27$
$\quad\quad\quad\quad\quad\quad x = \dfrac{27}{12}$, or $\dfrac{9}{4}$
$\quad\quad h^2 + x^2 = 16$
$\quad\quad\quad h^2 = 16 - \left(\dfrac{9}{4}\right)^2 = 16 - \dfrac{81}{16} = \dfrac{175}{16}$
Thus, $TU = \sqrt{\dfrac{175}{16}}$, or $\dfrac{5\sqrt{7}}{4}$.

36. Given: $\overline{CD} \perp \overline{AB}$, $BC = 4$, $CA = 3$, and $AB = 6$. Find CD.

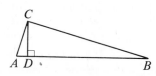

37. Given: $\overline{CD} \perp \overline{AB}$, $BC = 6$, and $AC = 4$, and $AB = 9$. Find CD.

THE PYTHAGOREAN THEOREM

313

A Challenge To You

The triple of numbers a, b, c is called a Pythagorean Triple if $a^2 + b^2 = c^2$ and a, b, and c are positive integers. For example, 3, 4, 5 is a Pythagorean Triple since $3^2 + 4^2 = 5^2$. Each set of such triples can be the lengths of the sides of a right triangle.

Pythagorean Triple			Check	
a	b	c	$a^2 + b^2$	c^2
3	4	5	9 + 16	25
5	12	13	25 + 144	169
7	24	25	49 + 576	625

1. Examine the three sets of triples in the table. What is true of the first number, a in each triple? How do b and c compare?
2. If a is any positive odd integer n, derive a formula for b and c in terms of n.
3. Let $n = 9, 11, 13 \ldots$ Do your formulas for b and c give Pythagorean Triples?

CALCULATOR ACTIVITIES

A calculator can help you to apply the Pythagorean Theorem:
$$a^2 + b^2 = c^2 \quad \text{or} \quad c^2 = a^2 + b^2.$$

Since a, b, and c represent positive numbers, properties of algebra lead to:
(1) $c^2 = a^2 + b^2$ and $c = \sqrt{a^2 + b^2}$
(2) $a^2 = c^2 - b^2$ and $a = \sqrt{c^2 - b^2}$
(3) $b^2 = c^2 - a^2$ and $b = \sqrt{c^2 - a^2}$

For example, if $a = 18$ and $c = 36$, you can find b by using $b = \sqrt{c^2 - a^2}$. You can then proceed as follows.

$\qquad\qquad$ *Find c^2.* $\quad\blacktriangleright\quad$ Press 36 $\otimes$ 36 $\ominus$
$\qquad\qquad\qquad\qquad\qquad\qquad$ Display 1296 $\quad\blacktriangleleft$ *Write down and clear.*
$\qquad\qquad$ *Find a^2.* $\quad\blacktriangleright\quad$ Press 18 $\otimes$ 18 $\ominus$
$\qquad\qquad\qquad\qquad\qquad\qquad$ Display 324 $\quad\blacktriangleleft$ *Write down and clear.*
$\qquad$ *Find $c^2 - a^2$.* $\quad\blacktriangleright\quad$ Press 1296 $\ominus$ 324 $\ominus$
$\qquad\qquad\qquad\qquad\qquad\qquad$ Display 972
$\qquad b = \sqrt{c^2 - a^2}$ $\quad\blacktriangleright\quad$ **Thus, $b = \sqrt{972}$, or 31.2.**

For each right triangle, find the indicated length to the nearest tenth.
1. $a = ?$ $b = 40$, $c = 41$ $\qquad$ 2. $a = 15$, $b = 36$, $c = ?$ $\qquad$ 3. $a = 60$, $b = ?$, $c = 61$
4. $a = ?$ $b = 75$, $c = 85$ $\qquad$ 5. $a = 17$, $b = ?$, $c = 34$ $\qquad$ 6. $a = 16$, $b = 32$, $c = ?$
7. $a = 24$, $b = 72$, $c = ?$ $\qquad$ 8. $a = ?$, $b = 18$, $c = 90$ $\qquad$ 9. $a = 32$, $b = ?$, $c = 96$

10.3 Converse of the Pythagorean Theorem

OBJECTIVE ▶ **To apply the converse of the Pythagorean Theorem**

Recall that you can obtain the converse of a statement that is written in the "If . . . then" form by interchanging the "if" and "then" clauses.

Pythagorean Theorem: If $\triangle ABC$ is a rt. $\triangle$, then $a^2 + b^2 = c^2$.

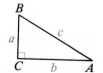

Converse: If $a^2 + b^2 = c^2$, then $\triangle ABC$ is a rt. $\triangle$.

Theorem 10.3 Converse of the Pythagorean Theorem If the sum of the squares of the lengths of two sides of a triangle is equal to the square of the length of the third side, then the triangle is a right triangle.

Given: $\triangle ABC$ with $a^2 + b^2 = c^2$,
Prove: $\triangle ABC$ is a rt. $\triangle$.

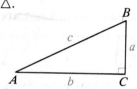

Analysis: Construct a $\triangle DEF$ with rt. $\angle F$, $DF = b$, and $EF = a$. Show that $\triangle ABC \cong \triangle DEF$.

Proof
(See Exercise 26.)

Given the length of each of the three sides of a triangle, you can use the converse of the Pythagorean Theorem to determine whether a triangle is a right triangle. Later you will be able to prove that the hypotenuse of a right triangle is the longest side, so the largest measure is the length of the hypotenuse.

Example 1 Is a triangle whose sides are 11 cm, 60 cm, and 61 cm long a right triangle? If so, which angle is the right angle?

$a^2 + b^2$	c^2	
$11^2 + 60^2$	61^2	◄ Use the largest measure, 61 for c.
$121 + 3{,}600$	$3{,}721$	◄ Apply Theorem 10.3.
$3{,}721$		

Thus, since $a^2 + b^2 = c^2$, the triangle is a right triangle. The right angle lies opposite the side measuring 61 cm.

Recall that if the diagonals of a quadrilateral are perpendicular bisectors of each other, then the quadrilateral is a rhombus. This is applied in the next example.

Example 2 Determine whether Quadrilateral $ABCD$ is a rhombus.

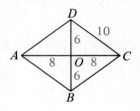

Since $AO = OC = 8$ and $DO = OB = 6$, the diagonals,
$\overline{AC}$ and $\overline{BD}$ bisect each other.
In $\triangle DOC$, $6^2 + 8^2 = 10^2$ so $\angle DOC$ is a right
angle and $\overline{OC} \perp \overline{DO}$. Hence, $\overline{AC} \perp \overline{BD}$
$\overline{AC}$ and $\overline{BD}$ are perpendicular bisectors of each other.
Thus, $ABCD$ is a rhombus.

Written Exercises

Which of the following are right triangles?

1.

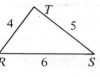

2.

3.

4.

Which of the following are lengths of sides of right triangles? For each right triangle, which angle is the right angle?

  5. $AB = 3$, $BC = 4$, $CA = 5$

  6. $DC = 0.5$, $CE = 1.2$, $ED = 1.3$

  7. $RT = 4$, $TQ = 7$, $QR = 9$

  8. $EF = \sqrt{3}$, $FG = \sqrt{4}$, $GE = \sqrt{5}$

  9. $AB = \sqrt{3}$, $BC = \sqrt{3}$, $CA = \sqrt{6}$

  10. $MN = 3$, $NO = 5$, $OM = \sqrt{34}$

Determine whether each quadrilateral is a rhombus. (Ex. 11–13)

11. **12.** **13.**

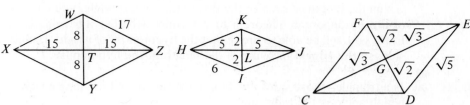

14. Given: $a^2 = (c - b)(c + b)$
    Prove: $\triangle ABC$ is a rt. $\triangle$.

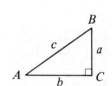

15. Given: $\dfrac{1}{a^2} + \dfrac{1}{b^2} = \dfrac{c^2}{a^2 b^2}$
    Prove: $\triangle ABC$ is a rt. $\triangle$.

Which of the following can be lengths of sides of a right triangle? (Ex. 16–21)

16. $3x, 4x, 5x$

17. $n, n, 2n$

18. $5y^2, 12y^2, 13y^2$

19. $n, m, n + m$

20. $s, \sqrt{t^2 - s^2}, t$

21. $\dfrac{1}{a}, \dfrac{1}{b}, \dfrac{1}{\sqrt{a^2 + b^2}}$

Ⓒ 22. Given: $\overline{CD} \perp \overline{AB}$, CD is the geometric mean of AD and DB.
Prove: $\triangle ABC$ is a rt. $\triangle$.

23. Given: $\overline{CD} \perp \overline{AB}$, AC is the geometric mean of AD and AB.
Prove: $\triangle ABC$ is a rt. $\triangle$.

24. Given: $a^2 + b^2 \neq c^2$. ($\overline{AB}$ is the longest side.)
Prove: $\triangle ABC$ is not a right $\triangle$.

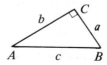

25. Given: $\triangle ABC$ is not a right triangle.
Prove: $a^2 + b^2 \neq c^2$

26. Prove Theorem 10.3.

Cumulative Review

1. The measure of a base angle of an isosceles triangle is 70°. Find the measure of each of the other two angles.

2. The measure of one of two complementary angles is twice the measure of the other. Find the measure of each angle.

Algebra Review

OBJECTIVE ► To perform operations with radicals
To add or subtract radicals: Simplify each radical and combine like terms.
To multiply radicals: Use $\sqrt{a} \cdot \sqrt{b} = \sqrt{ab}$.
To divide radicals: Use $\dfrac{\sqrt{a}}{\sqrt{b}} = \sqrt{\dfrac{a}{b}}$.

Examples Simplify.

$$5\sqrt{3} + 4\sqrt{12} - 2\sqrt{75}$$
$$5\sqrt{3} + 4\sqrt{4 \cdot 3} - 2\sqrt{25 \cdot 3}$$
$$5\sqrt{3} + 4 \cdot 2\sqrt{3} - 2 \cdot 5\sqrt{3}$$
$$5\sqrt{3} + 8\sqrt{3} - 10\sqrt{3}$$
$$3\sqrt{3}$$

$$3\sqrt{2} \cdot \sqrt{2}$$
$$3\sqrt{2 \cdot 2}$$
$$3 \cdot 2$$
$$6$$

$$\frac{12\sqrt{75}}{4\sqrt{3}}$$
$$\frac{12}{4} \cdot \sqrt{\frac{75}{3}}$$
$$3\sqrt{25} = 15$$

Simplify.

1. $8\sqrt{2} + 7\sqrt{2}$
2. $\sqrt{2} + \sqrt{50}$
3. $\sqrt{27} + \sqrt{75}$
4. $\sqrt{72} - \sqrt{50}$
5. $\sqrt{80} - \sqrt{5}$
6. $7\sqrt{2} - \sqrt{2}$
7. $\sqrt{5} + \sqrt{45} + \sqrt{80}$
8. $\sqrt{12} - \sqrt{48} + \sqrt{3}$
9. $\sqrt{98} - 4\sqrt{8} + 3\sqrt{128}$
10. $\sqrt{5} \cdot \sqrt{5}$
11. $\sqrt{32} \cdot \sqrt{2}$
12. $5\sqrt{8} \cdot 7\sqrt{3}$
13. $\dfrac{12\sqrt{20}}{3\sqrt{5}}$
14. $\dfrac{4\sqrt{48}}{8\sqrt{3}}$
15. $\dfrac{14\sqrt{150}}{7\sqrt{2}}$

CONVERSE OF THE PYTHAGOREAN THEOREM

10.4 Special Right Triangles

To find the lengths of segments in a 45°–45° (isosceles) right triangle
To find the lengths of segments in a 30°–60° right triangle

Two special right triangles occur frequently in many branches of mathematics. The first one that you will study is the *isosceles right triangle*, often called the *45°–45° right triangle*.

Examine the two isosceles right triangles shown below. In each case, the length of a leg of the triangle is given, so the Pythagorean theorem can be used to find the length of the hypotenuse.

By the Pythagorean th., $c^2 = 3^2 + 3^2$ $c^2 = 8^2 + 8^2$
$c^2 = 9 + 9$ $c^2 = 64 + 64$
$c^2 = 18$ $c^2 = 128$
$c = \sqrt{18}$, or $3\sqrt{2}$ $c = \sqrt{128}$, or $8\sqrt{2}$

leg	leg	hyp
3	3	$3\sqrt{2}$

◀ *Note the pattern.* ▶

leg	leg	hyp
8	8	$8\sqrt{2}$

These examples suggest a more general theorem.

Theorem 10.4   In a 45°–45° (isosceles) right triangle, the length of the hypotenuse is equal to the length of a leg times $\sqrt{2}$.
$$\text{hyp.} = l\sqrt{2}$$

(See Exercise 21.)

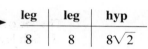

Example 1 $\triangle ABC$ is a 45°–45° right triangle and the length of the hypotenuse is 20. Find the length of a leg.

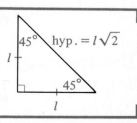

$$\text{hyp.} = l\sqrt{2}$$
$$20 = l\sqrt{2}$$
$$l = \frac{20}{\sqrt{2}} = \frac{20}{\sqrt{2}} \cdot \frac{\sqrt{2}}{\sqrt{2}} = \frac{20\sqrt{2}}{2} = 10\sqrt{2}$$

Thus, the length of a leg is $10\sqrt{2}$.

$\triangle ABC$ shown at the right is a 30°–60° right triangle. Suppose that $\overline{AC}$ is extended to D so that $\overline{CA} \cong \overline{CD}$ and $\overline{BD}$ is drawn. You can prove that $\triangle DCB \cong \triangle ACB$. It follows that $\triangle ABC$ is equiangular and therefore equilateral.

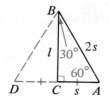

Let $BC = l$ and $CA = s$. Then $AB = AD = 2s$.
$$l^2 + s^2 = (2s)^2$$
$$l^2 = 4s^2 - s^2$$
$$l^2 = 3s^2$$
$$l = \sqrt{3s^2}, \text{ or } s\sqrt{3}$$

This argument suggests the next theorem.

┌ **Theorem 10.5**   In a 30°–60° right triangle, (1) the hypotenuse is twice as long as the leg opposite the 30° angle, and (2) the leg opposite the 60° angle is $\sqrt{3}$ times as long as the leg opposite the 30° angle.

(See Exercise 22.)

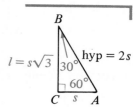

Example 2 The length of the hypotenuse of a 30°–60° right triangle is 10. Find the length of each leg.

Find s.   Find l.
hyp. $= 2s$ $l = s\sqrt{3}$
$10 = 2s$ $l = 5\sqrt{3}$
$s = 5$

Thus, the lengths of the legs are 5 and $5\sqrt{3}$.

Example 3 The length of the leg opposite the 60° angle of a 30°–60° right triangle is 9. Find the length of the leg opposite the 30° angle and the length of the hypotenuse.

Find s. ▶ $l = s\sqrt{3}$
        $9 = s\sqrt{3}$
$$s = \frac{9}{\sqrt{3}} = \frac{9}{\sqrt{3}} \cdot \frac{\sqrt{3}}{\sqrt{3}} = \frac{9\sqrt{3}}{3} = 3\sqrt{3}$$

Find hyp. ▶ hyp. $= 2s$
        hyp. $= 2(3\sqrt{3}) = 6\sqrt{3}$

SPECIAL RIGHT TRIANGLES

Written Exercises

Find the indicated lengths in each right triangle.

1.

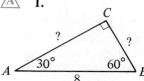

2.

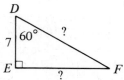

3.

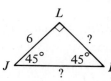

4.

△*XYZ* **is a 45°–45° rt. triangle. Find the indicated lengths.**

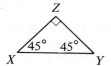

5. $XY = 12, XZ = ?, YZ = ?$
7. $XY = ?, XZ = 3\sqrt{2}, YZ = ?$
9. $XY = ?, XZ = ?, YZ = 4$

6. $XY = 27, XZ = ?, YZ = ?$
8. $XY = ?, XZ = ?, YZ = 9\sqrt{2}$
10. $XY = 8\sqrt{2}, XZ = ?, YZ = ?$

△*ABC* **is a 30°–60° rt. triangle. Find the indicated lengths. (Ex. 11–16)**

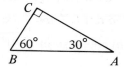

11. $AB = 36, BC = ?, CA = ?$
13. $AB = ?, BC = 9, CA = ?$
15. $AB = ?, BC = ?, CA = 6\sqrt{3}$

12. $AB = 27, BC = ?, CA = ?$
14. $AB = ?, BC = 4\sqrt{3}, CA = ?$
16. $AB = ?, BC = ?, CA = 10$

17. Given: △*DEF* is equilateral.
$\overline{DG}$ is an altitude and $DE = 18$
Find *DG*.

18. Given: △*DEF* is equilateral.
$\overline{DG}$ is an altitude and $DG = 12$.
Find *DE*.

19. Given: Isosceles right △*JKL*
with $\overline{LM}$ the altitude to
the hypotenuse and $JL = 16$.
Find *JK* and *LM*.

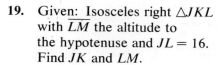

20. Given: Isosceles right △*JKL*
with $\overline{LM}$ the altitude to
the hypotenuse and $LM = 7$.
Find *JK* and *JL*.

21. Prove Theorem 10.4.

22. Prove Theorem 10.5.

23. Prove that if *d* is the length of a
diagonal of a square with side *s*,
then $d = s\sqrt{2}$.

24. Prove that in an isosceles right
triangle, the length *l* of a leg is
$\dfrac{\text{hyp.}}{2}\sqrt{2}$.

25. Given: Rhombus *DEFG*
m ∠*FGD* = 60.
Prove or disprove:
$$\frac{DE + EF + FG + GD}{GE \cdot DF} = \frac{1}{2\sqrt{3}}$$

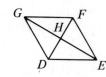

26. Given: Rhombus *DEFG*,
m ∠*FGD* = 60.
Prove or disprove:
$GE \cdot DF = \sqrt{3} \cdot GD \cdot FE$

10.5 Trigonometric Ratios

OBJECTIVE ► **To compute the tangent, sine, and cosine of an acute angle**

Right triangle *trigonometry* is a branch of mathematics that deals with the relationship between the sides and the angles in right triangles. The word "trigonometry" is derived from two Greek words meaning "triangle measurement."

Notice that if right triangles have a pair of corresponding acute angles that are congruent, then the triangles are similar. In the case shown below, the right triangles each have a 28° acute angle.

      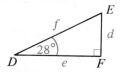

$\triangle ABC \sim \triangle DEF$ by AA for $\sim \triangle$'s.

Thus, $\dfrac{a}{b} = \dfrac{d}{e}$, $\dfrac{a}{c} = \dfrac{d}{f}$, and $\dfrac{b}{c} = \dfrac{e}{f}$.

You can conclude that for all right triangles with a given acute angle A, the ratio $\dfrac{a}{b}$ is determined. The ratios $\dfrac{a}{c}$ and $\dfrac{b}{c}$ are also determined. These ratios are defined below.

Definition:
tangent, sine,
cosine

> For all right triangles ABC, with acute angle A,
>
> $\text{tangent } A = \dfrac{\text{length of opposite leg}}{\text{length of adjacent leg}} \quad \tan A = \dfrac{a}{b}$
>
> $\text{sine } A = \dfrac{\text{length of opposite leg}}{\text{length of hypotenuse}} \quad \sin A = \dfrac{a}{c}$
>
> $\text{cosine } A = \dfrac{\text{length of adjacent leg}}{\text{length of hypotenuse}} \quad \cos A = \dfrac{b}{c}$

The values of the tangent, sine, and cosine ratios depend upon the measure of angle A and not upon the size of the right triangle. For this reason, these ratios are often called *functions of $\angle A$*.

Example 1 For rt. $\triangle ABC$, find $\tan A$, $\sin A$, and $\cos A$.

$$\tan A = \frac{\text{opp.}}{\text{adj.}} = \frac{3}{4}, \text{ or } 0.75$$

$$\sin A = \frac{\text{opp.}}{\text{hyp.}} = \frac{3}{5}, \text{ or } 0.6$$

$$\cos A = \frac{\text{adj.}}{\text{hyp.}} = \frac{4}{5}, \text{ or } 0.8$$

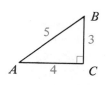

TRIGONOMETRIC RATIOS

Example 2 For rt. △ABC, find tan B, sin B, and cos B correct to three decimal places.

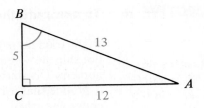

$$\tan B = \frac{\text{opp.}}{\text{adj.}} = \frac{12}{5} = 2.400$$

≐ *means approx =.* ▶ $\sin B = \dfrac{\text{opp.}}{\text{hyp.}} = \dfrac{12}{13} \doteq 0.923$

$$\cos B = \frac{\text{adj.}}{\text{hyp.}} = \frac{5}{13} \doteq 0.385$$

The properties of a 30°–60° right triangle and a 45°–45° right triangle can be used to find certain sine, cosine, and tangent ratios.

Example 3 Use rt. △ABC to find sin 30°, cos 30°, and tan 30°, correct to three decimal places.

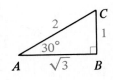

$$\sin 30° = \frac{1}{2} = 0.500$$

$$\cos 30° = \frac{\sqrt{3}}{2} \doteq \frac{1.732}{2} \doteq 0.866$$

$$\tan 30° = \frac{1}{\sqrt{3}} = \frac{1}{\sqrt{3}} \cdot \frac{\sqrt{3}}{\sqrt{3}} = \frac{\sqrt{3}}{3} \doteq \frac{1.732}{3} \doteq 0.577$$

Reading in Geometry

△JKL is a right triangle with right ∠L.

1. Name the hypotenuse.
2. Name the leg adjacent to ∠J.
3. Name the leg opposite ∠K.
4. Name the leg adjacent to ∠K.
5. Name the leg opposite ∠J.
6. What is sin J?
7. What is tan K?
8. What is cos J?
9. What is sin K?
10. What is tan J?
11. What is cos K?

Written Exercises

For each triangle, find tan A, sin A, cos A, tan B, sin B, and cos B, correct to three decimal places.

Ⓐ 1.

2.

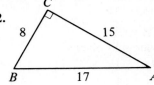

3.

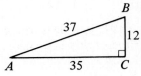

4.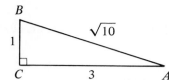

5.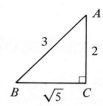

6.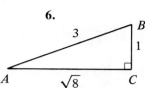

Find each value, correct to three decimal places. Use the triangle shown.

7. tan 60°
8. sin 60°
9. cos 60°

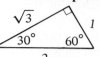

10. tan 45°
11. sin 45°
12. cos 45°

For each triangle, find tan A, sin A, cos A, tan B, sin B, and cos B, correct to three decimal places. [Hint: Use the Pythagorean theorem first.]

Ⓑ **13.**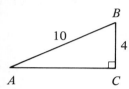

14.

15.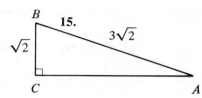

16.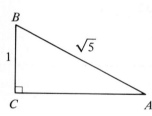

17.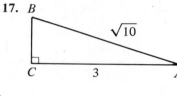

18.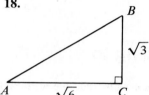

Show that each statement is true. Use the figure below. (Ex. 19–24)

Ⓒ **19.** sin B = cos A

21. tan $B = \dfrac{1}{\tan A}$

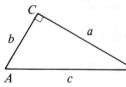

20. cos B = sin A
22. $(\sin B)^2 = 1 - (\cos B)^2$
[Hint: Use the Pythagorean theorem.]

23. The tangent of an acute angle is equal to the reciprocal of the tangent of its complement.

24. The sine of an acute angle is equal to the cosine of its complement.

CALCULATOR ACTIVITIES

$\triangle ABC$ is a right triangle with right $\angle C$.
Find each value correct to three decimal places.

1. sin A
2. tan B
3. cos B
4. tan A
5. cos A
6. sin B

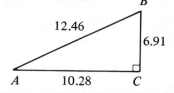

10.6 Trigonometric Tables

OBJECTIVES ► **To use a table to find sin A, cos A, and tan A, given m ∠A**
To use a table to find m ∠A, given sin A, cos A, or tan A

In the last lesson, you found sine, cosine, and tangent values for 30°, 45°, and 60° angles. You can find approximate values of sine, cosine, and tangent for angles of other degree measures by constructing right triangles, measuring the sides, and computing the ratios. For practical purposes, tables have been compiled to give these values. A portion of such a table is given below.

Angle Meas.	Sin	Cos	Tan	Angle Meas.	Sin	Cos	Tan
32°	0.5299	0.8480	0.6249	78°	0.9781	0.2079	4.704
33°	0.5446	0.8387	0.6494	79°	0.9816	0.1908	5.145
34°	0.5592	0.8290	0.6745	80°	0.9848	0.1736	5.671
35°	0.5736	0.8192	0.7002	81°	0.9877	0.1564	6.314
36°	0.5878	0.8090	0.7265	82°	0.9903	0.1392	7.115
37°	0.6018	0.7986	0.7536	83°	0.9925	0.1219	8.144
38°	0.6157	0.7880	0.7813	84°	0.9945	0.1045	9.514
39°	0.6293	0.7771	0.8098	85°	0.9962	0.0872	11.43
40°	0.6428	0.7660	0.8391	86°	0.9976	0.0698	14.30
41°	0.6561	0.7547	0.8693	87°	0.9986	0.0523	19.08

A complete table is found on page 592.

Example 1 Use the table to find sin 35°, cos 35°, and tan 35°.
Look in the appropriate column next to 35°.

Thus, sin 35° = 0.5736, cos 35° = 0.8192, and tan 35° = 0.7002.

Example 2 Find m ∠A if cos A = 0.1219.
Find 0.1219 in the cos column.
cos 83° = 0.1219

Thus, m ∠A = 83.

Example 3 Find m ∠B to the nearest degree, if tan B = 4.976.

4.976	5.145
−4.704	−4.976
0.272	0.169

→ Find the closest value to 4.976 in the tan column. Tan 78° = 4.704 and tan 79° = 5.145. 4.976 is closer to 5.145 than to 4.704. Thus, m ∠B = 79 to the nearest degree.

Oral Exercises

Find each indicated value. Use the table on page 592.

1. sin 56°	**2.** sin 29°	**3.** cos 5°	**4.** tan 35°
5. cos 38°	**6.** tan 81°	**7.** sin 55°	**8.** cos 74°
9. tan 15°	**10.** sin 12°	**11.** tan 52°	**12.** sin 41°
13. cos 21°	**14.** cos 85°	**15.** cos 73°	**16.** sin 76°

Find m $\angle B$. Use the table on page 592.

17. tan B = 3.487	**18.** tan B = 0.8693	**19.** cos B = 0.1736
20. cos B = 0.4695	**21.** cos B = 0.7771	**22.** tan B = 1.111
23. sin B = 0.9945	**24.** sin B = 0.6428	**25.** sin B = 0.7986
26. cos B = 0.9659	**27.** tan B = 0.4245	**28.** sin B = 0.4067

Written Exercises

Find m $\angle A$ to the nearest degree. Use the table on page 599.

1. tan A = 0.8721	**2.** cos A = 0.9931	**3.** cos A = 0.4295
4. sin A = 0.8392	**5.** tan A = 1.352	**6.** cos A = 0.1196
7. cos A = 0.8516	**8.** sin A = 0.9927	**9.** sin A = 0.2593
10. tan A = 0.4439	**11.** sin A = 0.5036	**12.** tan A = 12.57

True or false? Use the right triangle at the right and the table on page 599.

13. sin A = cos B	**14.** cos A = cos B
15. sin A = sin B	**16.** tan B = $\dfrac{1}{\tan A}$
17. m $\angle A$ + m $\angle B$ = m $\angle C$	**18.** sin A + sin B = sin C
19. sin A + cos A = 1	**20.** tan A · tan B = 1

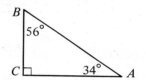

$\triangle ABC$ is a right triangle with right angle C. True or false?

21. m $\angle A$ < m $\angle B$ and m $\angle B$ < m $\angle C$.	**22.** If m $\angle A$ < m $\angle B$, then cos A > cos B.
23. If m $\angle A$ < m $\angle B$, then tan A < tan B.	**24.** If sin A > sin B, then m $\angle A$ < m $\angle B$.
25. (sin A)² + (sin B)² = 1	**26.** (sin A)² + (cos A)² = 1

27. Explain why sin A cannot be greater than 1.

28. Explain why cos A decreases as m $\angle A$ increases.

29. Show that tan A = $\dfrac{\sin A}{\cos A}$.
(Hint: Use a, b, and c as the lengths of the sides of rt. $\triangle ABC$.)

30. Explain why tan A get infinitely large as m $\angle A$ increases.

10.7 Measures in Right Triangles

OBJECTIVE ▶ **To find measures of sides and angles in right triangles by using sine, cosine, and tangent ratios**

Trigonometric ratios can be used to find the measures of sides and angles in right triangles. In Examples 1 and 2, you will find measures of sides.

Example 1 If m $\angle A = 48$ and $c = 9$, find a and b to the nearest tenth.

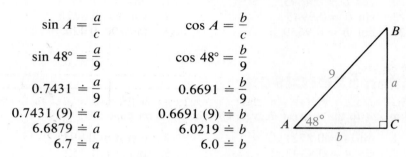

$$\sin A = \frac{a}{c} \qquad\qquad \cos A = \frac{b}{c}$$

$$\sin 48° = \frac{a}{9} \qquad\qquad \cos 48° = \frac{b}{9}$$

$$0.7431 \doteq \frac{a}{9} \qquad\qquad 0.6691 \doteq \frac{b}{9}$$

$$0.7431\,(9) \doteq a \qquad\qquad 0.6691\,(9) \doteq b$$

$$6.6879 \doteq a \qquad\qquad 6.0219 \doteq b$$

$$6.7 \doteq a \qquad\qquad 6.0 \doteq b$$

Thus, a is 6.7 and b is 6.0, to the nearest tenth.

───────◆◆◆───────

Sometimes there is more than one way to solve a problem involving trigonometric ratios. In the next example, you can use either tan A or tan B.

Example 2 If m $\angle A = 23$ and $a = 15$, find b to the nearest tenth.

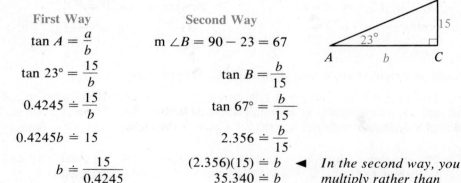

First Way

$$\tan A = \frac{a}{b}$$

$$\tan 23° = \frac{15}{b}$$

$$0.4245 \doteq \frac{15}{b}$$

$$0.4245b \doteq 15$$

$$b \doteq \frac{15}{0.4245}$$

$$b \doteq 35.3$$

Second Way

$$m \angle B = 90 - 23 = 67$$

$$\tan B = \frac{b}{15}$$

$$\tan 67° = \frac{b}{15}$$

$$2.356 \doteq \frac{b}{15}$$

$$(2.356)(15) \doteq b$$

$$35.340 \doteq b$$

$$35.3 \doteq b$$

◀ *In the second way, you multiply rather than divide.*

Thus, b is 35.3 to the nearest tenth.

In Example 3, you will use trigonometric ratios to find measures of angles.

Example If $a = 5$ and $c = 15$, find m $\angle B$ and m $\angle A$ to the nearest degree.

$$\cos B = \frac{a}{c}$$

$$\cos B = \frac{5}{15}$$

$$\cos B = \frac{1}{3}$$

$$\cos B \doteq 0.3333$$
$$\cos 71° \doteq 0.3256$$

Thus, m $\angle B \doteq 71$ and m $\angle A \doteq 90 - 71$, or 19.

Written Exercises

Find the indicated measure (sides to the nearest tenth and angles to the nearest degree).

 1.

2.

3.

4.
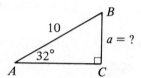

5.
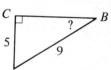

6.

7.

8.
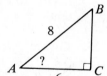

Find each indicated measure (sides to the nearest tenth and angles to the nearest degree). Use the figure at the right.

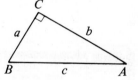

9. If $a = 6$ and m $\angle B = 18$, find b.
11. If $b = 9$ and $c = 15$, find m $\angle B$.
13. If $b = 15$ and $c = 20$, find m $\angle A$.
15. If $c = 18$ and m $\angle B = 40$, find a.
17. If $b = 17$ and m $\angle B = 49$, find c.
19. If $c = 10$ and m $\angle A = 38$, find a.
21. If $a = 3$ and $c = 5$, find m $\angle A$.
23. If $a = 14$ and $b = 17$, find m $\angle A$.

10. If $a = 12$ and $c = 19$, find m $\angle B$.
12. If $b = 21$ and m $\angle B = 76$, find a.
14. If $c = 28$ and m $\angle A = 31$, find a.
16. If $a = 9$ and $b = 13$, find m $\angle B$.
18. If $c = 26$ and m $\angle B = 62$, find a.
20. If $b = 16$ and m $\angle A = 12$, find c.
22. If $b = 18$ and m $\angle B = 38$, find a.
24. If $a = 16$ and m $\angle B = 8$, find c.

FINDING MEASURES IN RIGHT TRIANGLES

Find each of the missing measures (sides of the nearest tenth and angles to the nearest tenth and angles to the nearest degree). (Ex. 25–30)

Ⓑ 25.

26.

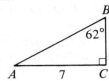

27.

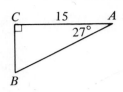

28.

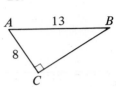

29.

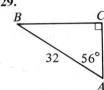

30.

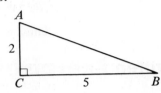

31. The lengths of the legs of a right triangle are in the ratio 1 to 4. Find the measure of each acute angle to the nearest degree.

32. One leg of a right triangle is $\frac{2}{3}$ as long as the hypotenuse. Find the measure of each acute angle to the nearest degree.

Ⓒ 33. Given: $\triangle ABC$ with $\overline{BC} \perp \overline{AC}$, m $\angle A = 27$, and $BC = 10$. Find the perimeter of $\triangle ABC$ to the nearest tenth.

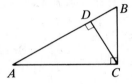

34. Given: $\triangle ABC$ with $\overline{BC} \perp \overline{AC}$, $\overline{CD} \perp \overline{AB}$, $BC = 8$, and m $\angle A = 32$. Find CD to the nearest tenth.

35. Given: $\triangle RST$ with $\overline{ST} \perp \overline{TR}$, m $\angle x = 51$, m $\angle R = 28$, and $SR = 20$. Find SU to the nearest tenth.

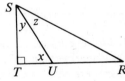

36. Given: $\triangle RST$ with m $\angle T = 90$, m $\angle y = 35$, m $\angle z = 18$, and $TU = 12$. Find SR to the nearest tenth.

CALCULATOR ACTIVITIES

$\triangle ABC$ is a right triangle with right $\angle C$ and $\overline{CE} \perp \overline{AB}$. Find each indicated length to the nearest hundredth.

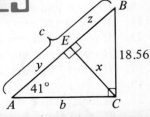

1. Find c.   **2.** Find b.   **3.** Find x.
4. Find y.   **5.** Find z.

10.8 Applications of Trigonometry

OBJECTIVE ▶ **To solve problems using trigonometric ratios**

Trigonometric ratios can be used to help solve measurement problems, especially problems involving lengths or distances that cannot be measured directly.

Example 1 A diagonal of a rectangle measures 5 cm. It makes an angle of 71° with a side of the rectangle. Find the dimensions of the rectangle to the nearest tenth of a centimeter.

$$\sin 71° = \frac{b}{5}$$

$$0.9455 \doteq \frac{b}{5}$$

$$0.9455(5) \doteq b$$

$$4.7275 \doteq b$$

$$4.7 \doteq b$$

$$\cos 71° = \frac{h}{5}$$

$$0.3256 \doteq \frac{h}{5}$$

$$0.3256(5) \doteq h$$

$$1.6280 \doteq h$$

$$1.6 \doteq h$$

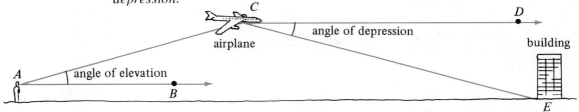

Thus, the length of a base is 4.7 cm and length of an altitude is 1.6 cm.

Surveyors and engineers often measure an *angle of elevation* or an *angle of depression*.

An observer at A, looking up at C, would have to elevate his line of sight from the horizontal $\overrightarrow{AB}$ to the direction $\overrightarrow{AC}$. $\angle CAB$ is called the *angle of elevation of C at A*. If the observer were at C, looking down at E, he would have to depress his line of sight from the horizontal $\overrightarrow{CD}$ to the direction $\overrightarrow{CE}$. $\angle DCE$ is called the *angle of depression of E at C*.

Example 2 When the angle of elevation of the sun measures 42°, a tower casts a 26-meter shadow. How tall is the tower?

$$\tan 42° = \frac{x}{26}$$

$$0.9004 \doteq \frac{x}{26}$$

$$0.9004(26) \doteq x$$

$$23.4104 \doteq x$$

$$23.4 \doteq x$$

Thus, the tower is about 23.4 m tall.

Example 3 From a treehouse, the angle of depression of the base of a house measures 53°. The tree is 12 m from the base of the house. How far is the treehouse from the base of the house?

$$\cos 53° = \frac{12}{x}$$

$$0.6018 \doteq \frac{12}{x}$$

$$0.6018\, x \doteq 12$$

$$x \doteq \frac{12}{0.6018}$$

$$x \doteq 19.9$$

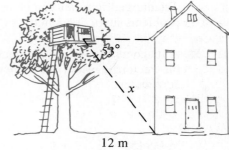

12 m

Thus, the treehouse is about 19.9 m from the base of the house.

Written Exercises

Find *x* to the nearest tenth.

A **1.**

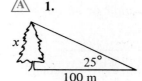

2.

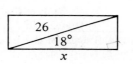

3.

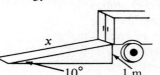

4.

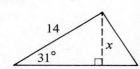

5.

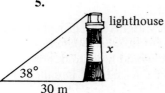

6.

7.

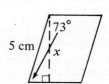

8.

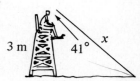

Find lengths to the nearest tenth and angle measures to the nearest degree.

9. The diagonal of a rectangle is 6 cm long. It makes an angle of 55° with a side of the rectangle. Find the dimensions of the rectangle.

10. The leg opposite the 50° angle in a right triangle measures 8 m. Find the length of the hypotenuse.

11. The angle of elevation from a ship to the top of a 35-m lighthouse on the coast measures 26°. How far from the coast is the ship?

12. A ramp is 60 m long. It rises a vertical distance of 8 m. Find the measure of the angle of elevation.

Find lengths to the nearest tenth and angle measures to the nearest degree.

13. A kite is flying at the end of a 150-m string (straight). The string makes an angle of 75° with the ground. How high above the ground is the kite?

14. A tree casts a 50-m shadow while the angle of elevation of the sun is 48°. How tall is the tree?

15. Two sides of a triangle measure 8 mm and 11 mm. The included angle measures 34°. Find the measure of the altitude to the 11-mm side.

16. A cliff is 90 m above the sea. From the cliff, the angle of depression of a boat measures 46°. How far is the boat from the base of the cliff?

17. In the trapezoid below, $AB \parallel CD$ and $\overline{DA} \perp \overline{AB}$. $DC = 12$, $CB = 9$, and m $\angle B = 52$. Find AB. [Hint: Draw $\overline{CE} \perp \overline{AB}$.]

18. The diagonals of the rhombus below measure 8 and 16. Find the measure of each angle of the rhombus.

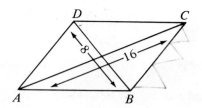

19. The diagonals of a rhombus measure 18 cm and 24 cm. Find the measure of each angle of the rhombus.

20. Each side of a rhombus is 9 cm long and an angle measures 76°. Find the length of the longer diagonal.

21. Two sides of an isosceles triangle each measure 10 cm, and the vertex angle measures 40°. Find the length of the altitude to the base.

22. In $\square ABCD$, m $\angle B = 20$ and $AD = 12$. Find the length of the altitude from C to $\overline{AB}$.

23. The sides of an isosceles triangle measure 14, 14, and 18. Find the measure of each angle of the triangle.

24. An angle of a rhombus measures 110° and the diagonal opposite that angle measures 30. Find the measure of the other diagonal.

25. The sides of a triangle measure 12, 12, and 18. Find the measure of each angle of the triangle.

26. $ABCD$ is an isosceles trapezoid with $\overline{AB} \parallel \overline{CD}$. If $AB = 20$, $CD = 14$, and m $\angle A = 72$. Find BC.

27. The longer base of a trapezoid measures 21 m, and the other three sides each measure 12 m. Find the measure of each angle of the trapezoid.

28. A diagonal of a rectangle divides one of its angles into two angles whose measures are in the ratio 4 to 5. Express the length of a base of the rectangle as a percentage of the length of a corresponding altitude.

APPLICATIONS OF TRIGONOMETRY

Applications

Read | Plan | Solve → Interpret

1. Ancient surveyors used a rope with equally spaced knots to lay out right-angled corners on land. By using the third, seventh, and twelfth knots as corners, they formed a right triangle. Why did this work?

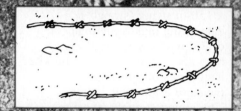

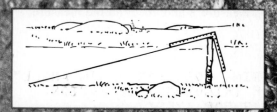

2. A land developer needs to measure the road frontage of some property. The only measuring tools he has with him are a 5 m tape and a carpenters square. There is a pole 1.5 m tall at one corner of the property. How can he use these tools to estimate the length of the road frontage?

3. An airplane is trying to fly due north. There is a strong wind blowing from the west. Suppose that the air speed of the plane is 300 km per hour and the speed of the wind is 20 km per hour. Where will the plane land after one hour of flight? How far has it actually flown? How many degrees is it off course?

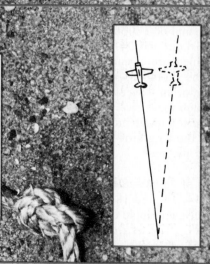

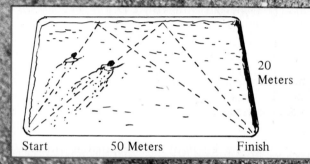

Start   50 Meters   Finish

20 Meters

4. In a swimming race, each swimmer is to start at one corner of the pool, swim to a point on the opposite side of the pool, and back to the other corner on the starting side. Each swimmer wants the shortest possible path. Does it matter where on the opposite side each aims for? If so, how much difference can it make in the distance each must swim?

Computer Activities

In BASIC, the ratios, sin, cos, and tan, can be found through computation, using the measures of the sides of triangles as indicated below.

Tan: $T = A/B$ Sin: $S = A/C$ Cos: $C1 = B/C$

The ratios can also be found through the built in BASIC functions: $TAN(x)$, $SIN(x)$, and $COS(x)$ where x is the angle measure in radians. The following program uses these built-in functions for finding trigonometric ratios. The angle is entered in degrees and the program converts it to radians. For example, if angle A measures 130°, then $130 * (3.14159/180)$ or 2.26893 radians.

See the computer section on p. 560 for more information.

PROGRAM

```
10 PRINT "PROGRAM COMPUTES THE SIN, COS, TAN OF AN ANGLE"
20 PRINT "DO YOU WANT A TABLE OF TRIGONOMETRIC RATIOS?"
30 PRINT "ANSWER 1 FOR 'NO' AND 2 FOR 'YES'"
40 INPUT A
50 IF A = 1 THEN 170
60 PRINT "FOR WHAT STARTING ANGLE DO YOU WANT THE TABLE?"
70 INPUT S
80 PRINT "FOR WHAT ENDING VALUE?"
90 INPUT F
100 PRINT "DEGREES RADIANS     SIN        COS        TAN"
110 LET C = 3.14159/180
120 FOR I = S TO F STEP 5
130 LET R = C * I
140 PRINT I; R; SIN{R}; COS{R}; TAN{R}
150 NEXT I
160 GO TO 999
170 PRINT "FOR WHAT ANGLE MEASURE DO YOU WANT SIN, COS, TAN?"
180 INPUT M
190 LET R = M * {3.14159/180}
200 PRINT "DEGREES RADIANS     SIN        COS        TAN"
210 PRINT M; R; SIN{R}; COS{R}; TAN{R}
999 END
```

Exercises

1. Run the program above to find the sin, cos, and tan for a 117° angle.
2. Run the program to produce a table going from a 25° angle to an 80° angle.
* 3. Write a program to convert radian measure to degree measure.

ACTIVITY: TRIGONOMETRIC RATIOS

Chapter Ten Review

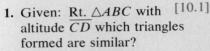

1. Given: Rt. $\triangle ABC$ with [10.1] altitude $\overline{CD}$ which triangles formed are similar?

2. Given: $\overline{AC} \perp \overline{CB}$, $\overline{CD} \perp \overline{AB}$, $AD = 3$, and $DB = 27$ Find CD and CB.

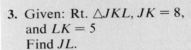

3. Given: Rt. $\triangle JKL$, $JK = 8$, and $LK = 5$ Find JL.

4. Given: Rt. $\triangle JKL$, $JL = 9$, and $LK = 4$ Find JK.

Which of the following can be lengths of sides of a right triangle? (Ex. 5–7) [10.2]

5. 9, 12, 15

6. 6, 8, 12

7. $x, 2x, \sqrt{5x}$

8. Find the length of the hypotenuse of a right triangle if the length of altitude to the hypotenuse is 6 and the length of a leg is 10.

*9. Find the length of a diagonal of a cube if the length of an edge is 6.

10. Given: $\triangle RST$ is a $45° - 45°$ rt. $\triangle$ and $RT = 6$ Find RS and TS. [10.4]

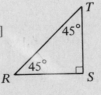

11. Given: $\triangle RST$ is a $45° - 45°$ rt. $\triangle$ and $RS = 6$ Find RT and TS.

Vocabulary
Pythagorean Theorem [10.2], trigonometry [10.5], sine [10.5], cosine [10.5], tangent [10.5]

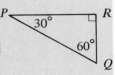

12. Given: $\triangle PQR$ is a $30° - 60°$ rt. $\triangle$ and $PR = 4$ Find PQ and QR. [10.4]

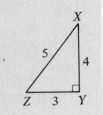

13. Given: Rt. $\triangle XYZ$, $XY = 4$, $YZ = 3$, and $XZ = 5$ Find $\tan X$. [10.5, 10.6]

14. Given: Rt. $\triangle XYZ$, $XY = 4$, $YZ = 3$, and $XZ = 5$ Find $\sin Z$.

Use the table of trigonometric ratios to find each of the following. [10.5, 10.6]

15. $\sin 32°$

16. $\tan 57°$

Use the table to find m $\angle A$ to the nearest degree. [10.6]

17. $\tan A = 0.5407$

18. $\cos A = 0.6633$

Find each indicated measure. [10.7]

19. Given: $\tan K = 0.5543$ and $JK = 10$ Find LJ.

20. Given: $\sin K = 0.6947$ and $JK = 8$ Find LK.

Find lengths to the nearest tenth. [10.8]

21. A flagpole casts a 20-meter shadow while the angle of elevation of the sun is 42°. How tall is the flagpole?

22. Two sides of an isosceles triangle each measure 12 cm, and the vertex angle measures 130°. Find the length of the altitude to the base.

*23. $ABCD$ is an isosceles trapezoid with $\overline{AB} \parallel \overline{CD}$. If $AB = 25$, $CD = 17$, and m $\angle A = 52$, find BC.

Chapter Ten Test

1. Given: Rt. △PQR with altitude $\overline{RS}$. Which triangles formed are similar?

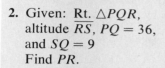

2. Given: Rt. △PQR, altitude $\overline{RS}$, $PQ = 36$, and $SQ = 9$ Find PR.

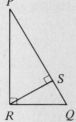

3. Given: Rt. △HJK, $HK = 4$, and $KJ = 7$ Find HJ.

4. Given: Rt. △HJK, $HJ = 9$, and $KJ = 7$ Find HK.

Which of the following can be lengths of sides of a right triangle? (Ex. 5–7)

5. 5, 12, 13

6. 2, 3, 5

7. $\sqrt{2}x$, $\sqrt{3}x$, $\sqrt{6}x$

8. Find the length of the altitude to the hypotenuse of a right triangle if the lengths of the legs are 10 and 24.

*9. If the edges of a rectangular solid are 5 cm, 6 cm, and 6 cm long, find the length of a diagonal of the solid.

10. Given: △XYZ is a 45°–45° rt. △ and $XY = 6$ Find YZ.

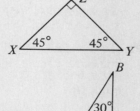

11. Given: △ABC is a 30°–60° rt. △ and $AB = 12$ Find CB and AC.

12. Given: Rt. △DEF, $DE = 13$, $EF = 5$, and $DF = 12$ Find cos D.

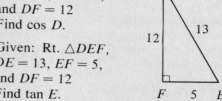

13. Given: Rt. △DEF, $DE = 13$, $EF = 5$, and $DF = 12$ Find tan E.

Use the table of trigonometric ratios below for Items 14–20.

Angle Measure	Sin	Cos	Tan
28	0.4695	0.8829	0.5317
29	0.4848	0.8746	0.5543
30	0.5000	0.8660	0.5774
60	0.8660	0.5000	1.732
61	0.8746	0.4848	1.804
62	0.8829	0.4695	1.881

14. Find cos 62°.

15. If tan $A = 1.839$, find m ∠A to the nearest degree.

16. Given: Rt. △RST, m ∠$R = 29$ and $ST = 10$ Find RT to the nearest tenth.

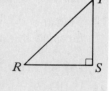

17. Given: Rt. △RST, m ∠$T = 62$ and $RT = 10$ Find ST to the nearest tenth.

Find lengths to the nearest tenth.

18. In ▱$ABCD$, m ∠$B = 29$, and $AD = 15$. Find the length of the altitude from C to $\overline{AB}$.

* 19. An angle of a rhombus measures, 124° and the diagonal opposite that angle measures 12. Find the measure of the other diagonal.

College Prep Test

Directions: Choose the one best answer to each question or problem.

1. Two highways meet at right angles. A post is 30 ft from one road and 50 ft from the other road. How far is the post from the intersection?

   (A) 40 ft (B) 60 ft (C) $2\sqrt{85}$ ft
   (D) $10\sqrt{34}$ ft (E) none of these

2. In the diagram below, $\angle BCA$, $\angle ADC$, $\angle ADE$ are right angles.

   $AB = 17$
   $BC = 8$
   $CD = 9$
   $DE = 5$

   Find EA

   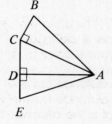

   (A) 12 (B) 13 (C) 15 (D) 25 (E) 17

3. In the diagram below, $\overline{BC} \perp \overline{AC}$.

   $CB = 12$
   $AC = 27$
   $AD = 1\frac{1}{4} CD$

   Find the measure of $\angle DBC$.

   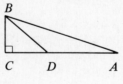

   (A) 45 (B) 30 (C) 60 (D) 50
   (E) none of these

4. A 25-foot ladder is placed against a vertical wall of a building. The foot of the ladder is 7 ft from the base of the building. If the top of the ladder slips 4 ft, how many feet will the bottom of the ladder slide?
   (A) 9 ft (B) 15 ft (C) 5 ft (D) 8 ft
   (E) 4 ft

5. In the figure below, $MP = OP$, $MN = 4$, $NP = 3$, $\overline{ON} \perp \overline{NM}$. Find MO.

   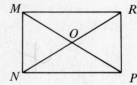

   (A) $4\sqrt{3}$ (B) 8 (C) $4\sqrt{5}$ (D) 12
   (E) $5\sqrt{2}$

6. $MNPR$ is a rectangle.
   $MN = 12$
   $MR = 16$
   Find NO.

   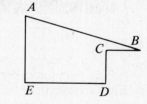

   (A) 8 (B) 20 (C) 14 (D) 15 (E) 10

7. Given: $\overline{AE} \perp \overline{ED}$
   $\overline{CD} \perp \overline{ED}$
   $\overline{DC} \perp \overline{CB}$
   $ED = 13$, $CD = 3$
   $CB = 2$, $AE = 11$
   Find AB.

   (A) 17 (B) 13 (C) 14 (D) 15 (E) 8

8. In right triangle ABC, $\overline{CD}$, the altitude to the hypotenuse $\overline{AB}$, measures 3. If DB exceeds AD by 8, find AB.
   (A) 9 (B) $8\frac{1}{2}$ (C) 10 (D) 12 (E) 15

9. Triangle ABC is equilateral.
   $\overline{BD} \perp \overline{AC}$
   $BD = 6\sqrt{3}$
   Find AB.

   (A) 6 (B) $12\sqrt{3}$
   (C) $3\sqrt{3}$ (D) 12 (E) $6\sqrt{3}$

11 CIRCLES AND LINES

A Square Circle?

RULE: The *distance* between two points in a jump-plane is defined as the least number of jumps from one point to another.

The distance from *A* to *B* is 1 jump.
The distance from *F* to *L* is 3 jumps.
What is the distance from *A* to *K*?

A	B	C	D
E	F	G	H
I	J	K	L

A *jump-circle* is defined as the set of all points in a jump-plane a given distance from a fixed point.

The set of points ringed in black is an an example of a jump-circle with center *P* and a "radius" of 2 jumps.

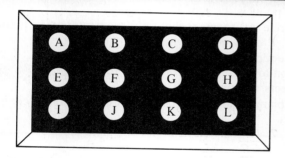

1. Construct a jump circle with a "radius" of 3 jumps. What appears to be true of jump circles?

2. If *r* is the length of a "radius" of a jump circle and *s* is the length of a "side," express *s* in terms of *r*.

Read	→	Plan	→	Solve	→	Interpret

11.1 Circles and Lines

To identify segments and lines related to circles
To prove and apply theorems about radii and chords

Segments and lines related to a circle are shown below. The symbol for circle is ⊙.

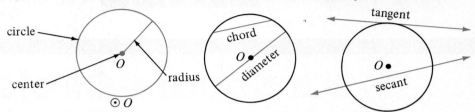

Definitions:	A circle is the set of all points in a plane that are a given distance from a given point in the plane. The given point is the **center** of the circle.
circle, center	
radius (radii)	A **radius** (plural: **radii**) of a circle is a segment that joins the center and a point on the circle.
chord	A *chord* is a segment whose endpoints lie on the circle.
diameter	A *diameter* is a chord that contains the center of the circle.
secant	A *secant* is a line that intersects the circle in two points.
tangent	A *tangent* is a line that is coplanar with the circle and intersects the circle in exactly one point.

Example 1 Identify a radius, a diameter, a chord, a secant, and a tangent of ⊙O.

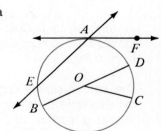

Radius: $\overline{OB}$, $\overline{OC}$, or $\overline{OD}$
Diameter: $\overline{BD}$
Chord: $\overline{EA}$ or $\overline{BD}$
Secant: $\overleftrightarrow{EA}$
Tangent: $\overleftrightarrow{FA}$

The following theorem follows from the definition of a circle.

Theorem 11.1 All radii of a circle are congruent. (See Exercise 19.)

From Theorem 11.1, you can also conclude that each diameter of a circle is twice as long as a radius of the circle; that is,
$$d = 2r.$$
Thus, if $r = 7$, then $d = 14$.

$d = 2r$

The next theorem states an important relationship between radii and chords of circle.

┌ **Theorem 11.2**   In a circle, a radius perpendicular to a chord bisects ┐
the chord.

Given: $\odot O$ with radius
$\overline{OA} \perp$ chord $\overline{XY}$ at B
Prove: $\overline{OA}$ bisects $\overline{XY}$.

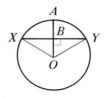

Analysis:
Draw radii $\overline{OX}$ and $\overline{OY}$.
Show $\triangle OBX \cong \triangle OBY$.

Proof

Statements	Reasons
1. $\odot O$, with radius $\overline{OA} \perp$ chord $\overline{XY}$ at B	1. Given
2. Draw radii $\overline{OX}$ and $\overline{OY}$.	2. Two points are contained in exactly one line.
3. $\overline{OX} \cong \overline{OY}$ (H)	3. All radii of a $\odot$ are $\cong$.
4. $\overline{OB} \cong \overline{OB}$ (L)	4. Reflexive property
5. $\triangle XOB$ and $\triangle YOB$ are rt. $\triangle$'s.	5. $\perp$'s form rt. $\angle$'s; def. of rt. $\triangle$.
6. $\triangle XOB \cong \triangle YOB$	6. HL for $\cong$ rt. $\triangle$'s.
7. $\overline{XB} \cong \overline{YB}$	7. CPCTC
8. $\therefore \overline{OA}$ bisects $\overline{XY}$.	8. Def. of bisector

Example 2   Given: Radius $\overline{OR} \perp$ chord $\overline{PQ}$;
$PS = 3x - 1$ and $SQ = x + 9$.
Find PS and SQ.

$$PS = SQ, \text{ by Th. 11.2}$$
$$3x - 1 = x + 9$$
$$2x = 10$$
$$x = 5$$
$$PS = 3x - 1 = 3 \cdot 5 - 1 = 14; \; SQ = x + 9 = 5 + 9 = 14$$
Thus, $PS = 14$ and $SQ = 14$.

Example 3   In a circle with a radius 10 cm long, a chord is 6 cm from the center. How long is the chord?

$\overline{OD} \perp \overline{AB}$
$(AO)^2 = (OD)^2 + (AD)^2$
$10^2 = 6^2 + (AD)^2$
$100 = 36 + (AD)^2$
$64 = (AD)^2$
$AD = 8$

◄ *Distance from a point to a line is the length of the $\perp$ segment.*

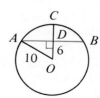

   ◄   *Th. 11.2*
Thus, $AB = 16$ cm.

Reading in Geometry

Write A if the statement is *always* true. Write S if the statement is *sometimes* true. Write N if the statement is *never* true.

1. A circle is a polygon.
2. All radii of a circle are congruent.
3. A secant is part of a chord.
4. A chord is part of a tangent.
5. A diameter is a chord.
6. A chord is a diameter.
7. The union of two radii of a circle is a diameter of the circle.
8. A diameter is twice as long as a radius.
9. A radius of a circle is part of the circle.
10. All points of a circle are equidistant from the center of the circle.

Written Exercises

For each ⊙O, name all radii and diameters. For each ⊙Q, name all secants, chords, and tangents.

1.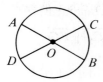

2.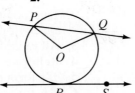

3.

4.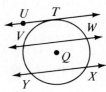

Which triangles are congruent? Why?

5. Given: $\overline{BD}$ is a diameter of ⊙O and $\overline{AB} \cong \overline{CB}$.

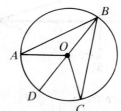

6. Given: $\overline{BD}$ is a diameter of ⊙O and $\angle AOB \cong \angle COB$.

In addition to the "given" in Exercises 7–16, ⊙O has $\overline{OP} \perp \overline{AB}$.

7. Given: $OP = 4$ and $OB = 5$
   Find AB.
8. Given: $AB = 10$ and $OB = 8$.
   Find OP.
9. Given: $OP = 6$ and m $\angle ABO = 30$.
   Find OB and AB.
10. Given: $OB = 10$ and m $\angle POB = 60$
    Find OP and AB.
11. Given: $OP = 7$ and m $\angle POB = 45$
    Find OB and AB.
12. Given: $OB = 8$ and m $\angle ABO = 45$
    Find OP and AB.
13. Given: $AB = 18$ and m $\angle POB = 45$
    Find OP and OB.
14. Given: $AB = 16$ and m $\angle ABO = 30$
    Find OP and OB.
15. Given: $AP = 3x + 4$ and $PB = 5x - 2$
    Find AB.
16. Given: $AO = x + 8$ and $OB = 2x - 1$
    Find AO and OB.

17. Given: Radii $\overline{OA}$ and $\overline{OB}$
Prove: $\angle OAB \cong \angle OBA$

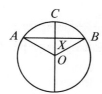

18. Given: $\angle AOC \cong \angle BOC$, $\overline{OA}$ and $\overline{OB}$ are radii.
Prove: $\overline{OC}$ is the $\perp$ bisector of $\overline{AB}$.

19. Prove Theorem 11.1.

20. Prove: In a circle, a radius that bisects a chord which is not a diameter is perpendicular to the chord.

21. Given: Diameters $\overline{AC}$ and $\overline{BD}$ of $\odot O$
Prove: $\overline{AD} \cong \overline{BC}$

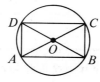

22. Given: Diameters $\overline{AC}$ and $\overline{BD}$ of $\odot O$
Prove: $ABCD$ is a rectangle.

23. Given: Diameter $\overline{XY}$ of $\odot O$, chord $\overline{RS} \parallel$ chord $\overline{TU}$, and $\overline{XY}$ bisects $\overline{RS}$ at M.
Prove: N is the midpoint of $\overline{TU}$.

24. Given: $\overline{DC}$ is a diameter of $\odot O$. $\overline{DC} \perp$ chord $\overline{AB}$.
Prove: $\overline{AC} \cong \overline{BC}$

25. Given: Diameter $\overline{AB}$ bisects chords $\overline{CD}$ and $\overline{FG}$.
Prove: $\overline{CD} \parallel \overline{FG}$

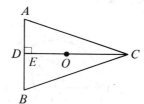

26. A chord is as long as its distance from the center of the circle. A second chord of the same circle is twice as long. How far is the second chord from the center?

27. Prove: The perpendicular bisector of a chord of a circle in the same plane as the circle goes through the center of the circle.

28. Prove: If two chords of a circle have a common endpoint and form congruent angles with the radius drawn to that endpoint, then the chords are congruent.

29. Prove: Two points of a circle each equidistant from two other points of the circle determine a diameter of the circle.

Cumulative Review

1. Given: $\overline{RV} \perp \overline{ST}$ and $\overline{TU} \perp \overline{SR}$
Prove: $\triangle RSV \sim \triangle TSU$

2. Given: $\overline{WZ} \parallel \overline{XY}$
Prove: $\triangle ZWP \sim \triangle XYP$

CIRCLES AND LINES

11.2 Congruent Circles

OBJECTIVES ► **To identify congruent circles**
To prove and apply theorems about chords and radii in congruent circles

In general, congruent figures are figures that have the same size and shape. Congruent circles are defined more specifically.

Definition:
congruent circles

Congruent circles are circles that have congruent radii. $\odot O \cong \odot P$ is read "$\odot O$ is congruent to $\odot P$.

$\odot O \cong \odot P$

In the diagram above, circles O and P are congruent since $\overline{OA} \cong \overline{PB}$. Some theorems in this book apply either to one circle or to congruent circles. Proofs will be presented for congruent circles only.

Theorem 11.3 If chords of a circle or of congruent circles are congruent, then the chords are equidistant from the center(s).

Given: $\odot O \cong \odot P$,
$OC \perp AB$,
$PF \perp DE$, and
$AB \cong DE$
Prove: $OC = PF$

Analysis: Show $\triangle AOB \cong$
$\triangle EPD$. Then $\overline{OC}$
and $\overline{PF}$ are corr.
altitudes of $\cong$
$\triangle$'s

Proof

Statements	Reasons
1. $\odot O \cong \odot P$, $\overline{OC} \perp \overline{AB}$, $\overline{PF} \perp \overline{DE}$, $AB \cong DE$	1. Given
2. $\overline{OA} \cong \overline{PE}$, $\overline{OB} \cong \overline{PD}$	2. Def. of $\cong$ circles
3. $\triangle AOB \cong \triangle EPD$	3. SSS for $\cong$ $\triangle$'s
4. $\therefore \overline{OC} \cong \overline{PF}$ and $OC = PF$	4. Corr. alt. of $\cong$ $\triangle$'s are $\cong$.

Example 1 Given: $\odot O$ with $JK = 12$, $MS = 6$,
$OS \perp MN$, $OR \perp JK$, and $OR = 3$
Find OS.

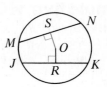

If $MS = 6$, then $MN = 12$ by Th. 11.2.
So $\overline{MN} \cong \overline{JK}$.
$\overline{OR} \cong \overline{OS}$ by Th. 11.3.
Thus, $OS = 3$.

The converse of Theorem 11.3 is stated below as Theorem 11.4.

Theorem 11.4   If chords of a circle or of congruent circles are equidistant front the center(s), then the chords are congruent.

Given: $\odot O \cong \odot P$,
         $OC = PF$,
         $\overline{OC} \perp \overline{AB}$, and
         $\overline{PF} \perp \overline{DE}$
Prove: $\overline{AB} \cong \overline{DE}$

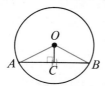 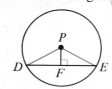

Analysis: Show
$\triangle OCA \cong$
$\triangle PFD$. Then
$\overline{AC} \cong \overline{DF}$.

Proof: (See Exercise 24.)

Recall that the distance from a point to a line is the length of the perpendicular segment from the point to the line. In Theorems 11.3 and 11.4, the term "equidistant" refers to equal lengths of the segments perpendicular to the chords.

    Theorems 11.3 and 11.4 can also be applied to a polygon inscribed in a circle.

**Definitions:
inscribed
polygon
circumscribed
circle**

An *inscribed polygon* is a polygon whose sides are chords of a circle. The polygon is *inscribed* in the circle, and the circle is *circumscribed* about the polygon.

Notice that when a polygon is inscribed in a circle, each vertex of the polygon lies on the circle.

Reading in Geometry

Draw each figure described.

1. An equilateral triangle inscribed in a circle
2. A circle circumscribed about an isosceles trapezoid
3. A scalene triangle inscribed in a circle and circumscribed about another circle
4. A circle with two congruent chords that intersect in a point that is not an endpoint of the chords
5. A circle with two congruent chords that have a common endpoint.
6. Two congruent quadrilaterals inscribed in two congruent circles

Written Exercises

In each case, determine whether $\odot O \cong \odot P$.

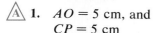

1. $AO = 5$ cm, and
   $CP = 5$ cm
3. $AB = 4$ cm, and
   $CD = 4$ cm
5. $AB = 3$ km, and
   $CD = 3$m
7. $OA = 8$ cm, and
   $CD = 1.6$ m

2. $AO = 8$ cm, and
   $DP = 8$ cm
4. $AB = 10$ cm, and
   $CP = 5$ cm
6. $AO = 12$ mm, and
   $CD = 2.4$ cm
8. $OB = 35$ cm, and
   $CD = 0.7$ m

CONGRUENT CIRCLES

In ⊙O, $\overline{OD} \perp \overline{AC}$ and $\overline{OE} \perp \overline{BC}$. **Find the indicated measures.**

9. Given: $OD = 4$, $AC = 16$.
and $OE = 4$
Find BC.

11. Given: $OD = 3$, $OE = 3$,
and m $\angle C = 40$
Find m $\angle A$ and m $\angle B$.

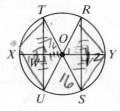

10. Given: $AC = 16$, $BE = 8$,
and $OE = 4$
Find OD.

12. Given: m $\angle A = 50$, m $\angle B = 50$,
and $AC = 30$
Find CE.

$\overline{XY}$ **is a diameter of ⊙O. Find the indicated measures.**

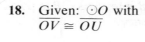

13. Given: $\overline{OY}$ bisects $\angle ROS$,
$OR = 12$, m $\angle ROS = 120$,
and $\overline{TU} \cong \overline{RS}$.
Find WX.

15. Given: $\overline{OY} \perp \overline{RS}$ at V,
$\overline{OX} \perp \overline{TU}$ at W, $\overline{TU} \cong \overline{RS}$,
$OW = 5$, and $OT = 9$
Find VY.

14. Given: $\overline{OY} \perp \overline{RS}$ at V,
$\overline{OX} \perp \overline{TU}$ at W, $OV = 12$,
$OS = 16$, and $\overline{TU} \cong \overline{RS}$
Find OW.

16. Given: $\overline{OY} \perp \overline{RS}$ at V,
$\overline{OX} \perp \overline{TU}$ at W, $\overline{OW} \cong \overline{OV}$,
m $\angle R = 45$, and $OS = 8$
Find TU.

On the basis of the given information, which segments can you conclude are congruent? [Ex. 17–19]

Ⓑ 17. Given: ⊙$A \cong$ ⊙B,
$\overline{RS} \cong \overline{TU}$, $\overline{AM} \perp \overline{RS}$,
and $\overline{BN} \perp \overline{TU}$

18. Given: ⊙O with
$\overline{OV} \cong \overline{OU}$

19. Given: Radii $\overline{OA} \cong \overline{QC}$,
$\overline{OE} \perp \overline{AB}$, and $\overline{QF} \perp \overline{CD}$

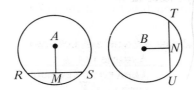
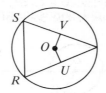

20. Given: ⊙O with $\overline{OT} \perp \overline{XY}$
$\overline{OU} \perp \overline{WZ}$, and $\overline{OT} \cong \overline{OU}$
Prove: $\triangle XOY \cong \triangle ZOW$

22. Given: ⊙O with $\overline{OT} \perp \overline{XY}$,
$\overline{OU} \perp \overline{WZ}$, and $\angle X \cong \angle Z$
Prove: $\overline{XY} \cong \overline{WZ}$

24. Prove Theorem 11.4.

21. Given: ⊙O with $\overline{OT} \perp \overline{XY}$,
$\overline{OU} \perp \overline{WZ}$, and $\angle XOY \cong$
$\angle ZOW$
Prove: $\overline{OT} \cong \overline{OU}$

23. Given: ⊙O with $\overline{OT} \perp \overline{XY}$,
$\overline{OU} \perp \overline{WZ}$, and $\angle XOT \cong$
$\angle ZOU$
Prove: $\overline{XY} \cong \overline{WZ}$

Prove each statement.

Ⓒ 25. If congruent chords are equidistant
from the centers of circles, then
the circles are congruent.

27. If the center of a circle is equidistant
from the sides of an inscribed
triangle, then the triangle is equilateral.

26. If a point on a circle is equidistant
from two radii, then the radius
from the point bisects the angle
formed by the two given radii.

28. If a chord of a circle makes an
angle of 30° with a diameter, then the
distance from the center to the chord is
one fourth the length of the diameter.

11.3 Properties of Tangents

To prove and apply theorems about tangents to circles

A circle separates the plane into three sets of points: the circle itself, the interior of the circle, and the exterior of the circle. The exterior of the circle is the set of all points in the plane of the circle whose distances from the center are greater than the length of a radius. Thus, for point Q in the exterior of $\odot O$, $OQ > OR$, where OR is a radius.

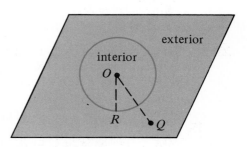

A *tangent* to a circle is a line, coplanar with the circle, that intersects the circle in exactly one point. The point is called the *point of tangency*. In the diagram at the right, $\overleftrightarrow{TB}$ intersects $\odot P$ at point T, so T is the point of tangency.

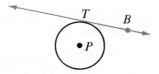

Theorem 11.5 If a line is tangent to a circle, then it is perpendicular to the radius drawn to the point of tangency.

Given: l is tangent to $\odot O$ at A.
Prove: $\overline{OA} \perp l$

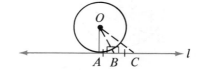

Analysis: Use an indirect proof. Assume $\overline{OA} \not\perp l$. Then some segment such as $\overline{OB}$, $\perp l$. This leads to a contradiction.

Outline of Proof

Assume $\overline{OA} \not\perp l$. Then there is a segment $\overline{OB}$ such that $\overline{OB} \perp l$. On the ray opposite $\overrightarrow{BA}$, choose a point C such that $\overline{BC} \cong \overline{BA}$. $\overline{OB} \cong \overline{OB}$ and rt. $\angle OBA \cong$ rt. $\angle OBC$, so $\triangle OBA \cong \triangle OBC$. Thus, $\overline{OC} \cong \overline{OA}$ and $\overline{OC}$ must also be a radius. Then both points A and C lie on $\odot O$.

Theorem 11.6 If a line is perpendicular to a radius at its endpoint on the circle, then the line is tangent to the circle.

Given: $\odot O$ with $\overline{OD} \perp l$ at D.
Prove: l is tangent to $\odot O$ at D.

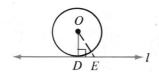

Analysis: Let E be any point on l other than D. Show E is in the exterior of $\odot O$.
Proof: (See Exercise 16.)

A **tangent** segment is a segment that joins the point of tangency and another point on the tangent. In Example 1 below, $\overline{PT}$ is a tangent segment.

Example 1 Given: $\overline{PT}$ tangent to $\odot O$.
$\overline{OT}$ is a radius, $OT = 6$ and $PO = 9$.
Find PT.

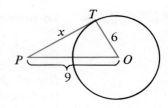

$\triangle OPT$ is a rt. $\triangle$ by Th. 11.5.
$$x^2 + 6^2 = 9^2$$
$$x^2 + 36 = 81$$
$$x^2 = 45$$
$$x = \sqrt{45}, \text{ or } 3\sqrt{5}$$
Thus, PT is $3\sqrt{5}$.

As indicated in Theorem 11.7, two tangent segments may be congruent.

Theorem 11.7 Tangent segments to a circle from the same point are congruent.

Given: $\odot O$ with tangent
segments $\overline{BA}$ and $\overline{BC}$
Prove: $\overline{BA} \cong \overline{BC}$

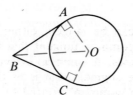

Analysis: Draw radii $\overline{OA}$ and
$\overline{OC}$. Draw $\overline{OB}$. Show
$\triangle OAB \cong \triangle OCB$.

Proof

Statements	Reasons
1. $\odot O$ with tangent segments $\overline{BA}$ and $\overline{BC}$	1. Given
2. Draw radii $\overline{OA}$ and $\overline{OC}$. Draw $\overline{OB}$.	2. Two points are contained in exactly one line.
3. $\overline{OA} \perp \overline{BA}$ and $\overline{OC} \perp \overline{BC}$	3. Radius drawn to tangency pt. is $\perp$.
4. $\triangle AOB$ and $\triangle COB$ are rt. $\triangle$'s.	4. Def. of $\perp$ and def. of rt. $\triangle$.
5. $\overline{BO} \cong \overline{BO}$	5. Reflexive property
6. $\overline{OA} \cong \overline{OC}$	6. All radii of a $\odot$ are $\cong$.
7. $\triangle AOB \cong \triangle COB$	7. HL for $\cong$ rt. $\triangle$'s
8. $\therefore \overline{BA} \cong \overline{BC}$	8. CPCTC

If a circle is *inscribed* in a polygon, then the sides of the polygon form tangent segments.

Definitions:
circumscribed polygon
inscribed circle

A *circumscribed polygon* is a polygon whose sides are tangent to a circle. The polygon is *circumscribed* about the circle, and the circle is *inscribed* in the polygon.

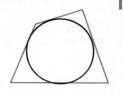

Example 2 Given: $\odot O$ with circumscribed $\triangle ABC$ and
chord $\overline{DE}$. m $\angle ADE = 6t - 2$ and
m $\angle AED = 4t + 22$.
Find m $\angle A$.

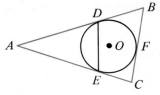

$\overline{AD} \cong \overline{AE}$ by Th. 11.7
So, $\angle ADE \cong \angle AED$. ◄ *∠'s opp. $\cong$ sides of $\triangle$ are $\cong$.*
$$6t - 2 = 4t + 22$$
$$2t = 24$$
$$t = 12$$
m $\angle ADE = 6(12) - 2 = 70$; m $\angle AED = 4(12) + 22 = 70$
Thus, m $\angle A = 180 - (70 + 70)$, or 40.
It is possible for a line to be tangent to two circles.

**Definition:
common
tangent**

> A *common tangent* is a line that is tangent to each of two coplanar circles.

A common tangent can be tangent either internally or externally. A **common internal tangent** is a common tangent that intersects the segment that joins the center of the two circles. A **common external tangent** is a common tangent that does not intersect the segment that joins the centers of the two circles. In the diagram below, l is a common internal tangent while m is a common external tangent.

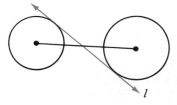
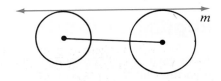

Two circles may also be tangent to each other.

**Definition:
tangent
circles**

> Two coplanar *circles* are *tangent* to each other if they are tangent to the same line at the same point.

Tangent circles may be tangent either internally or externally. Tangent circles are *tangent internally* if one lies in the interior of the other (except for the point of tangency). Tangent circles are *tangent externally* if each lies in the exterior of the other (except for the point of tangency). In the diagram below, $\odot P$ and $\odot Q$ are tangent internally while $\odot R$ and $\odot S$ are tangent externally.

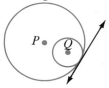
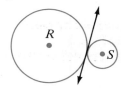

PROPERTIES OF TANGENTS

Example 3 Given two circles that are tangent externally, how many common internal tangents and how many common external tangents can be drawn?

Draw two circles that are tangent externally. Then draw all possible common tangents. ▶

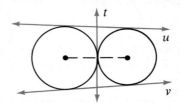

Thus, one common internal tangent, *t*, and two common external tangents, *u* and *v*, can be drawn.

Example 4 Given: $\odot O \cong \odot P$. $\odot O$ and $\odot P$ are tangent to $\overleftrightarrow{ST}$ at *T*.
Prove: $\overline{OS} \cong \overline{PS}$

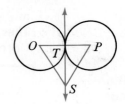

Proof

Statements	Reasons
1. $\odot O \cong \odot P$; $\odot O$ and $\odot P$ are tangent to $\overleftrightarrow{ST}$ at *T*.	1. Given
2. $\overline{OT} \perp \overleftrightarrow{ST}$, $\overline{PT} \perp \overleftrightarrow{ST}$	2. Radius drawn to pt. of tangency is $\perp$.
3. $\angle OTS \cong \angle PTS$	3. $\perp$'s form $\cong$ rt. $\angle$'s.
4. $\overline{OT} \cong \overline{PT}$	4. Radii of $\cong \odot$'s are $\cong$.
5. $\overline{ST} \cong \overline{ST}$	5. Reflexive property
6. $\triangle OTS \cong \triangle PTS$	6. SAS for $\cong \triangle$'s
7. $\therefore \overline{OS} \cong \overline{PS}$	7. CPCTC

Reading in Geometry

Draw each pair of coplanar circles as indicated below. Then tell (a) how many common internal tangents and (b) how many common external tangents can be drawn for each picture.

1. Two circles which are tangent internally
2. Two circles which intersect in two points
3. Two non-intersecting circles, one in the interior of the other
4. Two non-intersecting circles, each in the exterior of the other.

Oral Exercises

Tell whether each pair of circles is tangent internally, tangent externally, or neither. Then tell whether the line is a common internal tangent, a common external tangent, or neither.

1.

2.

3.

4.
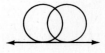

Tell whether the circle is inscribed in the polygon, the polygon is inscribed in the circle, or neither.

5.   6.   7.   8.

Written Exercises _____

Ⓐ 1. Given: Tangents $\overrightarrow{PR}$, $\overrightarrow{PS}$ and $\overrightarrow{PT}$, and $PR = 11$ Find PT.

2. Given: Circumscribed $\triangle ABC$, $AD = 4$, $DB = 6$, and $CE = 2$ Find $AB + BC + CA$.

3. Given: $\overrightarrow{PH}$ and $\overrightarrow{PJ}$ tangent to $\odot O$ and $\odot Q$, $IH = 7$, and $PI = 10$ Find PJ.

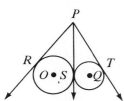   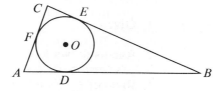   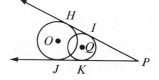

4. Given: Radii $\overline{OA}$ and $\overline{OC}$, tangents $\overleftrightarrow{AP}$ and $\overleftrightarrow{CP}$, and m $\angle AOC = 150$ Find m $\angle APC$.

5. Given: Circumscribed polygon $ACEG$, $AB = 5$, $CD = 4$, $DE = 3$, and $FG = 2$ Find $AC + CE + EG + GA$.

6. Given: Diameter $\overline{XY}$, tangent $\overleftrightarrow{WZ}$, $XY = 10$, and $WZ = 12$ Find YZ.

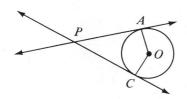   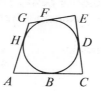   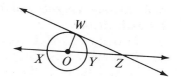

Which segments are congruent? Which angles are congruent? [Ex. 7–9]

7. Given: $\overleftrightarrow{PQ}$ tangent to $\odot O$ at Q, $\overleftrightarrow{PR}$ tangent to $\odot O$ and $\odot T$ at R, $\overleftrightarrow{PS}$ tangent to $\odot T$ at S

8. Given: $\overleftrightarrow{AB}$ tangent to $\odot O$ at A and $\odot P$ at B, $\overleftrightarrow{CD}$ tangent to $\odot O$ at C and $\odot P$ at D

9. Given: $\overline{FI}$ is a diameter of $\odot O$, $\overleftrightarrow{EG}$ tangent to $\odot O$ at F, $\overleftrightarrow{HJ}$ tangent to $\odot O$ at I

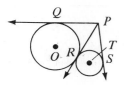   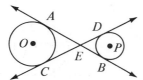   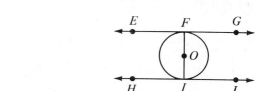

PROPERTIES OF TANGENTS

Ⓑ **10.** Given: $\overrightarrow{TB}$ tangent to ⊙O at B, and $\overrightarrow{TC}$ tangent to ⊙O at C. Prove: $\overrightarrow{TO}$ bisects ∠BTC

11. Given: Two circles with same center O, and chord $\overline{AB}$ of outer circle tangent to inner circle at X Prove: $\overline{AX} \cong \overline{BX}$

12. Given: $\overleftrightarrow{TC}, \overleftrightarrow{PD}, \overleftrightarrow{TP}$ tangent to ⊙O at C, D, and E respectively; $\overleftrightarrow{TC} \parallel \overleftrightarrow{PD}$. Prove: $\overline{TO} \perp \overline{PO}$

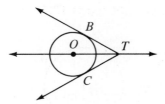

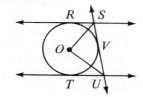

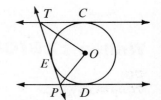

Ⓒ **13.** Given: $\overrightarrow{PA}$ tangent to ⊙O at A, and $\overrightarrow{PB}$ tangent to ⊙O at B Prove: m ∠P = 2 m ∠OAB

14. Given: $\overleftrightarrow{RS}$ tangent to ⊙O at R, $\overleftrightarrow{TU}$ tangent to ⊙O at T, $\overleftrightarrow{SU}$ tangent to ⊙O at V, and $\overline{OS} \perp \overline{OU}$ Prove: $\overleftrightarrow{RS} \parallel \overleftrightarrow{TU}$

15. Given: Radius $\overline{OA} \perp$ radius $\overline{OB}$ of ⊙O, chord $\overline{AD}$, $\overleftrightarrow{DE}$ tangent at D, and radius $\overline{OD}$ Prove: ∠ECD ≅ ∠EDC

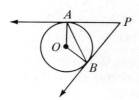

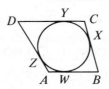

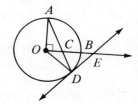

16. Prove Theorem 11.6.
17. Given: Circumscribed △XYZ, XY = 7, YZ = 8, and ZX = 5 Find AX, BY, and CZ.

18. Given: Circumscribed polygon ABCD, AB = 21, BC = 24, and CD = 30 Find AD.

19. Given: $\overleftrightarrow{XY}$ tangent to ⊙O and ⊙P, OX = 16, PY = 6, and OP = 26 Find XY.

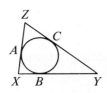

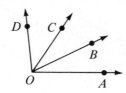

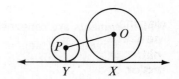

Cumulative Review

1. Given: m ∠BOD = b, m ∠AOC = a, and $\overrightarrow{OB}$ bisects ∠AOC Find m ∠AOD.

2. Given: ∠AOD = d, m ∠AOB = b, and $\overrightarrow{OC}$ bisects ∠DOB Find m ∠AOC.

11.4 Measures of Arcs

► **To find degree measures of minor arcs, major arcs, and semicircles**
To identify concentric circles

In this lesson, only degree measures of arcs are discussed. In Chapter 12, lengths of arcs will be discussed.

Definitions:
arc
central angle

An *arc* is part of a circle. $\overset{\frown}{AB}$ is an arc of circle O.

A *central angle* of a circle is an angle whose vertex is the center of the circle. $\angle AOB$ is a central angle of $\odot O$.

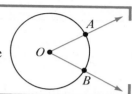

Different types of arcs are shown below. Their definitions follow.

Minor arc	Major arc	Semicircle

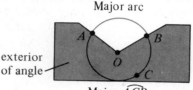
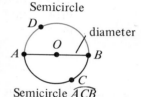

Minor $\overset{\frown}{AB}$
Read: Minor arc AB

Major $\overset{\frown}{ACB}$
Read: Major arc $\overset{\frown}{ACB}$

Semicircle $\overset{\frown}{ACB}$
Read: Semicircle ACB

Definitions:
minor arc
major arc
semicircle

Minor $\overset{\frown}{AB}$ consists of points A and B and all points of $\odot O$ that are in the interior of central $\angle AOB$.
Major $\overset{\frown}{ACB}$ consists of points A and B and all points of $\odot O$ that are in the exterior of central $\angle AOB$.
Semicircle $\overset{\frown}{ACB}$ (or $\overset{\frown}{ADB}$) consists of endpoints A and B of diameter $\overline{AB}$ and all points of $\odot O$ that lie on one side of $\overline{AB}$.

The degree measures of arcs are defined in terms of central angles.

Definitions:
degree
measure
minor arc
major arc
semicircle

The *degree measure of minor $\overset{\frown}{AB}$* is equal to the degree measure of central $\angle AOB$.
The *degree measure of major $\overset{\frown}{ACB}$* is equal to 360 minus the degree measure of central $\angle AOB$.
The *degree measure of semicircle $\overset{\frown}{ACB}$* is equal to 180.

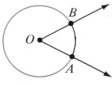
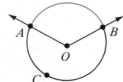
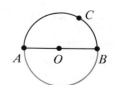

$m \overset{\frown}{AB} = m \angle AOB$
$m \overset{\frown}{ACB} = 360 - m \angle AOB$
m semicircle $\overset{\frown}{ACB} = 180$

MEASURES OF ARCS

Recall that the sum of the measures of the angles on one side of a line is 180°. This, along with the definition of *degree measure* can be used to show that the degree measure of a circle is equal to 360°.

Example 1

Given: m ∠AOB = 32
Find m$\widehat{AB}$

m $\widehat{AB}$ = 32

Given: m ∠QOR = 27
Find m$\widehat{QR}$

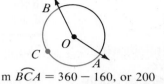

m $\widehat{QR}$ = 27

Given: m ∠BOA = 160
Find m$\widehat{BCA}$.

m $\widehat{BCA}$ = 360 − 160, or 200

The Arc Addition Postulate stated below applies to major arcs, minor arcs, and semicircles.

Postulate 23   Arc Addition Postulate   If P is a point on $\widehat{AB}$, then m$\widehat{AP}$ + m$\widehat{PB}$ = m$\widehat{APB}$.

In Example 2, the Arc Addition Postulate is used to add the measures of two arcs that form a circle.

Example 2

Given: m$\widehat{AB}$ = 62 and m$\widehat{BC}$ = 141
Find m$\widehat{ABC}$ and m$\widehat{ADC}$.

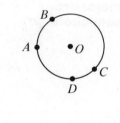

$$m\widehat{ABC} = 62 + 141, \text{ or}$$
$$203 \text{ by Post. 23.}$$

$$m\widehat{ADC} + m\widehat{ABC} = 360 \quad \blacktriangleright \quad m\widehat{ADC} = 360 - m\widehat{ABC}$$
$$= 360 - 203,$$
$$\text{or } 157$$

Thus, m$\widehat{ABC}$ = 203
and m$\widehat{ADC}$ = 157

If you toss a stone into a lake, the waves that are formed represent a model of concentric circles.

Definition:
concentric circles

Concentric circles are coplanar circles with a common center.

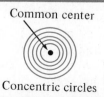

Common center

Concentric circles

Written Exercises _____

Are the circles concentric circles?

 1.　　　　2. 　　3. 　　4.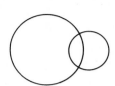

Find each indicated arc measure.

　　　　　　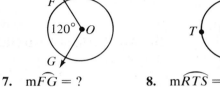

5.　m$\widehat{AB}$ = ?　　6.　m$\widehat{HKJ}$ = ?　　7.　m$\widehat{FG}$ = ?　　8.　m$\widehat{RTS}$ = ?

　　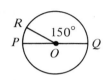

9.　m$\widehat{IJ}$ = ?　　10.　m$\widehat{WZ}$ = ?　　11.　m$\widehat{PR}$ = ?　　12.　m$\widehat{AB}$ = ?

For Exercises 13–15, use ⊙O with diameter $\overline{BD}$.

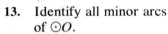

13.　Identify all minor arcs of ⊙O.
14.　Identify all major arcs of ⊙O.
15.　Identify all semicircles of ⊙O.

For Exercises 16–17, use ⊙Q.

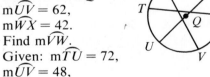

16.　Given: $\overline{UX}$ is a diameter of ⊙Q.
m$\widehat{UV}$ = 62,
m$\widehat{WX}$ = 42.
Find m$\widehat{VW}$.

17.　Given:　m$\widehat{TU}$ = 72,
m$\widehat{UV}$ = 48,
m$\widehat{VW}$ = 60,
m$\widehat{WX}$ = 72,
m$\widehat{XY}$ = 56,
m$\widehat{YT}$ = 52. Which chords (if any) are diameters?

For Exercises 18–21, use ⊙O with diameters $\overline{AC}$ and $\overline{BD}$ and m$\widehat{DC}$ = 79.

18.　Find m∠AOD.
19.　Find m∠AOB.
20.　Find m$\widehat{ADC}$.
21.　Find m$\widehat{BC}$.

For Exercises 22–25, use ⊙P with diameters $\overline{RT}$ and $\overline{SU}$ and m∠RPU = 143.

22.　Find m∠SPT.
23.　Find m$\widehat{RU}$.
24.　Find m∠RPS.
25.　Find m∠RSP.

MEASURES OF ARCS

Identify the contradictory information. [Ex. 26–27]

26. $\overline{GJ}$ and $\overline{HK}$ are diameters. $\mathrm{m}\widehat{GL} = 84$, $\mathrm{m}\widehat{LK} = 34$, $\mathrm{m}\widehat{KJ} = 62$, $\mathrm{m}\widehat{JI} = 27$, $\mathrm{m}\widehat{IH} = 79$, and $\mathrm{m}\widehat{HG} = 74$.

27. $\overline{GJ}$ is a diameter, $\mathrm{m}\widehat{GK} = 110$, $\mathrm{m}\widehat{LK} = 72$, $\mathrm{m}\widehat{LJ} = 142$, $\mathrm{m}\widehat{GI} = 113$, $\mathrm{m}\widehat{HI} = 44$, and $\mathrm{m}\widehat{IJ} = 77$.

28. Given: $\odot O$ with tangent $\overline{PA}$. and $\mathrm{m}\angle P = x$
Prove: $\mathrm{m}\widehat{AB} = 90 - x$

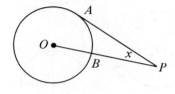

29. Given: $\odot O$ with tangents $\overline{PC}$ and $\overline{PD}$, and $\mathrm{m}\angle P = x$
Prove: $\mathrm{m}\widehat{CD} = 180 - x$

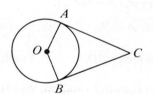

30. Given: $\odot O$ inscribed in $\triangle RST$, A, B, and C points of tangency, and $\mathrm{m}\angle R = 90$.
Prove: $\mathrm{m}\widehat{ABC} = 270$

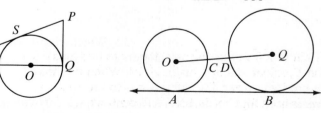

31. Given: $\odot O$ with tangents $\overline{AC}$ and $\overline{BC}$, $\mathrm{m}\widehat{AB} = 132$, and $OA = 8$
Find BC to the nearest tenth.

32. Given: $\odot O$ with tangents $\overline{AC}$ and $\overline{BC}$, $OB = 9$, and $AC = 14$
Find $\mathrm{m}\widehat{AB}$ to the nearest degree.

33. Given: $\odot O$ with $\triangle PQR$, and S and Q points of tangency
Prove: $\mathrm{m}\angle P = \mathrm{m}\widehat{TS}$

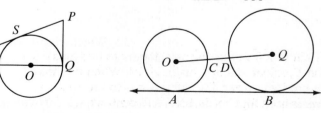

34. Given: $\overleftrightarrow{AB}$ tangent to $\odot O$ at A and to $\odot Q$ at B
Prove: $\mathrm{m}\widehat{AC} + \mathrm{m}\widehat{BD} = 180$

35. Given: $\odot O$ and $\odot Q$ with tangents $\overline{PR}$, $\overline{PS}$, and $\overline{PT}$
Prove: $\mathrm{m}\widehat{RS} + \mathrm{m}\widehat{ST} = 360 - \mathrm{m}\angle RPT$

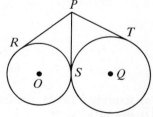

Cumulative Review

1. Find the length of a leg of an isosceles right triangle if the length of the hypotenuse is 10.

2. Find the length of a diagonal of a square if the length of a side is 7.

11.5 Arcs, Chords, and Central Angles

OBJECTIVES ▶ **To identify congruent arcs and congruent chords**
To prove relationships between arcs, chords, and central angles

This lesson deals with relationships between arcs, chords, and central angles of a circle or of congruent circles.

Definition:
congruent arcs

> In the same circle or in congruent circles, *congruent arcs* are arcs that have the same measure.

Notice that some arcs with the same measure are congruent and some are not.

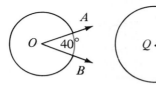

$\odot O \not\cong \odot Q$ and $m\overset{\frown}{AB} = m\overset{\frown}{CD}$.

But $\overset{\frown}{AB} \not\cong \overset{\frown}{CD}$.

$\odot O \cong \odot Q$ and $m\overset{\frown}{AB} = m\overset{\frown}{CD}$.

Also, $\overset{\frown}{AB} \cong \overset{\frown}{CD}$.

Example **1** Based on the given information, which arcs are congruent?

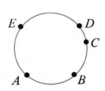

Given: $m\overset{\frown}{AB} = 48$, $m\overset{\frown}{AC} = 124$,
$\quad m\overset{\frown}{ABD} = 208$, and $m\overset{\frown}{ABE} = 312$
$m\overset{\frown}{EA} = 360 -$ ▶ $m\overset{\frown}{EA} = 48$ and $m\overset{\frown}{AB} = 48$.
$m\overset{\frown}{ABE}$
Thus, since $\overset{\frown}{EA}$ and $\overset{\frown}{AB}$ are in the same circle, $\overset{\frown}{EA} \cong \overset{\frown}{AB}$.

Notice that for chord $\overline{AB}$ in the diagram, there are two arcs with endpoints A and B, minor $\overset{\frown}{AB}$ and major $\overset{\frown}{ACB}$. When it is stated that a chord determines an arc, the reference is to the *minor* arc. This terminology is used for chords, arcs, and central angles. **Thus**

(1) $\overline{AB}$ determines $\overset{\frown}{AB}$ and $\angle O$.

(2) $\overset{\frown}{AB}$ determines $\overline{AB}$ and $\angle O$.

(3) $\angle O$ determines $\overline{AB}$ and $\overset{\frown}{AB}$.

Theorem 11.8 In a circle or in congruent circles, congruent arcs determine congruent central angles and congruent chords.

Given: $\odot O \cong \odot Q$ and
$\qquad \widehat{AB} \cong \widehat{CD}$
Prove; $\angle O \cong \angle Q$ and
$\qquad \overline{AB} \cong \overline{CD}$

Proof

Statements	Reasons
1. $\odot O \cong \odot Q$ and $\widehat{AB} \cong \widehat{CD}$	1. Given
2. $m\widehat{AB} = m\widehat{CD}$	2. Def. of $\cong$ arcs
3. $m\widehat{AB} = m \angle AOB;$ $m\widehat{CD} = m \angle CQD$	3. Def. of degree measure of minor arc
4. $m \angle O = m \angle Q$	4. Substitution
5. $\angle O \cong \angle Q$	5. Def. of $\cong$ $\angle$'s
6. $\overline{OA} \cong \overline{QC}; \overline{OB} \cong \overline{QD}$	6. Def. of $\cong$ $\odot$'s
7. $\triangle AOB \cong \triangle CQD$	7. SAS
8. $\therefore \overline{AB} \cong \overline{CD}$	8. CPCTC

Example 2 Which chords are congruent?

Use Post. 22 ► $m\widehat{AD} = 52 + 50 + 36 = 138$
$\qquad m\widehat{FC} = 50 + 36 + 43 = 129$
$\qquad m\widehat{EB} = 36 + 43 + 50 = 129$
$\qquad m\widehat{AB} = 360 - (52 + 50 + 36 + 43 + 50)$
$\qquad \qquad = 360 - 231 = 129$

$\widehat{FC} \cong \widehat{EB} \cong \widehat{AB}$ ► **Thus,** $\overline{FC} \cong \overline{EB} \cong \overline{AB}$ by Th. 11.8.

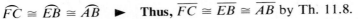

It is possible for two chords to be congruent while the central angles and arcs which they determine are not congruent. For example, $\overline{AB} \cong \overline{CD}$ as shown, but $\angle O \not\cong \angle P$. Also $\widehat{AB} \not\cong \widehat{CD}$ since $m\widehat{AB} = 78$ and $m\widehat{CD} = 112$. In this case, $\odot O \not\cong \odot P$. This suggests the following theorems.

Theorem 11.9 In a circle or in congruent circles, congruent chords determine congruent central angles and congruent arcs. (See Exercise 17.)

Theorem 11.10 In a circle or in congruent circles, congruent central angles determine congruent arcs and congruent chords. (See Exercise 18.)

Example 3 Prove: In a circle, a radius perpendicular to a chord bisects the arc determined by the chord.

Given: $\odot O$ with radius $\overline{OZ} \perp$ chord $\overline{XY}$
Prove: $\overset{\frown}{XZ} \cong \overset{\frown}{ZY}$

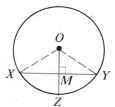

Proof

Statements	Reasons
1. $\odot O$ with radius $\overline{OZ} \perp$ chord $\overline{XY}$	1. Given
2. Draw radii $\overline{OX}$ and $\overline{OY}$.	2. Two pt. are contained in exactly one line.
3. $\overline{XM} \cong \overline{MY}$	3. Radius $\perp$ chord bisects the chord.
4. $\overline{OX} \cong \overline{OY}$	4. Radii of a $\odot$ are $\cong$.
5. $\overline{OM} \cong \overline{OM}$	5. Reflexive property
6. $\triangle XOM \cong \triangle YOM$	6. SSS
7. $\angle XOM \cong \angle YOM$	7. CPCTC
8. $\therefore \overset{\frown}{XZ} \cong \overset{\frown}{ZY}$	8. $\cong$ central $\angle$'s determine $\cong$ arcs.

Written Exercises

In which cases can you conclude that chord $\overline{WX} \cong$ chord $\overline{ST}$?

1. Given: $\overline{OW} \cong \overline{PS}$
2. Given: $\overset{\frown}{WX} \cong \overset{\frown}{ST}$
3. Given: m$\overset{\frown}{WYX}$ = m$\overset{\frown}{SUT}$

4. In $\odot O$, m$\overset{\frown}{XY}$ = 85, m$\overset{\frown}{XYZ}$ = 190, and m$\overset{\frown}{XYW}$ = 300. In $\odot P$, m$\overset{\frown}{ST}$ = 95, m$\overset{\frown}{STU}$ = 180, and m$\overset{\frown}{STV}$ = 240. Which arcs are congruent if $\odot O \cong \odot P$?

On the basis of the given information, which arcs are congruent?

5. Given: $\overline{CD} \cong \overline{AB}$

6. Given: Radius $\overline{OE} \cong$ radius $\overline{PH}$ and $\overline{EF} \cong \overline{HI}$

7. Given: $\angle TOU \cong \angle WQV$

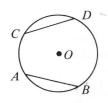
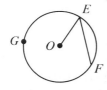
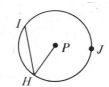

In $\odot O$, m$\overset{\frown}{AB}$ = 35, m$\overset{\frown}{AC}$ = 75, m$\overset{\frown}{AD}$ = 110, m$\overset{\frown}{AE}$ = 160, m$\overset{\frown}{ABF}$ = 180, m$\overset{\frown}{ADG}$ = 215, m$\overset{\frown}{ADH}$ = 240, m$\overset{\frown}{ADI}$ = 280, and m$\overset{\frown}{ADJ}$ = 305.

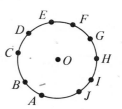

8. Which arcs are congruent to $\overset{\frown}{AB}$?
9. Which arcs are congruent to $\overset{\frown}{BC}$?
10. Which arcs are congruent to $\overset{\frown}{DF}$?

ARCS, CHORDS, AND CENTRAL ANGLES

11. Given: $\overset{\frown}{RS} \cong \overset{\frown}{RT}$
    Prove: $\triangle RST$ is isosceles.

12. Given: $\angle S \cong \angle T$
    Prove: $\overset{\frown}{RS} \cong \overset{\frown}{RT}$

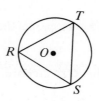

13. Given: $\overline{OX}, \overline{OY}, \overline{OZ}$ are radii of $\odot O$ and $\angle ZXY \cong \angle ZYX$.
    Prove: $\overset{\frown}{XZ} \cong \overset{\frown}{YZ}$

14. Given: $\overline{OX}, \overline{OY}, \overline{OZ}$ are radii of $\odot O$ and $\overset{\frown}{XZ} \cong \overset{\frown}{YZ}$.
    Prove: $\triangle XOZ \cong \triangle YOZ$

B 15. Given: $\overline{NL}$ is a diameter of $\odot O$ and $\overset{\frown}{KL} = \overset{\frown}{ML}$.
    Prove: $\angle KNL \cong \angle MNL$

16. Given: $\overline{NL}$ is a diameter of $\odot O$ and $\angle KNL \cong \angle MNL$.
    Prove: $\overset{\frown}{KL} \cong \overset{\frown}{ML}$

17. Prove Theorem 11.9.

18. Prove Theorem 11.10.

19. Given: Radii $\overline{OR}$ and $\overline{OT}$ of $\odot O$, $\overline{SU} \perp \overline{OR}$, $\overline{SV} \perp \overline{OT}$, and $\overset{\frown}{RS} \cong \overset{\frown}{TS}$
    Prove: $\overline{SU} \cong \overline{SV}$.

20. Given: Radii $\overline{OR}$ and $\overline{OT}$ of $\odot O$, $\overline{SU} \perp \overline{OR}$, $\overline{SV} \perp \overline{OT}$, and $\overline{SU} \cong \overline{SV}$
    Prove: $\overset{\frown}{RS} \cong \overset{\frown}{TS}$.

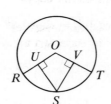

C 21. Given: Radii $\overline{OA}, \overline{OB}$ and $\overline{OC}$; B bisects $\overset{\frown}{AC}$; $m\overset{\frown}{AC} = 120$; and $AO = x$.
    Find AC in terms of x.

22. Given: Radii $\overline{OA}, \overline{OB}$, and $\overline{OC}$; B bisects $\overset{\frown}{AC}$; $m\overset{\frown}{AC} = 80$; and $AO = 5$.
    Find AC to the nearest tenth.

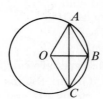

23. Given: Diameter $\overline{AB}$ of $\odot O$ and $\overset{\frown}{AC} \cong \overset{\frown}{BD}$
    Prove: $\angle ACD \cong \angle BDC$

24. Given: Diameter $\overline{AB}$ of $\odot O$ with chord $\overline{CD} \parallel \overline{AB}$
    Prove: $\overline{AC} \cong \overline{DB}$

25. Given: Diameter $\overline{AB}$ of $\odot O$ with chord $\overline{BD} \parallel \overline{OE}$
    Prove: $\overset{\frown}{AE} \cong \overset{\frown}{ED}$

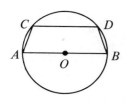

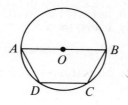

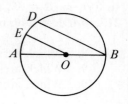

11.6 Inscribed Angles

OBJECTIVE ▶ **To apply measurement properties of inscribed angles**

$\angle B$ is *inscribed* in minor $\widehat{AC}$ of $\odot O$. $\angle B$ intercepts major $\widehat{ADC}$.

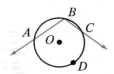

$\angle F$ is *inscribed* in semicircle $\widehat{EFG}$ of $\odot P$. $\angle F$ intercepts semicircle EHG.

$\angle J$ is *inscribed* in major $\widehat{IJK}$ of $\odot Q$. $\angle J$ intercepts minor $\widehat{IK}$.

Definition: **inscribed** **angle**	An *inscribed angle* is an angle whose vertex lies on a circle and whose sides contain chords of the circle.

There are three possible positions for inscribed angles, depending upon the location of the center of the circle.

Theorem 11.11 The measure of an inscribed angle is one half the measure of its intercepted arc.

Given: $\odot O$ with inscribed $\angle APB$ Prove: m $\angle APB = \frac{1}{2} m\widehat{AB}$

CASE I: O lies on $\angle APB$.

CASE II: O lies in the interior of $\angle APB$. (See Exercise 30.)

CASE III: O lies in the exterior of $\angle APB$. (See Exercise 31.)

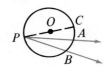

Proof of Case I

Statements	Reasons
1. Draw $\overline{OA}$.	1. Two pt. are contained in exactly one line.
2. $\overline{OA} \cong \overline{OP}$	2. Radii of a $\odot$ are $\cong$.
3. $\angle x \cong \angle P$ and m $\angle x =$ m $\angle P$	3. $\angle$'s opp. $\cong$ sides of a $\triangle$ are $\cong$.
4. m $\angle y =$ m $\angle x +$ m $\angle P$	4. Meas. of ext. $\angle$ of $\triangle =$ sum of meas. of remote int. $\angle$'s.
5. m $\angle y = 2 \cdot$ m $\angle P$	5. Substitution property
6. m $\angle P = \frac{1}{2} \cdot$ m $\angle y$	6. Multiplication property of equality
7. m $\angle y = m\widehat{AB}$	7. Meas. of minor arc $=$ meas. of central $\angle$.
8. $\therefore$ m $\angle APB = \frac{1}{2} m\widehat{AB}$	8. Substitution property

Example 1 Given: m $\angle ABC = 62$ and m$\overset{\frown}{BC} = 110$

Find m $\angle A$, m $\angle C$, and m$\overset{\frown}{AB}$.

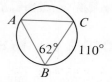

Sum of meas.
of $\angle$'s of a $\triangle$ ►
is 180°.

m $\angle A = \dfrac{1}{2}(110) = 55$ by Th. 11.11.

m $\angle C = 180 - (62 + 55) = 63$

m$\overset{\frown}{AB} = 2(63) = 126$ by Th. 11.11.

The following corollaries are direct results of Theorem 11.11.

Corollary 1 If two inscribed angles intercept the same arc (or congruent arcs), then the angles are congruent. (See Exercise 32.)

Given: $\odot O$ with inscribed
$\angle CAD$ and $\angle CBD$
Prove: $\angle CAD \cong \angle CBD$

The case of the same arc is shown.

Corollary 2 An angle inscribed in a semicircle is a right angle. (See Exercise 33.)

Given: $\odot O$ with semicircle $\overset{\frown}{ABC}$
Prove: $\angle ABC$ is a right angle.

Corollary 3 If two arcs of a circle are included between parallel secants, then the arcs are congruent.

Given: $\odot O$ with secants
$\overleftrightarrow{PQ}$ and $\overleftrightarrow{RS}$ and
$\overleftrightarrow{PQ} \parallel \overleftrightarrow{RS}$
Prove: $\overset{\frown}{PR} \cong \overset{\frown}{QS}$

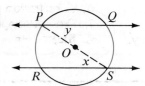

Analysis: Draw chord $\overline{PS}$.
Use $\angle x$ and $\angle y$ to show
$\overset{\frown}{PR} \cong \overset{\frown}{QS}$.

Proof

Statements	Reasons
1. $\odot O$ with $\overleftrightarrow{PQ} \parallel \overleftrightarrow{RS}$	1. Given
2. Draw chord $\overline{PS}$.	2. Two pts. are contained in exactly one line.
3. m $\angle x = $ m $\angle y$	3. Alt. int. $\angle$s of $\parallel$ lines are $\cong$.
4. m $\angle x = \dfrac{1}{2} \cdot $ m$\overset{\frown}{PR}$; m $\angle y = \dfrac{1}{2} \cdot $ m$\overset{\frown}{QS}$	4. Th. 11.11
5. $\dfrac{1}{2} \cdot $ m$PR = \dfrac{1}{2} \cdot $ m$\overset{\frown}{QS}$	5. Substitution property
6. m$\overset{\frown}{PR} = $ m$\overset{\frown}{QS}$	6. Multiplication property of equality
7. $\therefore \overset{\frown}{PR} \cong \overset{\frown}{QS}$	7. Def. of $\cong$ arcs

Example 2 Given: $\odot O$ with diameter $\overline{AC}$,
$\overline{BC} \parallel \overline{AD}$, and m $\angle COD = 50$.
Find m $\angle ABC$, m$\widehat{AB}$, and m$\widehat{BC}$.

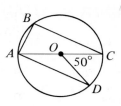

$\widehat{ABC}$ is a semicircle ▶ m $\angle ABC = 90$, by Cor. 2
m$\widehat{DC} = 50$, so m$\widehat{AB} = 50$, by Cor. 3.
m$\widehat{BC} = 180 - 50 = 130$

Corollary 4 is also a direct result of Theorem 11.1.

Corollary 4 Opposite angles of an inscribed quadrilateral are supplementary.

Given: Quad. $KLMN$ inscribed in $\odot O$
Prove: $\angle K$ and $\angle M$ are supplementary;
$\angle L$ and $\angle N$ are supplementary.

Proof

Statements	Reasons
1. Quad. $KLMN$ inscribed in $\odot O$.	1. Given
2. m $\angle K = \frac{1}{2}$ m$\widehat{LMN}$ m $\angle M = \frac{1}{2}$ m$\widehat{LKN}$	2. Meas. of inscribed $\angle = \frac{1}{2}$ meas. of intercepted arc.
3. m $\angle K + $ m $\angle M = \frac{1}{2}$ m$\widehat{LMN} + \frac{1}{2}$ m$\widehat{LKN}$	3. Addition property of equality
4. m $\angle K + $ m $\angle M = \frac{1}{2}$ (m$\widehat{LMN} + $ m$\widehat{LKN}$)	4. Distributive property
5. m$\widehat{LMN} + $ m$\widehat{LKN} = 360$	5. Arc addition postulate
6. m $\angle K + $ m $\angle M = 180$	6. Substitution property
7. $\therefore$ $\angle K$ and $\angle M$ are supplementary.	7. Def. of supplementary $\angle$'s
8. Similarly, $\angle L$ and $\angle N$ are supplementary.	8. Steps $1-6$

Reading in Geometry

Draw and label each figure described below.
1. An angle inscribed in a minor arc
2. An angle intercepting a minor arc
3. An angle inscribed in a semicircle
4. Two inscribed angles intercepting the same arc
5. An inscribed angle with the center of the circle on the angle
6. An inscribed angle with the center of the circle in the exterior of the angle

Oral Exercises

Find m $\angle AXB$ in each case.
1. m$\widehat{AB} = 72$
2. m$\widehat{AB} = 84$
3. m$\widehat{AB} = 110$
4. m$\widehat{AB} = 44$

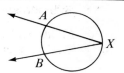

Find m$\widehat{AB}$ in each case.
5. m $\angle AXB = 25$
6. m $\angle AXB = 40$
7. m $\angle AXB = 63$
8. m $\angle AXB = 18$

INSCRIBED ANGLES

1. Given: $\overline{MN}$ is a diameter.
Find m ∠MPN.

2. Given: $\overline{AB} \cong \overline{BC}$ and m$\overarc{AB}$ = 110
Find m ∠ABC.

3. Given: m$\overarc{HK}$ = 112
Find m ∠I and m ∠J.

4. Given: m$\overarc{SVU}$ = 156
Find m ∠T and m ∠V.

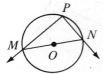

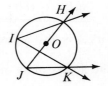

5. Given: m ∠I = 86 and m ∠L = 113
Find m ∠J and m ∠K.

6. Given: ⊙O with diameter $\overline{RS}$ and m$\overarc{QR}$ = 84
Find m ∠Q and m ∠R.

7. Given: ⊙O with diameter $\overline{AB} \parallel \overline{DC}$ and m$\overarc{AD}$ = 64
Find m ∠ACD and m$\overarc{BC}$.

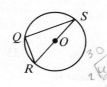

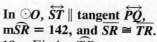

In ⊙O, m$\overarc{RU}$ = 86 and m$\overarc{SV}$ = 62.
8. Find m ∠SRV.
9. Find m ∠RSU.
10. Find m ∠RSQ.
11. Find m ∠RQU.

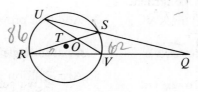

In ⊙O m ∠R = 36 and m ∠Q = 42.
12. Find m ∠RSU.
13. Find m$\overarc{RU}$.
14. Find m$\overarc{SV}$.
15. Find m ∠UTS.

In ⊙O, $\overleftrightarrow{ST} \parallel$ tangent $\overleftrightarrow{PQ}$, m ∠TSR = 61, and $\overarc{SR} \cong \overarc{TR}$.
16. Find m$\overarc{TR}$.
17. Find m$\overarc{SR}$.
18. Find m ∠STR.

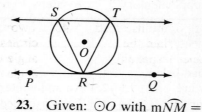

In ⊙O, $\overleftrightarrow{ST} \parallel$ tangent $\overleftrightarrow{PQ}$, m$\overarc{SR}$ = 142, and $\overarc{SR} \cong \overarc{TR}$.
19. Find m$\overarc{TR}$.
20. Find m ∠STR.
21. Find m ∠SRT.

22. Given: ⊙O with $\overline{DC} \parallel \overline{AB}$ and m$\overarc{AD}$ = 108
Find m ∠A and m ∠AOB.

23. Given: ⊙O with m$\overarc{NM}$ = 65 and ∠PNO ≅ ∠PMO
Find m ∠PNO and m ∠ONM.

24. Given: ⊙O with diameter $\overline{US}$, m$\overarc{RU}$ = 50 and m$\overarc{UT}$ = 30
Find m ∠RUS and m ∠STU.

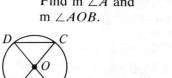

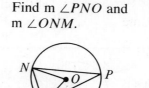

25. Given: ⊙O with diameters $\overline{SQ}$ and $\overline{PR}$
Prove: ∠PRQ ≅ ∠SQR

26. Given: ⊙O with diameter $\overline{DB}$ and m ∠ABD = $\frac{1}{2}$ · m ∠DOC
Prove: $\widehat{AD}$ ≅ $\widehat{DC}$

27. Given: ⊙O with $\overline{RS}$ ∥ $\overline{UT}$
Prove: $\overline{RT}$ ≅ $\overline{SU}$

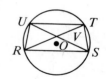

28. Given: ⊙O with diameter $\overline{AB}$ and $\overline{CD}$ ⊥ $\overline{AB}$.
Prove: △ADC ~ △ACB

29. Given: ⊙O with diameter $\overline{AB}$ and $\overline{CD}$ ⊥ $\overline{AB}$.
Prove: AD · CB = AC · CD

30. Prove Case II of Theorem 11.11. [Hint: Apply Case I to ∠APC and to ∠CPB. Then add the measures.]

31. Prove Case III of Theorem 11.11. [Hint: Apply Case I to ∠CPB and to ∠CPA. Then subtract the measures.]

32. Prove Corollary I to Theorem 11.11.

33. Prove Corollary 2 to Theorem 11.11.

34. Prove that if two angles are inscribed in the same arc, the angles are congruent.

Prove or disprove each of the following.

35. An angle inscribed in a major arc is acute.

36. An angle inscribed in a minor arc is acute.

37. Two triangles inscribed in congruent circles are congruent if two angles of one are congruent to two angles of the other.

38. If two secants intercept congruent arcs on a circle, then the secants are parallel.

39. If two consecutive angles of an inscribed quadrilateral are congruent, then the quadrilateral is an isosceles trapezoid.

40. Two triangles inscribed in congruent circles are congruent if a side and an angle of one are congruent to a side and angle of the other.

Cumulative Review

True or false?

1. The diagonals of a rhombus are congruent.

2. Each interior angle of a regular hexagon measures 120°.

3. The diagonals of an isosceles trapezoid are congruent.

4. The sum of the measures of the exterior angles of an octagon is 360°.

5. A parallelogram is a rhombus if the diagonals of the parallelogram are perpendicular.

6. A rhombus with at least one right angle is a square.

INSCRIBED ANGLES

11.7 Angles Formed by Secants

OBJECTIVE ▶ **To apply measurement properties for angles formed by two secants**

Two secants to a circle can intersect in three possible positions:

Case I On the circle	Case II In the interior of the circle	Case III In the exterior of the circle

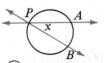

$\overset{\frown}{AB}$ is the intercepted arc with respect to $\angle x$.

$\overset{\frown}{CD}$ and $\overset{\frown}{EF}$ are the intercepted arcs with respect to $\angle x$.

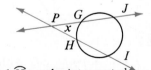

$\overset{\frown}{GH}$ and $\overset{\frown}{IJ}$ are the intercepted arcs with respect to $\angle x$.

In each case, there is a relationship between the measure of $\angle x$ and the measure(s) of the intercepted arc(s). For Case I, $\angle x$ is an inscribed angle, so its measure is one half the measure of the intercepted arc. The relationship for Case II is given in Theorem 11.12.

Theorem 11.12 The measure of an angle formed by two secants intersecting in the interior of a circle is one half the sum of the measures of the arcs intercepted by the angle and its vertical angle.

Given: $\odot O$ with secants $\overleftrightarrow{AB}$ and $\overleftrightarrow{CD}$ intersecting at P.

Prove: $m \angle x = \frac{1}{2} (m\overset{\frown}{BC} + m\overset{\frown}{AD})$

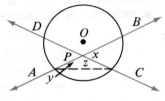

Analysis: Draw $\overline{AC}$. $m \angle x = m \angle y + m \angle z$. Express $m \angle y$ and $m \angle z$ in terms of their intercepted arcs.

Proof

Statements	Reasons
1. $\odot O$ with secants $\overleftrightarrow{AB}$ and $\overleftrightarrow{CD}$.	1. Given
2. Draw $\overline{AC}$.	2. Two pt. are contained in exactly one line.
3. $m \angle x = m \angle y + m \angle z$	3. Meas. of ext. $\angle$ of $\triangle$ = sum of meas. of remote int. $\angle$'s.
4. $m \angle y = \frac{1}{2} m\overset{\frown}{BC}$	4. Meas. of inscribed $\angle = \frac{1}{2}$ meas. of intercepted arc.
5. $m \angle z = \frac{1}{2} m\overset{\frown}{AD}$	5. Same as 4
6. $m \angle x = \frac{1}{2} m\overset{\frown}{BC} + \frac{1}{2} m\overset{\frown}{AD}$	6. Substitution property
7. $\therefore m \angle x = \frac{1}{2} (m\overset{\frown}{BC} + m\overset{\frown}{AD})$	7. Distributive property

In the diagram for Theorem 11.12, notice that the measure of $\angle APD$ is also equal to $\frac{1}{2} (m\overset{\frown}{BC} + m\overset{\frown}{AD})$.

You can use Theorem 11.12 to find the measures of angles and arcs, as shown in Examples 1 and 2.

Example 1 Given: $m\widehat{RS} = 58$, and $m\widehat{TU} = 36$
Find $m \angle RWS$.

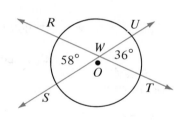

$m \angle RWS = \frac{1}{2}(m\widehat{RS} + m\widehat{TU})$ by Th 11.12

$m \angle RWS = \frac{1}{2}(58 + 36) = \frac{1}{2}(94)$

Thus, $m \angle RWS = 47$.

Example 2 Given: $m \angle AEB = 100$ and $m\widehat{CD} = 30$
Find $m\widehat{AB}$.

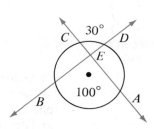

$m \angle AEB = \frac{1}{2}(m\widehat{CD} + m\widehat{AB})$

$100 = \frac{1}{2}(30 + m\widehat{AB})$

$200 = 30 + m\widehat{AB}$

Thus, $m\widehat{AB} = 170$.

Recall that in Case III on page 364, the two secants intersect in the exterior of the circle. Theorem 11.13 below deals with Case III.

Theorem 11.13 The measure of an angle formed by two secants inter-secting in the exterior of a circle is one half the difference of the measures of the intercepted arcs.

Given: $\odot O$ with secants $\overleftrightarrow{AB}$ and $\overleftrightarrow{CD}$
intersecting at P

Prove: $m \angle x = \frac{1}{2}(m\widehat{BD} - m\widehat{AC})$

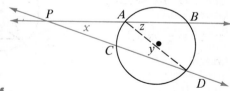

Proof

Statements	Reasons
1. $\odot O$ with secants $\overleftrightarrow{AB}$ and $\overleftrightarrow{CD}$	1. Given.
2. Draw $\overline{AD}$.	2. Two pts. are contained in exactly one line.
3. $m \angle z = m \angle x + m \angle y$	3. Meas. of ext. $\angle$ of $\triangle$ = sum of meas. of remote int. $\angle$'s.
4. $m \angle x = m \angle z - m \angle y$	4. Subtraction property of equality
5. $m \angle z = \frac{1}{2}m\widehat{BD}$; $m \angle y = \frac{1}{2}m\widehat{AC}$	5. Meas. of inscribed $\angle = \frac{1}{2}$ meas. of intercepted arc.
6. $m \angle x = \frac{1}{2}m\widehat{BD} - \frac{1}{2}m\widehat{AC}$	6. Substitution property
7. $\therefore m \angle x = \frac{1}{2}(m\widehat{BD} - m\widehat{AC})$	7. Distributive property

Notice that when two secants intersect in the exterior of a circle, two arcs are formed. As shown in Example 3, if you know the measure of each of these arcs, the measure of the angle can be found.

ANGLES FORMED BY SECANTS

Example 3

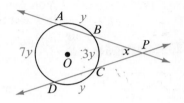

Given: $m\overset{\frown}{AB} = y$, $m\overset{\frown}{BC} = 3y$,
$m\overset{\frown}{CD} = y$, $m\overset{\frown}{DA} = 7y$
Find m $\angle x$.

$y + 3y + y + 7y = 360$

$12y = 360$

$y = 30$

$m\overset{\frown}{DA} = 7(30) = 210$; $m\overset{\frown}{BC} = 3(30) = 90$

$m \angle x = \frac{1}{2}(210 - 90)$

Thus, m $\angle x = \frac{1}{2} \cdot 120$, or 60.

Written Exercises

Ⓐ

1. Given: $m\overset{\frown}{RS} = 60$ and $m\overset{\frown}{UT} = 40$
Find m $\angle RPS$.

3. Given: $m\overset{\frown}{RS} = 20$ and $m\overset{\frown}{UT} = 100$
Find m $\angle UPT$.

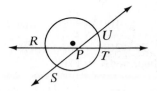

2. Given: $m\overset{\frown}{RU} = 100$ and $m\overset{\frown}{ST} = 80$
Find m $\angle RPU$.

4. Given: $m\overset{\frown}{RU} = 90$ and $m\overset{\frown}{ST} = 110$
Find m $\angle TPS$.

5. Given: $m\overset{\frown}{MJ} = 140$ and $m\overset{\frown}{LK} = 40$
Find m $\angle MPJ$.

7. Given: $m\overset{\frown}{MJ} = 90$ and $m\overset{\frown}{LK} = 30$
Find m $\angle MPJ$.

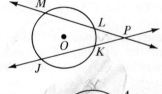

6. Given: $m\overset{\frown}{MJ} = 200$ and $m\overset{\frown}{LK} = 100$
Find m $\angle MPJ$.

8. Given: $m\overset{\frown}{MJ} = 120$ and $m\overset{\frown}{LK} = 60$
Find m $\angle MPJ$.

9. Given: $m\overset{\frown}{AB} = 115$ and $m \angle ATB = 63$
Find $m\overset{\frown}{DC}$.

11. Given: $m\overset{\frown}{AB} = 6x$, $m\overset{\frown}{BC} = 6x$, $m\overset{\frown}{CD} = x$, and $m\overset{\frown}{DA} = 2x$
Find m $\angle ATB$.

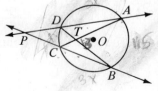

10. Given: m $\angle APC = 27$ and $m\overset{\frown}{DC} = 27$
Find $m\overset{\frown}{AB}$.

12. Given: $m\overset{\frown}{AB} = 4x$, $m\overset{\frown}{BC} = 3x$, $m\overset{\frown}{CD} = 2x$, and $m\overset{\frown}{DA} = 3x$
Find m $\angle APB$.

13. Given: m $\angle V = 103$, m $\angle VRT = 71$, and $\overline{RS} \parallel \overline{VU}$.
Find m $\angle TRS$ and m $\angle U$.

14. Given: Diameter $\overline{EG}$ $m\overset{\frown}{FG} = 41$, and $m\overset{\frown}{EH} = 53$
Find m $\angle E$ and m $\angle GPF$.

15. Given: $\overleftrightarrow{AB} \parallel \overleftrightarrow{DC}$, $m\overset{\frown}{CB} = 62$, and m $\angle DAB = 104$
Find m $\angle DEA$ and m $\angle ADB$.

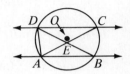

16. Given: m $\angle AOB = 70$ and m $\angle COD = 80$
Find m $\angle CTD$.

17. True or false? m $\angle CTD$ is equal to the average of $m\overset{\frown}{AB}$ and $m\overset{\frown}{CD}$.

18. Given: $m\widehat{EH} = 2x + 1$, $m\widehat{HG} = 3x - 2$, $m\widehat{GF} = 4x - 5$, and $m\widehat{FE} = x - 4$
Find $m \angle HIE$.

19. Given: $m\widehat{AB} = 7x + 3$, $m\widehat{BC} = 2x + 10$, $m\widehat{CD} = 6x$, and $m\widehat{DA} = 6x - 10$
Find $m \angle DPA$.

20. Given: $m \angle DEA = 42$, and $m \angle P = 18$
Find $m\widehat{AD}$ and $m\widehat{BC}$.

 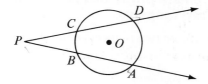

21. Given: $\overline{PQ} \perp \overline{RS}$ at T
Prove: $m\widehat{PR} + m\widehat{QS} = 180$

22. Given: $\overline{RT} \cong \overline{US}$
Prove: $\overline{UR} \cong \overline{TS}$

23. Given: Secants $\overleftrightarrow{LN}$ and $\overleftrightarrow{LQ}$
Prove: $\triangle LQM \sim \triangle LNP$

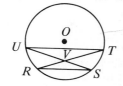 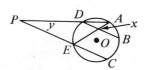

24. Given: $m\widehat{AB} = m\widehat{BC}$
Prove: $m \angle x + m \angle y = \frac{3}{2}m\widehat{AB}$

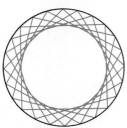

25. Given: $m\widehat{AB} = m\widehat{BC}$, $m \angle x = 60$, $m \angle y = 15$
Find $m\widehat{AC}$.

26. The vertex of an angle measuring 32° is in the exterior of a circle and its sides contain chords of the circle. If the sum of the measures of the intercepted arcs is 180°, find the measure of each intercepted arc.

27. Prove: If two circles are tangent internally and the center of the larger circle lies on the smaller circle, then any chord of the larger circle drawn from the point of tangency is bisected by the smaller circle.

A Challenge To You

Some figures that are constructed with segments appear to be curves. The figures below can be drawn on paper or sewn with yarn or string on heavy paper or cloth. Can you construct each figure?

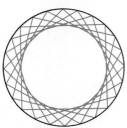 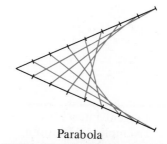 

Concentric circles   Parabola   Asteroid

ANGLES FORMED BY SECANTS

11.8 Tangents, Secants, and Angles

OBJECTIVE ▶ **To apply measurement properties for angles formed by a secant and a tangent or by two tangents**

A secant and a tangent or two tangents can intersect in three possible positions:

Case I
Secant and tangent
on the circle

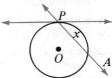

Case II
Secant and tangent in
the exterior of the circle

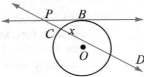

Case III
Two tangents in the
exterior of the circle

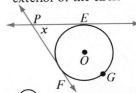

$\overset{\frown}{PA}$ is the intercepted arc
with respect to $\angle x$.

$\overset{\frown}{BC}$ and $\overset{\frown}{BD}$ are the intercepted
arcs with respect to $\angle x$.

$\overset{\frown}{EF}$ and $\overset{\frown}{EGF}$ are the intercepted
arcs with respect
to $\angle x$.

In each case, there is a relationship between the measure of $\angle x$ and the measure(s) of the intercepted arc(s). The relationship for Case I is given in Theorem 11.14.

Theorem 11.14 The measure of an angle formed by a secant and a tangent intersecting at the point of tangency is one half the measure of the intercepted arc.

Given: Secant $\overleftrightarrow{PA}$, tangent $\overleftrightarrow{PB}$,
intersecting at point P
on $\odot O$

Prove: m $\angle x = \frac{1}{2}$ m$\overset{\frown}{PA}$

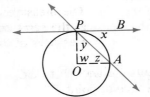

Analysis: Draw radii $\overline{OP}$ and
$\overline{OA}$. m $\angle x$ + m $\angle y$ =
90. Express m $\angle y$ in
terms of m $\angle z$. Then
use m $\angle w$ = m$\overset{\frown}{PA}$.

Outline of Proof

1. m $\angle x$ + m $\angle y$ = 90

2. m $\angle x$ = 90 − m $\angle y$

3. m $\angle y$ + m $\angle w$ + m $\angle z$ = 180

4. m $\angle z$ = m $\angle y$

5. m $\angle w$ = m$\overset{\frown}{PA}$

6. m $\angle y$ + m$\overset{\frown}{PA}$ + m $\angle y$ = 180

7. m $\angle y$ = $\frac{1}{2}$(180 − m$\overset{\frown}{PA}$)

8. m $\angle y$ = 90 − $\frac{1}{2}$m$\overset{\frown}{PA}$

9. m $\angle x$ = 90 − $\left(90 - \frac{1}{2}\text{m}\overset{\frown}{PA}\right)$

10. ∴ m $\angle x$ = $\frac{1}{2}$ m$\overset{\frown}{PA}$

If a secant and a tangent intersect at the point of tangency, then they intersect on the circle. In Example 1, Theorem 11.14 is applied to find the measure of an angle formed by a secant and a tangent.

Example 1 Given: Tangent $\overleftrightarrow{YZ}$ and $m\widehat{XY} = 124$
Find m $\angle XYZ$.

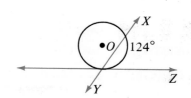

m $\angle XYZ = \dfrac{1}{2} m\widehat{XY}$, by Th. 11.14.

Thus, m $\angle XYZ = \dfrac{1}{2} \cdot 124$, or 62.

Theorem 11.15 deals with Case II on page 368. It involves the measure of an angle formed by a secant and a tangent that intersects in the exterior of a circle.

> **Theorem 11.15** The measure of an angle formed by a secant and a tangent intersecting in the exterior of a circle is one half the difference of the measures of the intercepted arcs.

Given: Tangent $\overleftrightarrow{PA}$ and secant $\overleftrightarrow{PB}$
intersecting at point P in the exterior of $\odot O$

Prove: m $\angle x = \dfrac{1}{2}(m\widehat{AB} - m\widehat{AC})$

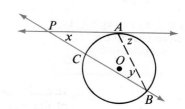

Proof: (See Exercise 24.)

Theorem 11.16 deals with Case III on page 368. It involves the measure of an angle formed by two tangents.

> **Theorem 11.16** The measure of an angle formed by two tangents to the same circle is one half the difference of the measures of the intercepted arcs.

Given: Tangents $\overleftrightarrow{PA}$ and $\overleftrightarrow{PB}$ to $\odot O$
intersecting at point P

Prove: m $\angle x = \dfrac{1}{2}(m\widehat{ACB} - m\widehat{AB})$

Proof: (See Exercise 25.)

Theorem 11.15 is used in Example 2 below.

Example 2 Given: Tangent $\overleftrightarrow{PW}$, $m\widehat{TW} = 173$,
and $m\widehat{JW} = 69$.
Find m $\angle JPW$.

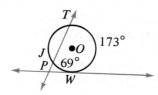

m $\angle JPW = \dfrac{1}{2}(173 - 69) = \dfrac{1}{2}(104) = 52$, by Th. 11.15.

TANGENTS, SECANTS, AND ANGLES

Theorem 11.16 is used in Example 3.

Example **3** Given: Tangents $\overline{PR}$ and $\overline{PS}$ and m $\angle P = 48$.
Find $m\widehat{RS}$ and $m\widehat{RQS}$.

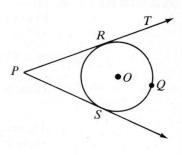

Let $x = m\widehat{RQS}$. Then $360 - x = m\widehat{RS}$.

$m\angle P = \dfrac{1}{2}(m\widehat{RQS} - m\widehat{RS})$ by Th. 11.16.

$48 = \dfrac{1}{2}[x - (360 - x)]$

$96 = 2x - 360$

$456 = 2x$

$x = 228;\ 360 - x = 132$

Thus, $m\widehat{RS} = 132$ and $m\widehat{RQS} = 228$.

You may use the following summary to help you find the measures of angles formed by intersecting secants or tangents.

Summary	**Angles Formed by Secants or Tangents**

If the intersection of two secants is in the interior of the circle, then the measure of the angle is one half the sum of the measures of the intercepted arcs.

If the intersection of a secant and a tangent is on the circle, then the measure of the angle is one half the measure of the intercepted arc.

If the intersection of secants or tangents is in the exterior of the circle, then the measure of the angle is one half the difference of the measures of the intercepted arcs.

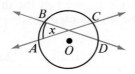

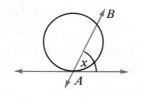

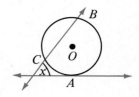

$m\angle x = \dfrac{1}{2}(m\,\widehat{AB} + m\,\widehat{CD})$

$m\angle x = \dfrac{1}{2}(m\,\widehat{AB})$

$m\angle x = \dfrac{1}{2}(m\,\widehat{AB} - m\,\widehat{CA})$

Written Exercises

For Exercises 1–20, you may assume that lines that appear to be tangents are tangents. Find each indicated measure.

Ⓐ **1.** Given: $m\widehat{AB} = 104$
Find m $\angle APB$.

2. Given: m $\angle APB = 71$
Find $m\widehat{AB}$.

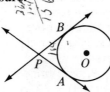

3. Given: $m\widehat{GE} = 42$
and $m\widehat{FE} = 138$
Find m $\angle FDE$.

4. Given: m $\angle FDE = 46$
and $m\widehat{FE} = 121$
Find $m\widehat{GE}$.

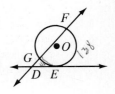

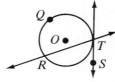

5. Given: m$\widehat{RT}$ = 142
Find m ∠RTS.

6. Given: m ∠RTS = 61
Find m$\widehat{RQT}$.

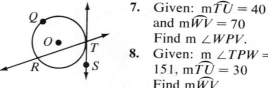

7. Given: m$\widehat{TU}$ = 40 and m$\widehat{WV}$ = 70
Find m ∠WPV.

8. Given: m ∠TPW = 151, m$\widehat{TU}$ = 30
Find m$\widehat{WV}$.

9. Given: m$\widehat{XVZ}$ = 212
Find m ∠XYZ.

11. Given: m$\widehat{XW}$ = 47, and m ∠XYV = 47
Find m$\widehat{XV}$.

13. Given: m$\widehat{XVZ}$ = 3 · m$\widehat{XZ}$
Find m ∠XYZ.

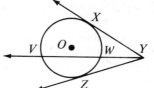
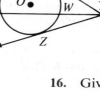

10. Given: m$\widehat{WX}$ = 60, m$\widehat{XV}$ = 130, and m$\widehat{VZ}$ = 110
Find m ∠VYZ.

12. Given: m$\widehat{WZ}$ = 40, m$\widehat{WX}$ = 70, and m$\widehat{XV}$ = 140
Find m ∠XYZ.

14. Given: m ∠XYZ = 58
Find m$\widehat{XZ}$ and m$\widehat{XVZ}$.

15. Given: m$\widehat{NMK}$ = 162
Find m ∠JKN

17. Given: m$\widehat{KGN}$ = $\frac{3}{2}$ m$\widehat{KMN}$

Find m ∠NKL.

19. Given: m$\widehat{MK}$ = 3m$\widehat{GK}$ and m$\widehat{GNM}$ = 160
Find m ∠MJL.

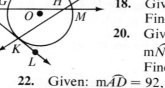

16. Given: m$\widehat{GK}$ + m$\widehat{NM}$ = 62
Find m ∠GHK.

18. Given: m$\widehat{GN}$ = 142 and m$\widehat{KM}$ = 160
Find m ∠NHM.

20. Given: m ∠GHK = 35, m$\widehat{GN}$ = 154, and m$\widehat{NM}$ = 20
Find m ∠NKL.

B 21. Given: Diameter $\overline{AC}$ and $\overline{AD} \cong \overline{AO}$
Find m ∠CAD and m ∠DBA.

22. Given: m$\widehat{AD}$ = 92, m$\widehat{CD}$ = 103, m$\widehat{BC}$ = 41, and tangent $\overleftrightarrow{AF}$
Find m ∠CQD and m ∠ECA.

23. Given: m$\widehat{AB}$ = 43, $\overline{AC} \cong \overline{BC}$, and tangent $\overleftrightarrow{DE}$
Find m ∠CAO and m ∠DAC.

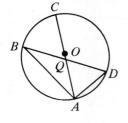
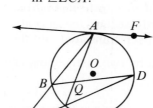
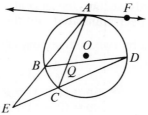

24. Prove Theorem 11.15.

26. Given: $\overline{US} \cong \overline{VS}$ and tangent $\overleftrightarrow{RT}$
Prove: $\overline{UV} \parallel \overleftrightarrow{RT}$

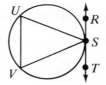

25. Prove Theorem 11.16.

27. Given: Tangent $\overleftrightarrow{RT} \parallel \overline{UV}$
Prove: $\overline{US} \cong \overline{VS}$

28. Prove: If two tangents to a circle are parallel, then the points of tangency divide the circle into two congruent arcs.

29. Prove: If two circles are tangent internally at point P, and chord $\overline{PA}$ of the larger circle intersects the smaller circle at B, then m$\widehat{PA}$ = m$\widehat{PB}$.

30. Prove: The bisector of the angle formed by a tangent and a chord drawn from the point of tangency divides the intercepted arc into two congruent arcs.

TANGENTS, SECANTS, AND ANGLES

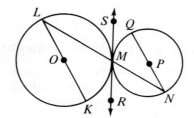

31. Given: $\overleftrightarrow{RS}$ tangent to
⊙O and ⊙P at M,
diameter $\overline{KL}$, diameter
$\overline{QN}$
Prove: $m\overgroup{LM} = m\overgroup{NM}$

32. Given: $\overleftrightarrow{RS}$ tangent to
⊙O and ⊙P at M,
diameter $\overline{KL}$, diameter
$\overline{QN}$
Prove: $\overline{KL} \parallel \overline{QN}$

33. Prove: If a quadrilateral is inscribed in a circle, then an exterior angle of the quadrilateral is congruent to its opposite interior angle.

34. Prove: If $\overline{RS}$ is the common chord of two intersecting circles and $\overline{ST}$ and $\overline{SU}$ are diameters, then $\angle TRU$ is a straight angle.

35. Prove: If two circles are tangent externally at point P and $\overleftrightarrow{AB}$ is a common external tangent which intersects the two circles at points A and B, respectively, then $\angle APB$ is a right angle.

36. Prove: If two circles are tangent internally at point P and $\overline{PA}$ and $\overline{PB}$ are chords of the larger circle which intersect the smaller circle at points C and D, respectively, then $\overline{AB} \parallel \overline{CD}$.

CALCULATOR ACTIVITIES

A calculator can be helpful to you in finding the measures of angles and arcs formed by intersecting chords, secants, or tangents. See if you can show how each of the formulas below has been translated into the "language" of the calculator.

Part 1   An angle formed by two intersecting chords

$x = (p + q) \div 2$ or
$p = (2 \times x) - q$ or
$q = (2 \times x) - p$

Part 2   An angle formed by secants or tangents intersecting outside the circle

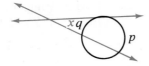

$x = (p - q) \div 2$
$p = (2 \times x) + q$
$q = p - (2 \times x)$ ◄   *(Be careful!)*

Use one of the formulas from Part 1 to find the indicated angle or arc measure.
1. If $p = 68$ and $q = 75$, find x.   **2.** If $x = 37$ and $p = 55$, find q.   **3.** If $x = 47$ and $q = 82$, find p.

Use one of the formulas from Part 2 to find the indicated angle or arc measure.
4. If $p = 158$ and $q = 65$, find x.   **5.** If $x = 39$ and $q = 73$, find p.   **6.** If $x = 43$ and $p = 162$, find q.

11.9 Products of Lengths

OBJECTIVE ► **To find ratios and products of lengths of segments related to a circle**

Intersecting chords, secants, and tangents often determine pairs of similar triangles. The resulting ratios can be useful in finding lengths of segments. Theorem 11.17 deals with intersecting chords.

┌ **Theorem 11.17** If two chords of a circle intersect, then the product ┐
of the lengths of the segments of one chord equals the product of the lengths of the segments of the other.

Given: $\odot O$ with chords $\overline{AB}$ and $\overline{CD}$ intersecting at point P

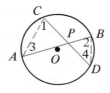

Analysis: Show $\dfrac{AP}{DP} = \dfrac{PC}{PB}$ by proving $\triangle APC \sim \triangle DPB$.

Prove: $AP \cdot PB = DP \cdot PC$

Proof

Statements	Reasons
1. $\odot O$ with chords $\overline{AB}$ and $\overline{CD}$	1. Given
2. Draw $\overline{AC}$ and $\overline{BD}$.	2. Two points are contained in exactly one line.
3. $\angle 1 \cong \angle 2$, $\angle 3 \cong \angle 4$	3. Inscribed $\angle$'s that intercept the same arc are $\cong$.
4. $\triangle APC \sim \triangle DPB$	4. AA for $\sim \triangle$'s
5. $\dfrac{AP}{DP} = \dfrac{PC}{PB}$	5. Corr. sides of $\sim \triangle$'s are proportional.
6. $\therefore AP \cdot PB = DP \cdot PC$	6. Prod. of extremes = prod. of means.

Example 1

Given: $VS = 4$, $RV = 8$, and $UV = 6$
Find VT.

$UV \cdot VT = RV \cdot VS$, by Th. 11.17

$\begin{aligned} 6 \cdot x &= 8 \cdot 4 \\ 6x &= 32 \\ x &= \frac{32}{6} = \frac{16}{3} \end{aligned}$

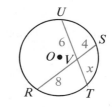

Thus, $VT = \dfrac{16}{3}$, or $5\dfrac{1}{3}$.

In the figure, $\overline{PA}$ is a *secant segment*, and $\overline{PB}$ is its external *secant segment*. Similarly, $\overline{PC}$ is a secant segment, and $\overline{PD}$ is its external segment. Theorem 11.18 deals with secants that intersect in the exterior of a circle.

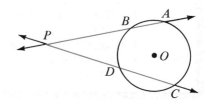

PRODUCTS OF LENGTHS

Theorem 11.18 If two secants intersect in the exterior of a circle, then the product of the lengths of one secant segment and its external secant segment equals the product of the lengths of the other secant segment and its external secant segment.

Given: ⊙O with secants $\overleftrightarrow{PA}$ and $\overleftrightarrow{PC}$ intersecting at point P

Prove: $PA \cdot PB = PC \cdot PD$

Proof: (See Exercise 16.)

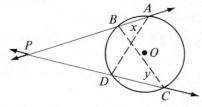

Analysis: Draw $\overline{AD}$ and $\overline{BC}$. Show $\dfrac{PA}{PC} = \dfrac{PD}{PB}$ by proving $\triangle PAD \sim \triangle PCB$.

You can use Theorem 11.18 to find the lengths of segments formed by two secants intersecting in the exterior of a circle.

Example 2 Given: $QR = 10$, $PR = 6$, and $PT = 8$
Find TS.

$$PS \cdot PT = PQ \cdot PR,$$
$$\text{by Th. 11.18.}$$

Let $TS = x$; then $PS = x + 8$. ▶

$$(x + 8)8 = 16 \cdot 6$$
$$8x + 64 = 96$$
$$8x = 32$$
$$x = 4$$

Thus, $TS = 4$.

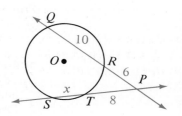

In the figure, $\overleftrightarrow{PA}$ is tangent to ⊙O, and $\overleftrightarrow{PB}$ is a secant. $\overline{PA}$ is a **tangent segment**, $\overline{PB}$ is a **secant segment**, and $\overline{PC}$ is an **external secant segment**. Theorem 11.19 is a statement about the products of lengths involving a tangent segment, a secant segment, and an external secant segment.

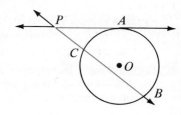

Theorem 11.19 If a tangent and a secant intersect in the exterior of a circle, then the square of the length of the tangent segment equals the product of the lengths of the secant segment and its external secant segment.

Given: ⊙O with tangent $\overleftrightarrow{PA}$ and secant $\overleftrightarrow{PB}$ intersecting at point P

Prove: $(PA)^2 = PB \cdot PC$

Proof: (See Exercise 17.)

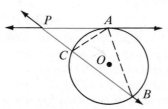

Analysis: Draw $\overline{AB}$ and $\overline{AC}$. Show $\dfrac{PA}{PB} = \dfrac{PC}{PA}$ by proving $\triangle PAB \sim \triangle PCA$.

Examples 3 and 4 are applications of Theorem 11.19.

Example 3 Given: Secant $\overleftrightarrow{AB}$, tangent $\overleftrightarrow{AD}$, $AC = 2$, and
$CB = 4$
Find AD.

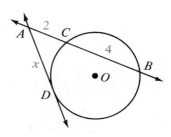

$(AD)^2 = AB \cdot AC$ by Th. 11.19.
Let $AD = x$. ▶ $\quad x^2 = 6 \cdot 2$
$\quad x^2 = 12$
$\quad x = \sqrt{12}$, or $2\sqrt{3}$

Thus, $AD = 2\sqrt{3}$.

Example 4 A tangent and a secant intersect in the exterior
of a circle. The tangent segment is 10 cm long
and the secant segment is 25 cm long. Find the
length of the external secant segment.

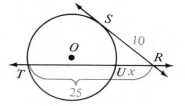

Draw and label a figure.
$(RS)^2 = RT \cdot RU$
Let $RU = x$. ▶ $\quad 10^2 = 25 \cdot x$
$\quad 100 = 25x$
$\quad 4 = x$

Thus, $RU = 4$ cm.

Written Exercises

For Exercises 1–15, you may assume that lines that appear to be tangents are
tangents. Find each indicated measure.

1. Given: $AP = 12$,
$PC = 9$, and $PD = 4$
Find PB.

2. Given: $AP = 12$,
$PC = 8$, and $PB = 4$
Find PD.

3. Given: $AP = 9$,
$AB = 17$, and $CP = 12$
Find CD.

4. Given: $AP = 18$,
$BP = 3$, and $CP = 9$
Find CD.

5. Given: $AP = 4x$,
$PB = x$, $CP = 6$, and
$PD = 6$
Find AP.

6. Given: $AP = 9x$,
$BP = 4x$, $CP = 16$, and
$DP = 9$
Find BP.

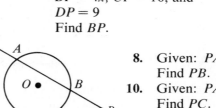

7. Given: $PB = 3$ and $PA = 12$
Find PC.

8. Given: $PA = 16$ and $PC = 8$
Find PB.

9. Given: $PA = 4x$, $PB = x$,
and $PC = 6$
Find PA.

10. Given: $PA = 7$ and $PB = 3$
Find PC.

PRODUCTS OF LENGTHS

11. Given: $RX = 16$, $RS = 5$, and $RU = 6$
Find RW and SX.

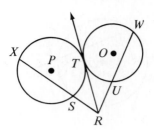

12. Given: $PW + WX = 12$ and $PY = 3$
Find $\dfrac{PW}{PZ}$.

13. Given: $SR = 20$, $WR = 4$, and $XR = 6$
Find YX and SY.

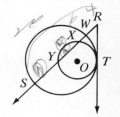

14. Given: $QR = 2x$, $PQ = 6$, $PT = 2x - 1$, and $PS = 8$
Find PR and PT.

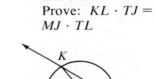

15. Given: $QR = 8$, $ST = 2$, and $PS = 6$
Find PR.

16. Prove Theorem 11.18.

17. Prove Theorem 11.19.

18. Given: Tangent $\overrightarrow{TX}$ and secant $\overleftrightarrow{TZ}$
Prove: $XT \cdot XY = XZ \cdot YT$

19. Given: Secants $\overrightarrow{TK}$ and $\overrightarrow{TM}$
Prove: $KL \cdot TJ = MJ \cdot TL$

20. Given: Diameter $\overline{GH}$, tangent $\overleftrightarrow{JH}$, and secant $\overleftrightarrow{JG}$
Prove: $IH = \sqrt{IJ \cdot IG}$

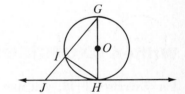

21. Given: Tangent $\overleftrightarrow{TM}$ and secant $\overrightarrow{MP}$
Prove: $MS \cdot MP = MR \cdot MQ$

22. Given: Secants $\overleftrightarrow{PC}$ and $\overleftrightarrow{PF}$
Prove: $\dfrac{PA}{PC} = \dfrac{PD}{PF}$

23. Given: $\overset{\frown}{ED} \cong \overset{\frown}{DC}$ and $\overset{\frown}{EA} \cong \overset{\frown}{BC}$
Prove: $AD \cdot FD = BD \cdot GD$

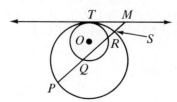

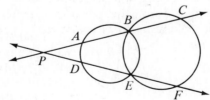

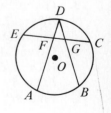

Cumulative Review

1. One base of a trapezoid measures 4 cm and the median measures 7 cm. Find the length of the other base.

2. In $\triangle ABC$, $AB = 6$, $BC = 9$, and $CA = 7$; D is the midpoint of $\overline{CA}$ and E is the midpoint of $\overline{BC}$. Find DE.

11.10 Constructions

OBJECTIVE ▶ To perform constructions related to circles

Recall that an angle inscribed in a semicircle is a right angle. Also, a line perpendicular to a radius at its endpoint on the circle is tangent to the circle. These two statements are the basis for the construction of tangents to a circle from an exterior point.

┌─**Construction:** Construct the tangents to a circle from a point in the exterior of the circle. ─────┐

Given: ⊙O and point P in the the exterior of ⊙O

Construct: Two tangents to ⊙O from P

Strategy: Construct a ⊙ with $\overline{OP}$ as its diameter. Apply Th. 11.7.

Draw $\overline{OP}$. Construct M, the midpoint of $\overline{OP}$.

With radius $\overline{MO}$, construct ⊙M intersecting ⊙O in points T and S.

Draw $\overleftrightarrow{PT}$ and $\overleftrightarrow{PS}$.

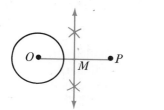
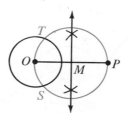
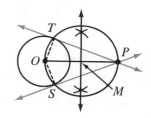

Conclusion: $\overleftrightarrow{PT}$ and $\overleftrightarrow{PS}$ are the desired tangents.

To justify the construction above, draw $\overline{OT}$ and $\overline{OS}$. ∠OTP and ∠OSP are right angles since each is inscribed in a semicircle. So $\overline{OT} \perp \overleftrightarrow{PT}$ and $\overline{OS} \perp \overleftrightarrow{PS}$. **Thus, $\overleftrightarrow{PT}$ and $\overleftrightarrow{PS}$ are tangents, since each is perpendicular to a radius at its endpoint on the circle.**

The next construction provides the basis for many beautiful designs.

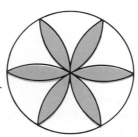

Construction   Inscribe a regular hexagon in a circle.

Given: $\odot O$
Construct: Inscribed hexagon
          $ABCDEF$ in $\odot O$.

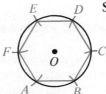

Strategy: Open compass to the length of a radius.
          Starting at any point A on the circle; mark
          successive arcs on the circle. Draw
          chords to form a regular hexagon.

Construction: (See Exercise 14.)

You can use a circle to construct segments whose lengths are in a particular proportion, as shown in the next construction.

Construction   Construct a segment whose length is the geometric
                   mean of the lengths of two given segments.

Given: Segments of lengths a and b
  Construct: A segment of length x such that
$$\frac{a}{x} = \frac{x}{b}$$

a _____

b _____

On a line, mark off $\overline{CD}$ with length a and $\overline{DE}$ with length b.

Construct M, the midpoint of $\overline{CE}$. Then construct $\odot M$ with radius $\overline{ME}$.

At D, construct a perpendicular to $\overline{CE}$ that intersects $\odot M$ at F. Then $DF = x$.

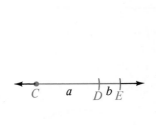

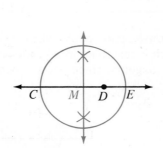

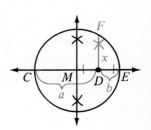

Conclusion: $\overline{DF}$ is the required segment of length x such that $\dfrac{a}{x} = \dfrac{x}{b}$.

Written Exercises

 1. Draw a segment 2 cm long. Construct a circle with a radius congruent to this segment.

2. Draw a segment 5 cm long. Construct a circle with a diameter congruent to this segment.

3. Draw a circle with a diameter approximately 6 cm long. Mark a point on the circle. Construct a tangent to the circle at this point.

4. Draw a circle with a diameter approximately 4 cm long. From a point outside this circle, construct two tangents to the circle.

5. Construct the two designs shown at the bottom of page 377.

6. Inscribe a regular hexagon and an equilateral triangle in the same circle.

7. Draw a segment 4 cm long and a line. Mark a point on the line. At that point, construct a circle tangent to the line with a radius congruent to the given segment.

8. Construct a segment whose length is the geometric mean of lengths p and q.

 9. Inscribe a circle in a given square.

10. Inscribe a square in a given circle.

11. Draw a circle and a point outside the circle. Construct two tangents to the circle from this point. Construct a second circle tangent both to the given circle and to the two tangents.

12. Draw two segments. Construct a right triangle with the hypotenuse congruent to the longer segment and the altitude to the hypotenuse congruent to the shorter segment. [*Hint:* An angle inscribed in a semicircle is a right angle.]

13. Inscribe a regular octagon in a given circle.

14. Inscribe a regular hexagon in a circle. Then justify your construction. [*Hint:* Draw radii to the vertices. Use equiangular triangles.]

15. Inscribe a regular polygon of 12 sides in a given circle.

16. Construct a segment whose length is the geometric mean of the lengths of two given segments. Then justify your construction.

17. Given segments with lengths a, b, and c, construct a segment with length x such that $\frac{a}{b} = \frac{c}{x}$.

 18. Inscribe a square in a semicircle.

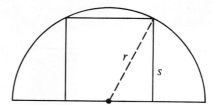

Draw two segments of lengths a and b. Then construct a segment with each indicated length.

19. $\sqrt{ab}$

20. $\sqrt{2ab}$

21. $2\sqrt{ab}$

22. $\sqrt{\frac{1}{2}ab}$

23. $\sqrt{\frac{a^2}{2}}$

24. $\sqrt{a^2 + b^2}$

CONSTRUCTIONS

Applications

1. A builder bought a used electric saw at a sale. The only saw blade included was broken, with one piece lost. How can the builder find the diameter of the original blade from the broken piece so that a new blade can be bought?

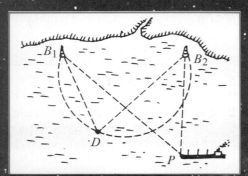

2. Two buoys are placed at points B_1 and B_2 to warn ships of shallow water in the circular region shown. As a ship sails towards this region, the navigator measures $\angle B_1PB_2$ by sighting the buoys. At a point D on the circle, the measure of $\angle B_1DB_2$ is known. The navigator knows that if he is too close to the shallow water, then the size of $\angle B_1PB_2$ will be greater than that of $\angle B_1DB_2$. Why is this so?

3. A landscape architect is laying out sidewalks. How can he find the center C of the arc $\overset{\frown}{AB}$ if this arc is to be tangent to the straight sides of the sidewalks at A and B?

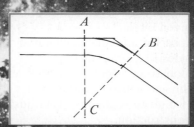

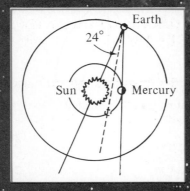

4. The orbits of Earth and Mercury around the sun are approximately circular. An astronomer on Earth can measure the angle formed by the sun, Earth, and Mercury. The measures will vary from 0° to 24°. If the average distance from the Earth to the sun is 149,504,000 kilometers or 92,897,000 miles and the maximum angle formed measures 24°, what is the average distance from Mercury to the sun?

APPLICATIONS

Computer Activities

Inscribed angle properties and formulas are used in creating arches, building domes, laying out baseball fields, and determining the areas that a circular sprinkler will water on a plot of land. Computers can be used to compute the necessary arc and angle measures for a finite number of combinations.

You can use the following program to find the measures of the angles of a triangle inscribed in a circle. You must indicate how many triangles you have and give two arc measures for each triangle.

See the Computer Section on p. 560 for more information.

PROGRAM

```
10 PRINT "PROGRAM FINDS MEASURES OF THE ANGLES OF A TRIANGLE"
20 PRINT "INSCRIBED IN A CIRCLE"
30 PRINT "FOR HOW MANY TRIANGLES DO YOU HAVE DATA?"
40 INPUT N
50 FOR I = 1 TO N
60 PRINT "ENTER ARCS G1, G2"
70 INPUT G1, G2
80 LET A = .5 * G1
90 LET C = .5 * G2
100 LET B = 180 - (A + C)
110 PRINT "A="; A; "B="; B; "C="; C
120 NEXT I
130 END
```

Exercises

Run this program for four triangles and for the following values for $G1$ and $G2$. (Ex 1–4)

1. $G1 = 120$, $G2 = 73$ **2.** $G1 = 110$, $G2 = 126$ **3.** $G1 = 150$, $G2 = 35$ **4.** $G1 = 180$, $G2 = 90$

5. Change the program to determine the measures of the three arcs AB, BC, and AC, given the measures of $\angle A$ and $\angle C$.

6. Write a BASIC program to determine the measure of $\angle APD$ given that $6y + y + 3y + 2y = 360$.

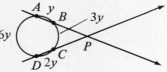

ACTIVITY: INSCRIBED ANGLES

Chapter Eleven Review

Use ⊙O for Exercises 1–6. [11.1]
1. Name all radii.

2. Name a secant.

3. Name a diameter.

4. Name all chords.

5. Name a tangent.

6. Name a minor arc. [11.4]

7. Given: $\overline{DA}$ is a
   diameter of ⊙O
   and chord $\overline{CB} \perp \overline{DA}$
   Prove: $\angle C \cong \angle B$ [11.1]

8. Given: ⊙O with
   m$\widehat{AB}$ = 82
   Find m $\angle AOB$. [11.5]

9. Given: ⊙O with
   m $\angle ACB$ = 32
   Find m$\widehat{AB}$. [11.6]

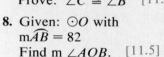

10. Given: ⊙O with
    m$\widehat{AD}$ = 84, m$\widehat{BC}$ = 62
    Find m $\angle AED$. [11.5]

11. Given: ⊙O with
    m$\widehat{AC}$ = 91, m $\angle AEC$ = 97
    Find m$\widehat{BD}$.

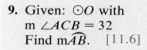

12. Given: ⊙O with
    m$\widehat{AD}$ = 113, m$\widehat{BC}$ = 48
    Find m $\angle AED$. [11.7]

13. Given: ⊙O with
    m$\widehat{BC}$ = 21, m $\angle AED$ = 47
    Find m$\widehat{AD}$.

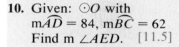

14. Given: ⊙O with tangents
    $\overrightarrow{EA}$ and $\overrightarrow{EC}$ and
    m$\widehat{AC}$ = 115
    Find m $\angle AEC$. [11.8]

15. Given: ⊙O with tangents
    $\overrightarrow{EA}$ and $\overrightarrow{EC}$, diameter
    $\overline{BD}$, and m$\widehat{BC}$ = 50
    Find m $\angle DEC$.

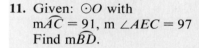

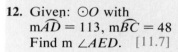

Vocabulary

circle [11.1], radius [11.1], chord [11.1], diameter [11.1], secant [11.1], tangent [11.1 and 11.3], arc [11.4], central angle [11.4], inscribed angle [11.6]

16. Given: $\overleftrightarrow{AB} \parallel \overleftrightarrow{GC} \parallel$
    tangent $\overleftrightarrow{FE}$, $\overline{AB} \cong \overline{GC}$,
    m$\widehat{BD}$ = 140, and
    m$\widehat{AB}$ = 80
    Find m $\angle FDB$
    and m $\angle BGC$. [11.6]

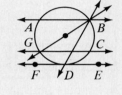

17. Given: ⊙O with
    AB = 14
    Find BD. [11.3]

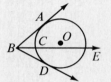

18. Given: ⊙O with
    AB = 12, BC = 9
    Find BE.

19. Draw a circle and a point outside the circle. Construct a tangent to the circle through the point. [11.10]

*20. Draw two segments with lengths a and c. Construct a segment with length $\sqrt{c^2 - a^2}$.

21. Given: Radius $\overline{OA} \cong$ radius $\overline{PC}$ and
    $\angle A \cong \angle C$
    Prove: $\widehat{AB} \cong \widehat{CD}$ [11.5]

*22. Prove that if two circles intersect in two points, then the line joining those points bisects a common external tangent segment. [11.8]

Chapter Eleven Test

Use ⊙O or ⊙P for Items 1–5.

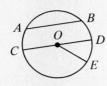 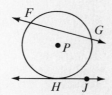

1. Name a diameter of ⊙O.

2. For which circle is there no secant drawn?

3. Name a tangent of ⊙P.

4. Name a semicircle of ⊙O.

5. Name a minor arc of ⊙P.

6. Given: Diameter $\overline{AB}$
   bisects chord $\overline{CD}$
   and chord $\overline{EF}$.
   Prove: $\overline{CD} \parallel \overline{EF}$

7. Given: ⊙O with
   m$\widehat{SRT}$ = 200
   Find m ∠SOT.

8. Given: ⊙O with
   m$\widehat{RS}$ = 71, m$\widehat{UT}$ = 43
   Find m ∠RNS.

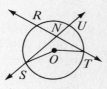

9. Given: ⊙O with tangent
   $\overleftrightarrow{AB} \parallel \overleftrightarrow{CD}$, m ∠ECD = 80
   Find m$\widehat{EC}$.

10. Given: $\overleftrightarrow{AB}$ tangent to
    ⊙O $\overleftrightarrow{AB} \parallel \overleftrightarrow{CD}$, and
    m$\widehat{CD}$ = 140
    Find m ∠CEB.

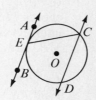

11. Given: $\overline{FH}$ is a diameter of ⊙O, m$\widehat{FJ}$ = 100,
    m$\widehat{FJ}$ = 100, and m$\widehat{GF}$ = 120.
    Find m ∠FPJ.

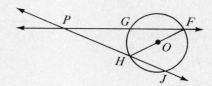

12. Given: $\overrightarrow{WT}$ is tangent
    to ⊙O, WS = 9, and
    WR = 4.
    Find WT.

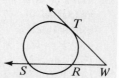

*13. Draw two segments with lengths a and b.
    Construct a segment with length $\dfrac{\sqrt{ab}}{2}$.

14. Given: ⊙O with
    diameter $\overline{AC}$ and
    $\widehat{DC} \cong \widehat{AB}$
    Prove: ABCD is
    a rectangle.

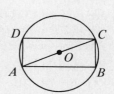

*15. Given: $\overleftrightarrow{XY}$ tangent to ⊙O and ⊙P, $\overleftrightarrow{ZT}$ tangent to ⊙O and ⊙P, $\overline{XT} \cong \overline{YT}$.
    Prove: $\overleftrightarrow{TZ} \perp \overleftrightarrow{XY}$

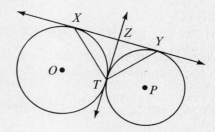

College Prep Test

Directions: Choose the one best answer to each question or problem.

1. In $\odot O$ m$\overset{\frown}{ACB} = 120$.
Find m $\angle BAO$.
(A) 12 (B) 30
(C) 45 (D) 60 (E) 120

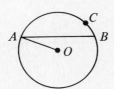

2. $MNPQ$ is an inscribed quadrilateral.
m $\angle P = 60$.
Find m $\angle M$.
(A) 120 (B) 110 (C) 130
(D) 125 (E) 115

3. In the figure,
$\overline{PA}$, $\overline{PB}$, $\overline{MN}$
are tangent to $\odot O$.
$AP = 20$.
Find the perimeter
of $\triangle PMN$.

(A) 20 (B) 30 (C) 40 (D) $35\frac{1}{2}$ (E) 50

4. In the figure,
A, B, C, D are on
the circle.
m $\angle B = 20$
m $\angle DPC = 70$
Find m $\angle D$.
(A) 30 (B) 100 (C) 50 (D) 120 (E) 90

5. What is the measure of the angle formed
by the hour and minute hands of a clock at
2:15?

(A) 30° (B) $22\frac{1}{2}^\circ$ (C) $157\frac{1}{2}^\circ$ (D) $172\frac{1}{2}^\circ$

(E) $27\frac{1}{2}^\circ$

6. In the figure,
$\overline{AO}$, $\overline{BO}$ are
radii of $\odot O$,
$PC = OA$,
POA is a st. line,
m $\angle BOA = 60$.
Find m $\angle P$.
(A) 10 (B) 15 (C) 20 (D) 30 (E) 40

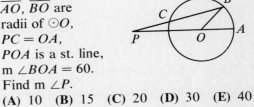

7. In the figure,
m$\overset{\frown}{RS} = 40$.
Find m $\angle W$ + m $\angle T$.
(A) 320 (B) 160
(C) 150 (D) 200
(E) 250

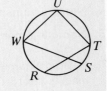

8. In $\odot O$,
m $\angle OMN = 50$.
Find m $\angle MSN$.
(A) 80
(B) 100
(C) 260
(D) 40
(E) 130

9. What is the length of a tangent drawn from
a point 3 inches from a circle whose radius
is 12 inches?
(A) 9 in. (B) $6\sqrt{2}$ in. (C) 6 in.
(D) $3\sqrt{5}$ in. (E)

10. In the figure
chords $\overline{MN}$ and $\overline{RS}$
intersect at P.
$MP = 25$, $PN = 8$.
$\dfrac{RP}{PS} = \dfrac{1}{2}$.
Find RS.

(A) 33 (B) 30 (C) $\dfrac{10}{3}\sqrt{6}$ (D) 20

(E) 22

Proofs of the Pythagorean Theorem

A. Cut out four identical right triangles.

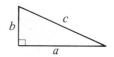

B. Arrange them as shown at the right. Verify that the figure in the center is a square.

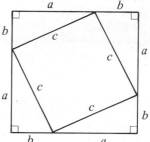

C. Find the area of the big square in two ways.

$$\begin{pmatrix}\text{Area of} \\ \text{big square}\end{pmatrix} = \begin{pmatrix}\text{length} \\ \text{of side}\end{pmatrix} \cdot \begin{pmatrix}\text{length} \\ \text{of side}\end{pmatrix}$$

$$= (a + b)(a + b)$$

$$= a^2 + 2ab + b^2$$

$$\begin{pmatrix}\text{Area of} \\ \text{big square}\end{pmatrix} = \begin{pmatrix}\text{4 times area} \\ \text{of triangle}\end{pmatrix} + \begin{pmatrix}\text{area of} \\ \text{small square}\end{pmatrix}$$

$$= 4\left(\frac{1}{2}ab\right) + c^2$$

$$= 2ab + c^2$$

Both expressions represent the area of the big square.
Thus, $a^2 + 2ab + b^2 = 2ab + c^2$
or, $a^2 + b^2 = c^2$!

| Read |
| Plan |
| Solve |
| Interpret |

PROBLEM

Prove the Pythagorean Theorem by making the arrangement at the right. [Hint: Find the area of the big square in two ways.]

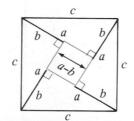

A Challenge To You

President Garfield discovered another proof by arranging two identical right triangles as shown in the picture.

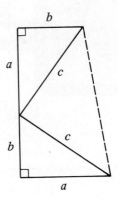

PROBLEM

Follow these steps to prove the Pythagorean Theorem by President Garfield's method.

1. Verify that the figure in the center is a right triangle.
2. Verify that the large figure is a trapezoid with a and b the lengths of the bases and $(a + b)$ the length of an altitude.
3. Find the area of the trapezoid in two ways and complete the proof. [Hint: See page 398.]

The square below is determined by four identical right triangles.

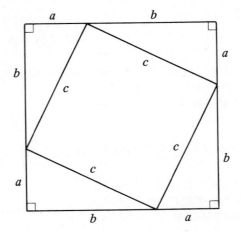

PROBLEM

4. Use the figure above to prove the Pythagorean Theorem. [*Hint:* Suppose the four triangles are removed from the big square.]

12.1 Areas of Rectangles and Squares

OBJECTIVE ► **To apply the formula for the area of a rectangle**

A **polygonal region** is the union of a polygon and its interior.
A **circular region** is the union of a circle and its interior.

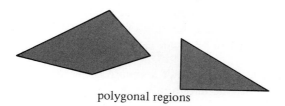

polygonal regions

circular
region

One way to measure a polygonal region or a circular region is to find its **area.** To simplify language, the area of a polygonal region or a circular region will be referred to as the area of the polygon or circle.

A **square unit** of area is a region bounded by a square whose sides are each one unit long. For example, a square with sides each 1 centimeter long can be used as a unit of area. It is called a square centimeter (cm²).

1 cm

1 cm
1 square
centimeter (cm^2)

To find the *area of a polygon,* you find the number of square units of area which are contained in the region bounded by the polygon. First consider the area of a rectangle.

Example 1 If the small square is the unit of area, find the area of the rectangle shown.

 There are 3 rows of 7 unit squares in the region.
The rectangle contains 21 square units.
$(3 \times 7) = 21$

Thus, the area is 21 square units.

Example 2 Find the area of the rectangle in square centimeters.

1.5 cm

4 cm

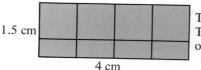

1.5 cm

4 cm

The first row contains 4 squares.
The second row contains 4 half–squares, or 2 squares. The total is 6 squares. $(1.5 \times 4 = 6)$

Thus, the area is 6 cm².

Examples 1 and 2 suggest a formula for the area of a rectangle.

Postulate 24 The area of a rectangle is the product of the length of a base and the length of a corresponding altitude.

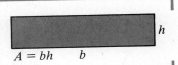

$A = bh$

A square is a rectangle, so you can use the formula $A = bh$ to find the area of any square. However, since each side of a square has the same length, there is another formula that can be used.

Corollary The area of a square is the square of the length of a side.

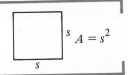

$A = s^2$

Examples 3 and 4 apply the formula $A = bh$.

Example 3 Find the area of a rectangle with a base of length 15 cm and a diagonal of length 17 cm.

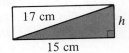

Use the Pythagorean theorem to find h.
$$h^2 + 15^2 = 17^2$$
$$h^2 + 225 = 289$$
$$h^2 = 64, \text{ or } h = 8$$
$$A = bh = 15 \cdot 8 = 120$$
Thus, the area is 120 cm².

Find the length of a base of a rectangle if $A = x^2 + 2x - 3$ and $h = x - 1$.

Example 4
$$A = b\,h$$
$$x^2 + 2x - 3 = (\quad)(x - 1)$$ ◄ *Substitute for A and h.*
Find the missing factor.
Thus, $b = x + 3$, since $(x + 3)(x - 1) = x^2 + 2x - 3$.

The next postulate enables you to add areas of regions.

Postulate 25 Area Addition Postulate If a region is the union of two or more nonoverlapping regions, then its area is the sum of the areas of these nonoverlapping regions.

Example 5 Find the area of the polygon.
Each angle is a right angle.

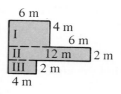

Divide the polygon into rectangles.
  Area of rectangle I $= 6 \times 4$, or 24 m²
  Area of rectangle II $= 12 \times 2$, or 24 m²
  Area of rectangle III $= 4 \times 2$, or 8 m²
Thus, the area of the polygon is $24 + 24 + 8$, or 56 m².

Oral Exercises

If the sides of a rectangle are measured in the following units, what is the corresponding unit for the area?
    1. millimeters   **2.** centimeters   **3.** meters   **4.** kilometers

Find the area of each rectangle.
    5. $b = 6$ cm, $h = 3$ cm   **6.** $b = 8$ m, $h = 4$ m   **7.** $b = 7$ km, $h = 9$ km
    8. $b = 5$ m, $h = 9$ m   **9.** $b = 9$ cm, $h = 3$ cm   **10.** $b = 6$ m, $h = 5$ m

Find the indicated length for each rectangle.
    11. $A = 20$ mm², $b = 4$ mm, $h = ?$ **12.** $A = 63$ km², $b = ?$, $h = 7$ km
    13. $A = 52$ cm², $b = ?$, $h = 13$ cm   **14.** $A = 120$ m², $b = 10$ m, $h = ?$

Find the area of each square.
    15. $s = 7$ mm   **16.** $s = 9$ cm   **17.** $s = 30$ m

Written Exercises

Find the area of each rectangle or square.

    1. $b = 6.5$ m, $h = 3.5$ m   **2.** $b = 4.27$ mm, $h = 3.94$ mm   **3.** $b = 5.7$ cm, $h = 4.3$ cm
    4. $b = 3.5$ m, $h = 2.25$ m   **5.** $b = \sqrt{5}$ m, $h = 7$ m   **6.** $b = 5$ km, $h = \sqrt{7}$ km
    7. Square with $s = 5$ cm   **8.** Square with $s = \sqrt{6}$ cm   **9.** Square with $s = (x + y)$
    10. $b = (x - y)$, $h = (x + y)$ **11.** $b = (x + y)$, $h = (x + y)$ **12.** $b = (2x + 3)$, $h = (3x - 5)$

Find the length of the base of each rectangle.
    13. $A = 78$ cm², $h = 1.5$ cm   **14.** $A = 9.86$ km², $h = 3.4$ km   **15.** $A = 5$ m², $h = \sqrt{5}$ m
    16. $A = x^2 + 2x + 1$,   **17.** $A = x^2 - 3x - 4$,   **18.** $A = 2x^2 - 5x - 12$,
        $h = x + 1$ $h = x - 4$ $h = x - 4$

Find the area of each rectangle. (Ex. 19–22)

    19. $b = 6$, length of diagonal $= 10$ **20.** $h = 40$, length of diagonal $= 41$
    21. $b = 3$, length of diagonal $= 7$ **22.** $h = \sqrt{2}$, length of diagonal $= \sqrt{3}$
    23. A diagonal of a rectangle makes an   **24.** Two consecutive sides of a rectangle
        angle of 30° with a base. The diagonal   are in a ratio of 2 to 3. The
        measures 12 cm. Find the area of   area is 216 m². Find the lengths
        the rectangle.   of the two sides.

AREAS OF RECTANGLES AND SQUARES

25. A diagonal of a square measures 16 cm. Find the area.

26. The dimensions of a rectangle are 4 cm by 5 cm. Find the length of a side of a square with the same area as the rectangle.

Find the area of each polygon. Each angle is a right angle. (Ex. 27–29)

27.

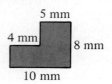

5 mm
4 mm
8 mm
10 mm

28.

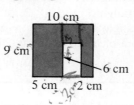

10 cm
9 cm
6 cm
5 cm   2 cm

29.

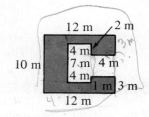

12 m   2 m
4 m
10 m   7 m   4 m
4 m
1 m   3 m
12 m

C **30.** Find the area of a square inscribed in a circle with a radius 6 cm long.

31. A circle with a radius 8 cm long is inscribed in a square. Find the area of the square.

32. Prove or disprove: The ratio of the areas of two rectangles is equal to the ratio of the products of the lengths of their bases and altitudes.

$$\frac{A}{A'} = \frac{bh}{b'h'}$$

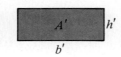

A h
b
A' h'
b'

33. Prove or disprove: The ratio of the areas of two rectangles with congruent altitudes is equal to the ratio of the lengths of their bases.

$$\frac{A}{A'} = \frac{b}{b'}$$

A h
b
A' h'
b'

34. Prove or disprove: If the length of a base of a rectangle is doubled and the length of a corresponding altitude remains the same, then the area is doubled.

35. Prove or disprove: If the lengths of the sides of one square are twice the lengths of the sides of another, then the area of the first square is twice the area of the second.

Algebra Review

OBJECTIVE ► **To solve an equation for one of its variables**

Example Solve $5xy = 4x + 3z$ for x.

$$5xy = 4x + 3z$$
$$5xy - 4x = 3z \qquad \blacktriangleleft \quad Add\ -4x\ to\ each\ side.$$
$$(5y - 4)x = 3z \qquad \blacktriangleleft \quad Distributive\ property$$
$$x = \frac{3z}{5y - 4} \qquad \blacktriangleleft \quad Divide\ each\ side\ by\ 5y - 4.$$

Solve each equation for the indicated variable.

1. $5x = b;\ x$
2. $4 + x = k;\ x$
3. $rx + s = t;\ x$
4. $9y - 24a = 6a + 4y;\ y$
5. $5t + 2b = t + 6b;\ t$
6. $rsx - 2s = 3;\ s$
7. $x + y = 3;\ y$
8. $2x + y = 8;\ y$
9. $3x - y = 12;\ y$
10. $4ab = 3a - 2c;\ a$
11. $-6xy + 4z = 3x;\ x$
12. $5rs - 3t = 7s;\ s$
13. $-6pq + 2q = 3p;\ q$
14. $abc + 2b = 4a;\ a$
15. $3x = 2yz - 5xyz;\ x$

12.2 Areas of Triangles and Rhombi

OBJECTIVES ► **To apply the formula for the area of a triangle**
To apply the formula for the area of a rhombus

Since congruent figures have the same size and shape, it is reasonable to assume that they have the same area. This is stated in Postulate 26.

Postulate 26 Congruent figures have the same area.

Recall that a diagonal of a rectangle divides the rectangle into two congruent right triangles. This leads to the following theorem.

Theorem 12.1 Area rt. $\triangle = \frac{1}{2}bh$ The area of a right triangle is one half the product of the lengths of the two legs. (See Exercise 22.)

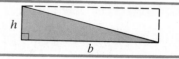

You can use Theorem 12.1 to prove a general theorem about the area of a triangle.

Theorem 12.2 Area $\triangle = \frac{1}{2}bh$ The area of any triangle is one half the product of the length of a base and the length of a corresponding altitude.

Given: $\triangle XYZ$, length of base $XY = b$, and length of altitude $ZD = h$

Prove: Area $\triangle XYZ = \frac{1}{2}bh$

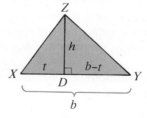

Analysis: Area $\triangle XYZ =$ area rt. $\triangle ZDY +$ area rt. $\triangle DZX$. Use the formula for the area of a rt. $\triangle$ and the area addition postulate.

Proof

Statements	Reasons
1. $\triangle XYZ$ with altitude $\overline{ZD}$, $XY = b$, $ZD = h$	1. Given
2. $\triangle ZDY$ and $\triangle DZX$ are rt. $\triangle$'s.	2. Def. of altitude and def. of rt. $\triangle$
3. Area $\triangle ZDY = \frac{1}{2}(b - t)h$ Area $\triangle DZX = \frac{1}{2}th$	3. Area rt. $\triangle = \frac{1}{2}bh$
4. Area $\triangle XYZ =$ area $\triangle DZX +$ area $\triangle ZDY$	4. Area Addition Postulate
5. Area $\triangle XYZ = \frac{1}{2}th + \frac{1}{2}(b - t)h$	5. Substitution property
6. Area $\triangle XYZ = \frac{1}{2}h\,(t + b - t)$	6. Distributive property
7. $\therefore$ Area $\triangle XYZ = \frac{1}{2}bh$	7. Algebraic properties

Theorem 12.2 can also be proved if the triangle is obtuse. (See Exercise 29.) In Example 1, the area is computed for a right triangle, an acute triangle, and an obtuse triangle.

Example 1 Find the area of each shaded triangular region.

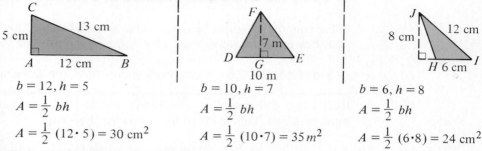

$b = 12, h = 5$

$A = \dfrac{1}{2} bh$

$A = \dfrac{1}{2} (12 \cdot 5) = 30 \text{ cm}^2$

$b = 10, h = 7$

$A = \dfrac{1}{2} bh$

$A = \dfrac{1}{2} (10 \cdot 7) = 35 \, m^2$

$b = 6, h = 8$

$A = \dfrac{1}{2} bh$

$A = \dfrac{1}{2} (6 \cdot 8) = 24 \text{ cm}^2$

Example 2 Given: $\triangle ABC$ with $\overline{AE} \perp \overline{BC}, \overline{CD} \perp \overline{AB}$, $AB = 8, CD = 4$, and $BC = 6$.

Find AE.

$\text{Area } \triangle ABC = \dfrac{1}{2} (AB)(CD) \quad \text{or} \quad \text{Area } \triangle ABC = \dfrac{1}{2} (BC)(AE)$

$A = \dfrac{1}{2} \cdot 8 \cdot 4$

$A = 16$

$16 = \dfrac{1}{2} \cdot 6 \, (AE)$

$\dfrac{16}{3} = AE$

Thus, $AE = \dfrac{16}{3}$.

Recall that the diagonals of a rhombus are perpendicular bisectors of each other. Also, either diagonal divides a rhombus into two congruent triangles. These reminders should help you to prove the following theorem.

Theorem 12.3 The area of a rhombus is one half the product of the lengths of the diagonals.

Given: Rhombus $ABCD$ with diagonals of lengths d_1 and d_2
Prove: Area rhombus $ABCD = \dfrac{1}{2} d_1 d_2$

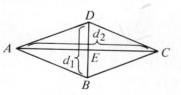

Analysis:
Find the area of $\triangle ACD$ in terms of d_2 and d_1. Then double that area to find the area of the rhombus. (See Exercise 23.)

Example 3 One diagonal of a rhombus is 12 cm long. The area is 48 cm². Find the length of the other diagonal.

$A = \dfrac{1}{2} d_1 \cdot d_2$

$48 = \dfrac{1}{2} \cdot 12 \cdot d_2$

$48 = 6 \cdot d_2$

Thus, $d_2 = 8$ cm.

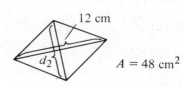

$A = 48 \text{ cm}^2$

The length of an altitude and the area of an equilateral triangle can be represented in terms of the length of a side, as stated below.

Theorem 12.4 Area $\bigtriangleup = \dfrac{S^2}{4}\sqrt{3}$ If S is the length of a side of an equilateral triangle, then the length of the altitude is $\dfrac{s}{2}\sqrt{3}$ and the area is $\dfrac{s^2}{4}\sqrt{3}$.

Given: Equilateral $\triangle ABC$ with side of length s and altitude $\overline{CD}$ of length h

Prove: $h = \dfrac{s}{2}\sqrt{3}$ and $A = \dfrac{s^2}{4}\sqrt{3}$

Analysis:
$\overline{CD}$ forms a $30°-60°$ rt. $\triangle$. Find h in terms of s. Then use the formula $A = \dfrac{1}{2}bh$.

Proof (See Exercise 24.)

Example 4 is an application of Theorem 12.4.

Example 4 Find the length of an altitude and the area of an equilateral triangle if each side is 8 cm long.

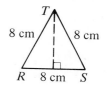

$$h = \frac{s}{2}\sqrt{3} = \frac{8}{2}\sqrt{3} = 4\sqrt{3}$$

$$A = \frac{s^2}{4}\sqrt{3} = \frac{8^2}{4}\sqrt{3} = \frac{64}{4}\sqrt{3} = 16\sqrt{3}$$

Thus, the length of an altitude is $4\sqrt{3}$ cm and the area is $16\sqrt{3}$ cm².

Written Exercises

Find the area of each shaded triangular region.

A

1.

4 m
6 m

2.
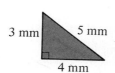
3 mm 5 mm
4 mm

3.

4 cm 4 cm

4.
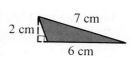
7 cm
2 cm
6 cm

5.
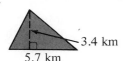
3.4 km
5.7 km

6.

$5\frac{1}{4}$ m $3\frac{1}{2}$ m

7.

$\sqrt{5}$ cm $\sqrt{5}$ cm

8.
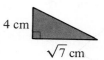
4 cm
$\sqrt{7}$ cm

Supply the missing information for each triangle.

	Length of base (b)	Length of altitude (h)	Area (A)
9.	9 cm	?	72 cm²
10.	7 m	?	63 m²
11.	?	0.7 km	0.56 km²

AREAS OF TRIANGLES AND RHOMBI

12. The diagonals of a rhombus measure 7 m and 10 m. Find the area.

13. One diagonal of a rhombus is 18 cm long. The area is 45 cm². Find the length of the other diagonal.

14. Find the length of an altitude and the area of an equilateral triangle if each side is 10 cm long.

15. Find the length of an altitude and the area of an equilateral triangle if each side is 12 cm long.

In $\triangle XYZ$, $\overline{XW} \perp \overline{ZY}$ and $\overline{ZT} \perp \overline{XY}$. Find each indicated length.

16. Given: $XY = 12$, $ZT = 8$, $YZ = 16$. Find XW.

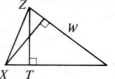

18. Given: $XW = 4$, $YZ = 7$, $ZT = 6$. Find XY.

17. Given: $XY = 15$, $ZT = 9$, $XW = 12$. Find YZ.

19. Given: $XY = 22$, $YZ = 33$, $XW = 12$. Find ZT.

20. The length of an altitude of an equilateral triangle is $7\sqrt{3}$. Find the length of a side.

22. Prove Theorem 12.1.

24. Prove Theorem 12.4.

21. The area of an equilateral triangle is $9\sqrt{3}$. Find the length of a side.

23. Prove Theorem 12.3.

25. Prove that the area of a square is one half the square of the length of a diagonal.

HERO'S FORMULA

Hero's Formula can be used to find the area of a triangle if the lengths of the three sides are known.

Area of a triangle $= \sqrt{s(s-a)(s-b)(s-c)}$, where a, b, and c are the lengths of the three sides and $s = \dfrac{1}{2}(a+b+c)$.

Example

Find the area of a triangle with sides 3 m, 4 m, and 5 m long.

$$s = \frac{1}{2}(a+b+c) = \frac{1}{2}(3+4+5) = \frac{1}{2} \cdot 12 = 6$$

$$A = \sqrt{s(s-a)(s-b)(s-c)} = \sqrt{6(6-3)(6-4)(6-5)} = \sqrt{6 \cdot 3 \cdot 2 \cdot 1} = \sqrt{36} = 6$$

Thus, the area is 6 m².

Find the area of each triangle. The lengths of the three sides are given.

26. 5 cm, 12 cm, 13 cm

27. 4 m, 5 m, 6 m

28. 4 km, 5 km, 8 km

29. Prove Theorem 12.2 for an obtuse triangle.

Prove or disprove each of the following.

30. The areas of two similar triangles have the same ratio as the squares of the lengths of any two corresponding sides.

31. The ratio of the areas of two similar triangles is equal to the ratio of the squares of the lengths of the corresponding altitudes.

32. If two triangles have equal areas, then the ratio of the lengths of their bases is equal to the ratio of the lengths of their altitudes.

33. The ratio of the areas of two triangles with congruent bases is equal to the ratio of the lengths of their altitudes.

34. Any angle bisector of a triangle separates the region into two regions with equal areas.

35. Any median of a triangle separates the region into two regions with equal areas.

CHAPTER TWELVE

12.3 Areas of Parallelograms

OBJECTIVE ►   **To apply the formula for the area of a parallelogram**

You can show that if a parallelogram and a rectangle have congruent bases and congruent altitudes, then they have the same area. This enables you to prove Theorem 12.5.

Theorem 12.5 Area $\square = bh$ The area of any parallelogram is the product of the length of a base and the length of a corresponding altitude.

Given: $\square ABCD$, length of base $\overline{AB} = b$, and length of altitude $\overline{CE} = h$

Prove: Area $\square ABCD = bh$

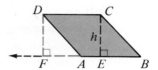

Analysis:
Show $\triangle FAD \cong \triangle EBC$.
Then Area $\square ABCD =$ area rect. $FECD$.

Proof

Statements	Reasons
1. $\square ABCD$ with altitude $\overline{CE}$, $AB = b$, $CE = h$	1. Given
2. Draw $\overrightarrow{DF} \perp \overrightarrow{BA}$.	2. There is exactly one $\perp$ from a pt. to a line.
3. $\overrightarrow{DC} \parallel \overrightarrow{BA}$	3. Opp. sides of a $\square$ are $\parallel$.
4. $\overline{DF} \cong \overline{CE}$	4. $\parallel$ lines are equidistant at all points.
5. $\overline{AD} \cong \overline{BC}$	5. Opp. sides of a $\square$ are $\cong$.
6. $\triangle FAD \cong \triangle EBC$	6. Def. of rt. $\triangle$ and HL for $\cong$ rt. $\triangle$'s
7. Area $\triangle FAD =$ area $\triangle EBC$	7. $\cong$ figures have the same area.
8. Area $\triangle FAD +$ area $AECD =$ area $\triangle EBC +$ area $AECD$	8. Add. prop. of equality
9. Area rect. $FECD =$ area $\square ABCD$	9. Area Add. Post. and substitution property
10. Area rect. $FECD = bh$	10. Area $\square = bh$
11. $\therefore$ Area $\square ABCD = bh$	11. Substitution property

Example 1 Find the area of $\square ABCD$.

$b = 9.2$, $h = 4.5$
$A = bh = 9.2\ (4.5) = 41.4$ cm²

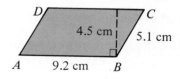

Example 2 The area of a parallelogram is 36 m². The length of a base is 8 m. Find the length of a corresponding altitude.

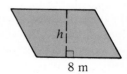

$A = bh$
$36 = 8h$ ◄   *Substitute 36 for A and 8 for b.*
$4.5 = h$

Thus, the length of a corresponding altitude is 4.5 m.

Notice that you can use any of the four sides of a parallelogram as a base. The area can be found by multiplying the length of any base by the length of any altitude drawn to that base, as shown in Example 3.

Example 3 Given: $\Box ACEF$ with $\overline{AD} \perp \overline{EC}$, $\overline{EB} \perp \overline{AC}$,
$AC = 12$, $BE = 6$, and $CE = 8$
Find AD.

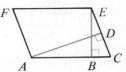

Area $\Box ACEF = (AC)(BE)$　　or　　Area $\Box ACEF = (CE)(AD)$
$A = 12 \cdot 6$　　　　　　　　　　　$\rightarrow 72 = 8\,(AD)$
$A = 72$　　　　　　　　　　　　　　$9 = AD$

Thus, $AD = 9$.

In Example 4, an altitude of a parallelogram is drawn so that a $30°-60°$ right triangle is formed. After the length of the altitude is completed, then the area of the parallelogram is found.

Example 4 The lengths of two consecutive sides of a parallelogram are 12 m and 14 m, respectively. The included angle measures $30°$. Find the area of the parallelogram.

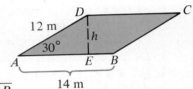

Let $h = DE$, the length of the altitude from D to $\overline{AB}$.
$\triangle AED$ is a $30°-60°$ rt. $\triangle$, so $h = 6$.
Area $\Box ABCD = bh = 14 \cdot 6 = 84$.
Thus, the area is 84 m².

Reading in Geometry

Write *A* if the statement is *always* true, *S* if it is *sometimes* true, and *N* if it is *never* true. Draw a figure, if necessary.

1. Congruent parallelograms have the same area.

2. Parallelograms with the same area are congruent.

3. Parallelograms with equal areas have congruent bases and congruent corresponding altitudes.

4. Parallelograms with congruent bases and congruent corresponding altitudes have the same area.

5. If the measure of an angle of a parallelogram is $30°$, then the area is equal to one half the product of the lengths of two consecutive sides.

6. If two consecutive sides of a parallelogram are 5 cm and 8 cm long, then the area is greater than 40 cm².

7. If two sides of a triangle have the same measures as a base and a corresponding altitude of a parallelogram, respectively, then the area of the triangle is equal to one half the area of the parallelogram.

8. If b_1 and b_2 represent the lengths of two consecutive sides of a parallelogram, and h_1 and h_2 represent the lengths of the corresponding altitudes, then $b_1 \cdot h_1 = b_2 \cdot h_2$.

Oral Exercises

In each case, tell whether enough information is given to find the area of the parallelogram.

1.
10 cm
9 cm

2.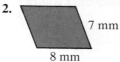
7 mm
8 mm

3.
8 m
7 m

4.
6 km
8 km

Written Exercises

Find the area of each parallelogram.

 1.
5 m
6 m

2.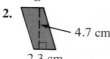
4.7 cm
2.3 cm

3.
8.9 cm
6.2 cm

4.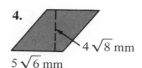
$4\sqrt{8}$ mm
$5\sqrt{6}$ mm

Supply the missing information for each parallelogram.

	Length of base (b)	Length of altitude (h)	Area (A)
5.	9 cm	?	81 cm²
6.	?	0.9 mm	0.72 mm²
7.	0.05 m	?	0.1695 m²
8.	?	$\sqrt{7}$ km	7 km²

In $\square ACEG$, $\overline{FB} \perp \overline{AC}$ and $\overline{GD} \perp \overline{CE}$. Find each indicated length.

 9. Given: $AC = 18$,
$BF = 6$,
and $CE = 12$
Find DG.

11. Given: $AC = 35$,
$CE = 24$,
and $DG = 21$
Find BF.

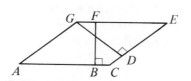

10. Given: $AC = 24$,
$BF = 8$,
and $DG = 12$
Find CE.

12. Given: $CE = 12$,
$DG = \sqrt{6}$,
and $BF = \sqrt{8}$
Find AC.

Find the area of $\square ABCD$ in each case. (Ex. 13–16)

13. Given: $AB = 10$,
$AD = 6$, and
m $\angle A = 30$

15. Given: $AB = 12$,
$BC = 10$, and
m $\angle A = 45$

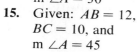

17. Prove that the area of a
parallelogram can be found
by the formula
Area $= ab \sin A$.

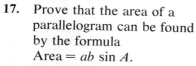

19. Find the area of $\square ABCD$
if $a = 16$, $b = 5$, and
m $\angle A = 42$.

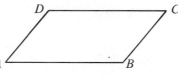

14. Given: $DC = 9$,
$BC = 8$, and
m $\angle C = 60$

16. Given: $DC = 16$,
$AD = 12$, and
m $\angle D = 135$

18. Prove that the area of $\triangle ABC$
can be found by the formula
Area $= \frac{1}{2} ab \sin A$, where
$\angle A$ is acute.

20. Find the area of $\triangle ABC$
if $a = 5$, $b = 6$, and
m $\angle A = 56$.

AREAS OF PARALLELOGRAMS

12.4 Areas of Trapezoids

OBJECTIVE ▶ **To apply the formula for the area of a trapezoid**

Recall that a trapezoid has two bases which are parallel. An altitude is a perpendicular segment from any point on one base to the line containing the other base.

Consider trapezoid $RSTU$ below. You can find its area by dividing the region into two triangular regions and adding the areas. Notice that $\triangle RSU$ and $\triangle UTS$ have congruent altitudes.

$$\text{Area trap. } RSTU = \text{area } \triangle RSU + \text{area } \triangle UTS.$$
$$= \frac{1}{2} \cdot 6 \cdot 9 + \frac{1}{2} \cdot 6 \cdot 7$$
$$= \frac{1}{2} \cdot 6 \,(9 + 7) \quad \blacktriangleleft \quad \textit{Distributive Property}$$

Thus, Area trap. $RSTU = 48$.

The proof of Theorem 12.6 follows the strategy used above.

Theorem 12.6   The area of a trapezoid is one half the product of the length of an altitude and the sum of the lengths of the two bases.

Given: Trap. $ABCD$ with base
lengths b_1 and b_2,
and altitude length h
Prove: Area trap. $ABCD =$
$\frac{1}{2} h \,(b_1 + b_2)$

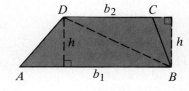

Proof

Statements	Reasons
1. Trap. $ABCD$ with base lengths b_1 and b_2 and altitude length h.	1. Given
2. Draw diagonal $\overline{DB}$.	2. Two points are contained in exactly one line.
3. Area $\triangle ABD = \frac{1}{2} b_1 \, h$	3. Area $\triangle = \frac{1}{2} bh$
4. Area $\triangle DBC = \frac{1}{2} b_2 \, h$	4. Same as 3
5. Area trap. $ABCD = $ area $\triangle ABD + $ area $\triangle DBC$	5. Area Addition Postulate
6. Area trap. $ABCD = \frac{1}{2} b_1 \, h + \frac{1}{2} b_2 \, h$	6. Substitution property
7. ∴ Area trap. $ABCD = \frac{1}{2} h \,(b_1 + b_2)$	7. Distributive property

Example 1 Find the area of trap. *ABCD*.

$b_1 = 15$, $b_2 = 10$, $h = 8$

$A = \dfrac{1}{2}h(b_1 + b_2) = \dfrac{1}{2} \cdot 8(15 + 10) = 4 \cdot 25 = 100$

Thus, the area is 100 cm².

Example 2 The area of a trapezoid is 36 m². The length of one base is 7 m and the length of an altitude is 6 m. Find the length of the other base.

Let $x =$ the length of the other base.

$A = \dfrac{1}{2}h(b_1 + b_2)$ $36 = 3(7 + x)$

$36 = \dfrac{1}{2} \cdot 6(7 + x)$ $12 = 7 + x$
                                       $5 = x$

Thus, the length of the other base is 5 m.

In Example 3, the length of one base must be expressed in terms of the length of the other. In Example 4, a 30°–60° right triangle must be used.

Example 3 The area of a trapezoid is 175 cm². An altitude is 10 cm long. If the length of one base is 8 cm greater than twice the length of the other base, find the length of each base.

Let $x =$ the length of one base.
$2x + 8 =$ the length of other base.

$A = \dfrac{1}{2}h(b_1 + b_2)$

$175 = \dfrac{1}{2} \cdot 10[x + (2x + 8)]$

$175 = 5(3x + 8)$
$35 = 3x + 8$
$27 = 3x$
$9 = x$
$2x + 8 = 2 \cdot 9 + 8 = 26$

Thus, the lengths of the bases are 9 cm and 26 cm.

Example 4 In trap. *ABCD*, $AB = 11$, $DA = 4$, $DC = 9$, and m $\angle A = 60$. Find the area of trap. *ABCD*.

Draw altitude $\overline{DE}$ from D to $\overline{AB}$.
$\triangle ADE$ is a 30°–60° rt. $\triangle$.

So, $DE = \dfrac{4}{2}\sqrt{3} = 2\sqrt{3}$.

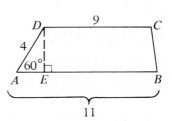

$A = \dfrac{1}{2}h(b_1 + b_2) = \dfrac{1}{2} \cdot 2\sqrt{3}(11 + 9)$

$= \sqrt{3} \cdot 20 = 20\sqrt{3}$

Thus, the area is $20\sqrt{3}$.

AREAS OF TRAPEZOIDS

Oral **Exercises**

In which cases is enough information given to find the area of the trapezoid?

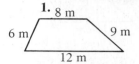

1.
8 m
6 m
9 m
12 m

2.
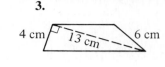
12 m
10 m
16 m

3.
4 cm
13 cm
6 cm

4.
5 cm
4 cm
8 cm

Written **Exercises**

Find the area of each trapezoid.

Ⓐ 1.
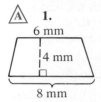
6 mm
4 mm
8 mm

2.
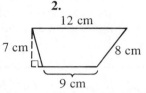
12 cm
7 cm
8 cm
9 cm

3.
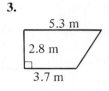
5.3 m
2.8 m
3.7 m

4.
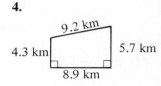
9.2 km
4.3 km
5.7 km
8.9 km

Supply the missing information for each trapezoid. (Ex. 5–13)

	b_1	b_2	h	Area
5.	7 m	9 m	5 m	?
6.	12 mm	11 mm	9 mm	?
7.	9 cm	15 cm	?	72 cm²
8.	12 mm	16 mm	?	56 mm²
9.	8 m	?	10 m	55 m²
10.	4 cm	?	7 cm	21 cm²

Ⓑ 11.	$x + 2$	$3x - 6$	$2x + 1$	?
12.	$3x - 1$	$5x + 7$	?	$4x^2 - 13x - 12$
13.	?	$2x + 3$	$2x + 1$	$4x^2 + 4x + 1$

14. The area of a trapezoid is 136 cm².
An altitude is 8 cm long. If one
base is 4 cm longer than the other
base, find the length of each base.

15. The area of a trapezoid is 234 m². An
altitude is 12 m long. If the length of one
base is 9 m less than twice the length of
the other base, find the length of each
base.

16. $\overline{AB}$ and $\overline{CD}$ are the bases of trap. $ABCD$.
If $AB = 30$, $CD = 20$, $AD = 8$, and
m $\angle A = 60$, find the area of the trapezoid.

17. $\overline{XY}$ and $\overline{ZW}$ are the bases of trap. $XYZW$.
If $XY = 15$, $ZW = 3$, $XW = 8$, and
m $\angle X = 45$, find the area of the trapezoid.

Ⓒ **18.** $\overline{AB}$ and $\overline{CD}$ are the bases of
isosceles trapezoid $ABCD$. If
$AB = 12$, $CD = 6$, and $AD = 5$, find
the area of the trapezoid.

19. $\overline{XY}$ and $\overline{ZW}$ are the bases of isosceles
trapezoid $XYZW$. If $XY = 11$,
$ZW = 7$, and m $\angle X = 60$, find
the area of the trapezoid.

20. In trapezoid $ABCD$, the lengths of bases $\overline{AB}$ and $\overline{CD}$ are 17 and 13, respectively. The length of $\overline{AD}$ is 4. If m $\angle A = 37$, find the area of trapezoid $ABCD$ to the nearest tenth.

21. In trapezoid $XYZW$, the lengths of bases $\overline{XY}$ and $\overline{WZ}$ are 9 and 4, respectively. The length of $\overline{XW}$ is 3. If m $\angle X = 72$, find the area of trapezoid $XYZW$ to the nearest tenth.

22. Prove or disprove: If two trapezoids have equal areas, then the sums of the lengths of the bases are inversely proportional to the lengths of the corresponding altitudes.

23. Prove or disprove: The ratio of the areas of two trapezoids with bases of one congruent to bases of the other is equal to the ratio of the lengths of their altitudes.

24. Construct an isosceles trapezoid with the same bases and area as a given nonisosceles trapezoid.

25. Construct a rectangle with the same area as a given trapezoid. [Hint: Use the median of the trapezoid.]

Cumulative Review

1. In $\square ABCD$, if m $\angle A = 120$, find the measure of each angle.

2. If $\triangle ABC \sim \triangle DEF$, write 3 proportions showing the correspondence between the sides.

CALCULATOR ACTIVITIES

The formula for the area of a trapezoid can be written as follows:

$$\text{Area trap.} = \frac{(b_1 + b_2)\,h}{2}$$

Example Find the area of trap. $ABCD$ to the nearest tenth.

Formula ▶ $\text{Area trap.} = \dfrac{(b_1 + b_2)\,h}{2}$

$= \dfrac{(8.2 + 5.7)\,4.8}{2}$

Press ▶ $8.2 \oplus 5.7 \otimes 4.8 \ominus 2$
Display ▶ 33.36

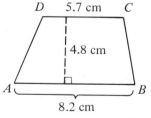

Thus, the area is 33.4 cm² to the nearest tenth.

Use a calculator to find the area of each trapezoid, to the nearest tenth.

	b_1	b_2	h		b_1	b_2	h
1.	6.9 cm	7.2 cm	4.6 cm	**4.**	5.23 cm	6.92 cm	4.37 cm
2.	10.1 mm	14.7 mm	9.5 mm	**5.**	18.64 m	12.81 m	9.47 m
3.	23.8 m	17.9 m	30.6 m	**6.**	21.71 m	16.05 m	8.56 m

AREAS OF TRAPEZOIDS

12.5 Similar Polygons: Areas and Perimeters

Consider the following experiment with similar triangles $\triangle ABC$ and $\triangle DEF$. Find the area of each triangle.

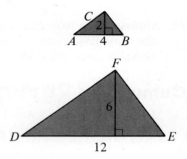

Area $\triangle ABC = \frac{1}{2}bh = \frac{1}{2} \cdot 4 \cdot 2 = 4$

Area $\triangle DEF = \frac{1}{2}bh = \frac{1}{2} \cdot 12 \cdot 6 = 36$

Notice that the ratio of the lengths of corresponding sides is $\frac{4}{12}$, or $\frac{1}{3}$. The ratio of the areas is $\frac{4}{36}$, or $\frac{1}{9}$. This leads to the following theorem.

> **Theorem 12.7** The ratio of the areas of two similar triangles is the square of the ratio of the lengths of any two corresponding sides. (See Exercise 23.)

You can use Theorem 12.7 to find the ratio of the areas of two similar triangles or to find the length of one of the sides.

Example 1 The ratio of the lengths of two corresponding sides of two similar triangles is $\frac{5}{6}$. Find the ratio of the areas.

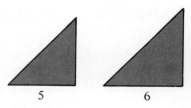

$$\frac{\text{Area of 1st } \triangle}{\text{Area of 2nd } \triangle} = \left(\frac{5}{6}\right)^2 = \frac{25}{36}$$

Example 2 Given: $\triangle ABC \sim \triangle DEF$. The ratio of the areas of the triangles is $\frac{9}{16}$. $BC = 6$. Find EF.

$$\frac{\text{Area } \triangle ABC}{\text{Area } \triangle DEF} = \left(\frac{BC}{EF}\right)^2 \text{ by Th. 12.7}$$

Let $x = EF$. ► $\dfrac{9}{16} = \left(\dfrac{6}{x}\right)^2$

$$\frac{9}{16} = \frac{36}{x^2}$$
$$9x^2 = 16 \cdot 36$$
$$x^2 = 64$$
$$x = 8, \text{ so } EF = 8.$$

You have learned to find the *perimeter* of a triangle by adding the lengths of the three sides. Now the concept of the perimeter will be extended to apply to any polygon.

Definition:
perimeter

> The **perimeter** of a polygon is the sum of the lengths of its sides.

The definition of perimeter is applied in Example 3.

Example 3 Find the perimeter of a rhombus with a side 7.2 cm long.

7.2 cm

All sides of a rhombus are the same length.
$p = 7.2 + 7.2 + 7.2 + 7.2$, or $p = 4 \cdot 7.2 = 28.8$

Thus, the perimeter is 28.8 cm.

Consider the following experiment with similar quadrilaterals $ABCD$ and $EFGH$, and their perimeters.

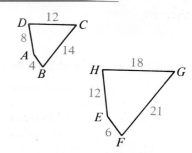

The ratio of the lengths of two corresponding sides is $\frac{8}{12}$, or $\frac{2}{3}$. The ratio of the perimeters is $\frac{8 + 4 + 14 + 12}{12 + 6 + 21 + 18} = \frac{38}{57} = \frac{2}{3}$. This suggests the following theorem.

> **Theorem 12.8** The ratio of the perimeters of two similar polygons is the same as the ratio of the lengths of any two corresponding sides. (See Exercise 24.)

Theorem 12.8 can sometimes be used to find the perimeter of one of two similar polygons.

Example 4 The ratio of the lengths of corresponding sides of similar triangles is $\frac{2}{5}$. If the perimeter of the larger triangle is 15 cm, find the perimeter of the smaller triangle.

$$
\begin{aligned}
\text{Let } p = \text{ perimeter of} & \\
\text{the smaller } \triangle. & \\
\frac{p}{15} = \frac{2}{5} \text{ by Th. 12.8} & \\
5p = 30 & \\
p = 6 &
\end{aligned}
$$

Thus, the perimeter of the smaller triangle is 6 cm.

SIMILAR POLYGONS: AREAS AND PERIMETERS

Written Exercises

Find the ratio of the areas and the ratio of the perimeters for each pair of similar triangles.

A **1.** Given: $\triangle ABC \sim \triangle DEF$

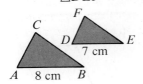

2. Given: $\triangle GHI \sim \triangle JKL$

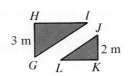

3. Given: Rt. $\triangle TUV \sim \triangle XYZ$

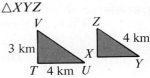

4. Given: Equilateral $\triangle ABC \sim \triangle DEF$

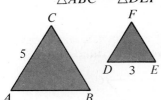

5. Given: Rt. $\triangle EFG \sim \triangle HIJ$

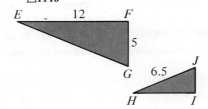

6. Given: $\triangle PQR \sim \triangle STU$ and $\overline{PQ} \cong \overline{QR}$

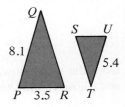

Find the perimeter of each polygon. (Ex. 7–10)

7. An equilateral triangle with a side 7 cm long

8. A square with a side 3 m long

9. A parallelogram with consecutive sides 5.2 cm and 3.9 cm long

10. A rhombus with a side 6.8 mm long

11. The ratio of the lengths of corresponding sides of similar triangles is $\frac{3}{4}$. If the perimeter of the smaller triangle is 51 cm, find the perimeter of the larger triangle.

12. The ratio of the perimeters of two similar polygons is $\frac{5}{8}$. One side of the larger polygon is 28 cm long; find the length of the corresponding side of the smaller polygon.

Find the perimeter of each polygon. (Ex. 13–18)

B **13.** A square with a diagonal 8 cm long

14. A rectangle with a side 8 m long and a diagonal 17 m long

15. A right triangle with legs 9 cm and 12 cm long

16. A right triangle with a leg 6 m long and the hypotenuse 12 m long

17. A 30°–60° right triangle with the hypotenuse 14 m long

18. An isosceles right triangle with a leg 9 cm long

19. Given: $\triangle ABC \sim \triangle DEF$. The ratio of the areas is $\frac{16}{25}$. $AC = 12$. Find DF.

20. Given: $\triangle ABC \sim \triangle DEF$. The ratio of the areas is $\frac{4}{9}$. $AB = 5$, $BC = 9$, and $CA = 10$. Find the perimeter of $\triangle DEF$.

21. The area of one triangle is 9 cm². The area of a similar triangle is 4 cm². If the perimeter of the first is $5x - 3$ and the perimeter of the second is $2x + 2$, what is the perimeter of each?

22. In two similar triangles, corresponding sides are 4 m and 2 m long. If the area of the smaller is 18 m² less than the area of the larger, find the area of the larger.

23. Prove Theorem 12.7.

24. Prove Theorem 12.8.

25. A side of a triangle measures 1 unit. What is the measure of the corresponding side of a similar triangle with an area three times the area of the original triangle?

26. A side of a triangle measures x units. What is the measure of the corresponding side of a similar triangle with an area y times the area of the original triangle?

A Challenge To You

Approximating Areas

Two different methods are used to estimate the area of a quadrilateral-shaped land plot. In most cases, the area obtained is only an approximation since the shapes are not exactly rectangles or kites.

Sides Method

To find the approximate area of a quadrilateral that is almost rectangular-shaped, use

$$\text{Area} \doteq \left(\frac{AB + CD}{2}\right)\left(\frac{AD + BC}{2}\right)$$

$$\text{Area} \doteq \left(\frac{90 + 100}{2}\right)\left(\frac{45 + 55}{2}\right)$$
$$\doteq (95)(50)$$
$$\doteq 4{,}750 \text{ square units}$$

Diagonal Method

To find the approximate area of a quadrilateral that is almost kite-shaped, use

$$\text{Area} \doteq \frac{1}{2}(AC)(DB)$$

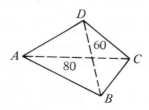

$$\text{Area} \doteq \frac{1}{2}(80)(60)$$
$$\doteq (40)(60)$$
$$\doteq 2{,}400 \text{ square units}$$

PROJECT **For the two figures below, measure carefully in centimeters. Approximate the area of each using both formulas. Which formula gives a better estimate. Why?**

12.6 Areas of Regular Polygons

OBJECTIVE ► **To apply the formula for the area of a regular polygon**
To find lengths of segments related to a regular polygon

Recall that a regular polygon is both equilateral and equiangular. It can be proved that a circle can be inscribed in any regular polygon. Also, a circle can be circumscribed about any regular polygon. The following definitions pertain to a regular polygon.

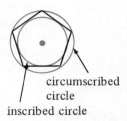

circumscribed circle

inscribed circle

Definitions:
center, apothem
radius of
regular polygon

The *center of a regular polygon* is the common center of its inscribed and circumscribed circles.
An *apothem of a regular polygon* is a segment from the center of the polygon perpendicular to a side of the polygon.
A *radius of a regular polygon* is a segment that joins the center of the polygon and a vertex of the polygon.

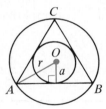

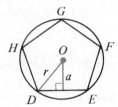

In the figures above, note that an apothem (a) is also a radius of the inscribed circle, and a radius (r) is also a radius of the circumscribed circle.

It can be proved that an apothem of a regular polygon bisects a side of the polygon. (See Exercise 20.) Also, a radius of a regular polygon bisects an angle of the polygon. (See Exercise 21.) These two statements are applied in Example 1.

Example 1 The length of an apothem of a square is 8. Find the length of a radius, the length of a side, and the area of the square.

Radius $\overline{OB}$ bisects $\angle ABC$, so m $\angle OBE = 45$.
Then $\triangle OEB$ is a 45°–45° rt. $\triangle$.
So $EB = 8$ and $OB = 8\sqrt{2}$.
Apothem $\overline{OE}$ bisects $\overline{AB}$, so $AB = 16$.
Area $\square ABCD = s^2 = 16^2 = 256$.
Thus, the length of a radius is $8\sqrt{2}$, the length of a side is 16, and the area is 256.

Theorem 12.9

The area of a regular polygon is one half the product of the lengths of an apothem and the perimeter.

Given: Regular polygon $ABCD \cdots$ with n sides, a is the length of an apothem, and p is the perimeter.

Prove: Area regular polygon $ABCD \cdots = \frac{1}{2} ap$.

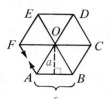

Outline of Proof

For a regular polygon with n sides, its radii divide it into n congruent triangles. If a is the length of an apothem and s is the length of a side, then the area of each triangle is $\frac{1}{2} as$. The area of the polygon is $n \cdot \left(\frac{1}{2} as \right)$, or $\frac{1}{2} a (ns)$. But ns is the perimeter of the polygon. **Thus,** the area of the polygon is $\frac{1}{2} ap$.

You can use Theorem 12.9 to find the area of any regular polygon.

Example 2

The length of an apothem of a regular hexagon is $5\sqrt{3}$. Find the area.

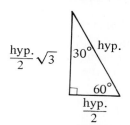

Radius $\overline{OB}$ bisects $\angle ABC$, so m $\angle OBG = 60$.
Then $\triangle OBG$ is a $30°\!-\!60°$ rt. $\triangle$, and $GB = 5$.
Apothem $\overline{OG}$ bisects $\overline{AB}$, so $AB = 10$.
$p = 6 \cdot 10 = 60$
$A = \frac{1}{2} ap = \frac{1}{2} \cdot 5\sqrt{3} \cdot 60 = 150\sqrt{3}$
Thus, the area is $150\sqrt{3}$.

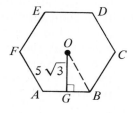

Written Exercises

Find the area of each of the following regular polygons.

	Number of sides	Length of side	Length of apothem	Area
1.	5	2	1.4	?
2.	5	1.4	1	?
3.	8	10	12.1	?
4.	8	0.5	0.6	?

Supply the missing information for each regular polygon.

	Number of sides	Length of side	Length of apothem	Length of radius
5.	3	?	7	?
6.	3	8	?	?
7.	4	?	6	?
8.	4	?	?	$5\sqrt{2}$
9.	6	10	?	?
10.	6	?	$4\sqrt{3}$	?

Find the area of each of the following regular polygons.

	Number of sides	Length	Area
11.	3	apothem: 4 cm	?
12.	3	radius: 6 m	?
13.	4	apothem: 3 mm	?
14.	4	radius: 8 m	?
15.	6	radius: 10 cm	?
16.	6	apothem: 6 cm	?

Find the missing measures for each regular polygon.

	Number of sides	Area	Length of apothem	Length of radius	Length of side
17.	3	$12\sqrt{3}$	?	?	?
18.	4	25	?	?	?
19.	6	$8\sqrt{3}$	?	?	?

Prove each of the following.

20. An apothem of a regular polygon bisects a side of the polygon.

21. A radius of a regular polygon bisects an angle of the polygon.

22. If an equilateral triangle is inscribed in a circle, and another equilateral triangle is circumscribed about the same circle, what is the ratio of the areas of the two triangles?

23. If a square is inscribed in a circle, and another square is circumscribed about the same circle, what is the ratio of the areas of the two squares?

Prove or disprove each of the following.

24. The ratio of the areas of two similar regular polygons is equal to the ratio of their perimeters.

25. The ratio of the areas of two similar regular polygons is equal to the square of the ratio of the lengths of their apothems.

For each regular polygon, use sine, cosine, or tangent to find the missing measures. Give each answer to the nearest hundredth.

	Number of sides	Length of radius	Length of apothem	Area
26.	5	4	?	?
27.	5	?	4	?
28.	5	?	?	4
29.	9	6	?	?
30.	9	?	10	?
31.	9	?	?	12
32.	10	8	?	?

12.7 Circumferences of Circles

OBJECTIVE ▶ **To apply the formula for the circumference of a circle**

Suppose several regular polygons are inscribed in congruent circles, as shown.

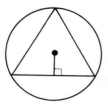
3 sides

6 sides

As you move from one regular polygon to the next, the number of sides is doubled. As this continues, the following describes the results.
1. The length of an apothem approaches the length of a radius of the circle as a limit.
2. The perimeter of the polygons approaches the "distance around" the circle as a limit.
3. The area of the polygons approaches the area of the circle as a limit.
These observations lead to the following definition.

Definition:
circumference

> The **circumference** of a circle is the limit of the perimeters of inscribed regular polygons of the circle as the number of sides of the polygons increases indefinitely.

Examine the relationship between the perimeter of an inscribed regular hexagon and the length of a diameter of its circumscribed circle. Suppose three regular hexagons are inscribed in circles. You can compute the ratio of the perimeter of each hexagon to the length of a diameter of the circle.

I

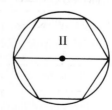
II

III

Since a side of a regular hexagon has the same length as a radius of the circle,

$$\frac{\text{Perimeter}}{\text{Length of Diameter}} = \frac{p}{d} = \frac{6r}{2r} = \frac{3}{1}.$$

Thus, in each case, the ratio is a constant, $\frac{3}{1}$.

Now suppose the number of sides of the inscribed regular polygons is increased. Then the perimeters of the polygons approach the circumferences of the circles as a limit. So it is reasonable to assume that the ratio of the circumference of a circle to the length of a diameter is also a constant. This can be proved with the help of a set of postulates and theorems about limits. However, in this book the theorem is presented without proof.

> **Theorem 12.10** For all circles, the ratio of the circumference to the length of a diameter is the same.

π (pi) is the symbol used for the ratio of the circumference to the length of a diameter of a circle.

$$\frac{c}{d} = \pi$$

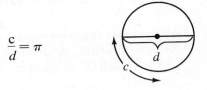

π is an irrational number which can be approximated correct to thousands of decimal places with the help of a computer. $\pi \doteq 3.141592653589793$, correct to fifteen decimal places. Commonly used approximations are 3.14, $\frac{22}{7}$, and 3.1416.

Since $\frac{c}{d} = \pi$, there are two formulas for the circumference of a circle. These formulas are given in the following corollary to Theorem 12.10.

> **Corollary** If c is the circumference of a circle with a diameter of length d and a radius of length r, then $c = \pi d$ or $c = 2\pi r$.

Either $c = \pi d$ or $c = 2\pi r$ can be used in problems involving circumference.

Example 1 If a diameter of a circle measures 8 cm, find the circumference in terms of π.

$c = \pi d = \pi \cdot 8$, or 8π cm

Example 2 If the circumference of a circle is 20π, find the length of a radius.

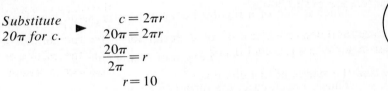

Substitute 20π for c. ▶
$$c = 2\pi r$$
$$20\pi = 2\pi r$$
$$\frac{20\pi}{2\pi} = r$$
$$r = 10$$

$c = 20\pi$

Reading in Geometry

Translate into symbols. Use *c* for circumference, *d* for length of diameter, *r* for length of radius, and *A* for area.

1. The circumference of a circle is equal to π times the length of a diameter.

2. π is equal to the ratio of the circumference of a circle to twice the length of a radius.

3. One half the circumference of a circle is equal to the length of a radius times π.

4. The area of a square inscribed in a circle is twice the square of the length of a radius of the circle.

Written Exercises

Find each missing measurement for each circle. For the last column, use 3.14 for π.

Ⓐ

	1.	2.	3.	4.	5.	6.	7.	8.
r	2 m				32 mm			
d		8 cm					5.2 mm	
c in terms of π			12π mm			15π cm		
c to two decimal places				6.28 cm				72.22 cm

For each given circumference, find the length of a radius and the circumference correct to the nearest hundredth. Use 3.14 for π. (Ex. 9–12)

Ⓑ 9. $\frac{3}{4}$ m

10. $\frac{2}{3}$ m

11. $\sqrt{3}$ mm

12. $\sqrt{7}$ km

13. Two approximations, $3\frac{1}{7}$ and 3.14 are often used for π. Which is closer to π?

14. Archimedes found π to be between $3\frac{1}{7}$ and $3\frac{10}{71}$. Which is closer to π?

15. If a radius of a circle is increased by *d*, express the increase in the circumference in terms of *d*.

16. Find the length of the equator if the radius of the earth is 6,400 kilometers.

Ⓒ 17. Using the Pythagorean theorem, find the length of each side of a square inscribed in a circle with a 1 cm radius. Compare the perimeter of the square to the circumference of the circle.

18. Using the appropriate trigonometric ratio, find the length of each side of an octagon inscribed in a circle with a 1-cm radius. Compare the perimeter of the octagon with the circumference of the circle.

19. The circumference of a circle is equal to the perimeter of a square with side s. Show that the radius of this circle is $\frac{2s}{\pi}$.

20. The circumference of a circle is 20π. Find the perimeter and area of a regular inscribed hexagon.

CIRCUMFERENCES OF CIRCLES

12.8 Areas of Circles

OBJECTIVE ▶ **To apply the formula for the area of a circle**

Recall that as you increase the number of sides of a regular polygon inscribed in a circle,
1. The length of an apothem approaches the length of a radius $(a \rightarrow r)$;
2. The perimeter approaches the circumference $(p \rightarrow c)$;
3. The area of the polygon approaches the area of the circle (Area polygon $\rightarrow$ Area $\odot$).

Consider the formula for the area of a regular polygon, $A = \frac{1}{2} ap$. Suppose you increase the number of sides of the inscribed regular polygon indefinitely. You can derive a formula for the area of a circle as follows:

$$\text{Area regular polygon} = \frac{1}{2} a\, p$$

$$\downarrow \qquad\qquad \downarrow\downarrow$$

Since $a \rightarrow r$ and $p \rightarrow c$, Area $\odot = \frac{1}{2} r\, c$ But $c = 2\pi r.$

$$\text{Area } \odot = \frac{1}{2} r\, (2\pi r)$$

$$\text{Area } \odot = \pi r^2$$

This leads to the following theorem. It is given without proof.

> **Theorem 12.11** Area $\odot = \pi r^2$ The area of a circle with a radius of length r is πr^2.

Since $r = \frac{1}{2} d$, you can also write the area formula in terms of the length of a diameter.

$$A = \pi r^2 = \pi\left(\frac{1}{2} d\right)^2, \text{ or } A = \frac{\pi d^2}{4}$$

Example 1 The length of a radius of a circle is 6 cm. Find the area. (Use 3.14 for π.)

$$A = \pi r^2 = \pi(6)^2 = 36\pi = 36(3.14) = 113.04 \text{ cm}^2$$

Example 2 The area of a circle is $12\pi\, m^2$. Find the length of a diameter.

$$A = \frac{\pi d^2}{4}$$

Substitute 12π for A.   ▶ $12\pi = \frac{\pi d^2}{4}$

Multiply each side by $\frac{4}{\pi}$.

$$48 = d^2$$

$$d = \sqrt{48} = \sqrt{16.3}, \text{ or } 4\sqrt{3}\ m$$

Example 3 Find the area of a circle if the circumference is 5π.

$$c = 2\pi r$$
$$5\pi = 2\pi r$$
$$\frac{5}{2} = r$$
$$A = \pi r^2 = \pi \left(\frac{5}{2}\right)^2 = \frac{25}{4}\pi$$

Example 4 Regular hexagon $ABCDEF$ is inscribed in $\odot O$, $AO = 1$. Find the area of the shaded region in terms of π.

Area shaded region = Area $\odot$ − Area hex.

Area $\odot = \pi r^2 = \pi \cdot 1^2 = \pi$

Area $\triangle AOB = \frac{s^2}{4}\sqrt{3} = \frac{r^2}{4}\sqrt{3}$

Area hex. $= 6 \cdot$ Area $\triangle AOB$

$$= 6 \cdot \frac{r^2}{4}\sqrt{3} = 6 \cdot \frac{(1)^2}{4}\sqrt{3} = \frac{3\sqrt{3}}{2}$$

Thus, the area of the shaded region is $\pi - \dfrac{3\sqrt{3}}{2}$.

Written Exercises

Find the area of each circle in terms of π.

Ⓐ   1. $r = 2$ m   2. $r = 1$ mm   3. $d = 4$ km   4. $d = 16$ cm

Find the length of a radius of each circle whose area is given.

5. 25π m²   6. 16π cm²   7. 49π mm²   8. π cm²

Find the length of a diameter of each circle whose area is given.

9. 9π m²   10. 25π cm²   11. 144π mm²   12. 36π cm²

Find the area of a circle with each given radius length. (Use 3.14 for π.)

13. $r = 0.6$ m   14. $r = 5.6$ mm   15. $r = .75$ cm   16. $r = \sqrt{5}$ km

Find the area of a circle with each given diameter length. (Use 3.14 for π.)

17. $d = 3$ cm   18. $d = 6.2$ mm   19. $d = 0.3$ m   20. $d = \sqrt{3}$ m

Find the lengths of a radius and a diameter of a circle with each given area. (Use 3.14 for π.)

21.   314 cm²   22.   78.5 m²   23.   1.1304 mm²   24.   4.5216 cm²

Find the area of a circle with each given circumference. (Use 3.14 for π.)

25. $c = 25.12$ mm   26. $c = 6.28$ cm   27. $c = 9$ m   28. $c = 100$ cm

AREAS OF CIRCLES

B **29.** Find the area of a square with an apothem of length 1 m and a perimeter of 8 m. Compare this to the area of a circle with a 1 m radius.

30. Find the area of a regular octagon with an apothem of length 1 m and a perimeter of 6.6 m. Compare this with the area of a circle with a 1 m radius.

Find the area of the shaded region. Each polygon is regular with sides 2 cm long. (Hint: Find the length of the radius of each circle. Then find the difference between the larger and smaller areas.)

31.   **32.**   **33.**   **34.**

Each circle is tangent to the adjacent circles. Find the area of the shaded region. (Ex. 35–37)

35. $\overline{AB}$ is a diameter of $\odot O$, $\overline{AO}$ is a diameter of $\odot P$, $\overline{OB}$ is a diameter of $\odot Q$. $AB = 10$.

36. Each circle is tangent to the square. All $\odot$'s are $\cong$. $AB = 2$.

37. All circles, except the center circle, are tangent to the square. All $\odot$'s are $\cong$. $AB = 2$.

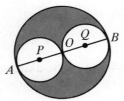   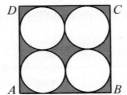   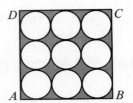

C **38.** Prove or disprove: The ratio of the areas of two circles equals the ratio of the lengths of the radii.

39. Prove or disprove: The ratio of the areas of two circles equals the ratio of the squares of the circumferences.

40. If a circle is inscribed in an equilateral triangle, and another circle is circumscribed about the same triangle, what is the ratio of the areas of the two circles?

41. If a circle is inscribed in a square, and another circle is circumscribed about the same square, what is the ratio of the areas of the two circles?

CALCULATOR ACTIVITIES

Find the area of the shaded region correct to the nearest hundredth. Use 3.1416 for π.

1.   **2.**

12.9 Arc Lengths

OBJECTIVE ▶ **To apply the formula for the length of an arc**

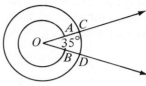

Recall that two arcs may have the same measure, yet not be congruent. For the two concentric circles shown, $\angle COD$ intercepts $\overset{\frown}{AB}$ and $\overset{\frown}{CD}$. If $m \angle COD = 35$, then $m\overset{\frown}{AB} = 35$ and $m\overset{\frown}{CD} = 35$. But $\overset{\frown}{CD}$ is not congruent to AB.

When you find the length of an arc, you are actually finding a part of the circumference of the circle. Consider $\odot Q$ with $m \angle EQF = 60$ and $QE = 6$ cm. $\angle EQF$ intercepts $\frac{60}{360}$, or $\frac{1}{6}$ of the circle, so you can find the length of $\overset{\frown}{EF}$ by finding $\frac{1}{6}$ of the circumference.

$$c = 2\pi r = 2\pi \cdot 6 = 12\pi \text{ cm}$$
$$\text{length of } EF = \frac{1}{6} \cdot 12\pi = 2\pi \text{ cm}$$

This suggests the following theorem. It is given without proof.

> **Theorem 12.12** $\quad l = \dfrac{m}{360} \cdot 2\pi r \quad$ If the degree measure of an arc is m and the length of a radius of the circle is r, then the length l of the arc is given by the formula,
>
> $$l = \frac{m}{360} \cdot 2\pi r.$$

Since $d = 2r$, it is also true that $l = \dfrac{m}{360} \cdot \pi d$. You can use either of these two formulas to find lengths of arcs, as shown in the following examples.

Example 1 Find the length of $\overset{\frown}{RS}$ if $m\overset{\frown}{RS} = 90$ and $OS = 2$ cm.

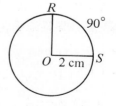

$$l = \frac{m}{360} \cdot 2\pi r = \frac{90}{360} \cdot 2\pi \cdot 2$$
$$= \frac{1}{4} \cdot 4\pi = \pi$$

Thus, the length of $\overset{\frown}{RS}$ is π cm.

Example 2 Given: $\odot O$ with diameter $\overline{RP}$, $RP = 16$, and $m \angle PRQ = 60$.
Find the length of $\overset{\frown}{PQ}$.

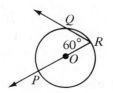

$\angle PRQ$ is inscribed, so $m\overset{\frown}{PQ} = 120$.

$$l = \frac{m}{360} \cdot \pi d = \frac{120}{360} \cdot \pi \cdot 16$$
$$= \frac{1}{3} \cdot 16\pi = \frac{16}{3}\pi$$

ARC LENGTHS

Example 3 Given: $\odot O$ with length of $\overset{\frown}{AB} = 0.75\pi$ cm
and $OA = 4.5$ cm.
Find $m\overset{\frown}{AB}$ and $m \angle AOB$.

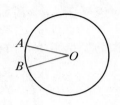

$$l = \frac{m}{360} \cdot 2\pi r$$

$$0.75\pi = \frac{m}{360} \cdot 2\pi \cdot 4.5$$

$$0.75\pi = \frac{m}{40}\pi$$

$$0.75\pi \left(\frac{40}{\pi}\right) = m \quad \blacktriangleleft \quad \textit{Multiply each side by } \frac{40}{\pi}.$$

$$30 = m$$

Thus, $m\overset{\frown}{AB} = 30$ and $m \angle AOB = 30$.

Written Exercises

Find each missing measure. Answers may be left in terms of π.

	Degree Measure of Arc	Length of Radius	Length of Diameter	Length of Arc
Ⓐ 1.	45	10 mm	?	?
2.	30	?	6 km	?
3.	120	2.5 cm	?	?
4.	270	?	3.2 m	?
5.	300	1.8 cm	?	?
6.	15	120 m	?	?
7.	60	12 mm	?	?
8.	75	?	21.6 cm	?

Find each indicated arc length.

9. In a circle with a 6-cm radius, find, correct to the nearest cm, the length of an arc with a measure of 120°.

10. In a circle with a 10-cm diameter, find, correct to the nearest cm, the length of an arc determined by a central angle with a measure of 75°.

Find each missing measure. Answers may be left in terms of π. (Ex. 11−16)

	Degree measure of Arc	Length of Radius	Length of Diameter	Length of Arc
Ⓑ 11.	180	?	?	π km
12.	120	?	?	0.8π cm
13.	?	8 m	?	π m
14.	?	?	10 cm	3π cm
15.	?	2.5 mm	?	5π mm
16.	?	?	0.8 m	0.4π m

17. Given: $\odot O$ with $\overline{OB} \perp \overleftrightarrow{AC}$, $OB = 9$, and $m \angle DBC = 60$ Find the length of $\overset{\frown}{DEB}$.

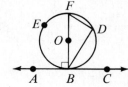

18. Given: $\odot O$ with diameter $\overline{BF}$, $BF = 20$, and $m \angle BFD = 72$ Find the length of $\overset{\frown}{BD}$, of $\overset{\frown}{FD}$, and $\overset{\frown}{BEF}$.

Find each indicated measure.

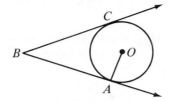
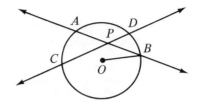

C 19. Given: $\overrightarrow{BA}$ and $\overrightarrow{BC}$ are
tangent to $\odot O$,
m $\angle ABC = 48$,
and $OA = 8$
Find the length of $\widehat{AC}$.

20. Given: $\overrightarrow{BA}$ and $\overrightarrow{BC}$ are
tangent to $\odot O$, $OA = 10$,
the length of $\widehat{AC} = 12$
Find m $\angle ABC$. (Use 3.14
for π.)

21. Given: $\odot O$ with
m$\widehat{BD} = 30$,
m $\angle APC = 50$,
and $OB = 10$
Find the length of $\widehat{AC}$.

22. Given: $\odot O$ with
m$\widehat{BD} = 40$, length of
$\widehat{AC} = 12$, and $OB = 10$
Find m $\angle APC$. (Use 3.14
for π.)

Algebra Review

OBJECTIVE ► **To simplify radical expressions by rationalizing the denominator**

To simplify expressions like

$$\frac{3 + \sqrt{5}}{\sqrt{5}} \quad \text{and} \quad \frac{1 + \sqrt{2}}{3 - \sqrt{7}}$$

(1) Rationalize the denominator.
(2) Write in simplest form.

Example 1 Simplify $\dfrac{2 + \sqrt{7}}{\sqrt{3}}$.

*Make the denominator
a perfect square.* ► $\dfrac{2 + \sqrt{7}}{\sqrt{3}} \cdot \dfrac{\sqrt{3}}{\sqrt{3}} = \dfrac{(2 + \sqrt{7}) \cdot \sqrt{3}}{\sqrt{3} \cdot \sqrt{3}} = \dfrac{2\sqrt{3} + \sqrt{21}}{3}$

Example 2 Simplify $\dfrac{2}{1 + \sqrt{3}}$.

$$\frac{2}{1 + \sqrt{3}} \cdot \frac{1 - \sqrt{3}}{1 - \sqrt{3}} = \frac{2 - 2\sqrt{3}}{1 - 3}$$

$$= \frac{2 - 2\sqrt{3}}{-2}, \text{ or } -1 + \sqrt{3}$$

Simplify.

1. $\dfrac{\sqrt{7} - 1}{\sqrt{7}}$

2. $\dfrac{4\sqrt{3} + 2}{\sqrt{3}}$

3. $\dfrac{2\sqrt{5} - 1}{\sqrt{5}}$

4. $\dfrac{3\sqrt{6} + 2}{\sqrt{2}}$

5. $\dfrac{3}{1 + \sqrt{2}}$

6. $\dfrac{6}{4 - \sqrt{2}}$

7. $\dfrac{4}{2 + \sqrt{5}}$

8. $\dfrac{2 + \sqrt{3}}{1 - \sqrt{6}}$

9. $\dfrac{1}{2\sqrt{2} + 3}$

10. $\dfrac{3}{3\sqrt{2} - 3}$

11. $\dfrac{3\sqrt{3}}{2\sqrt{6} - 1}$

12. $\dfrac{2\sqrt{3} + 1}{2\sqrt{3} - 1}$

12.10 Areas of Sectors and Segments

OBJECTIVES ▶ To find the area of a sector and a segment of a circle
To find the area of the ring bounded by two concentric circles

In this lesson, you will learn about some other areas in relation to circles.

Definition:
sector of
circle

A *sector of a circle* is the region bounded by two radii of the circle and the arc determined by the radii.

When you find the area of a sector, you are actually finding a part of the area of the circle. Consider $\odot O$ with m $\angle COD =$ 36 and $OC = 10$ cm. $\angle COD$ intercepts $\frac{36}{360}$, or $\frac{1}{10}$ of the circle, so you can find the area of the sector bounded by $\overline{OC}$, $\overline{OD}$, and $\overarc{CD}$ by finding $\frac{1}{10}$ of the area of $\odot O$.

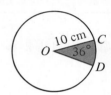

Area $\odot O = \pi r^2 = \pi \cdot 10^2 = 100\pi$ cm²

Area sector $= \frac{1}{10} \cdot 100\pi = 10\pi$ cm²

This leads to the following theorem, which is given without proof.

Theorem 12.13 Area sector $= \frac{m}{360} \cdot \pi r^2$ In a circle, the area of a sector bounded by an arc of measure m and radii of length r is given by the formula, Area $= \frac{m}{360} \cdot \pi r^2$.

The formula in Theorem 12.13 can be used to find the area of a sector of a circle.

Example 1 The length of a radius of a circle is 8. The arc of a sector of the circle measures 90°. Find the area of the sector.

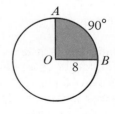

Area sector $= \frac{m}{360} \cdot \pi r^2 = \frac{90}{360} \cdot \pi \cdot (8)^2$

$= \frac{1}{4} \cdot 64\pi = 16\pi$

Another region associated with a circle is a segment of the circle.

Definition:
segment of
circle

A *segment of a circle* is a region bounded by an arc of the circle and the chord determined by the arc.

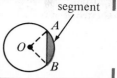

You can find the area of a segment of a circle by subtracting the area of the triangle formed by the radii and the chord from the area of the corresponding sector, as shown in the next example.

Example 2 The length of a radius of a circle is 10 cm. Find the area of a segment bounded by an arc measuring 60° and the corresponding chord.

Area segment = Area sector − Area $\triangle AOB$

Area sector $= \dfrac{m}{360} (\pi r^2) = \left(\dfrac{60}{360}\right)(\pi \cdot 10^2) = \dfrac{1}{6} \cdot 100\pi = \dfrac{50}{3} \pi$ cm²

$\triangle AOB$ is equilateral. ▶ Area $\triangle AOB = \dfrac{s^2}{4} \sqrt{3} = \dfrac{10^2}{4} \sqrt{3} = \dfrac{100}{4} \sqrt{3} = 25\sqrt{3}$ cm²

Thus, the area of the segment is $\left(\dfrac{50}{3} \pi - 25\sqrt{3}\right)$ cm².

Subtraction can also be used to find the area of the region bounded by two concentric circles.

Example 3 Find the area of the ring bounded by two concentric circles with 8-cm and 5-cm radii.

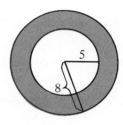

Area outer $\odot = \pi r^2 = \pi \cdot 8^2 = 64\pi$ cm²
Area inner $\odot = \pi r^2 = \pi \cdot 5^2 = 25\pi$ cm²
Thus, the area of the ring is $64\pi - 25\pi$, or 39π cm².

Written Exercises

The length of a radius of a circle is 10. The arc of a sector of the circle has the given measure. What is the area of the sector?

1. 36°   2. 90°   3. 54°   4. 72°
5. 180°   6. 60°   7. 270°   8. 45°

Find each indicated measure.

9. The length of a radius of a circle is 6 cm. The arc of a sector measures 72°. Find the area of the sector.

11. Find the area of the ring bounded by concentric circles with 10-cm and 8-cm radii.

10. The length of a radius of a circle is 5 cm. The arc of a sector measures 60°. Find the area of the sector.

12. Find the area of the ring bounded by concentric circles with 8-m and 5-m radii.

AREAS OF SECTORS AND SEGMENTS

Find the missing measures. $\overline{OA}$ and $\overline{OB}$ are radii of $\odot O$. **Answers may be left in terms of π. (Ex. 13−17)**

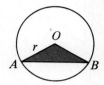

	m $\angle O$	Length of Radius r	m$\widehat{AB}$	Area of Sector Shown	Area of Segment Shown
13.	60	5 cm	?	?	?
14.	?	5 m	90	?	?
15.	120	8 mm	?	?	?
16.	?	10 cm	?	25π cm²	?
17.	?	?	120	12π m²	?

18. Find the area of a sector of a circle with a 12-cm radius and an arc length of 3π cm.

19. Find the area of a sector of a circle with a 10-cm radius and an arc length of 4π cm.

20. Find the area of a segment of a circle with an 8-cm radius and an arc length of 4π cm.

21. Find the area of a segment of a circle with a 9-m radius and an arc length of 3π m.

22. If the area of a ring is 48π cm² and the outer circle has an 8-cm radius, find the length of a radius of the inner circle.

23. If the area of a ring is 48π m² and the inner circle has an 8-m radius, find the length of a radius of the outer circle.

Find the change in the area of a sector of a circle. (Ex. 24−26)

24. The measure of the angle is doubled.

25. The length of the radius of the circle is doubled.

26. The measure of the angle is halved and the length of the radius is doubled.

27. Find a formula for the area of a ring bounded by two given concentric circles with radii of length R and $r (R > r)$.

28. Show that in a circle of radius r the segment cut off by a 60° central angle has area $= \dfrac{r^2 (2\pi - 3\sqrt{3})}{12}$.

29. Find the area of a segment of a circle with a 10-cm radius and an arc measure of 68°. [*Hint:* Use the appropriate trigonometric ratio.]

30. Find the area of a segment of a circle with a 12-cm radius and an arc measure of 32°. [*Hint:* Use the appropriate trigonometric ratio.]

Cumulative Review

1. Given: $\overline{BC} \perp \overline{AC}$ and $\overline{DE} \perp \overline{AB}$
   Find $ED \cdot AB$.

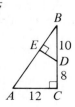

2. Given: $\triangle ABC \sim \triangle BDE$
   Find $BE \cdot BC$.

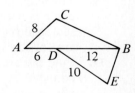

420

Applications

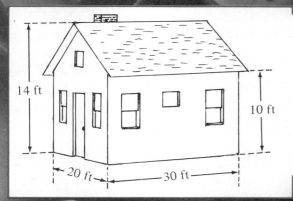

1. A painter is buying paint for a house. One gallon will cover approximately 500 square feet of surface. The size of the house is shown in the picture. There are twelve windows, each $2\frac{1}{2}$ feet wide and 3 feet tall. There are two doors, each $2\frac{1}{2}$ feet wide and 6 feet tall. The doors and windows will not be painted. How many gallons of paint are needed for painting the house?

2. The area of an irregularly shaped region can be estimated by dividing the region into narrow strips, all the same width. Each strip is assumed to be a trapezoid. A plot map of some land shows the given dimensions. Approximately how many square meters of land is in the parcel? If a hectare is 10,000 square meters, how many hectares are there?

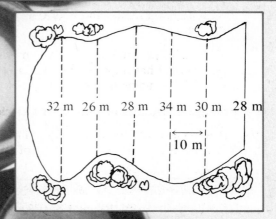

3. An engineering firm is gathering data for a new water supply for a city. They need to know the water flow in a nearby river. At the site of the water intake they must find the cross-sectional area of the river. At four points 17 meters apart, the depth of the water is measured. Using this data, approximate the cross-sectional area of the river.

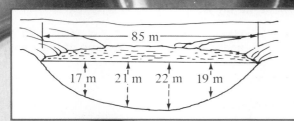

Chapter Twelve Review

Vocabulary

area [12.1]   sector [12.10]
apothem [12.6]   segment [12.10]
circumference [12.7]

Find the area of each figure

1. Rectangle *ABCD*
   with *AB* = 15 m
   and *BC* = 8 m
   [12.1]

2. Square *EFGH*
   with *EF* = 14 mm
   [12.1]

3. Parallelogram
   WXYZ   [12.3]

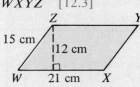

4. Triangle *PQR*
   [12.2]

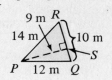

5. Trapezoid *HIJK*
   [12.4]

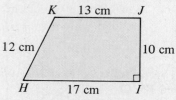

6. Equilateral triangle
   RST   [12.2]

7. Regular pentagon
   ABCDE   [12.6]

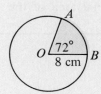

8. Regular hexagon
   FGHIJK whose
   perimeter is 18.
   [12.6]

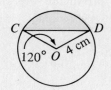

9. Sector *AOB*
   [12.10]

10. Segment *CD*
    [12.10]

Find each indicated area.

11. Find the area of a rhombus whose diagonals are 8 m and 11 m long. [12.2]

12. Find the area of a circle whose diameter measures 12 cm. [12.8]

13. Find the area of the ring bounded by circles with 9 cm and 7 cm radii. [12.10]

*14. $\overline{AB}$ and $\overline{CD}$ are the bases of isosceles trapezoid *ABCD*. If *AB* = 9, *CD* = 5, and *AD* = 4, find the area of the trapezoid. [12.2]

Find each indicated measure.

15. The radius of a circle measures 7 cm. Find the circumference. [12.7]

16. Each side of a rhombus is 23 mm long. Find the perimeter. [12.5]

17. Each side of a regular hexagon measures 6 cm. Find the length of an apothem. [12.6]

18. The area of an equilateral triangle is $16\sqrt{3}$. Find the length of a side.

*19. The circumference of a circle is 18π. Find the perimeter of a regular inscribed hexagon. [12.7]

20. In $\odot O$, m $\angle AOB$ = 50 and *OA* = 8. Find the length of $\overset{\frown}{AB}$. [12.9]

21. In $\odot P$, the length of $\overset{\frown}{CD} = 8\pi$ and *PC* = 6. Find m$\overset{\frown}{CD}$.

22. Given: $\triangle RST \sim \triangle XYZ$, $\angle R \cong \angle S$, *RT* = 18, and *ZX* = 12. Find the ratio of the areas. [12.5]

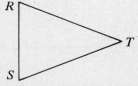

23. Given: In the figure above, $\triangle RST \sim \triangle XYZ$, $\angle R \cong \angle S$, *RT* = 21, *RS* = 18, and *YZ* = 14. Find the ratio of the perimeters.

Chapter Twelve Test

Find the area of each shaded figure.

1. Parallelogram *ABCD*

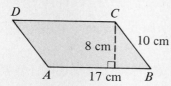

2. Square *RSTU*

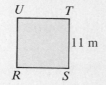

3. Triangle *XYZ*

4. Rhombus *EFGH*

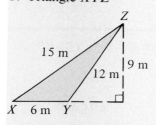
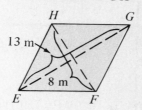

5. Equilateral triangle *PQR*

6. Trapezoid *JKLM*

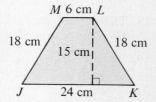

7. Regular octagon *ABCDEFGH*

8. Regular hexagon *UVWXYZ*

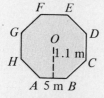
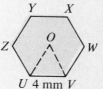

9. Sector *COD*

10. Segment *AB*

Find each indicated area.

11. Find the area of a circle whose radius measures 7 cm.

12. Find the area of a ring bounded by circles with 10 cm and 5 cm radii.

*13. $\overline{AB}$ and $\overline{CD}$ are the bases of isosceles trapezoid *ABCD*. If $AB = 15$, $CD = 9$, and m $\angle A = 45$, find the area of the trapezoid.

Find each indicated measure.

14. Each side of a square is 17 cm long. Find the length of an apothem.

15. The area of an equilateral triangle is $25\sqrt{3}$. Find the length of an altitude.

*16. The circumference of a circle is 16π. Find the perimeter of an inscribed square.

17. In $\odot O$, m $\angle COD = 40$ and $CO = 9$. Find the length of $\overset{\frown}{CD}$.

18. Given: $\triangle ABC \sim \triangle XYZ$, $\overline{CD} \perp \overline{AB}$, $AB = 8$, $CD = 6$, and $WZ = 9$

Find the ratio of the areas of the two triangles.

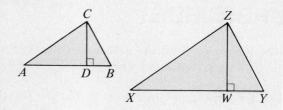

Computer Activities

Computing the area of a geometric figure often requires that you look up the correct formula or that you have the proper measurements to apply a given formula. The computer can be used to find the area of any regular polygon given the number of sides, the length of a side, and the length of the apothem for a given figure.

The program below, uses the following BASIC formula to compute the area of a regular polygon.

$$A = .5 * P * (N * L)$$

where A = area, P = length of the apothem, N = number of sides, and L = length of one side.

See the Computer Section on p. 560 for more information.

PROGRAM

```
10 PRINT "PROGRAM COMPUTES THE AREA OF A REGULAR POLYGON"
20 READ N, L, P
30 PRINT "# SIDES      LENGTH      APOTHEM       AREA"
40 LET A = .5 * P * (N * L)
50 PRINT N, L, P, A
60 GO TO 20
70 DATA 3, 6, 1.73, 4, 8, 4, 5, 1.4, 1, 8, .5, .6
80 END
```

Exercises

Run the program for the following values in the DATA statement. (Ex 1–4)
1. $N = 3$, $L = 6$, $P = 1.73$ 2. $N = 4$, $L = 8$, $P = 4$ 3. $N = 5$, $L = 1.4$, $P = 1$
4. $N = 8$, $L = .5$, $P = .6$
5. Alter the program above to find the length of the side of a regular polygon given the area, the number of sides, and the length of the apothem.
6. Write a program to compute the area of a sector of a circle, given the measures of arc AB (M), and of the radius (R) of the circle. Use the BASIC formula: $A = (M/360) * (3.14159 * R \uparrow 2)$.

College Prep Test

Directions: Choose the one best answer to each question or problem.

1. The area of square *GAEF* is 36 and the area of square *HEBK* is 81. Find the area of square *ABCD*.

   (A) 90
   (B) 225
   (C) 117
   (D) 54
   (E) 45

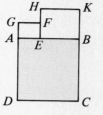

2. In rectangle *MNPR*, $PQ = \frac{1}{3}PR$, Area of $\triangle NPQ = 8$.

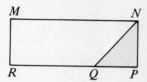

   Find the area of rectangle *MNPR*.

   (A) 24 (B) 32 (C) 48 (D) 72 (E) 96

3. In $\odot O$, $OA = 6$, $\overline{AO} \perp \overline{OB}$. Find the area of the shaded portion.

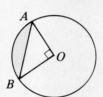

   (A) 2π (b) $\pi - 2$
   (C) $6\pi - 9\sqrt{3}$ (D) $9\pi - 18$ (E) $36\pi - 9\sqrt{3}$

4. What is the radius of a circle if it is equal in area to a triangle with an altitude of 4π and a base of 16?

   (A) 4 (B) $4\sqrt{2}$ (C) 8 (D) $4\sqrt{2\pi}$ (E) 8π

5. Four equal circles with 1 foot diameters touch as shown. What is the area of the shaded portion?

   (A) $1 - \frac{\pi}{4}$ (B) $1 - \pi$ (C) $1 - 4\pi$ (D) π (E) $\frac{\pi}{4}$

6. A picture in an art museum is 6 feet wide by 8 feet long. If the frame has a width of 6 inches, what is the ratio of the area of the frame to the area of the picture?

   (A) $\frac{5}{16}$ (B) $\frac{5}{4}$ (C) $\frac{4}{5}$ (D) $\frac{5}{12}$ (E) $\frac{16}{5}$

7. On each side of a regular hexagon, an isosceles right triangle is drawn. If the perimeter of the hexagon is 36, what is the area of the shaded portion?

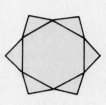

   (A) 54 (B) $54\sqrt{3}$ (C) 108
   (D) $108\sqrt{3} + 108$ (E) $54 + 54\sqrt{3}$

8. $\overline{AB} \parallel \overline{CD}$, $DC = 8$, $AB = 12$, m $\angle A =$ m $\angle B = 45$. Find the area of Trapezoid *ABCD*.

   (A) 20 (B) 40 (C) $20\sqrt{2}$
   (D) 32 (E) 28

9. A rectangular field is half as wide as it is long and is completely enclosed by *x* yards of fencing. What is the area of the field?

   (A) $\frac{x^2}{2}$ (B) $2x^2$ (C) $\frac{x^2}{18}$ (D) $3\frac{1}{2}$

   (E) $\frac{x^2}{72}$

10. What is the area of *PQRS*?

    (A) 5 (B) 8
    (C) 20 (D) 16
    (E) 10

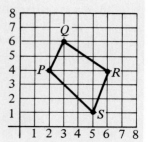

Write the letter that indicates the best answer.

1. In the figure below, the measure of $\angle x$ is
   (A) 60°   (B) 52°
   (C) 172°   (D) none of these

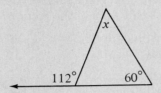

2. In the figure below, the two right triangles are
   (A) congruent by leg-leg
   (B) congruent by hypotenuse-leg
   (C) congruent by leg-acute angle
   (D) none of these

 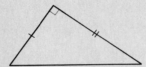

3. The diagonals of an isosceles trapezoid
   (A) are congruent   (B) bisect each other
   (C) are perpendicular   (D) none of these

4. If $4x = 3y$, then the ratio of x to y is
   (A) $\frac{4}{3}$ (B) $\frac{3}{4}$

   (C) $\frac{y}{x}$ (D) none of these

5. The geometric mean of 3 and 12 is
   (A) 36   (B) 15
   (C) 6   (D) none of these

6. If $\frac{8}{x} = \frac{10}{13}$, then x is equal to
   (A) 10.4   (B) 11
   (C) 6.2   (D) none of these

7. Which of the following can be lengths of sides of a right triangle?
   (A) 9, 12, 15   (B) $\sqrt{3}x$, $\sqrt{4}x$, $\sqrt{7}x$
   (C) both of these   (D) neither of these

8. Given: $\triangle RST$ is a 30°–60° rt. $\triangle$ and $RT = 16$. Then RS is equal to

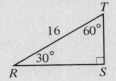

   (A) 8   (B) $8\sqrt{3}$
   (C) 16   (D) $16\sqrt{3}$

9. If $\angle A$ is inscribed in a circle, and $\angle A$ intercepts an arc which measures 32°, then m $\angle A$ is equal to
   (A) 16   (B) 32
   (C) 64   (D) none of these

10. An angle inscribed in a semicircle is
    (A) acute   (B) obtuse
    (C) right   (D) none of these

11. The legs of a right triangle measure 8 cm and 7 cm. The area of the triangle is
    (A) 28 cm²   (B) 56 cm²
    (C) 112 cm²   (D) none of these

12. The area of an equilateral triangle is $16\sqrt{3}$. The length of an altitude is
    (A) 4   (B) $4\sqrt{3}$
    (C) 8   (D) $8\sqrt{3}$

True or false.

13. Any two right angles are complementary.

14. All angles of a rhombus are congruent.

15. All squares are rectangles.

16. A pentagon is a polygon with seven sides.

17. Each interior angle of a regular hexagon measures $120°$.

18. The sum of the measures of the exterior angles of any polygon is $360°$.

19. If an angle bisector of a triangle is also an altitude, then the triangle is equilateral.

20. An isosceles trapezoid has two pairs of congruent angles.

21. A square has four lines of symmetry.

Find each indicated measure.

22. The bases of a trapezoid measure 6 cm and 13 cm. Find the length of the median.

23. The length and the width of a rectangle have the ratio 5 to 2. The area is 1,440. Find the length and the width.

24. One leg of a $45' - 45°$ right triangle measures 7 cm. Find the length of the hypotenuse.

*25. If the edges of a rectangular solid are 3 cm, 4 cm, and 8 cm long, find the length of a diagonal of the solid.

26. Given: $\odot O$ with
    $\overgroup{mCA} = 50$ and
    $\overgroup{mBD} = 36$
    Find m $\angle CEA$.

27. Given: $\odot O$ with
    tangent $\overrightarrow{PQ}$
    $\overgroup{mRQ} = 80$ and
    $\overgroup{mRS} = 162$.
    Find m $\angle P$.

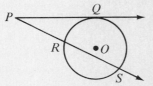

28. In the figure for Exercise 26, $AE = 8$, $EB = 5$, and $CE = 6$. Find ED.

29. In the figure for Exercise 27, $PR = 9$ and $RS = 7$. Find PQ.

30. Find the area of a square if each side measures 9 m.

31. Two adjacent sides of a parallelogram measure 8 cm and 11 cm. An angle of the parallelogram measures $45°$. Find the area of the parallelogram.

32. A side of an equilateral triangle is 5 cm long. Find the area of the triangle.

33. The radius of a circle measures 7 m. Find the circumference of the circle.

34. A central angle of a circle measures $120°$ and a radius is 6 cm long. Find the area of the sector bounded by the central angle and its intercepted arc.

Find lengths to the nearest tenth.

35. Find x.

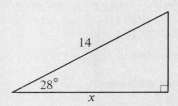

36. In $\square ABCD$, m $\angle B = 125°$ and $BC = 16$. Find the length of the altitude from D to $\overline{AB}$.

37. An angle of a rhombus measures $154°$ and the diagonal opposite that angle measures 20. Find the measure of the other diagonal.

13 COORDINATE GEOMETRY

Applying Formulas

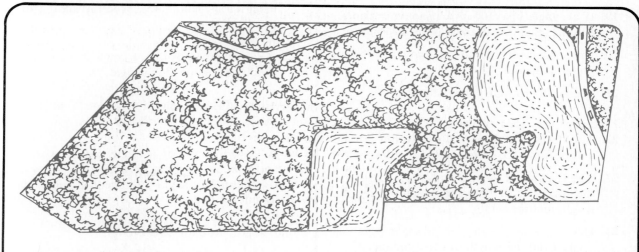

A farmer obtained this copy of an aerial photograph of her land. This shows the location of fields, forest, and roads.

1 in   = 300 ft
1 acre = 43,560 ft²

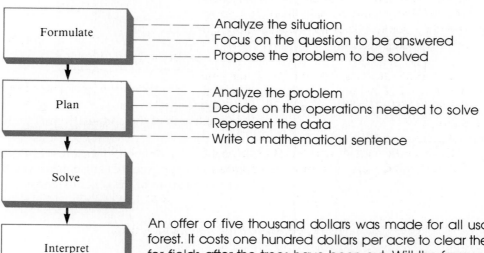

Formulate
— — — — Analyze the situation
— — — — Focus on the question to be answered
— — — — Propose the problem to be solved

Plan
— — — — Analyze the problem
— — — — Decide on the operations needed to solve
— — — — Represent the data
— — — — Write a mathematical sentence

Solve

Interpret

An offer of five thousand dollars was made for all usable timber in the forest. It costs one hundred dollars per acre to clear the land in the forest for fields after the trees have been cut. Will the farmer make a net profit or a loss after selling the timber and clearing the land?

13.1 The Coordinate Plane

OBJECTIVES ► To give the coordinates of a point in a coordinate plane
To graph ordered pairs of numbers in a coordinate plane
To determine if a line is vertical or horizontal, given the coordinates of two of its points

An ordered pair of numbers such as $(2, -8)$ can be graphed in a *coordinate plane*. In general an ordered pair is represented by (x, y).

ordered pair

(x, y)
x-coordinate   *y*-coordinate
abscissa   ordinate

A coordinate plane is determined by two perpendicular number lines intersecting at O. The horizontal line is called the *x-axis*, and the vertical line is called the *y-axis*. The point of intersection is called the *origin*. The *axes* divide the plane into four *quadrants* labeled with Roman numerals in the diagram.

coordinate plane

For every point in a coordinate plane, there is a corresponding ordered pair of numbers, and for every ordered pair, there is a corresponding point. The point is called the *graph* of the ordered pair.

To graph the ordered pair $(2, 4)$ on your paper, start at the origin and move 2 units to the right. Then move 4 units up and mark point *A*.

Observe that $(2, 4)$ and $(4, 2)$ are two different ordered pairs. The order is important.

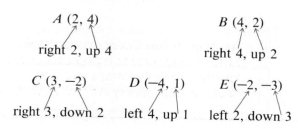

$A\ (2, 4)$
right 2, up 4

$B\ (4, 2)$
right 4, up 2

$C\ (3, -2)$
right 3, down 2

$D\ (-4, 1)$
left 4, up 1

$E\ (-2, -3)$
left 2, down 3

THE COORDINATE PLANE

Example 1 Give the coordinates of each labeled point. Then tell which quadrant or axis contains each point.

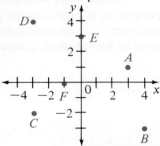

Answers

$A(3, 1)$; Quadrant I
$B(4, -3)$; Quadrant IV
$C(-3, -2)$; Quadrant III
$D(-3, 4)$; Quadrant II
$E(0, 3)$; y-axis
$F(-1, 0)$; x-axis

Examples 2 and 3 below lead to important properties of horizontal and vertical lines.

Example 2 Graph each ordered pair. Then draw a line through the points. What do you observe?

$A(-4, 3)$
$B(-1, 3)$
$C(0, 3)$
$D(2, 3)$

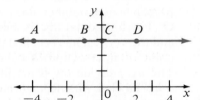

Every point has the same y-coordinate, 3.
The points appear to lie on a horizontal line.

Property of horizontal lines

> Every point on a horizontal line has the same y-coordinate.

Example 3 Graph each ordered pair. Then draw a line through the points. What do you observe?

$R(-2, 4)$
$S(-2, 0)$
$T(-2, -2)$
$U(-2, -3)$

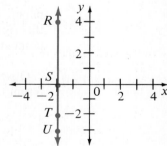

Every point has the same x-coordinate, -2.
The points appear to lie on a vertical line.

Property of vertical lines

> Every point on a vertical line has the same x-coordinate.

Oral Exercises

Give the coordinates of each labeled point. Then tell which quadrant or axis contains each point.

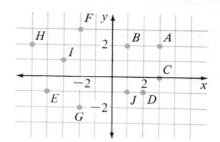

1. A
2. B
3. C
4. D
5. E
6. F
7. G
8. H
9. I
10. J

Tell in which directions and how many units to move from the origin in order to graph each ordered pair.

11. $A(2, 3)$ 12. $B(-4, 2)$ 13. $C(6, -4)$ 14. $D(-3, -5)$ 15. $E(0, 8)$ 16. $F(0, -3)$
17. $G(3, 0)$ 18. $H(-5, 0)$ 19. $I(-3, 8)$ 20. $J(0, 0)$ 21. $K(-1, -4)$ 22. $L(6, -2)$

Written Exercises

 1. On the same coordinate plane, graph and label each ordered pair in Exercises 11–16 above.

2. On the same coordinate plane, graph and label each ordered pair in Exercises 17–22 above.

Is $\overleftrightarrow{PQ}$ a vertical line, a horizontal line, or neither?

3. $P(6, 1), Q(6, -2)$
4. $P(4, 0), Q(1, 0)$
5. $P(2, 6), Q(6, 2)$
6. $P(-3, 4), Q(-2, 4)$
7. $P(-1, 3), Q(-1, -4)$
8. $P(5, 1), Q(1, 2)$
9. $P(-3, 6), Q(-3, -6)$
10. $P(4, -1), Q(4, 1)$
11. $P(-4, 5), Q(4, -5)$
12. $P(1, -1), Q(1, -2)$
13. $P(4, -3), Q(0, -3)$
14. $P(6, -1), Q(1, 6)$

For what value of a will $\overleftrightarrow{AB}$ be vertical or horizontal, as indicated?

15. $A(-4, a), B(6, 2)$; horizontal
16. $A(a, 6), B(6, -6)$; vertical
17. $A(3, 1), B(a, -1)$; vertical
18. $A(4, 3), B(a, -1)$; vertical
19. $A(7, a), B(-1, -3)$; horizontal
20. $A(6, 5), B(-2, a)$; horizontal

In which quadrant(s) will a point have the following coordinate(s)?

 21. Positive y-coordinate
22. Negative x-coordinate
23. Positive x-coordinate and negative y
24. Positive y-coordinate and positive x
25. Negative x-coordinate and positive y
26. Negative x-coordinate and negative y

Give the coordinates of D so that $ABCD$ is a rectangle. Graph $ABCD$. (Ex. 27–30)

27. $A(1, 2), B(5, 2), C(5, 5), D(?, ?)$
28. $A(-1, -6), B(-5, -6), C(-5, -2), D(?, ?)$
29. $A(4, 0), B(7, 0), C(7, 3), D(?, ?)$
30. $A(-3, -2), B(-3, 4), C(4, 4), D(?, ?)$

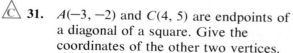

31. $A(-3, -2)$ and $C(4, 5)$ are endpoints of a diagonal of a square. Give the coordinates of the other two vertices.
32. $R(1, 3), S(-2, -1)$, and $T(5, -1)$ are vertices of a parallelogram. Give the coordinates of three possible points for the other vertex.
33. $E(-1, -2)$ and $F(4, -2)$ are vertices of a square. Give the coordinates of three possible pairs of points for the other two vertices.
34. $J(-6, 2)$ and $K(3, 2)$ are endpoints of the base of an isosceles triangle. Give the x-coordinate of the third vertex.

THE COORDINATE PLANE

13.2 The Distance Formula

In this lesson, you will find the distance between pairs of points in a coordinate plane. You will consider points which lie on a horizontal line or a vertical line, and then points which lie on any line. Recall that the distance between two points is the length of the segment that connects them.

Notice that for the points $A(1, 2)$ and $B(6, 2)$, the y-coordinate, 2, is the same. A and B lie on a horizontal line. To find the distance between A and B, you need only to consider the x-coordinates, 1 and 6. By the definition of distance,

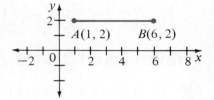

$$AB = |6 - 1| = |5| = 5$$

This suggests the following formula.

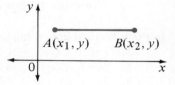

Length of a horizontal segment For a horizontal segment $\overline{AB}$ with $A(x_1, y)$ and $B(x_2, y)$,

$$AB = |x_2 - x_1|$$

Now examine the vertical segment $\overline{CD}$ with $C(4, 3)$ and $D(4, -1)$. The x-coordinate, 4, is the same. To find the distance between C and D, you need only to consider the y-coordinates, 3 and -1.

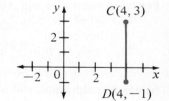

$$CD = |-1 - 3| = |-4| = 4$$

This suggests the following formula.

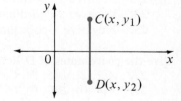

Length of a vertical segment For a vertical segment $\overline{CD}$ with $C(x, y_1)$ and $D(x, y_2)$,

$$CD = |y_2 - y_1|$$

Example 1 Find RS for $R(6, -2)$ and $S(-1, -2)$. Then find TU for $T(3, 1)$ and $U(3, -5)$.

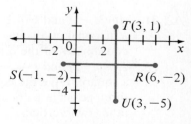

$\overline{RS}$ is horizontal. ▶ $RS = |x_2 - x_1| = |-1 - 6| = |-7| = 7$
$\overline{TU}$ is vertical. ▶ $TU = |y_2 - y_1| = |1 - (-5)| = |6| = 6$

Thus, $RS = 7$ and $TU = 6$.

Suppose you want to find the distance between $A(3, 2)$ and $B(7, 5)$ in the coordinate plane at the right. The horizontal segment $\overline{AC}$ intersects the vertical segment $\overline{BC}$ at C. $\triangle ABC$ is a right triangle. You can use the Pythagorean Theorem to find AB. First find AC and BC.

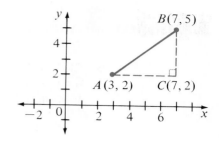

$AC = |7 - 3| = 4 \quad BC = |2 - 5| = 3$

$(AB)^2 = (AC)^2 + (BC)^2$ by the Pythagorean Th.
$AB = \sqrt{(AC)^2 + (BC)^2} = \sqrt{4^2 + 3^2} = \sqrt{16 + 9} = \sqrt{25} = 5$

Thus, $AB = 5$. This suggests the following formula for finding the distance between any two points, P and Q, in a coordinate plane.

> ### Theorem 13.1 The Distance Formula
>
> The distance d between $P(x_1, y_1)$ and $Q(x_2, y_2)$ is given by the formula
>
> $$d = \sqrt{(x_2 - x_1)^2 + (y_2 - y_1)^2}.$$
>
> (See Exercise 29.)

Notice that the formula above can be used to find the distance between any two points in a coordinate plane. However, if the segment connecting the points is horizontal or vertical, you may want to use one of the shorter formulas given on page 432.

Example 2 Use the Distance Formula to find the distance between $P(-2, -5)$ and $Q(2, -3)$.

$$
\begin{array}{cccc}
P(-2, -5) & & Q(2, -3) \\
\uparrow \quad \uparrow & & \uparrow \quad \uparrow \\
x_1 \quad y_1 & & x_2 \quad y_2
\end{array}
$$

$d = \sqrt{(x_2 - x_1)^2 + (y_2 - y_1)^2}$
$= \sqrt{[2 - (-2)]^2 + [-3 - (-5)]^2}$
$= \sqrt{4^2 + 2^2}$
$= \sqrt{16 + 4}$
$= \sqrt{20}$
$= 2\sqrt{5}$

Thus, the distance PQ is $2\sqrt{5}$.

In the next example, you must apply the Distance Formula several times.

THE DISTANCE FORMULA

433

Example 3

$\triangle RST$ has vertices $R(-3, 5)$, $S(6, 3)$, and $T(-1, -3)$. Show that $\triangle RST$ is isosceles.

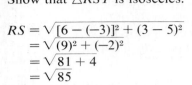

$$RS = \sqrt{[6 - (-3)]^2 + (3 - 5)^2}$$
$$= \sqrt{(9)^2 + (-2)^2}$$
$$= \sqrt{81 + 4}$$
$$= \sqrt{85}$$

$$RT = \sqrt{[-1 - (-3)]^2 + (-3 - 5)^2} \qquad ST = \sqrt{(-1 - 6)^2 + (-3 - 3)^2}$$
$$= \sqrt{(2)^2 + (-8)^2} \qquad\qquad\qquad = \sqrt{(-7)^2 + (-6)^2}$$
$$= \sqrt{4 + 64} \qquad\qquad\qquad\qquad = \sqrt{49 + 36}$$
$$= \sqrt{68} \qquad\qquad\qquad\qquad\quad = \sqrt{85}$$

Thus, since $RS = ST = \sqrt{85}$, $\triangle RST$ is isosceles.

Written Exercises

Find PQ.

  A

1. $P(4, 1)$, $Q(2, 1)$
4. $P(4, 1)$, $Q(4, -1)$
7. $P(6, -3)$, $Q(4, -5)$
10. $P(4, 7)$, $Q(-3, -5)$
13. $P(6, -2)$, $Q(-7, 1)$
16. $P(r, s)$, $Q(t, u)$

2. $P(2, -1)$, $Q(2, 5)$
5. $P(1, 4)$, $Q(4, 2)$
8. $P(-1, 7)$, $Q(5, 0)$
11. $P(-2, 8)$, $Q(6, -4)$
14. $P(1, 9)$, $Q(-1, 7)$

3. $P(6, 3)$, $Q(-6, 3)$
6. $P(-1, 3)$, $Q(7, -2)$
9. $P(-3, -2)$, $Q(-6, 7)$
12. $P(0, 0)$, $Q(-8, -1)$
15. $P(2, 5)$, $Q(m, n)$

Find the length of each side of $\triangle ABC$. Then tell whether $\triangle ABC$ is isosceles or scalene. (Ex. 17–22)

B

17. $A(1, 1)$, $B(3, 6)$, $C(5, 1)$
19. $A(3, 4)$, $B(5, -3)$, $C(-2, 2)$
21. $A(-6, 2)$, $B(5, -1)$, $C(4, 4)$

18. $A(-3, 4)$, $B(2, -1)$, $C(4, 5)$
20. $A(0, 2)$, $B(-3, -2)$, $C(4, -1)$
22. $A(-3, -3)$, $B(1, -6)$, $C(-2, -2)$

23. Show that $\triangle RST$ is a right triangle for $R(-5, 4)$, $S(5, 2)$, and $T(1, -2)$. [*Hint:* Use the converse of the Pythag. Th.]

24. Show that the diagonals of $MNPQ$ are congruent for $M(3, 2)$, $N(3, -1)$, $P(7, -1)$, and $Q(7, 2)$.

C

25. $\overline{AB}$ is the hypotenuse of isosceles right triangle ABC for $A(2, 3)$ and $B(7, 3)$. Find all possible coordinates of C.

26. Repeat Exercise 25 for $A(-6, -2)$ and $B(-6, 5)$.

27. $Q(2, a)$ is 5 units from $P(-2, -1)$. Find all possible values of a.
29. Prove Theorem 13.1.

28. $Q(-1, a)$ is $4\sqrt{5}$ units from $P(3, -2)$. Find all possible values of a.

Cumulative Review

1. In $\triangle XYZ$, $XZ = 10$ and $YZ = 15$. A line parallel to $\overline{XY}$ divides $\overline{XZ}$ into segments measuring 2 and 8. Find the measures of the segments into which the line divides $\overline{YZ}$.

2. In $\triangle ABC$, $\overline{AC} \perp \overline{BC}$. If $c = 16$ and m $\angle B = 48$, find a to the nearest tenth. (Use a table.)

13.3 The Midpoint Theorem

OBJECTIVES ▶ To find the coordinates of the midpoint of a segment in a coordinate plane

To apply the Midpoint Theorem

You can use the coordinates of the endpoints of a segment in a coordinate plane to find the coordinates of the midpoint of the segment. First, examine a horizontal segment and a vertical segment.

Consider points $A(1, 3)$ and $B(9, 3)$. $\overline{AB}$ is horizontal, so the y-coordinate of the midpoint must also be 3. The midpoint lies halfway between points A and B, so the x-coordinate of the midpoint will be the average of the x-coordinates of the endpoints, 1 and 9. **Thus,** the coordinates of the midpoint are $\left(\dfrac{1+9}{2}, 3\right)$, or (5, 3).

Now consider the vertical segment $\overline{BC}$ with endpoints $B(9, 3)$ and $C(9, 5)$. The x-coordinate of the midpoint must also be 9. The y-coordinate will be the average of the y-coordinates of the endpoints, 5 and 3. **Thus,** the coordinates of the midpoint are $\left(9, \dfrac{5+3}{2}\right)$, or (9, 4).

Now examine the segment with endpoints $A(1, 3)$ and $C(9, 5)$. Form a right triangle with $B(9, 3)$. To find the coordinates of M, the midpoint of $\overline{AC}$, use the midpoints of $\overline{AB}$ and $\overline{BC}$ as guides. **Thus,** the coordinates of M are $\left(\dfrac{1+9}{2}, \dfrac{5+3}{2}\right)$, or (5, 4). This suggests the following theorem.

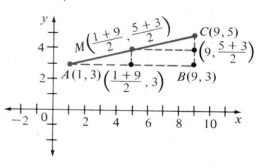

┌─ **Theorem 13.2**   The Midpoint Formula   If $P(x_1, y_1)$ and $Q(x_2, y_2)$ are any two points in a coordinate plane, then the midpoint M of $\overline{PQ}$ has the coordinates $\left(\dfrac{x_1 + x_2}{2}, \dfrac{y_1 + y_2}{2}\right)$.

(See Exercise 31.)

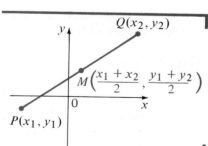

THE MIDPOINT THEOREM

Example 1 Find the coordinates of the midpoint of $\overline{AB}$ for $A(5, -4)$ and $B(-3, -6)$.

$$\begin{array}{cc} A(5, -4) & B(-3, -6) \\ \uparrow\ \uparrow & \uparrow\ \uparrow \\ x_1\ y_1 & x_2\ y_2 \end{array}$$

$$\frac{x_1 + x_2}{2} = \frac{5 + (-3)}{2} = \frac{2}{2} = 1 \qquad \frac{y_1 + y_2}{2} = \frac{-4 + (-6)}{2} = \frac{-10}{2} = -5$$

Thus, the midpoint of $\overline{AB}$ has coordinates $(1, -5)$.

Example 2 M is the midpoint of $\overline{CD}$. Find the coordinates of D for $C(-5, 4)$ and $M(-2, 1)$.

Let C have coordinates (x_1, y_1)
and D have coordinates (x_2, y_2).

$$\left(\frac{x_1 + x_2}{2}, \frac{y_1 + y_2}{2}\right) = (-2, 1)$$

$$\frac{-5 + x_2}{2} = -2 \qquad \frac{4 + y_2}{2} = 1$$

$$-5 + x_2 = -4 \qquad 4 + y_2 = 2$$

$$x_2 = 1 \qquad y_2 = -2$$

Thus, D has coordinates $(1, -2)$.

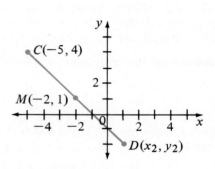

Example 3 requires the use of both the Midpoint Theorem and the Distance Formula.

Example 3 $\triangle ABC$ has vertices $A(-4, -3)$, $B(4, -1)$, and $C(-2, 3)$. Find the length of median $\overline{CM}$.

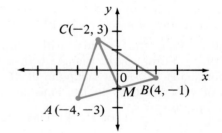

First find the coordinates of M.
Use the Midpoint Theorem.

$$\frac{x_1 + x_2}{2} = \frac{-4 + 4}{2} = \frac{0}{2} = 0$$

$$\frac{y_1 + y_2}{2} = \frac{-3 + (-1)}{2} = \frac{-4}{2} = -2$$

M has coordinates $(0, -2)$.

Then find CM for $C(-2, 3)$ and $M(0, -2)$.
Use the Distance Formula.

$$d = \sqrt{(x_2 - x_1)^2 + (y_2 - y_1)^2}$$

$$CM = \sqrt{[0 - (-2)]^2 + (-2 - 3)^2}$$

$$= \sqrt{2^2 + (-5)^2}$$

$$= \sqrt{4 + 25}$$

$$= \sqrt{29}$$

Thus, the length of median $\overline{CM}$ is $\sqrt{29}$.

Reading in Geometry

Write A if the statement is *always* true. Write S if it is *sometimes* true. Write N if it is *never* true.

1. The *x*-coordinate of the midpoint of a segment is the average of the *x*-coordinates of its endpoints.
2. The *y*-coordinate of the midpoint of a segment is the average of the *y*-coordinates of its endpoints.
3. The *y*-coordinate of the midpoint of a vertical segment is the same as the *y*-coordinate of an endpoint.
4. The *y*-coordinate of the midpoint of a horizontal segment is the same as the *y*-coordinate of an endpoint.

Written Exercises

Find the coordinates of the midpoint of $\overline{AB}$.

1. $A(7, 1), B(-3, 5)$ 2. $A(5, 2), B(-3, -6)$ 3. $A(4, 7), B(-2, 5)$ 4. $A(3, 8), B(-5, 2)$
5. $A(5, 0), B(-4, 1)$ 6. $A(5, -8), B(4, 7)$ 7. $A(-1, 5), B(9, -2)$ 8. $A(3, 7), B(-3, -7)$
9. $A(1, 6), B(-1, 3)$ 10. $A(-3, 1), B(8, -5)$ 11. $A(4, -6), B(3, -8)$ 12. $A(-2, 6), B(5, -5)$

M is the midpoint of $\overline{AB}$. Find the coordinates of B.

13. $M(-3, 2), A(4, 7)$ 14. $M(6, 1), A(-8, 2)$ 15. $M(-3, -1), A(7, 5)$ 16. $M(-4, 7), A(8, -2)$
17. $M(1, 4), A(-4, 2)$ 18. $M(6, 4), A(-2, -3)$ 19. $M(5, 0), A(-8, 2)$ 20. $M(-6, 1), A(0, -3)$

Find the coordinates of the midpoints of each side of $\triangle PQR$. Then find the length of the median to PQ (Ex. 21–23)

21. $P(-2, -4), Q(6, -2), R(2,6)$ 22. $P(-4,1), Q(2, -4), R(-2, 5)$ 23. $P(-1, -1), Q(4, -2), R(5, 4)$

24. In $\triangle ABC$, M is the midpoint of $\overline{AB}$. Show that $AM = MB = MC$ for $A(7, 1), B(1, -7)$ and $C(1, 1)$.

25. In $\triangle PQR$, M is the midpoint of $\overline{PQ}$ and N is the midpoint of $\overline{QR}$. Show that $MN = \frac{1}{2}(PR)$ for $P(-3, -2), Q(2, 2)$ and $R(3, -7)$.

26. Show that $\overline{AC}$ and $\overline{BD}$ have the same midpoint for $A(-3, -5), B(2, -3), C(3, 5)$, and $D(-2, 3)$.

27. M is the midpoint of $\overline{AD}$ and N is the midpoint of $\overline{BC}$. Show that $MN = AB = CD$ for $A(-1, -4), B(2, 2), C(-2, 6)$, and $D(-5, 0)$.

28. For $\triangle ABC$ with $A(-5, -4), B(3, -2)$, and $C(-1, 6)$, M is the midpoint of $\overline{AB}$ and N is the midpoint of $\overline{BC}$. Show that $MN = \frac{1}{2}(AC)$.

29. For quadrilateral $ABCD$ with $A(-3, -4), B(3, 0), C(5, 6)$ and $D(-7, 2)$, M, N, P, and Q are midpoints of $\overline{AB}, \overline{BC}, \overline{CD}$, and $\overline{DA}$, respectively. Show that $MN = PQ$ and $PN = QM$.

30. For $\triangle RST$ with $R(a, b), S(c, d)$, and $T(e, f)$, M is the midpoint of $\overline{RS}$.

    Show that $TM = \sqrt{\left(\frac{a+c}{2} - e\right)^2 + \left(\frac{b+d}{2} - f\right)^2}$.

31. Prove Theorem 13.2.

CALCULATOR ACTIVITIES

Find the coordinates of the midpoint of $\overline{CD}$.

1. $C(6.1, 4.2), D(3.8, 7.9)$ 2. $C(5.4, 7.2), D(-2.3, -3.8)$
3. $C(-9.6, 3.1), D(7.2, -4.7)$ 4. $C(-3.9, -4.1), D(-6.3, -8.9)$
5. $C(12.46, -8.23), D(-16.53, 9.47)$ 6. $C(-26.58, -13.53), D(-12.75, -9.23)$

THE MIDPOINT THEOREM

13.4 Slope of a Line

OBJECTIVES ▶ **To find the slope of a line in a coordinate plane**
To determine the position of a line from its slope

Just as the slope of a roof refers to its "steepness," the slope of a line in a coordinate plane refers to its steepness. Consider lines *l* and *m* shown at the right. Line *l* appears to be steeper than line *m*, or the slope of line *l* appears to be greater than the slope of line *m*. The mathematical definition of slope gives you a precise method for assigning a numerical value to the slope of a line.

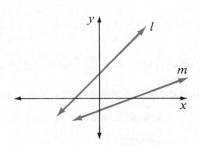

Definition:

The **slope** *m* **of a line** passing through $P(x_1, y_1)$ and $Q(x_2, y_2)$ is defined as follows:

$$m = \frac{y_2 - y_1}{x_2 - x_1} \qquad [x_2 \neq x_1]$$

Slope $(\overleftrightarrow{PQ})$ means the slope of $\overleftrightarrow{PQ}$.

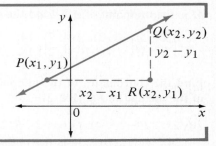

Notice that $y_2 - y_1$ represents the change in the *y*-coordinates, and $x_2 - x_1$ the change in the *x*-coordinates. For any two points on a line, the slope of the line is the ratio of the change in the *y*-coordinates to the change in the *x*-coordinates.

Example 1 Find slope $(\overleftrightarrow{CD})$ for $C(-3, -1)$ and $D(3, 2)$.

$$C(\underset{\underset{x_1}{\uparrow}}{-3}, \underset{\underset{y_1}{\uparrow}}{-1}) \qquad D(\underset{\underset{x_2}{\uparrow}}{3}, \underset{\underset{y_2}{\uparrow}}{2})$$

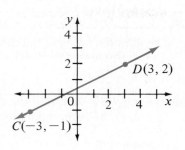

$$m = \frac{y_2 - y_1}{x_2 - x_1} = \frac{2 - (-1)}{3 - (-3)} = \frac{3}{6} = \frac{1}{2}$$

Thus, slope $(\overleftrightarrow{CD}) = \frac{1}{2}$.

In Example 1, suppose (x_1, y_1) and (x_2, y_2) were reversed. Then $m = \frac{y_2 - y_1}{x_2 - x_1} = \frac{-1 - 2}{-3 - 3} = \frac{-3}{-6} = \frac{1}{2}$. Notice that the resulting slope is still $\frac{1}{2}$. When computing the slope of a line, any point on the line can be (x_1, y_1) and any other point (x_2, y_2).

In Examples 2 and 3, you will compare the slope of a line with its position in the coordinate plane.

Example 2 Find the slope of $\overleftrightarrow{AB}$ in each case. Then describe the position of $\overleftrightarrow{AB}$ in the coordinate plane.

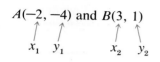

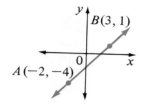

$$m = \frac{y_2 - y_1}{x_2 - x_1} = \frac{1 - (-4)}{3 - (-2)} = \frac{5}{5} = 1$$

Slope ($\overleftrightarrow{AB}$) is positive.
$\overleftrightarrow{AB}$ slants up to the right.

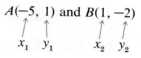

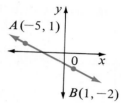

$$m = \frac{y_2 - y_1}{x_2 - x_1} = \frac{-2 - 1}{1 - (-5)} = \frac{-3}{6} = -\frac{1}{2}$$

Slope ($\overleftrightarrow{AB}$) is negative.
$\overleftrightarrow{AB}$ slants down to the right.

Example 3 deals with horizontal and vertical lines.

Example 3 Find the slope of $\overleftrightarrow{AB}$ in each case. Then describe the position of $\overleftrightarrow{AB}$ in the coordinate plane.

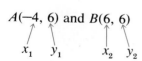

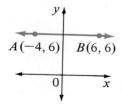

$$m = \frac{y_2 - y_1}{x_2 - x_1} = \frac{6 - 6}{6 - (-4)} = \frac{0}{10} = 0$$

Slope ($\overleftrightarrow{AB}$) is zero.
$\overleftrightarrow{AB}$ is horizontal.

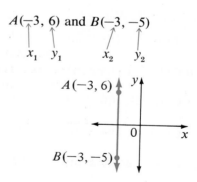

$$m = \frac{y_2 - y_1}{x_2 - x_1} = \frac{-5 - 6}{-3 - (-3)} = \frac{-11}{0}$$

The denominator is 0; division by zero is undefined.
Slope ($\overleftrightarrow{AB}$) is undefined. $\overleftrightarrow{AB}$ is vertical.

SLOPE OF A LINE

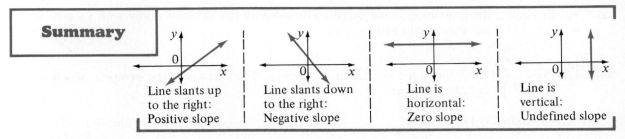

Summary

Line slants up to the right: Positive slope

Line slants down to the right: Negative slope

Line is horizontal: Zero slope

Line is vertical: Undefined slope

Oral Exercises

Classify the slope of each line *l* as positive, negative, zero, or undefined.

1.   2.   3.   4.   5.

Describe the position of each line whose slope is indicated.

6. 6   7. $\dfrac{0}{4}$ 8. -3 9. $\dfrac{-5}{0}$ 10. $\dfrac{8}{5}$ 11. $-\dfrac{3}{4}$ 12. $\dfrac{7}{0}$

Written Exercises

Find the slope of the line joining each pair of points. Then describe the position of the line in a coordinate plane.

1. $C(4, -2), D(3, 4)$
2. $P(-1, 1), Q(7, 4)$
3. $A(6, -7), B(-3, -7)$
4. $S(1, 4), T(8, 1)$
5. $R(-2, -3), S(-2, -6)$
6. $E(6, 2), F(-4, -1)$
7. $A(5, -4), B(-5, -4)$
8. $G(1, -6), H(5, 3)$
9. $K(-1, 3), L(3, -1)$
10. $P(6, -2), Q(-4, 1)$
11. $A(1, 7), B(1, -7)$
12. $R(-2, 6), S(-6, 2)$
13. $M(5, 2), N(5, -4)$
14. $P(4, -1), Q(3, -4)$
15. $U(-1, -4), V(-4, -1)$
16. $E(6, -1), F(-2, 8)$
17. $C(6, -3), D(-6, 3)$
18. $P(-2, 7), Q(-2, 0)$

Find *a* so that $\overleftrightarrow{CD}$ will have the given slope.

B 19. $C(4, -2), D(6, a); 1$
20. $C(3, -3), D(-3, a); -\dfrac{4}{3}$
21. $C(3, a), D(8, 1); -2$
22. $C(-5, a), D(1, -a); -\dfrac{1}{3}$
23. $C(a, -1), D(-3, 2);$ undefined
24. $C(2, a), D(3, -6); \dfrac{2}{3}$
25. $C(5, -2), D(-4, a); 0$
26. $C(2, a), D(-a, 3); \dfrac{5}{4}$
27. $C(-3, -2), D(1, a); 2$

Graph *A*, *B*, *C*, and *D*. Draw $\overline{AB}$ and $\overline{CD}$. Find slope $(\overleftrightarrow{AB})$ and slope $(\overleftrightarrow{CD})$. What relationship appears to exist between $\overline{AB}$ and $\overline{CD}$ in each case?

C 28. $A(-4, -6), B(-1, -3), C(2, 0), D(6, 4)$
29. $A(-5, 7), B(-1, 4), C(3, 1), D(7, -2)$
30. $A(-3, -3), B(-1, 3), C(1, -5), D(3, 1)$
31. $A(-4, 1), B(2, -3), C(-3, 6), D(3, 2)$

440

CHAPTER THIRTEEN

32. Justify each conclusion about the slope in the summary at the top of page 440. [*Hint:* For the line that slants up to the right, $y_2 > y_1$, so $y_2 - y_1 > 0$. Also $x_2 > x_1$, so $x_2 - x_1 > 0$. **Thus,** $\dfrac{y_2 - y_1}{x_2 - x_1} > 0$.]

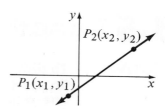

Algebra Review

OBJECTIVES ► **To square a binomial**
To complete the square

To square a binomial:
Use $(a + b)^2 = a^2 + 2ab + b^2$.

To complete the square of a binomial such as $x^2 - 8x$:
(1) Take one half of the middle coefficient;
(2) Square it and add the result to the binomial;
(3) The trinomial formed is a perfect square.

Example 1 Simplify $(2x + 3)^2$.

$$(a + b)^2 = a^2 + 2ab + b^2$$

$$(2x + 3)^2 = (2x)^2 + 2(2x)(3) + 3^2$$
$$= 4x^2 + 12x + 9$$

Example 2 Complete the square: $x^2 - 6x + ?$.

Take one half of -6, square it, and add it to $x^2 - 6x$.
$$\left(\frac{-6}{2}\right)^2 = (-3)^2 = 9$$
$x^2 - 6x + 9$ is a perfect square.

Simplify.

1. $(x + 2)^2$ **2.** $(x - 3)^2$ **3.** $(y + 5)^2$ **4.** $(a - 8)^2$

5. $(2x + 1)^2$ **6.** $(3y - 2)^2$ **7.** $(2c - 5)^2$ **8.** $(4x + 1)^2$

9. $(3a + b)^2$ **10.** $(x + 3y)^2$ **11.** $(2c - d)^2$ **12.** $(5x - 4y)^2$

Complete the square.

13. $x^2 + 2x$ **14.** $y^2 - 4y$ **15.** $m^2 - 8m$
16. $a^2 + 12a$ **17.** $x^2 + 5x$ **18.** $y^2 - 9y$
19. $z^2 - 24z$ **20.** $a^2 + 15a$ **21.** $x^2 - 25x$
22. $a^2 + 6ab$ **23.** $x^2 - 12xy$ **24.** $c^2 + 7cd$

13.5 Equation of a Line

OBJECTIVES ▶
To draw the graph of a linear equation of the form $ax + by = c$
To draw a line, given the coordinates of one point and the slope of the line, and then write its equation
To write an equation of a line in standard form, given the coordinates of two points on the line

Suppose you could graph all ordered pairs (x, y) that are solutions of the equation $2x + 4y = 10$. A few of the ordered pairs are listed below and graphed on the coordinate plane.

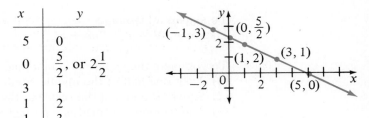

$2x + 4y = 10$

x	y
5	0
0	$\frac{5}{2}$, or $2\frac{1}{2}$
3	1
1	2
-1	3

Notice that the points corresponding to the ordered pairs appear to lie on a line. This leads to Theorem 13.3, which is stated without proof.

┌─**Theorem 13.3** **Standard Form** The graph of an equation that can──┐
be written in the form $ax + by = c$ [a and b not both
equal to 0] is a line.
└───┘

An equation whose graph is a line is called a *linear equation*. The form $ax + by = c$ [a, b, and c integers] is called the **standard form** of a linear equation.

Example 1 Write $y + 3 = -\frac{1}{2}(x - 5)$ in standard form.

$$y + 3 = -\frac{1}{2}(x - 5) \quad \blacktriangleleft \quad \textit{Multiply each side by } -2.$$

$-x$ is the same as $-1 \cdot x$. ▶
$$-2y - 6 = x - 5$$
$$-x - 2y = 1 \text{ is in standard form.}$$

Theorem 13.3 enables you to graph a linear equation such as $2x + 4y = 10$ by graphing only two ordered pairs that satisfy the equation. It is usually wise to graph a third ordered pair as a check. Thus, the first two or three ordered pairs in the chart at the top of the page are sufficient to graph $2x + 4y = 10$.

You can also draw a line if you are given its slope and the coordinates of a point on the line, as shown in Example 2.

Example 2 Draw a line passing through $P(-1, 4)$ and having slope -2.

1. Start at $P(-1, 4)$.
2. $m = \dfrac{-2}{1} \begin{array}{l}\leftarrow \text{ down 2} \\ \leftarrow \text{ right 1}\end{array}$
   Move down 2 units and to the right 1 unit. Thus, a second point on the line is $Q(0, 2)$.
3. Draw a line through P and Q.

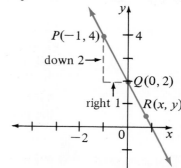

You can write an equation for the line drawn in Example 2. Let $R(x, y)$ be any other point on $\overleftrightarrow{PQ}$. You will use the definition of slope, $m = \dfrac{y_2 - y_1}{x_2 - x_1}$. Consider points P and R and the slope.

$$\underset{\substack{\nearrow \quad \uparrow \\ x_1 \quad y_1}}{P(-1, 4)} \qquad \underset{\substack{\nearrow \quad \uparrow \\ x_2 \quad y_2}}{R(x, y)} \qquad m = \dfrac{y_2 - y_1}{x_2 - x_1}$$

$$-2 = \dfrac{y - 4}{x - (-1)}$$

$$-2 = \dfrac{y - 4}{x + 1}$$

$$y - 4 = -2(x + 1)$$

The form $y - 4 = -2(x + 1)$ is convenient because you can easily determine both the slope of the line and the coordinates of a point on the line simply by examining the equation.

$$y - 4 = -2(x + 1)$$
$$y - 4 = -2\,[x - (-1)]$$

$$\underset{y\text{-coordinate of point}}{\uparrow} \qquad \underset{\text{slope}}{\uparrow} \qquad \underset{x\text{-coordinate of point}}{\uparrow}$$

Thus, the line has slope -2 and passes through $P(-1, 4)$. This suggests Theorem 13.4.

Theorem 13.4 **Point-Slope Form** If a line passes through $P(x_1, y_1)$ and has slope m, then an equation of the line is

$$y - y_1 = m(x - x_1).$$

(See Exercise 42.)

Example 3

Write an equation of the line with slope -4 and passing through the point $P(3, -5)$.

$$P(3, -5) \quad m = -4$$

$x_1 \quad y_1$

$y - y_1 = m(x - x_1)$ by theorem 13.4.

$y - (-5) = -4(x - 3)$

$y + 5 = -4(x - 3)$

You can also write an equation of a line, given the coordinates of two points on the line, as shown in the next example.

Example 4

Write an equation in standard form of the line through $C(-1, -7)$ and $D(3, 5)$.

$C(-1, -7) \quad D(3, 5)$

$x_1 \quad y_1 \quad x_2 \quad y_2$

First find the slope.

$$m = \frac{y_2 - y_1}{x_2 - x_1} = \frac{-7 - 5}{-1 - 3} = \frac{-12}{-4} = 3$$

Then use the Point-slope form.

$$y - y_1 = m(x - x_1)$$
$$y - 5 = 3(x - 3)$$
$$y - 5 = 3x - 9$$
$$y = 3x + 4$$
$$-3x + y = 4$$

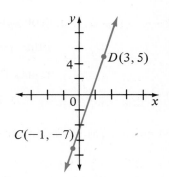

Oral Exercises

Points P and Q lie on the line whose equation is given. Find the missing coordinate for P and for Q.

1. $2x + y = -8$; $P(0, ?)$, $Q(?, 0)$
2. $x - 3y = 6$; $P(0, ?)$, $Q(?, 0)$
3. $4x + 2y = -4$; $P(0, ?)$, $Q(?, 0)$
4. $5x - 2y = 10$; $P(0, ?)$, $Q(?, 0)$
5. $y = 3x - 12$; $P(0, ?)$, $Q(?, 0)$
6. $y = -7x$; $P(0, ?)$, $Q(?, 0)$
7. $-3x + 5y = 9$; $P(0, ?)$, $Q(?, 0)$
8. $4x - 3y = -8$; $P(0, ?)$, $Q(?, 0)$

Give an expression for the slope of $\overleftrightarrow{AB}$.

9. $A(2, 3)$, $B(x, y)$
10. $A(1, 0)$, $B(x, y)$
11. $A(6, -2)$, $B(x, y)$
12. $A(-2, 4)$, $B(x, y)$
13. $A(5, -7)$, $B(x, y)$
14. $A(3, -2)$, $B(x, y)$
15. $A(-1, -4)$, $B(x, y)$
16. $A(0, 0)$, $B(x, y)$

For each line whose equation is given, find the slope and the coordinates of one point on the line.

17. $y - 6 = 2(x - 5)$
18. $y - 3 = -\frac{4}{5}(x - 2)$
19. $y + 4 = \frac{2}{3}(x - 1)$
20. $y - \frac{7}{3} = \left(x + \frac{3}{4}\right)$
21. $y - 7 = -(x + 5)$
22. $y = -\frac{4}{3}(x - 2)$
23. $y + 6 = -x + 8$
24. $y = x$
25. $y = -x$

Written Exercises _____

Graph each equation.

  1. $2x + y = -8$ **2.** $x - 3y = 6$ **3.** $4x + 2y = -4$

     4. $5x - 2y = 10$ **5.** $y = 3x - 12$ **6.** $y = -7x$

     7. $-3x + 5y = 9$ **8.** $4x - 3y = -8$ **9.** $y = \dfrac{3}{4}x$

Write each equation in standard form.

     10. $6y = -3x - 9$ **11.** $y = 4x - 7$ **12.** $-6y = 2x$

     13. $y - 8 = 3(x + 2)$ **14.** $y - 3 = -(x + 7)$ **15.** $y + 6 = -\dfrac{1}{3}(x - 9)$

     16. $y = -\dfrac{2}{3}x + 8$ **17.** $y = -\dfrac{1}{3}x - \dfrac{1}{2}$ **18.** $y = \dfrac{2}{5}x - \dfrac{3}{10}$

Draw a line with slope m and passing through point p. Then write an equation for the line.

     19. $m = 3$; $P(2, 5)$ **20.** $m = -4$; $P(3, -2)$ **21.** $m = -6$; $P(-1, -5)$

     22. $m = \dfrac{1}{2}$; $P(-4, 3)$ **23.** $m = -\dfrac{4}{3}$, $P(-6, -1)$ **24.** $m = 0$; $P(2, 4)$

     25. $m = 0$; $P(-1, -6)$ **26.** $m = 1$; $P(0, 0)$ **27.** $m = -1$; $P(0, 0)$

Write an equation in standard form of the line through points P and Q.

B   **28.** $P(6, 3)$, $Q(4, 1)$ **29.** $P(-5, 2)$, $Q(3, -2)$ **30.** $P(0, 4)$, $Q(6, -2)$

     31. $P(3, -1)$, $Q(5, -5)$ **32.** $P(4, 7)$, $Q(0, -2)$ **33.** $P(6, -1)$, $Q(3, -2)$

     34. $P(0, 3)$, $Q(-4, 2)$ **35.** $P(-7, -2)$, $Q(-1, 4)$ **36.** $P(-3, -1)$, $Q(-8, 2)$

For Exercises 37–40, graph each triangle. Then write the indicated equations in standard form.

37. The vertices of a triangle are $A(-2, -4)$, $B(-3, 1)$, and $C(2, 6)$. Write an equation for the line containing each side.

38. The vertices of a triangle are $D(5, -1)$, $E(4, 3)$, and $F(-3, 0)$. Write an equation for the line containing each side.

39. The vertices of a triangle are $G(0, 0)$, $H(0, 8)$, and $I(6, 4)$. Write an equation for the line containing each median.

40. The vertices of a triangle are $J(-4, 0)$, $K(0, 7)$, and $L(0, -5)$. Write an equation for the line containing each median.

C   **41.** Show that an equation of the line containing points (x_1, y_1) and (x_2, y_2) is $\dfrac{y - y_1}{x - x_1} = \dfrac{y_2 - y_1}{x_2 - x_1}$.

42. Prove Theorem 13.4. [*Hint:* Let $R(x, y)$ be another point on the line.]

43. Show that the slope of a line that makes an angle of 30° with the y-axis is either $\sqrt{3}$ or $-\sqrt{3}$.

44. Show that the slope of a line that makes an angle of 30° with the x-axis is either $\dfrac{\sqrt{3}}{3}$ or $-\dfrac{\sqrt{3}}{3}$.

45. Write an equation for each line that passes through (4, 3) and makes an angle of 45° with the x-axis.

46. What are the possible slopes of all lines that make an angle of 70° with the x-axis? [*Hint:* Use a trigonometric ratio.]

EQUATION OF A LINE   **445**

13.6 Slope-Intercept Form of an Equation

OBJECTIVE ▶ **To draw a line and write its equation by using its slope and y-intercept**

In this lesson you will learn a shortcut for drawing the graph of a linear equation. Consider the equation $2x - 3y = 6$. If you let $x = 0$, then $y = -2$, and $P(0, -2)$ is the point where the graph of $2x - 3y = 6$ intersects the y-axis. The y-coordinate, -2, is called the *y-intercept* of the line.

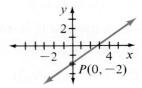

Definition:
y-intercept

> The **y-intercept** of a line is the y-coordinate of the point where the line intersects the y-axis.

Every nonvertical line intersects the y-axis at exactly one point. The x-coordinate of that point is 0 and the y-coordinate is the y-intercept. Generally, b is used to represent the y-intercept of a line. Thus, $(0, b)$ are the coordinates of the point where the line intersects the y-axis. Using the point-slope form of an equation and substituting $(0, b)$ for (x_1, y_1), you can derive another valuable form of the equation of a line.

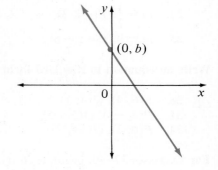

$$y - y_1 = m(x - x_1)$$
$$y - b = m(x - 0)$$
$$y - b = mx$$
$$y = mx + b$$

This argument represents a proof of the next theorem.

> ┌ **Theorem 13.5** Slope-intercept Form If a line has slope m and y-intercept b, then an equation of the line is $y = mx + b$. ┐

The slope-intercept form can be useful in drawing the graph of a linear equation.

Example 1 Draw the graph of $y = \dfrac{2}{3}x - 1$.

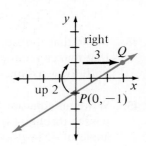

$m = \dfrac{2}{3}$ $b = -1$

1. Start at $P(0, -1)$.
2. $m = \dfrac{2}{3}$ ← up 2
   ← right 3
   Move up 2 and to the right 3 to Q.
3. Draw $\overleftrightarrow{PQ}$, the graph of $y = \dfrac{2}{3}x - 1$.

Example 2 The equation of a line is $-2x - 6y = 12$. Find the slope and the y-intercept of the line. Then draw the graph of the equation.

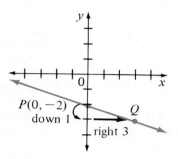

First find the slope and the y-intercept.
$$-2x - 6y = 12$$
$$-6y = 2x + 12$$
$$y = -\frac{1}{3}x - 2 \quad \blacktriangleleft \quad m = -\frac{1}{3}, b = -2$$

Thus, the slope is $-\frac{1}{3}$ and the y-intercept is -2.

Now draw the graph of the equation.
1. Start at $P(0, -2)$.
2. $m = \dfrac{-1}{3} \; \begin{matrix} \leftarrow \text{down } 1 \\ \leftarrow \text{right } 3 \end{matrix}$
   Move down 1 and to the right 3 to $Q(3, -3)$.
3. Draw $\overleftrightarrow{PQ}$, the graph of $-2x - 6y = 12$.

In the next two examples, you will consider equations for horizontal and vertical lines.

Example 3 Draw the graph of $y = 3$.

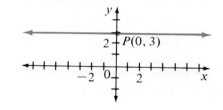

$y = 3$ is the same as $y = 0 \cdot x + 3$.
$m = 0 \quad b = 3$
1. Start at $P(0, 3)$.
2. $m = 0$. **Thus,** the line is horizontal. Draw a horizontal line through $P(0, 3)$.

From Example 3, you can conclude that the equation of a horizontal line is $y = b$, where b is the y-intercept. Now consider a vertical line.

Example 4 Draw the graph of $x = -2$.

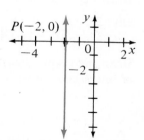

The x-coordinate of each point must be -2, so the line is vertical.
1. Start at $P(-2, 0)$.
2. m is undefined. Draw a vertical line through $P(-2, 0)$.

From Example 4, you can conclude that the equation of a vertical line cannot be in the form $y = mx + b$ since the slope is undefined and there is no y-intercept. In general, the equation of a vertical line is $x = a$, where $(a, 0)$ are the coordinates of the point where the line intersects the x-axis.

SLOPE-INTERCEPT FORM OF AN EQUATION

Oral Exercises

Give the slope and the y-intercept of each line whose equation is given. Then tell whether the line slants up to the right, down to the right, is horizontal, or is vertical.

1. $y = 4x - 2$
2. $y = -7x + 3$
3. $y = 6x + 4$
4. $y = -3x - 5$
5. $y = \frac{3}{5}x + 4$
6. $x = 2$
7. $y = 3x$
8. $y = -\frac{2}{3}x + 2$
9. $x = -3$
10. $y = -x + 5$
11. $y = 0$
12. $y = -3$
13. $y = x - 7$
14. $y = -\frac{7}{2}x + \frac{3}{2}$
15. $y = x$
16. $y = -\frac{4}{5}x$

Tell whether $\overleftrightarrow{PQ}$ is vertical or horizontal in each case. Then give its equation.

17. $P(6, -2), Q(4, -2)$ 18. $P(3, 8), Q(3, -2)$ 19. $P(5, 0), Q(4, 0)$ 20. $P(4, 5), Q(-3, 5)$
21. $P(1, 1), Q(1, 2)$ 22. $P(0, 1), Q(0, -6)$ 23. $P(3, 6), Q(-3, 6)$ 24. $P(4, 7), Q(4, -2)$
25. $P(5, -3), Q(5, 3)$ 26. $P(3, -1), Q(-1, -1)$ 27. $P(-6, 2), Q(-6, -2)$ 28. $P(-4, 4), Q(-4, -4)$

Written Exercises

Write an equation of each line with slope m and y-intercept b.

1. $m = 3, b = 5$
2. $m = -3, b = 4$
3. $m = 7, \ b = -2$
4. $m = -1, b = -2$
5. $m = 0, b = -\frac{1}{2}$
6. $m = 1, \ b = 0$
7. $m = -1, b = \frac{1}{4}$
8. $m = 0, \ b = 0$

Write each equation in the form $y = mx + b$. Identify the slope and the y-intercept.

9. $3y = 6x + 12$
10. $-4y = 2x - 3$
11. $5x + y = -2$
12. $-3x - y = 4$
13. $y - 5 = 0$
14. $4x - 3y = 0$
15. $-2x = 6y + 3$
16. $y - 8 = \frac{1}{3}(x + 12)$

Draw the graph of each equation.

17. $y = 3x + 1$
18. $y = \frac{1}{2}x - 4$
19. $y = -\frac{4}{3}x - 2$
20. $y = -2x + 3$
21. $y = \frac{1}{3}x$
22. $x = -5$
23. $y = -3$
24. $y = -x - 4$
25. $y = x - 4$
26. $y = x$
27. $-3x - 2y = 8$
28. $4x - 5y = 10$

Draw $\overleftrightarrow{PQ}$. Then write an equation of $\overleftrightarrow{PQ}$ in the form $y = mx + b$. Identify the slope and the y-intercept.

B 29. $P(3, 0), Q(5, -4)$ 30. $P(5, 3), Q(3, 1)$ 31. $P(0, 3), Q(6, -3)$ 32. $P(5, -1), Q(2, -2)$
33. $P(0, -1), Q(2, -4)$ 34. $P(-3, 3), Q(3, 3)$ 35. $P(6, 6), Q(-2, -2)$ 36. $P(-4, 4), Q(1, -1)$

Draw the graph of each pair of equations in the same coordinate plane. Find the coordinates of the point of intersection of the two lines. Check these coordinates in each equation.

37. $y = 6$
$x = -1$

38. $y = 3x - 5$
$y = -\frac{2}{3}x + 6$

39. $3x - 2y = 6$
$x - y = 2$

40. $y = 2x$
$x + y = 9$

C 41. Prove that if $P(a, 0)$ is the point where a nonvertical line intersects the x-axis, then $x = \frac{1}{m} \cdot y + a$.

42. Prove that if a line intersects the x-axis at $P(a, 0)$ and the y-axis at $(0, b)$, then $\frac{x}{a} + \frac{y}{b} = 1$.

13.7 Slopes of Parallel and Perpendicular Lines

OBJECTIVES ► **To determine from their slopes if lines are parallel or perpendicular**
To find the slope of a line parallel or perpendicular to a given line
To write an equation of a line parallel or perpendicular to a given line

Examine the graphs of the equations $y = \frac{3}{2}x + 2$ and

$y = \frac{3}{2}x - 4$. Notice that both lines have the same slope, $\frac{3}{2}$.

It appears that the lines are parallel. This result is generalized in Theorem 13.6.

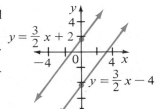

┌─ **Theorem 13.6**   If two nonvertical lines have the same slope, then the
lines are parallel.

Lines with slope 0 are horizontal and therefore
are parallel. Lines with undefined slope are
vertical and are also parallel.

Given: Slope $(\overleftrightarrow{AB})$ = slope $(\overleftrightarrow{DE})$
Prove: $\overleftrightarrow{AB} \parallel \overleftrightarrow{DE}$

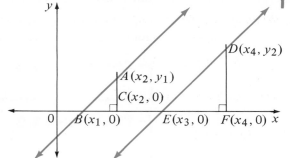

Outline of proof

1. Draw $\overline{AC}$ and $\overline{DF}$ perpendicular to the x-axis. Let the points have coordinates as shown.
2. $AC = |y_1 - 0| = y_1$ $(y_1 > 0)$
   $BC = |x_2 - x_1| = x_2 - x_1$ $(x_2 > x_1)$
   $DF = |y_2 - 0| = y_2$ $(y_2 > 0)$
   $EF = |x_4 - x_3| = x_4 - x_3$ $(x_4 > x_3)$
3. Slope $(\overleftrightarrow{AB}) = \dfrac{y_1 - 0}{x_2 - x_1} = \dfrac{y_1}{x_2 - x_1}$

   Slope $(\overleftrightarrow{DE}) = \dfrac{y_2 - 0}{x_4 - x_3} = \dfrac{y_2}{x_4 - x_3}$

4. slope $(\overleftrightarrow{AB})$ = slope $(\overleftrightarrow{DE})$
5. $\dfrac{y_1}{x_2 - x_1} = \dfrac{y_2}{x_4 - x_3}$
6. $\dfrac{AC}{BC} = \dfrac{DF}{EF}$
7. $\angle ACB \cong \angle DFE$
8. $\triangle ABC \sim \triangle DEF$
9. $\angle ABC \cong \angle DEF$
10. $\therefore \overleftrightarrow{AB} \parallel \overleftrightarrow{DE}$

The converse of Theorem 13.6 is also true.

┌─ **Theorem 13.7**   If two nonvertical lines are parallel, then the lines
have the same slope. (See Exercise 26.)

Example 1 Use slopes to show that $\overleftrightarrow{PQ} \parallel \overleftrightarrow{RS}$ for $P(-3, 2)$, $Q(5, 0)$, $R(-4, -3)$, and $S(0, -4)$.

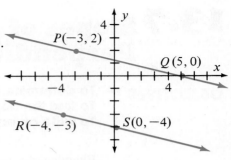

Slope $(\overleftrightarrow{PQ}) = \dfrac{y_2 - y_1}{x_2 - x_1} = \dfrac{0 - 2}{5 - (-3)} = \dfrac{-2}{8} = -\dfrac{1}{4}$

Slope $(\overleftrightarrow{RS}) = \dfrac{-4 - (-3)}{0 - (-4)} = \dfrac{-1}{4} = -\dfrac{1}{4}$

Slope $(\overleftrightarrow{PQ}) =$ slope $(\overleftrightarrow{RS})$

Thus, $\overleftrightarrow{PQ} \parallel \overleftrightarrow{RS}$ by Theorem 13.6.

Examine the graphs of the equations $y = \dfrac{2}{3}x - 2$ and

$y = -\dfrac{3}{2}x + 1$. Notice that the slopes of the lines are

$\dfrac{2}{3}$ and $-\dfrac{3}{2}$; $\dfrac{2}{3}$ and $-\dfrac{3}{2}$ are negative reciprocals of each

other since their product is -1 $\left(\dfrac{2}{3} \cdot -\dfrac{3}{2} = -1\right)$. It ap-

pears that the lines are perpendicular. This result and converse are stated in Theorems 13.8 and 13.9.

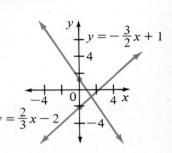

Theorem 13.8 If the slopes of two lines are negative reciprocals, then the lines are perpendicular. (See Exercise 27.)

Theorem 13.9 If two nonvertical lines are perpendicular, then their slopes are negative reciprocals. (See Exercise 28.)

Theorems 13.8 and 13.9 deal with nonvertical lines. A vertical line and a horizontal line in the same coordinate plane are always perpendicular.

Example 2 Show that $ABCD$ is a rectangle for $A(-1, -2)$, $B(3, 2)$, $C(1, 4)$, and $D(-3, 0)$.

Slope $(\overline{AD}) = \dfrac{0 - (-2)}{-3 - (-1)} = \dfrac{2}{-2} = -1$

Slope $(\overline{BC}) = \dfrac{4 - 2}{1 - 3} = \dfrac{2}{-2} = -1$

Slope $(\overline{AB}) = \dfrac{2 - (-2)}{3 - (-1)} = \dfrac{4}{4} = 1$

Slope $(\overline{DC}) = \dfrac{4 - 0}{1 - (-3)} = \dfrac{4}{4} = 1$

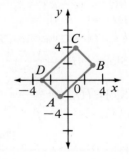

$\overline{AD} \parallel \overline{BC}$ and $\overline{AB} \parallel \overline{DC}$ by Th. 13.6, so $ABCD$ is a parallelogram.
Slopes of consecutive sides of $ABCD$ are negative reciprocals $(-1 \times 1 = -1)$.
$\overline{AD} \perp \overline{DC}$, $\overline{BC} \perp \overline{DC}$, $\overline{AB} \perp \overline{BC}$, and $\overline{AD} \perp \overline{AB}$ by Th. 13.8.
Since four right angles are formed, $ABCD$ is a rectangle.

Reading in Geometry

Copy and complete to make each statement true.

1. The negative reciprocal of −1 is _____.

2. The negative reciprocal of $-\frac{1}{5}$ is _____.

3. Any two vertical lines are _____ to each other.

4. If the slope of $\overleftrightarrow{AB}$ is 0 and the slope of $\overleftrightarrow{CD}$ is undefined, then $\overleftrightarrow{AB}$ is _____ to $\overleftrightarrow{CD}$.

5. Line l has slope 4. Any line parallel to l has slope _____. Any line perpendicular to l has slope _____.

6. Line l has slope $-\frac{2}{3}$. Any line parallel to l has slope _____. Any line perpendicular to l has slope _____.

7. If two lines have the equations $y = 3x - 2$ and $y = -\frac{1}{3}x - 2$, then the lines are _____ and intersect at the point with coordinates _____.

8. If two lines have the equations $y = x$ and $y = -x$, then the lines are _____ and intersect at the point with coordinates _____.

Oral Exercises

Give the negative reciprocal of each slope.

1. $\frac{2}{3}$ 2. 4   3. −7   4. 1   5. $\frac{5}{2}$ 6. −1   7. $-\frac{3}{4}$ 8. 0

Give the slope of a line parallel to the line with the given equation. Then give the slope of a line perpendicular to the line with the given equation.

9. $y = 3x - 1$ 10. $y = -2x + 4$ 11. $y = x + 3$ 12. $y = -\frac{4}{3}x - \frac{2}{3}$

Written Exercises

Give the slope of a line parallel to $\overleftrightarrow{AB}$. Then give the slope of a line perpendicular to $\overleftrightarrow{AB}$.

1. $A(0, -5)$, $B(7, 2)$ 2. $A(3, 5)$, $B(-2, 5)$ 3. $A(4, -5)$, $B(6, 0)$ 4. $A(-3, 2)$, $B(6, -1)$
5. $A(2, -8)$, $B(2, 9)$ 6. $A(-4, 3)$, $B(7, -1)$ 7. $A(-3, -1)$, $B(5, -8)$ 8. $A(1, 6)$, $B(2, 5)$

Use slopes to show that $\overleftrightarrow{PR} \perp \overleftrightarrow{SQ}$.

9. $P(2, -1)$, $Q(5, 3)$, $R(1, 6)$, $S(-2, 2)$ 10. $P(-2, -2)$, $Q(6, -1)$, $R(0, 4)$, $S(-6, 3)$

Use slopes to show that $\overline{AB} \parallel \overline{CD}$ and $\overline{AD} \parallel \overline{BC}$.

11. $A(-1, 0)$, $B(4, 5)$, $C(3, 9)$, $D(-2, 4)$ 12. $A(5, -8)$, $B(7, -6)$, $C(6, 1)$, $D(4, -1)$

Show that $ABCD$ is a parallelogram.

13. $A(-2, -5)$, $B(0, -3)$, $C(-1, 4)$, $D(-3, 2)$ 14. $A(2, -7)$, $B(7, -2)$, $C(6, 2)$, $D(1, -3)$

Show that $EFGH$ is a rectangle.

15. $E(1, 4)$, $F(7, 0)$, $G(9, 3)$, $H(3, 7)$ 16. $E(-4, -5)$, $F(1, 0)$, $G(-1, 2)$, $H(-6, -3)$

SLOPES OF PARALLEL AND PERPENDICULAR LINES

Show that the diagonals of *MNPQ* are perpendicular.

17. $M(5, -2)$, $N(8, 2)$, $P(4, 5)$, $Q(1, 1)$

18. $M(0, -3)$, $N(6, -2)$, $P(5, 4)$, $Q(-1, 3)$

Write an equation in slope-intercept form of the line passing through the given point and parallel to the line whose equation is given.

19. $(5, -2)$; $y = -6x + 1$ [*Hint:* Use the point-slope form for $m = -6$.]

20. $(0, 6)$; $2x + 4y = 10$

Write an equation in slope-intercept form of the line passing through the given point and perpendicular to the line whose equation is given. (Ex. 21–22)

21. $(-3, 1)$; $y = \dfrac{2}{3}x - 4$

22. $(-4, -5)$; $3x + 2y = -7$

 23. Write an equation of the line containing the altitude to $\overline{AB}$ of $\triangle ABC$ with $A(-1, 2)$, $B(-3, -4)$ and $C(-2, 5)$.

24. Write an equation of the line containing the median to $\overline{BC}$ of $\triangle ABC$ with $A(3, 5)$, $B(-4, 1)$, and $C(-2, -4)$.

25. Write an equation of the perpendicular bisector of $\overline{RS}$ for $R(-2, -3)$ and $S(4, 7)$.

26. Prove Theorem 13.7.

27. Prove Theorem 13.8.

28. Prove Theorem 13.9.

A Challenge To You

On one full-page coordinate plane, graph each segment described below. Get the message?

1. $y = -2x - 16$ between $(-11, 6)$ and $(-10, 4)$
2. $y = 2x + 24$ between $(-10, 4)$ and $(-9, 6)$
3. $x = -10$ between $(-10, 2)$ and $(-10, 4)$
4. $x = -7$ between $(-7, 6)$ and $(-7, 2)$
5. $y = 6$ between $(-7, 6)$ and $(-5, 6)$
6. $x = -5$ between $(-5, 6)$ and $(-5, 2)$
7. $y = 2$ between $(-7, 2)$ and $(-5, 2)$
8. $x = -3$ between $(-3, 6)$ and $(-3, 2)$
9. $y = 2$ between $(-3, 2)$ and $(-1, 2)$
10. $x = -1$ between $(-1, 6)$ and $(-1, 2)$
11. $x = 1$ between $(1, 7)$ and $(1, 6)$
12. $x = 2$ between $(2, 6)$ and $(2, 2)$
13. $y = 6$ between $(2, 6)$ and $(4, 6)$
14. $x = 4$ between $(4, 6)$ and $(4, 4)$
15. $y = 4$ between $(2, 4)$ and $(4, 4)$
16. $y = -2x + 10$ between $(3, 4)$ and $(4, 2)$
17. $x = 6$ between $(6, 6)$ and $(6, 2)$
18. $y = 6$ between $(6, 6)$ and $(8, 6)$
19. $y = 4$ between $(6, 4)$ and $(7, 4)$
20. $y = 2$ between $(6, 2)$ and $(8, 2)$
21. $y = -2$ between $(-11, -2)$ and $(-9, -2)$
22. $x = -11$ between $(-11, -2)$ and $(-11, -6)$
23. $y = -6$ between $(-11, -6)$ and $(-9, -6)$
24. $x = -9$ between $(-9, -5)$ and $(-9, -6)$
25. $y = -5$ between $(-10, -5)$ and $(-8, -5)$
26. $x = -7$ between $(-7, -2)$ and $(-7, -6)$
27. $y = -2$ between $(-7, -2)$ and $(-5, -2)$
28. $x = -5$ between $(-5, -2)$ and $(-5, -4)$
29. $y = -4$ between $(-7, -4)$ and $(-5, -4)$
30. $y = -2x - 16$ between $(-6, -4)$ and $(-5, -6)$
31. $x = -3$ between $(-3, -2)$ and $(-3, -6)$
32. $y = -2$ between $(-3, -2)$ and $(-1, -2)$
33. $y = -4$ between $(-3, -4)$ and $(-2, -4)$
34. $y = -6$ between $(-3, -6)$ and $(-1, -6)$
35. $x = 1$ between $(1, -2)$ and $(1, -6)$
36. $y = -2$ between $(1, -2)$ and $(3, -2)$
37. $x = 3$ between $(3, -2)$ and $(3, -6)$
38. $y = -4$ between $(1, -4)$ and $(3, -4)$
39. $x = 6$ between $(6, -2)$ and $(6, -6)$
40. $y = -2$ between $(5, -2)$ and $(7, -2)$

13.8 Using Coordinates in Proofs

OBJECTIVES ► To find an appropriate placement for a polygon in a coordinate plane and assign coordinates to its vertices
To use coordinate geometry to prove statements

Many statements can be proved quite simply by the use of coordinate geometry. As a first step, the given geometric figure must be placed in a coordinate plane. The placement is crucial. For example, if a proof involves a square, you can rely on the definition of a square in placing it. Since the angles of a square are right angles, you can place the square so that two of its sides lie on the axes. Let a be the length of a side. Since all four sides have the same length, the coordinates of the vertices are as shown at the right.

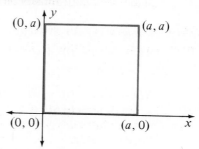

If the square were in one of the positions shown below, the coordinates of the vertices would become much more complicated.

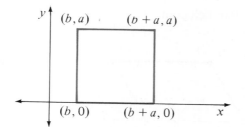
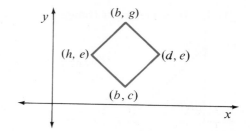

To find an appropriate placement for a polygon in a coordinate plane
(1.) Place one vertex at the origin;
(2.) Place one side on the x-axis.

In Example 1, notice that the placement of the square in the coordinate plane helps to simplify the proof of the statement.

Example 1 Prove that the diagonals of a square are perpendicular.

Given: Square $ABCD$, diagonals $\overline{AC}$ and $\overline{BD}$
Prove: $\overline{AC} \perp \overline{BD}$

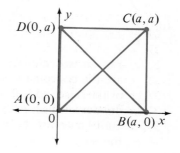

Place square $ABCD$ in a coordinate plane with coordinates as shown.

Slope $(\overleftrightarrow{AC}) = \dfrac{a - 0}{a - 0} = \dfrac{a}{a} = 1$ ◄

Slope $(\overleftrightarrow{BD}) = \dfrac{0 - a}{a - 0} = \dfrac{-a}{a} = -1$ ◄   *Def. of slope*

Thus, $\overline{AC} \perp \overline{BD}$ by Theorem 13.8.

USING COORDINATES IN PROOFS

Example 2 Prove that the diagonals of a rectangle are congruent.

Given: Rect. $ABCD$ with diagonals $\overline{AC}$ and $\overline{BD}$
Prove: $\overline{AC} \cong \overline{BD}$

Place rect. $ABCD$ in a coordinate plane with coordinates as shown.

$d = \sqrt{(x_2 - x_1)^2 + (y_2 - y_1)^2}$ ◄ *Dist. formula*
$AC = \sqrt{(a - 0)^2 + (b - 0)^2}$
$\quad = \sqrt{a^2 + b^2}$
$BD = \sqrt{(a - 0)^2 + (0 - b)^2}$
$\quad = \sqrt{a^2 + (-b)^2}$
$\quad = \sqrt{a^2 + b^2}$
So $AC = BD$.
Thus, $\overline{AC} \cong \overline{BD}$.

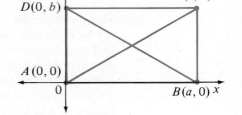

Written Exercises

Give the missing coordinates for each figure. (Ex. 1–6)

Ⓐ **1.** Isosceles right triangle

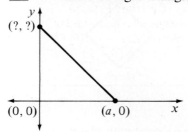

2. Parallelogram

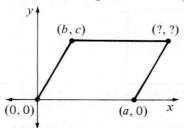

3. Isosceles triangle

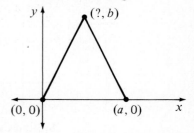

4. Isosceles trapezoid

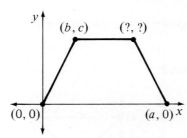

5. Midpoints of sides of a triangle

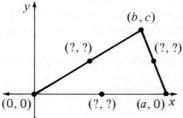

6. 30°–60° right triangle

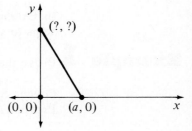

7. For an isosceles triangle, if $(a, 0)$ are the coordinates of an endpoint of the base, and $(0, b)$ are the coordinates of the vertex angle, give the coordinates of the other endpoint of the base.

8. If the coordinates of the endpoints of a segment are $(a, 0)$ and $(0, b)$, give the coordinates of the midpoint of the segment.

Use coordinate geometry to prove each statement.

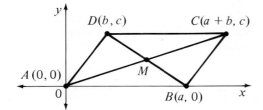

B **9.** The diagonals of a parallelogram bisect each other. [*Hint:* Show that the diagonals have the same midpoint.]

10. The segment joining the midpoint of two sides of a triangle is parallel to the third side and is one half as long.

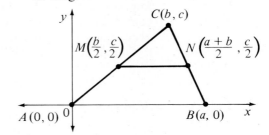

11. The diagonals of an isosceles trapezoid are congruent.

12. The midpoint of the hypotenuse of a right triangle is equidistant from the vertices.

C **13.** The segments joining the midpoints of the opposite sides of a quadrilateral bisect each other.

14. The length of the median of a trapezoid is equal to one half the sum of the lengths of the bases.

15. The length of the segment joining the midpoints of the diagonals of a trapezoid is equal to one half the difference of the lengths of the bases.

16. The segments joining the midpoints of the sides of a triangle form another triangle which is similar to the given triangle.

Algebra Review

OBJECTIVE ▶ **To solve equations involving absolute value**

$|a|$ is read *the absolute value of a.*
$|a| = 3$ means $a = 3$ or $a = -3$.

Example Solve $|2x - 1| = 5$.

$|2x - 1| = 5$ means $\quad 2x - 1 = 5$ or $2x - 1 = -5$
Solve each equation: $\qquad 2x = 6 \qquad\quad 2x = -4$
$\qquad\qquad\qquad\qquad\qquad x = 3 \qquad\quad x = -2$
Check: $|2 \cdot 3 - 1| = |5| = 5 \quad |2(-2) - 1| = |-5| = 5$

Thus, the solutions are 3 and −2.

Solve each equation.

1. $|x - 2| = 7$ **2.** $|x + 6| = 10$ **3.** $|7 - x| = 4$ **4.** $|2 + x| = 9$

5. $|2x - 6| = 4$ **6.** $|5 - 3y| = 7$ **7.** $|2z - 14| = 1$ **8.** $|2 - 5y| = 8$

9. $|3k + 2| = 10$ **10.** $|4 + 2y| = 0$ **11.** $|5a + 3| = 6$ **12.** $|6z - 8| = 4$

13.9 Equation of a Circle

OBJECTIVE ► **To apply equations of circles**

Suppose circle Q lies in a coordinate plane with (h, k) the coordinates of its center. Let $P(x, y)$ be any point on the circle and r be the length of a radius. Since every point P is the same distance r from Q, you can use the Distance Formula to find an equation which describes all points $P(x, y)$ on the circle.

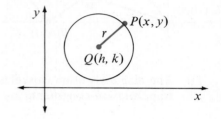

$$Q(h, k) \quad P(x, y) \quad d = r$$
$$x_1 \ y_1 \qquad x_2 \ y_2$$
$$d = \sqrt{(x_2 - x_1)^2 + (y_2 - y_1)^2}$$
$$r = \sqrt{(x - h)^2 + (y - k)^2}$$
$$r^2 = (x - h)^2 + (y - k)^2$$

Theorem 13.10 The equation of a circle with (h, k) the coordinates of the center and a radius of length r is

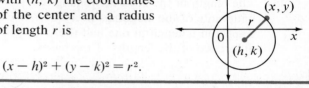

$$(x - h)^2 + (y - k)^2 = r^2.$$

The equation derived above is the general equation of a circle in a coordinate plane. Examples 1 and 2 are applications of Theorem 13.10.

Example 1 Write an equation for a circle with its center at the origin and a radius of length 8.

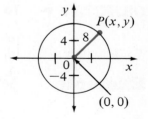

$$(h, k) = (0, 0) \text{ and } r = 8.$$
$$(x - h)^2 + (y - k)^2 = r^2 \text{ by Theorem 13.10}$$
$$(x - 0)^2 + (y - 0)^2 = 8^2$$
$$x^2 + y^2 = 64$$

Example 2 Show that $R(-4, 3)$ and $S(1, -2\sqrt{6})$ lie on a circle with equation $x^2 + y^2 = 25$.

$x = -4$ and $y = 3$		$x = 1$ and $y = -2\sqrt{6}$	
$x^2 + y^2$	25	$x^2 + y^2$	25
$(-4)^2 + 3^2$	25	$1^2 + (-2\sqrt{6})^2$	25
$16 + 9$		$1 + 24$	
25		25	

Thus, $R(-4, 3)$ and $S(1, -2\sqrt{6})$ lie on the circle.

To simplify an equation of a circle means to express it with only the variable terms on the left side. This is shown in Example 3.

Example 3 Write an equation of a circle with center $Q(-2, 1)$ and radius of length 6. Simplify the equation.

$(h, k) = (-2, 1)$ and $r = 6$.

$$(x - h)^2 + (y - k)^2 = r^2$$
$$[x - (-2)]^2 + (y - 1)^2 = 6^2$$
$$(x + 2)^2 + (y - 1)^2 = 6^2$$
$$x^2 + 4x + 4 + y^2 - 2y + 1 = 36$$
$$x^2 + 4x + y^2 - 2y = 31$$

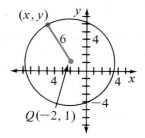

Thus, the equation is $x^2 + 4x + y^2 - 2y = 31$.

The process of completing the square is required in the next example. If necessary, you can refer to the Algebra Review on page 441.

Example 4 Find the coordinates of the center and the length of a radius of a circle whose equation is $x^2 + y^2 + 8x - 14y = 16$.

$$x^2 + y^2 + 8x - 14y = 16$$
$$(x^2 + 8x + \quad) + (y^2 - 14y + \quad) = 16$$

$$(x^2 + 8x + 16) + (y^2 - 14y + 49) = 16 + 16 + 49$$
$$(x + 4)^2 + (y - 7)^2 = 81$$
$$\text{or } [x - (-4)]^2 + (y - 7)^2 = 9^2$$
$$\qquad\qquad h \qquad\qquad k \qquad r$$

Thus, the coordinates of the center are $(-4, 7)$ and the length of a radius is 9.

Oral **Exercises**

Identify the coordinates of the center and the length of a radius of each circle whose equation is given.

1. $(x - 1)^2 + (y - 3)^2 = 5^2$
2. $(x + 5)^2 + (y - 4)^2 = 2^2$
3. $(x - 2)^2 + (y + 6)^2 = 100$
4. $(x + 4)^2 + (y - 6)^2 = 4$
5. $(x + 10)^2 + (y + 5)^2 = 16$
6. $(x - 6)^2 + y^2 = 1$
7. $x^2 + (y + 8)^2 = 7$
8. $x^2 + y^2 = 5$

EQUATION OF A CIRCLE

Written Exercises

Write an equation of each circle with center A and radius of length r. Leave the equation in the form $(x - h)^2 + (y - k)^2 = r^2$.

A
1. $A(0, 0); r = 3$ 2. $A(3, 1); r = 5$ 3. $A(-1, 4); r = 1$ 4. $A(-2, -6); r = 5$
5. $A(6, -1); r = 7$ 6. $A(-3, -8); r = \sqrt{12}$ 7. $A(5, 5); r = 8$ 8. $A(6, -2); r = \sqrt{10}$

Write an equation of each circle with center A and radius of length r. Simplify the equation.

9. $A(3, 1); r = 4$ 10. $A(2, 5); r = 3$ 11. $A(0, -4); r = 2$ 12. $A(-1, 5); r = 8$
13. $A(-8, -1); r = \sqrt{15}$ 14. $A(7, 0); r = 8$ 15. $A(-2, -9); r = \sqrt{7}$ 16. $A(6, -7); r = 20$

Show that each point P lies on a circle with the given equation.

17. $P(4, 0); x^2 + y^2 = 16$ 18. $P(5, -3); x^2 + y^2 = 34$
19. $P(5, -3); (x - 1)^2 + y^2 = 25$ 20. $P(-1, -1); (x - 2)^2 + (y + 1)^2 = 9$
21. $P(-\sqrt{3}, -2); x^2 + y^2 + 6y = -5$ 22. $P(-3, 4); x^2 + y^2 + 2x - 8y = -13$

Find the coordinates of the center and the length of a radius of the circle with each given equation. Draw the graph of the equation.

23. $x^2 + y^2 = 16$ 24. $x^2 + y^2 = 4$ 25. $x^2 + y^2 = 10$
26. $(x - 3)^2 + y^2 = 9$ 27. $(x - 3)^2 + (y + 4)^2 = 16$ 28. $(x + 2)^2 + (y - 6)^2 = 64$

Find the coordinates of the center and the length of a radius of a circle with each given equation.

B
29. $x^2 + y^2 = 18$ 30. $x^2 + y^2 + 6x = 7$ 31. $x^2 + y^2 + 2x - 10y = 1$
32. $x^2 + y^2 - 12y = 4$ 33. $x^2 + y^2 - 16x - 6y = -72$ 34. $x^2 + y^2 + 18x - 20y = -177$

Write an equation of each circle with center Q and passing through the origin. Draw the graph of the equation.

35. $Q(4, 3)$ 36. $Q(-1, 2)$ 37. $Q(-2, -\sqrt{5})$

Write an equation of each circle with R and S the endpoints of a diameter. Draw the graph of the equation.

38. $R(-4, -1), S(4, 5)$ 39. $R(-2, -5), S(6, -1)$ 40. $R(1, 2), S(-3, -4)$

Show that the two circles with the given equations are congruent.

C
41. $x^2 + y^2 + 4x = 32; x^2 + y^2 - 2x + 6y = 26$ 42. $x^2 + y^2 - 8y = 1; x^2 + y^2 + 10x = -8$

Show that the two circles with the given equations are concentric.

43. $(x - 3)^2 + (y + 2)^2 = 10; x^2 + y^2 - 6x + 4y = 52$ 44. $x^2 + (y - 8)^2 = 7; x^2 + y^2 - 16y = 46$

Find the coordinates of all common points of the two circles with the given equations.

45. $(x - 4)^2 + (y + 5)^2 = 16; (x - 4)^2 + (y - 2)^2 = 9$ 46. $x^2 + y^2 = 10; (x + 3)^2 + (y + 3)^2 = 4$

The equation of a circle is given. Write an equation of a line which is tangent to the circle at the given point P.

47. $x^2 + y^2 + 4x - 6y = 12; P(-6, 6)$ 48. $x^2 + y^2 - 10x + 8y = -28; P(7, -8)$

CHAPTER THIRTEEN

13.10 Coordinates in Space

OBJECTIVES ▶ **To graph ordered triples in a three-dimensional coordinate system**
To find the distance between points in a three-dimensional coordinate system

Suppose you take a coordinate plane and add a third axis, called the z-axis, perpendicular to the plane at the origin. You now have a three dimensional coordinate system. On it you can locate points in space by means of *ordered triples* of numbers.

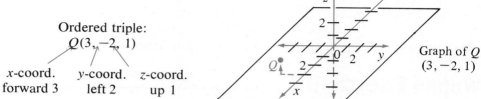

Ordered triple:
$Q(3, -2, 1)$

x-coord. y-coord. z-coord.
forward 3   left 2   up 1

Graph of Q
$(3, -2, 1)$

The chart below can serve as a guide for graphing ordered triples.

GRAPHING ORDERED TRIPLES					
x-coordinate		**y-coordinate**		**z-coordinate**	
Positive	Negative	Positive	Negative	Positive	Negative
Forward	Back	Right	Left	Up	Down

Example 1   Graph $P(3, 2, -1)$.

x-coord. y-coord. z-coord.
forward 3   right 2   down 1

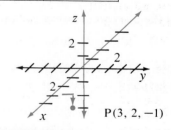

$P(3, 2, -1)$

The next theorem gives a formula for the distance between two points in a three-dimensional coordinate system.

┌─ **Theorem 13.11**   If d is the distance between points
$A(x_1, y_1, z_1)$ and $B(x_2, y_2, z_2)$, then

$$d = \sqrt{(x_2 - x_1)^2 + (y_2 - y_1)^2 + (z_2 - z_1)^2}.$$

(See Exercise 30.)

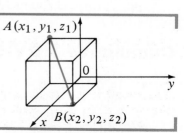

Example 2 Find the distance between $P(-2, -8, 5)$ and $Q(3, -4, 2)$.

$$P(-2, -8, 5) \qquad Q(3, -4, 2)$$
$$\overset{\uparrow}{x_1}\ \overset{\uparrow}{y_1}\ \overset{\uparrow}{z_1} \qquad \overset{\uparrow}{x_2}\ \overset{\uparrow}{y_2}\ \overset{\uparrow}{z_2}$$

$$d = \sqrt{(x_2 - x_1)^2 + (y_2 - y_1)^2 + (z_2 - z_1)^2}$$
$$PQ = \sqrt{(-2 - 3)^2 + (-8 + 4)^2 + (5 - 2)^2}$$
$$= \sqrt{(-5)^2 + (-4)^2 + 3^2}$$
$$= \sqrt{25 + 16 + 9}$$
$$= \sqrt{50}, \text{ or } 5\sqrt{2}$$

Thus, $PQ = 5\sqrt{2}$.

Written Exercises

Graph each ordered triple on a three-dimensional coordinate system.

Ⓐ
1. $A(3, 1, 2)$ 2. $B(4, -2, 1)$ 3. $C(-2, 1, 5)$ 4. $D(4, -1, -5)$ 5. $E(-3, -2, 1)$
6. $F(-1, 0, 5)$ 7. $G(0, -3, 4)$ 8. $H(-3, 0, -5)$ 9. $J(-1, 0, 0)$ 10. $K(0, -4, 0)$

On which axis does each of the following points tie?
11. $P(5, 0, 0)$ 12. $Q(0, -3, 0)$ 13. $R(0, 0, -6)$

Which pair of axes determines the plane on which each of the following points lies?

Ⓑ
14. $S(0, 1, -2)$ 15. $T(4, -3, 0)$ 16. $U(-5, 0, -1)$

Find the distance between each pair of points. (Ex. 17–25)

17. $A(3, 5, 2), B(6, -2, 8)$ 18. $C(6, 2, 8), D(-3, 4, -2)$ 19. $E(-7, -3, 0), F(4, -1, 6)$

20. $G(6, 2, -9), H(1, -1, -2)$ 21. $J(-5, 1, 0), K(7, -6, 3)$ 22. $L(0, 8, 0), M(-5, -2, 1)$

23. $P(4, -6, 5), Q(0, 3, 1)$ 24. $R(0, -6, 5), S(3, -8, 4)$ 25. $T(0, -2, -1), U(-3, -7, 0)$

Ⓒ 26. Derive a formula for the midpoint of $\overline{PQ}$ for $P(x_1, y_1, z_1)$ and $Q(x_2, y_2, z_2)$.

Find the coordinates of the midpoint of $\overline{RS}$. (Ex. 27–29)

27. $R(1, -3, 6), S(5, 7, -2)$ 28. $R(-3, 6, 0), S(5, -2, 6)$ 29. $R(4, 0, -1), S(5, -7, 3)$
30. Prove Theorem 13.11.

Cumulative Review

1. In $\triangle ABC$, $AB = 9$, $BC = 8$, and $AC = 13$. Find the perimeter of the triangle formed by joining the midpoints of the three sides of $\triangle ABC$.

2. If each angle of a regular polygon measures 120°, how many sides does the polygon have?

Applications

At the beginning of the year a teacher assigns seats in his class. An assignment of (3, 2) means the seat that is 3 columns from the left and 2 seats back.

1. Assign coordinates to each student in your math class according to his or her regular seat in the class. Which students have the same first and second coordinates?
2. Which students have coordinates whose sum is ten?

Maps of the United States give degrees latitude and longitude for cities. These are a type of coordinates.

3. Using a map, find these coordinates for your city or town.
4. What city has the coordinates 118° latitude and 34° longitude, 84° latitude and 36° longitude?

A carpenter needs to know the "pitch" or "slope" of a roof when building it. This is usually expressed as the number of inches of vertical rise in 12 in. of horizontal run. A slope of 4 in. 12 means a vertical rise of 4 in., in 12 in. of horizontal run.

5. How many inches would it rise in a run of 15 ft?
6. If a roof rises 2 ft in a run of 16 ft, what is the slope of the roof?

4″
12″

7. If an equation were written of the roof line, what number would you use for the slope in the equation?

In some cities, the streets are laid out in a rectangular grid. Those streets running north–south are called avenues; those running east–west are called streets.

8. If you could not take any short cuts through the blocks, how many blocks would you walk to go from the corner of 5th Avenue at 47th Street to the corner of 3rd Avenue at 51st Street?
9. If you could walk straight through the blocks, how far would you walk?

7th Ave.	6th Ave.	5th Ave.	4th Ave.	3rd Ave.	2nd Ave.	1st Ave.

52nd St.
51st St.
50th St.
49th St.
48th St.
47th St.
46th St.

Chapter Thirteen Review

On the same coordinate system, graph and label each ordered pair.

1. $P(3, 6)$ **2.** $Q(-2, 1)$ [13.1]
3. $R(-4, -3)$ **4.** $S(0, -2)$

Is $\overleftrightarrow{AB}$ a vertical line, a horizontal line, or neither?

5. $A(-3, 1)$, $B(-3, 2)$ **6.** $A(1, 5)$, $B(2, 5)$

Find RS. [13.2]
7. $R(2, 5)$, $S(3, 1)$ **8.** $R(4, -6)$, $S(5, 0)$

Find the coordinates of the midpoint [13.3]
of $\overline{AB}$.

9. $A(6, 5)$, $B(-2, 3)$ **10.** $A(-1, 2)$, $B(-3, 4)$

M is the midpoint of $\overline{AB}$. Find the coordinates of B. (Ex. 11–12)

11. $M(-5, 1)$, $A(3, 0)$ **12.** $M(-2, -4)$, $A(-5, 7)$

*13. For $\triangle ABC$ with $A(-3, -2)$, $B(5, 0)$, and $C(1, 8)$, M is the midpoint of $\overline{AB}$ and N is the midpoint of $\overline{BC}$. Show that $MN = \frac{1}{2}(AC)$.

Find the slope of $\overleftrightarrow{RS}$ in each case. Then [13.4]
determine its position in a coordinate plane. (Ex. 14–15)

14. $R(4, 3)$, $S(-1, -3)$ **15.** $R(-1, 6)$, $S(2, -3)$

16. Find a so that $\overleftrightarrow{CD}$ will have slope 2 for $C(-2, -1)$, $D(2, a)$.

Vocabulary
x-coordinate, y-coordinate [13.1]
x-axis, y-axis [13.1]
origin [13.1]
slope [13.4]
horizontal line, vertical line [13.4]
y-intercept [13.5]

Graph each equation. [13.5]
17. $2x - 3y = 6$ **18.** $x + 4y = -2$
19. $-2x = y + 8$ **20.** $y = -x + 1$

Draw a line with slope m and passing [13.6]
through point P. Then write an equation for the line.

21. $m = 2$; $P(1, 3)$ **22.** $m = -4$, $P(-2, 1)$
23. $m = \frac{1}{3}$; $P(4, -5)$ **24.** $m = -\frac{3}{2}$, $P(-1, 0)$

Write an equation in Standard Form for the line through P and Q.

25. $P(2, 1)$, $Q(-1, -3)$ **26.** $P(-4, 3)$, $Q(2, 0)$

Write an equation of each line with slope m and y-intercept b.

27. $m = 3$, $b = -5$ **28.** $m = -\frac{1}{2}$, $b = 3$

For each equation, identify the slope m and the y-intercept b. Then draw the graph of the equation. (Ex. 29–30)

29. $y = 6x - 4$ **30.** $y = -x$

31. Give the slope of a line parallel to [13.7]
$\overleftrightarrow{AB}$ for $A(-3, 4)$, $B(2, -1)$.

32. Give the slope of a line perpendicular to $\overleftrightarrow{CD}$ for $C(4, -6)$, $D(-2, 3)$.

33. Show that the diagonals of $ABCD$ [13.8]
are perpendicular for $A(2, -1)$, $B(8, 0)$, $C(7, 6)$, and $D(1, 5)$.

*34. Use coordinate geometry to prove that the diagonals of a rhombus are perpendicular.

35. Write an equation of the circle with [13.9]
center $A(5, -2)$ and radius of length 3.

36. Find the coordinates of the center and the length of a radius of a circle with the equation $x^2 + y^2 + 4x - 6y = 30$.

Chapter Thirteen Test

On the same coordinate system, graph and label each ordered pair.

1. $E(2, 3)$

2. $F(-4, -1)$

3. $G(0, -6)$

4. $H(-5, 4)$

Is $\overleftrightarrow{AB}$ a vertical line, a horizontal line, or neither?

5. $A(7, 0)$, $B(-2, 0)$

6. $A(-2, 3)$, $B(3, -2)$

7. Give the coordinates of D so that $ABCD$ is a rectangle for $A(-2, -4)$, $B(5, -4)$, $C(5, 1)$, and $D(?, ?)$.

Find PQ.

8. $P(-3, 4)$, $Q(2, -7)$

9. $P(6, 0)$, $Q(-4, 1)$

10. Find the coordinates of the midpoint of $\overline{RS}$ for $R(3, -6)$, $S(-1, 4)$.

11. M is the midpoint of $\overline{AB}$. Find the coordinates of B for $M(4, 2)$ and $A(-1, 5)$.

*__12.__ For quadrilateral $ABCD$ with $A(-2, 5)$, $B(6, 5)$, $C(4, -1)$, and $D(-6, 1)$, M, N, P, and Q are midpoints of $\overline{AB}$, $\overline{BC}$, $\overline{CD}$, and $\overline{DA}$, respectively. Show that $MN = PQ$.

Find the slope of $\overleftrightarrow{CD}$ in each case. Then determine its position in a coordinate plane.

13. $C(-2, -4)$, $D(5, 3)$

14. $C(0, 6)$, $D(0, -3)$

15. Find b so that $\overleftrightarrow{PQ}$ will have slope -1 for $P(2, 3)$, $Q(-4, b)$.

Graph each equation.

16. $x + 3y = -9$

17. $5x - 2y = 8$

18. Draw a line with slope $\frac{1}{2}$ and passing through point $P(-3, 4)$. Then write an equation for the line.

19. Write an equation in Standard Form for the line through $P(-2, -1)$ and $Q(-4, 5)$.

Write an equation of each line with slope m and y-intercept b.

20. $m = 4$, $b = -2$

21. $m = -\frac{2}{3}$, $b = 1$

For each equation, identify the slope m and the y-intercept b. Then draw the graph of the equation.

22. $y = -3x + 2$

23. $y = x - 3$

24. Give the slope of a line parallel to $\overleftrightarrow{PQ}$ for $P(2, 1)$, $Q(-3, 4)$.

25. Give the slope of a line perpendicular to $\overleftrightarrow{RS}$ for $R(3, 7)$, $S(-4, 2)$.

*__26.__ Use coordinate geometry to prove that the opposite sides of a parallelogram have the same length.

27. Write an equation of the circle with center $A(-4, 1)$ and radius of length 2.

28. Find the coordinates of the center and the length of a radius of a circle with the equation $x^2 + y^2 - 10x + 2y = 39$.

Computer Activities

You can determine the shape of this geometric figure by using these relationships:

SLOPES EQUAL–LINES PARALLEL SLOPES NEGATIVE RECIPROCALS–LINES PERPENDICULAR

See the computer section on p. 560 for more information.

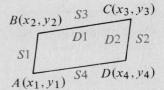

PROGRAM

```
10 PRINT "PROGRAM DETERMINES IF FIGURE IS A"
20 PRINT "PARALLELOGRAM, RECTANGLE OR SQUARE"
30 PRINT "ENTER X1, Y1, X2, Y2, X3, Y3, X4, Y4"
40 INPUT X1, Y1, X2, Y2, X3, Y3, X4, Y4
50 IF X2 = X1 THEN 90
60 IF X3 = X4 THEN 90
70 IF X3 = X2 THEN 90
80 IF X4 < > X1 THEN 110
90 PRINT "THE SLOPE IS UNDEFINED FOR LINES PARALLEL TO Y AXIS"
100 GO TO 270
110 LET S1 = {Y2 — Y1}/{X2 — X1}
120 LET S2 = {Y3 — Y4}/{X3 — X4}
130 IF S1 < > S2 THEN 260
140 LET S3 = {Y3 — Y2}/{X3 — X2}
150 LET S4 = {Y4 — Y1}/{X4 — X1}
160 IF S3 < > S4 THEN 260
170 PRINT "ABCD IS A PARALLELOGRAM"
180 IF {S2 * S4} < > —1 THEN 270
190 PRINT "ANGLE D IS A RIGHT ANGLE"
200 PRINT "ABCD IS A RECTANGLE"
210 LET D1 = SQR {{X3 — X2} ↑ 2 + {Y3 — Y2} ↑ 2}
220 LET D2 = SQR {{X3 — X4} ↑ 2 + {Y3 — Y4} ↑ 2}
230 IF D1 < > D2 THEN 270
240 PRINT "ABCD IS A SQUARE"
250 GO TO 270
260 PRINT "ABCD IS NOT A PARALLELOGRAM"
270 END
```

Exercises

Run this program for the following vertices. (Ex 1–2)

1. $A(-1, -2)$, $B(-3, 0)$, $C(1, 4)$, $D(3, 2)$

2. $A(-2, -4)$, $B(-2, 4)$, $C(2, 5)$, $D(1, 3)$

3. Write a program for the equation of a circle, given the center $(X2, Y2)$ and the length of radius R.

College Prep Test

Directions: Choose the one best answer to each question or problem.

1. A line segment has one end point at $(3, -2)$ and its midpoint at $(2, -5)$. What are the coordinates of the other endpoint?

   (A) $(1, -8)$ (B) $(5, -7)$ (C) $(1, -3)$
   (D) $(1, 8)$ (E) $(-1, 8)$

2. What is the length of a line segment joining the points whose coordinates are $(-2, -7)$ and $(6, 8)$?

   (A) 4 (B) 5 (C) $7\frac{1}{2}$ (D) $8\frac{1}{2}$ (E) 17

3. A circle whose center is the point $(-2, 6)$ is tangent to the x-axis. The coordinates of the point of tangency are

   (A) $(0, 6)$ (B) $(-2, 0)$ (C) $(0, -2)$
   (D) $(6, 0)$ (E) $(-2, -2)$

4. Which point lies at the greatest distance from the origin?

   (A) $(0, -9)$ (B) $(-2, 9)$ (C) $(-7, -6)$
   (D) $(8, 5)$ (E) $(0, 0)$

5. $\triangle AOB$ and $\triangle PCB$ are isosceles right triangles with equal area. What are the coordinates of point P?

   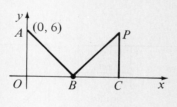

   (A) $(6, 0)$ (B) $(6, 12)$ (C) $(12, 0)$
   (D) $(0, 12)$ (E) $(12, 6)$

6. An equation of the line parallel to the x-axis and passing through point $(4, 2)$ is

   (A) $x = -4$ (B) $y = 2$ (C) $x = 2$
   (D) $x = 4$ (E) $y = 0$

7. The endpoints of the diameter of a circle are M and N. The coordinates of M and N are $(-1, 3)$ and $(5, 5)$. What are the coordinates of the center of the circle?

   (A) $(2, 4)$ (B) $(3, 4)$ (C) $(4, 8)$
   (D) $(4, 4)$ (E) $(0, 0)$

8. The coordinates of A are $(4, 0)$ and of C are $(15, 0)$. Find the area of $\triangle ABC$ if the equation of $\overleftrightarrow{AB}$ is $y = 2x - 8$.

   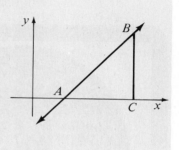

   (A) 100 (B) 121 (C) 144 (D) 169
   (E) 132

9. What is the equation of the line $\overleftrightarrow{AB}$

   (A) $y = \frac{3}{4}x + 3$

   (B) $y = \frac{3}{4}x - 4$

   (C) $y = \frac{4}{3}x + 3$

   (D) $y = -\frac{4}{3}x + 3$ (E) $y = -\frac{3}{4}x + 3$

10. The vertices of rectangle $ABCD$ are the points $A(0, 0)$, $B(8, 0)$, $C(8, k)$, $D(0, 5)$. The value of k is

    (A) 4 (B) 5 (C) 6 (D) 3 (E) 2

11. The area of a circle whose center is at $(0, 0)$ is 36π. This circle passes through all of the following points except

    (A) $(-6, 0)$ (B) $(0, 6)$ (C) $(6, 0)$
    (D) $(6, 6)$ (E) $(0, -6)$

14 GEOMETRIC LOCI

The Golden Spiral

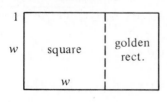

This half-shell of a chambered nautilus forms a golden spiral.

Spirals have been of great interest to mathematicians throughout the ages.

Descartes discovered the golden spiral. Archimedes wrote a book on spirals.

You can construct a golden spiral as follows.

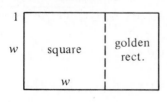 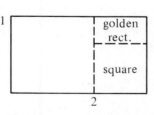 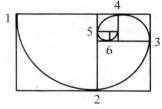

A. Start with a golden rectangle of length l and width w. Within the rectangle, construct a square with each side measuring w. The small rectangle formed is also a golden rectangle. Label the corner of the square 1, as shown.

B. Subdivide the new rectangle into a square and a golden rectangle. Label the corner of the square 2, as shown.

C. Continue subdividing golden rectangles into squares and smaller golden rectangles. Join the points labeled 1, 2, 3, 4, . . . with a smooth curve. The curve is a golden spiral.

14.1 Locus of Points

OBJECTIVE ► **To sketch and describe geometric figures that satisfy given conditions**

Recall that a geometric figure is a set of points. In this chapter you will be concerned with locating and describing sets of points which satisfy given conditions. You can assume that all points lie in the same plane, unless otherwise stated.

Example 1 Locate all points that are 3 cm from a given point Q. Then describe, as completely as possible, the figure formed.

Start with a given point Q.

Locate several points 3 cm from Q.

Draw a smooth dashed curve through the points.

The figure formed is a circle with center Q and a 3-cm radius.

In Example 1, the circle formed is called a **locus.**

Definition:
locus

A *locus* is a geometric figure containing all points, and only those points, that satisfy given conditions. [plural: loci (lō'sī)]

The word **locus** is a Latin word that means "place" or "location." There are several steps involved in determining a locus.

Summary

To determine a locus

1. Start with the given figure(s);

2. Locate several points that satisfy the given conditions;

3. Draw a smooth dashed curve through the points;

4. Describe the locus completely by naming the geometric figure formed and indicating its location.

Example 1 leads to the following postulate.

Postulate 27 The locus of points at a given distance d from a given point P is a circle with center P and the length of radius d.

It is possible to locate points that are a given distance from a given line.

Example 2 Sketch and describe the locus of points 2 cm from a given line l.

Start with a given line l.

Locate several points 2 cm from line l.

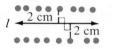

Draw dashed lines through the points.

The locus is a pair of lines each parallel to l and 2 cm from it.

The next postulate is based on Example 2.

Postulate 28 The locus of points a given distance d from a given line l is a pair of lines each parallel to l and at the distance d from l.

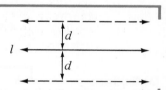

Example 3 presents a different situation from that of Postulate 27. In Example 3, you are given two parallel lines and asked to find the locus of all points that are the same distance from each of the lines.

Example 3 Sketch and describe the locus of points equidistant from two given parallel lines r and s.

Start with two given parallel lines, r and s.

Locate several points the same distance from r as from s.

Draw a dashed line through the points.

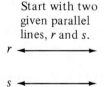

The locus is a line parallel to r and s and midway between them.

Example 3 suggests the next Postulate.

Postulate 29 The locus of points equidistant from two given parallel lines is a line parallel to each of the given lines and midway between them.

m

n

Written Exercises

Sketch and describe each locus.

 1. The locus of points equidistant from two given parallel lines that are 7 cm apart

2. The locus of points equidistant from points C and D that are 4 cm apart

3. The locus of points 8 mm from a given line

4. The locus of points 5 cm from a given point

5. The locus of points equidistant from two given points R and S

6. The locus of points 6 mm from a given line

7. The locus of points 2.5 cm from a given point G

8. The locus of points equidistant from the sides of a given angle

 9. The locus of points less than 2 cm from a given point

10. The locus of points less than or equal to 30 mm from a given point

11. The locus of points greater than 4 cm from a given point

12. The locus of points greater than or equal to 2.5 cm from a given point

The *locus of a moving point* is the set of all points traced by the point as it moves according to given conditions. **Sketch and describe each locus.**

 13. The locus of the center of a given circle that rolls along a given line and is always tangent to the line

14. The locus of the center of a circle that rolls between two parallel lines and is always tangent to both lines

15. The locus of the center of a given circle that rolls around the outside of a second given circle and is always tangent to it

16. The locus of the center of a given circle that rolls around the inside of a larger given circle and is always tangent to it

Cumulative Review

1. The area of a triangle is 52 cm². One side measures 13 cm. Find the length of the corresponding altitude.

2. The bases of a trapezoid measure 5 cm and 8 cm, respectively, and an altitude measures 10 cm. Find the area.

LOCUS OF POINTS

14.2 Locus Theorems

OBJECTIVES ►To state the postulate or theorem that applies to a locus
To state theorems about loci and identify what is to be proved

Consider two given points C and D. Observe the result when you sketch the locus of points equidistant from C and D.

Start with two given points C and D.

Locate several points the same distance from C as from D.

Draw a smooth dashed line through the points.

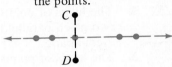

Conclusion: The locus is the perpendicular bisector of $\overline{CD}$.

It is possible to prove the conclusion stated above as a theorem. Recall that a locus of points consists of *all points* and *only those points* that satisfy the given conditions. Thus, there are two parts to a locus theorem that must be proved.

PART I Prove that every point on the locus satisfies the conditions.
PART II Prove that every point that satisfies the conditions lies on the locus.

The conclusion determined above is stated as Theorem 14.1.

Theorem 14.1 The locus of points equidistant from two given points is the perpendicular bisector of the segment joining the two points.

PART I
If a point lies on the perpendicular bisector of a segment, then it is equidistant from the endpoints of the segment.

Given:
P lies on the $\perp$ bisector of $\overline{AB}$.
Prove:
$PA = PB$

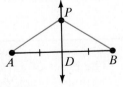

PART II
If a point is equidistant from the endpoints of a segment, then it lies on the perpendicular bisector of the segment.

Given:
$PA = PB$
Prove:
P lies on the $\perp$ bisector of $\overline{AB}$.

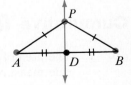

(See Exercise 15.)

Recall that in Exercise 8 on page 469, you found that the locus of points equidistant from the sides of an angle is the bisector of the angle. This conclusion is stated in Theorem 14.2.

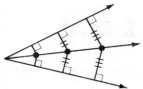

┌ **Theorem 14.2** The locus of points equidistant from the sides of an ┐
angle is the angle bisector.

PART I If a point is on the bisector of an angle, then it is equidistant from the sides of the angle.

Given: $\overrightarrow{BE}$ bisects $\angle ABC$, P is on $\overrightarrow{BE}$,
$\overrightarrow{PF} \perp \overrightarrow{BC}$, and $\overrightarrow{PG} \perp \overrightarrow{BA}$
Prove: $PF = PG$

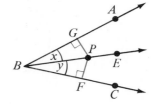

Proof

Statements	Reasons
1. $\overrightarrow{BE}$ bisects $\angle ABC$, $\overrightarrow{PF} \perp \overrightarrow{BC}$, $\overrightarrow{PG} \perp \overrightarrow{BA}$.	1. Given
2. $\angle PFB \cong \angle PGB$	2. $\perp$'s form $\cong$ rt. $\angle$'s.
3. $\angle x \cong \angle y$	3. Def. of $\angle$ bisector
4. $\overline{BP} \cong \overline{BP}$	4. Reflexive property
5. $\triangle PFB \cong \triangle PGB$	5. AAS
6. $\therefore PF = PG$	6. CPCTC

PART II If a point is equidistant from the sides of an angle, then it lies on the bisector of the angle.

Given: $\angle ABC$, with $\overrightarrow{PF} \perp \overrightarrow{BC}$, $\overrightarrow{PG} \perp \overrightarrow{BA}$, and
$PF = PG$
Prove: $\overrightarrow{BP}$ is the bisector of $\angle ABC$.
(P lies on $\overrightarrow{BP}$.)

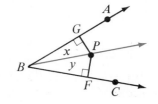

Proof

Statements	Reasons
1. $\angle ABC$, with $\overrightarrow{PF} \perp \overrightarrow{BC}$, $\overrightarrow{PG} \perp \overrightarrow{BA}$, $PF = PG$	1. Given
2. $\triangle PFB$ and $\triangle PGB$ are rt. $\triangle$'s.	2. Def. of $\perp$ and def. of rt. $\triangle$
3. $\overline{PF} \cong \overline{PG}$	3. Def. of $\cong$ segments
4. $\overline{BP} \cong \overline{BP}$	4. Reflexive property
5. $\triangle PFB \cong \triangle PGB$	5. HL for $\cong$ rt. $\triangle$'s
6. $\angle x \cong \angle y$	6. CPCTC
7. $\overrightarrow{BP}$ is the bisector of $\angle ABC$.	7. Def. of $\angle$ bisector

So far, three locus postulates and two locus theorems have been presented. The locus problem given in Example 2 is an application of one of the postulates.

Example 1 Sketch and describe the locus of the midpoints of all radii of a given circle. Then give the postulate that applies.

Start with a given circle *O*.

Locate the midpoints of several radii.

Draw a smooth dashed curve through the midpoints.

The locus is a circle concentric to the given circle and with a radius one half the length of the radius of the given circle. Since every point on the locus is the same distance from point *O*, the locus is an application of Postulate 27.

The locus problem given in the next example is an application of one of the locus theorems.

Example 2 Sketch and describe the locus of the centers of all circles that pass through two given points. Then give the theorem that applies.

Start with two given points *G* and *H*.

Draw several circles through *G* and *H*. Mark their centers.

Draw a smooth dashed line through the centers.

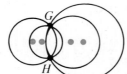
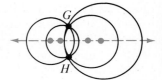

The locus is the perpendicular bisector of $\overline{GH}$. Since every point on the locus is equidistant from *G* and *H*, the locus is an application of Theorem 14.1.

Reading in Geometry

Explain the meaning of each phrase.

1. Equidistant from

2. At a given distance from

Match a figure name on the right with each description on the left.

3. The locus of points *equidistant from* two given parallel lines

4. The locus of points *at a given distance from* a given point

5. The locus of points *equidistant from* two given points

6. The locus of points *at a given distance from* a given line

a. circle

b. line

c. two parallel lines

Written Exercises

Sketch and describe each locus. Then give the postulate or theorem that applies.

1. The locus of the centers of all circles that are tangent to both sides of a given angle

2. The locus of the centers of all circles that are tangent to each of two parallel lines

3. The locus of the centers of all circles of the same size that are tangent to a given line

4. The locus of points equidistant from two intersecting lines

5. The locus of the midpoints of all chords parallel to a given chord of a circle

6. The locus of the midpoints of all chords of the same length in a given circle

7. The locus of points within a circle that are equidistant from the endpoints of a given chord

8. For all triangles with a given base and a given altitude, the locus of the vertices opposite that base

Sketch and describe each locus. Then write the locus statement as a theorem. Then write Part I and Part II of the theorem.

9. The locus of the midpoints of all radii of a given circle

10. The locus of points equidistant from two concentric circles

11. The locus of the centers of all circles tangent to a given line at a given point

12. The locus of the midpoints of all chords drawn from a given point of a circle

Prove each locus statement as a theorem.

13. The locus of the centers of all circles tangent to a given line at a given point is a line perpendicular to the given line at the given point.

14. The locus of the vertex of the right angle of a right triangle with a given hypotenuse is a circle with the hypotenuse as a diameter.

15. Prove Theorem 14.1.

LOCUS THEOREMS

A Challenge To You

The figures formed by a plane intersecting the surface of a cone are called *conic sections*.

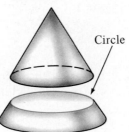

Circle

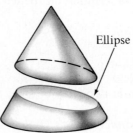

Ellipse

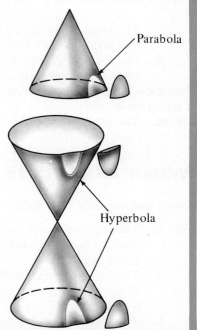

Parabola

Hyperbola

You have already seen that a circle can be interpreted as a locus of points. On page 482, you will see that each of the other three conic sections can also be defined as a locus.

Describe the way in which a cone is cut by a plane to form each of the following conic sections.
1. A circle   2. An ellipse
3. A parabola   4. A hyperbola

Algebra Review

OBJECTIVE ▶ To solve quadratic equations by factoring

Example   Solve. $6x^2 + x - 2 = 0$

Factor. ▶ $(3x + 2)(2x - 1) = 0$

Set each factor ▶ $3x + 2 = 0$ or $2x - 1 = 0$
equal to 0 and solve. $3x = -2$ $2x = 1$

$x = -\dfrac{2}{3}$ $x = \dfrac{1}{2}$ **Thus,** the solutions are $-\dfrac{2}{3}$ and $\dfrac{1}{2}$.

Solve.

1. $x^2 + 3x - 28 = 0$ 2. $x^2 + 5x + 6 = 0$ 3. $x^2 - 8x + 15 = 0$
4. $x^2 - 9x + 14 = 0$ 5. $x^2 + 10x + 25 = 0$ 6. $x^2 - 49 = 0$
7. $2x^2 - 11x + 5 = 0$ 8. $3x^2 + 8x - 3 = 0$ 9. $2x^2 + 3x - 9 = 0$
10. $x^2 = -5x + 24$ 11. $24 - 10x = -x^2$ 12. $x^2 + 35 = -12x$

14.3 Specific Conditions for Loci

OBJECTIVE ▶ **To sketch and describe loci determined by more than one specific condition**

The distance between two objects is generally defined to be the length of the shortest path between the objects. This is also true for the distance from a point to a circle.

Definition:
distance from a point to a circle

The **distance from point** P **to circle** O is measured along $\overleftrightarrow{PO}$ and is the length of the shortest segment joining P and circle O.

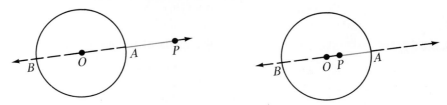

P in exterior of $\bigcirc O$. P in interior of $\bigcirc O$.

In each figure above, $\overline{PB}$ lies on $\overleftrightarrow{PO}$, but PA is the distance since $PA < PB$.

In each of the next three examples, you will find the locus of points at a given distance from a circle with a 6-cm radius. Notice that changing the given distance changes the resulting locus.

Example 1 Sketch and describe the locus of points 10 cm from a circle with a 8-cm radius.

1. Start with a circle with a 8-cm radius.
2. Locate several points 10 cm from the circle. The points lie in the exterior of the circle.
3. Draw a smooth dashed curve through the points.
4. Describe the locus:
   The locus is a circle concentric to the given circle and with a 18-cm radius.

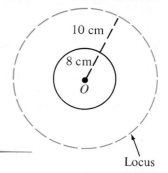

In Example 1, the given distance is greater than the length of a radius. In Examples 2 and 3, notice what happens when the given distance is equal to or less than the length of a radius.

Example 2 Sketch and describe the locus of points 8 cm from a circle with a 8-cm radius.

Follow steps similar to those in Example 1.

Note that the center is also 8 cm from the circle. ▶

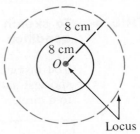

Locus

The locus is a circle concentric to the given circle and with a 16-cm radius, plus the center of the given circle.

Example 3 Sketch and describe the locus of points 5 cm from a circle with a 8-cm radius.

The points of the locus form an outer and an inner circle. ▶

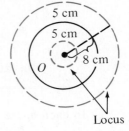

Locus

The locus is two circles concentric to the given circle, one with a 13-cm radius and one with a 3-cm radius.

In the next three examples, you will look for the intersection of two distinct loci.

Example 4 Sketch and describe the locus of points 6 cm from line *m* and 8 cm from point *P* on line *m*.

Use Post. 28 for the locus 6 cm from line m. ▶
Use Post. 27 for the locus 8 cm from point P. Look for the intersection of the parallel lines and the circle. ▶

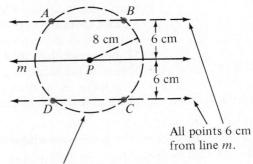

All points 6 cm from line *m*.

All points 8 cm from point *P*.

A, *B*, *C*, and *D* are the only points 6 cm from *m* and 8 cm from *P*. **Thus,** the locus is the set of points *A*, *B*, *C*, and *D*.

Example 5 Points *A* and *B* are 3 cm apart. Sketch and describe the locus of points 2 cm from *A* and 2 cm from *B*.

Use Post. 27 for each locus. ►
Look for the intersection of the two circles. ►

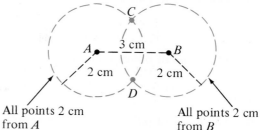

All points 2 cm from *A*

All points 2 cm from *B*

C and *D* are the only points 2 cm from *A* and 2 cm from *B*.
Thus, the locus is the set of points *C* and *D*.

Two loci may not intersect at all, as shown in the next example. In such a case, there are no points that meet all of the given conditions.

Example 6 Point *Q* is 4 cm below line *l*. Sketch and describe the locus of points 1 cm from *Q* and 2 cm from *l*.

Use Post. 27 and Post. 28. Sketch each locus. ►

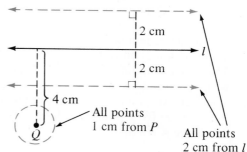

All points 1 cm from *P*

All points 2 cm from *l*

The circle and the parallel lines do not intersect.

Thus, there are no points in the locus.

Written Exercises

Sketch and describe each locus.

Ⓐ 1. The locus of points 6 cm from circle *Q*
   2. The locus of points 3 cm from circle *Q*
   3. The locus of points 1 cm from circle *Q*

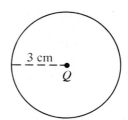

4. The locus of points 3 cm from A and 4 cm from B
5. The locus of points 1 cm from A and 5 cm from B
6. The locus of points 1.5 cm from A and 4 cm from B

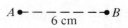

7. The locus of points equidistant from m and n and 2 cm from O

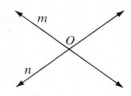

8. The locus of points equidistant from r and s and 3 cm from P

9. The locus of points equidistant from r and s and 4 cm from P

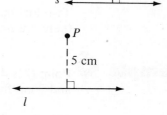

10. The locus of points 2 cm from l and 4 cm from P
11. The locus of points 2 cm from l and 3 cm from P

12. The locus of points 2 cm from l and 7 cm from P

13. The locus of points 2 cm from l and 9 cm from P

14. The locus of points 2 cm from l and 2 cm from P

B 15. The locus of points 5 cm from a circle with a 3-cm radius

16. The locus of points 6 cm from a circle with a 6-cm radius

17. The locus of points 3 m from a circle with a 7-m radius

18. The locus of points equidistant from two concentric circles

19. The locus of points 3 cm from point A and 2 cm from point B, where A and B are 4 cm apart

20. Repeat Exercise 19 but with A and B 5 cm apart.

C 21. The locus of points equidistant from intersecting lines r and s, and 3 cm from line l which is 2 cm above r

22. The locus of points equidistant from lines m and n and 8 cm from point P, where P is 3 cm above m, $m \parallel n$, and m is 6 cm above n

23. Repeat Exercise 22, but with P 5 cm above m.

24. Repeat Exercise 22, but with P 6 cm above m.

Cumulative Review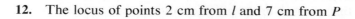

1. Each side of an equilateral triangle is 16 cm long. Find the length of an apothem of the triangle.

2. An apothem of a square is 7 m long. Find the area of the square.

14·4 General Conditions for Loci

OBJECTIVE ▶ **To sketch and describe loci determined by two or more general conditions**

In the preceding lesson, you found loci determined by very specific conditions. This lesson deals with more general conditions. In Example 1, you will examine all possible cases of the locus of points at a given distance from a given circle.

Example 1 Sketch and describe the locus of points at a given distance d from a given circle with a radius of length r.

There are three possible cases, depending upon the relationship between d and r.

Case I: $d > r$

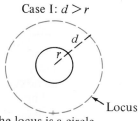

The locus is a circle concentric to the given circle with radius of length $r + d$.

Case II: $d = r$

The locus is a circle concentric to the given circle with radius of length $2r$, plus the center of the given circle.

Case III: $d < r$

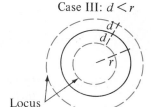

The locus is two circles concentric to the given circle and with radii of lengths $r + d$ and $r - d$, respectively.

Example 2 Sketch and describe the locus of points p cm from line m and q cm from point R on line m.

Case I: $p < q$

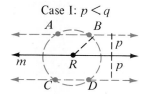

The locus is the set of points A, B, C, and D.

Case II: $p = q$

The locus is the set of points E and F.

Case III: $p > q$

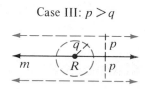

There are no points in the locus.

In Example 2, you found the locus of points at a given distance from a given line and at a given distance from a point on the line. The results varied according to the relationship between the two given distances. The next example also produces three different results depending upon given distances.

Example 3 Points P and Q are d meters apart. Sketch and describe the locus of points r meters from P and s meters from Q.

Case I: $r + s > d$	Case II: $r + s = d$	Case III: $r + s < d$
		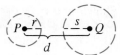
The locus is the set of points A and B.	The locus is the point C.	There are no points in the locus

In Example 3, points P and Q are given to be d meters apart. In the next example, three given points are not restricted in their relative positions. The result is a "free-floating" locus problem.

Example 4 Sketch and describe the locus of points equidistant from two given points and at a given distance from a third given point.

Let A and B be the two given points and P be the third point. Apply Theorem 14.1 and Postulate 26. Then look for all possible intersections of the two loci.

Case I: The circle and the perpendicular bisector intersect in 2 points.	Case II: The circle and the perpendicular bisector intersect in 1 point.	Case III: The circle and the perpendicular bisector do not intersect.
		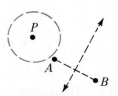
The locus is the set of points C and D.	The locus is the point E.	There are no points in the locus.

Oral **Exercises**

Give all possible intersections of the following figures.

1. Two lines
2. A line and a pair of parallel lines
3. A circle and a pair of parallel lines
4. A ray and a circle
5. Two circles with different radii
6. Two circles with the same radii
7. A line and a pair of concentric circles
8. A line and a pair of intersecting lines

Written **Exercises**

Sketch and describe each locus. Show all possible cases.

 1. The locus of points equidistant from intersecting lines r and s and y units from line r

2. The locus of points equidistant from the sides of $\angle A$ and d cm from point A

3. The locus of points equidistant from two parallel lines m and n and d meters from point A on line m, where m and n are f meters apart

4. The locus of points equidistant from intersecting lines p and q and x units from A, the point of intersection of p and q

5. The locus of points r meters from point A and r meters from point B, where A and B are d meters apart

6. The locus of points equidistant from points A and B and h cm from point A, where A and B are d cm apart

 7. The locus of points at a given distance from a given point and equidistant from the sides of a given angle

8. The locus of points equidistant from two given points and equidistant from two given parallel lines

9. The locus of points equidistant from two given concentric circles and at a given distance from each of two given parallel lines

10. The locus of points at a given distance d_1 from a given point and at a given distance d_2 from a second given point, where $d_1 \neq d_2$

11. The locus of points equidistant from a pair of intersecting lines and at a given distance from a given point

12. The locus of points equidistant from two given parallel lines and at a given distance from another given line

13. The locus of points equidistant from the sides of a given angle and equidistant from two given parallel lines

14. The locus of points equidistant from a pair of intersecting lines and at a given distance from a given line

 15. The locus of points equidistant from the sides of a given triangle [*Hint:* Take the sides two at a time.]

16. The locus of points equidistant from three given points [*Hint:* Take the points two at a time.]

17. The locus of points at the distance of a radius from a given circle and equidistant from two given points

18. The locus of points at a given distance from a given circle and equidistant from two given lines that intersect at the center of the given circle

GENERAL CONDITIONS FOR LOCI

A Challenge To You

Recall that a circle, an ellipse, a parabola, and a hyperbola are called *conic sections*. (See page 474.) A circle is the locus of points at a given distance from a given point. Each of the other conic sections is defined as a locus below.

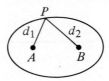

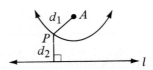

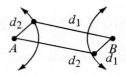

An *ellipse* is the locus of points the sum of whose distances from two given points is a constant. $(d_1 + d_2 = \text{constant})$

A *parabola* is the locus of points equidistant from a given point and a given line. $(d_1 = d_2)$

A *hyperbola* is the locus of points the difference of whose distances from two given points is a constant. $(|d_1 - d_2| = \text{constant})$

A circle can be constructed using a compass. You can also locate any number of points of a parabola or hyperbola by using a compass and straightedge. However, to draw an ellipse you will need a piece of string.
1. Use a compass and straightedge to construct seven points of a parabola and eight points for each branch of a hyperbola.
2. Use a piece of string to draw an ellipse.

Algebra Review

OBJECTIVE ► **To solve quadratic equations by the quadratic formula**

Example   Solve $2x^2 + 5x - 2 = 0$ by the quadratic formula.

Quadratic formula ► $x = \dfrac{-b \pm \sqrt{b^2 - 4ac}}{2a}$ $a = 2$ $b = 5$ $c = -2$

$$x = \frac{-5 \pm \sqrt{5^2 - 4(2)(-2)}}{2(2)} = \frac{-5 \pm \sqrt{25 + 16}}{4} = \frac{-5 \pm \sqrt{41}}{4}$$

Solve each equation by the quadratic formula.

1. $x^2 + 2x - 3 = 0$
2. $x^2 + x - 6 = 0$
3. $x^2 - 12x - 13 = 0$
4. $2x^2 - 11x + 12 = 0$
5. $3x^2 + 5x - 2 = 0$
6. $5x^2 - 3x - 2 = 0$
7. $x^2 - 6x - 10 = 0$
8. $2x^2 + 5x - 6 = 0$
9. $3x^2 - 7x = -3$
10. $-3x^2 = 4x - 2$
11. $6 - x = 5x^2$
12. $2x - 3x^2 = -5$

14.5 Concurrent Bisectors in a Triangle

OBJECTIVE ► **To prove and apply concurrence theorems about perpendicular bisectors in a triangle**

Three or more lines are **concurrent** if they pass through the same point.

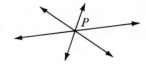

Suppose you were to construct the perpendicular bisectors of all three sides of a triangle. Each perpendicular bisector is the locus of points equidistant from two of the vertices of the triangle. You would find that the three loci appear to be concurrent, as shown in the figures below. This result leads to theorem 14.3.

Acute triangle   Right triangle   Obtuse triangle

Theorem 14.3   The perpendicular bisectors of the sides of a triangle are concurrent at a point that is equidistant from the vertices of the triangle.

Given: $\triangle ABC$ with l, m, and n the $\perp$ bisectors of $\overline{AB}$, $\overline{AC}$, and $\overline{BC}$, respectively

Prove: l, m, and n are concurrent at a point equidistant from A, B, and C.

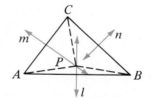

Analysis:
Let P be the point where two of the $\perp$ bisectors intersect. Show that the third $\perp$ bisector passes through P.

Proof

Statements	Reasons
1. $\triangle ABC$, with l, m, n the $\perp$ bisectors of $\overline{AB}$, $\overline{AC}$, and $\overline{BC}$, respectively	1. Given
2. l and m intersect at some point P.	2. $l \parallel m$ or $l \not\parallel m$; l cannot be $\parallel m$ by Th. 3.2.
3. $PB = PA$ and $PA = PC$	3. A point on the $\perp$ bisector of a segment is equidistant from its endpoints.
4. $PB = PC$	4. Transitive property
5. P lies on n.	5. A point equidistant from the endpoints of a segment lies on its $\perp$ bisector.
6. $\therefore$ l, m, and n are concurrent at a point equidistant from A, B, and C.	6. Steps 1–5 and def. of concurrent lines

The construction in Example 1 is an important application of Theorem 14.3.

Example 1 Circumscribe a circle about △ABC.

Strategy: Construct the perpendicular bisectors of two of the sides. The point
where they intersect is the center of the circumscribed circle.

Start with △ABC.

Construct the ⊥ bisectors of $\overline{AB}$ and of $\overline{AC}$. Let P be the point where they intersect.

With PA as a radius length, draw circle P.

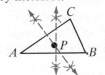

Conclusion; ⊙P is the circumscribed circle.

Now suppose you were to construct the bisectors of the three angles of a triangle.
As shown below, whether the triangle is acute, right, or obtuse, the angle bisectors
appear to be concurrent. This leads to Theorem 14.4.

Acute triangle

Right triangle

Obtuse triangle

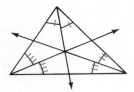

Theorem 14.4 The bisectors of the angles of a triangle are concurrent at a
point which is equidistant from the sides of the triangle.

Given: △ABC with rays r, s,
and t bisecting ∠B,
∠A, and ∠C, respectively
Prove: r, s, and t are concurrent
at a point equidistant
from $\overline{AB}$, $\overline{AC}$, and $\overline{BC}$

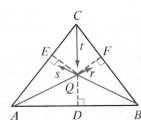

Analysis:
Let Q be the point where
two of the angle bisectors
intersect. Show that the
third bisector passes through
Q. Use Th. 14.2.

(See Exercise 15.)

Theorem 14.4 is applied in the construction in the next example.

Example 2 Inscribe a circle in △ABC.

Strategy: Bisect two angles of the triangle. The point where the bisectors intersect is the center of the inscribed circle.

Start with △ABC. Bisect ∠A and ∠B. Let Q be the point where the bisectors intersect.

Construct a perpendicular $\overline{QR}$ from Q to $\overline{AB}$.

With QR as a radius length, draw circle Q.

 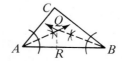 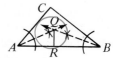

Conclusion: ⊙O is the inscribed circle.

Notice that in Examples 1 and 2, only two bisectors are constructed. In each case, since the bisectors are concurrent, it is not necessary to construct the third bisector.

From Examples 1 and 2, you can conclude that a circle can be circumscribed about any triangle. Also, a circle can be inscribed in any triangle. This leads to the following definitions.

Definitions:
circumcircle
and
circumcenter

The *circumcircle* of a triangle is the circle that is circumscribed about the triangle. The *circumcenter* of a triangle is the center of the circumcircle.

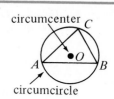

Definitions:
incircle and
incenter

The *incircle* of a triangle is the circle that is inscribed in the triangle. The *incenter* of a triangle is the center of the incircle.

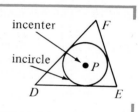

CONCURRENT BISECTORS IN A TRIANGLE

Written Exercises

1. Draw a right triangle *RST*. Construct the perpendicular bisector of each side. Label the point of intersection *P*.

2. Draw an acute triangle *PQR*. Construct the bisector of each angle. Label the point of intersection *S*.

3. Draw an obtuse triangle *EFG*. Inscribe a circle in triangle *EFG*. Label the incenter *I*.

4. Draw an acute triangle *ABC*. Circumscribe a circle about triangle *ABC*. Label the circumcenter *C*.

5. Draw a right triangle. Construct a circle that passes through all three vertices.

6. Draw a triangle *PQR*. Construct a circle tangent to all three sides.

7. Construct an equilateral triangle. Construct the incenter and the circumcenter. What appears to be true of the two centers?

8. Construct an isosceles triangle. Construct the incenter and the circumcenter. Where do the two centers appear to lie?

9. Trace a circle by drawing around a fifty-cent piece or similar object. Locate the center of the circle by construction. [*Hint:* Select three points on the circle.]

10. Consider an acute, a right, and an obtuse triangle. For each triangle, tell whether the circumcenter lies in the interior, on, or in the exterior of the triangle.

11. Repeat Exercise 10, but for the incenter instead of the circumcenter.

12. Given three noncollinear points, where is the point in their plane equidistant from all three?

13. Sketch and describe the locus of points equidistant from the three sides of a triangle.

14. Sketch and describe the locus of points equidistant from three noncollinear points.

15. Supply a reason for each step 3–6 in this proof of Theorem 14.4.

Statements	Reasons
1. Rays *r*, *s*, and *t* bisect $\angle B$, $\angle A$, and $\angle C$, respectively.	1. Given
2. Let *Q* be the point where *r* and *s* intersect.	2. $r \parallel s$ or $r \nparallel s$; *r* cannot be $\parallel$ *s* by Th. 3.2.
3. Draw $\overline{QD} \perp \overline{AB}$, $\overline{QE} \perp \overline{AC}$, $\overline{QF} \perp \overline{BC}$.	3.
4. $QE = QD$, $QD = QF$	4.
5. $QE = QF$	5.
6. *Q* lies on *t*.	6.
7. *r*, *s*, and *t* are concurrent at a point equidistant from $\overline{AB}$, $\overline{AC}$, and $\overline{BC}$.	7. Steps 1–6 and def. of concurrent lines

ABCD is any convex *quadrilateral*. (Ex. 16–18)

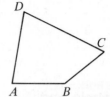

16. Explain how to locate a point equidistant from $\overleftrightarrow{AB}$ and $\overleftrightarrow{AD}$ and also equidistant from *D* and *C*

17. Explain how to locate a point equidistant from $\overleftrightarrow{AB}$, $\overleftrightarrow{AD}$, and $\overleftrightarrow{DC}$.

18. Do the points of Exercises 16 and 17 necessarily coincide?

19. For an equilateral triangle, what is the ratio of the length of the radius of the incircle to the length of the radius of the circumcircle, $\frac{x}{y}$?

20. For an equilateral triangle, what is the ratio of the area of the incircle to the area of the circumcircle? Justify your answer.

21. A side of an equilateral triangle measures 24 cm. Find the area of the incircle and the area of the circumcircle.

14.6 Concurrent Altitudes and Medians

OBJECTIVE ► **To prove and apply concurrence theorems about altitudes and medians of a triangle**

In the preceding lesson, you found that in a triangle the perpendicular bisectors of the sides are concurrent and the angle bisectors are concurrent. In the figure below, observe that the three altitudes of a triangle appear to be concurrent. This leads to Theorem 14.5.

Acute triangle   Right triangle   Obtuse triangle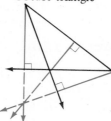

Theorem 14.5 The lines containing the altitudes of a triangle are concurrent.

Given: $\triangle ABC$ with altitudes $\overleftrightarrow{AD}$, $\overleftrightarrow{BE}$, and $\overleftrightarrow{CF}$

Prove: $\overleftrightarrow{AD}$, $\overleftrightarrow{BE}$, and $\overleftrightarrow{CF}$ are concurrent.

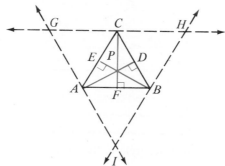

Analysis:
Form another $\triangle$ and show that the given altitudes are the $\perp$ bisectors of its sides and are therefore concurrent by Th. 14.3.

Proof

Statements	Reasons
1. $\triangle ABC$ with altitudes $\overline{AD}$, $\overline{BE}$, and $\overline{CF}$	1. Given
2. Through C draw $\overleftrightarrow{GH} \parallel \overline{AB}$; through B draw $\overleftrightarrow{HI} \parallel \overline{AC}$; through A draw $\overleftrightarrow{GI} \parallel \overline{BC}$.	2. Parallel postulate.
3. $ABCG$ and $ABHC$ are $\square$'s.	3. Def. of $\square$
4. $\overline{GC} \cong \overline{AB}$ and $\overline{AB} \cong \overline{CH}$	4. Opp. sides of a $\square$ are $\cong$.
5. $\overline{GC} \cong \overline{CH}$	5. Transitive property
6. $\overline{CF} \perp \overline{AB}$	6. Def. of altitude
7. $\overline{CF} \perp \overline{GH}$	7. If a line is $\perp$ to one of two $\parallel$ lines, it is $\perp$ to the other.
8. $\overleftrightarrow{CF}$ is the $\perp$ bisector of $\overline{GH}$.	8. Def. of $\perp$ bisector
9. Similarly, $\overleftrightarrow{AD}$ is the $\perp$ bisector of $\overline{GI}$; $\overleftrightarrow{BE}$ is the $\perp$ bisector of $\overline{HI}$.	9. Steps 3–8
10. $\overleftrightarrow{AD}$, $\overleftrightarrow{BE}$, and $\overleftrightarrow{CF}$ are concurrent	10. The $\perp$ bisectors of the sides of a $\triangle$ are concurrent.

CONCURRENT ALTITUDES AND MEDIANS

The *orthocenter* of a triangle is the point at which the altitudes of the triangle are concurrent

From the figures below, it also appears that the three medians of a triangle are concurrent. This is stated in Theorem 14.6.

Acute triangle

Right triangle

Obtuse triangle

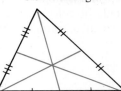 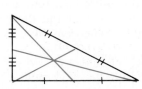 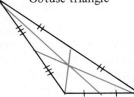

Theorem 14.6 The medians of a triangle are concurrent at a point which is two thirds of the distance from each vertex to the midpoint of the opposite side.

Given: $\triangle ABC$ with medians $\overline{AD}$, $\overline{BE}$, and $\overline{CF}$

Prove: $\overline{AD}$, $\overline{BE}$, and $\overline{CF}$ are concurrent at point O.

$AO = \frac{2}{3}(AD)$;

$BO = \frac{2}{3}(BE)$;

$CO = \frac{2}{3}(CF)$

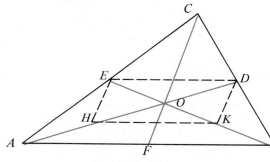

(See Exercise 19.)

Analysis:
Let H be the midpoint of $\overline{AO}$ and K be the midpoint of $\overline{BO}$. Show that $HKDE$ is a $\square$. Then use Th. 7.2.

The *centroid* of a triangle is the point at which the medians are concurrent.

Theorem 14.6 is applied in Example 1 which follows. Point S is the centroid of the triangle.

Example 1 In $\triangle PQR$, medians $\overline{QU}$ and $\overline{PT}$ intersect at S. If $PT = 3x$ and $PS = 8x - 12$, find PT, PS, and ST.

$$PS = \frac{2}{3}(PT) \text{ by Th. 14.6}$$

$$8x - 12 = \frac{2}{3} \cdot 3x$$

$$8x - 12 = 2x$$
$$6x = 12$$
$$x = 2$$

Thus, $PT = 3 \cdot 2 = 6$
$PS = 8 \cdot 2 - 12 = 4$
$ST = 6 - 4 = 2.$

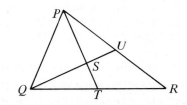

Reading in Geometry

Ortho comes from the Greek word *orthos* meaning *straight* or *right*.

1. Explain why *orthocenter* is an appropriate name for the point at which the altitudes of a triangle are concurrent.

Give the meaning of each word. Use a dictionary, if necessary.

2. orthodontist   3. orthogonal   4. orthorhombic   5. orthognathous

The centroid of a triangle is the center of gravity of the triangle. A triangular shaped board or piece of cardboard will balance at its centroid. The suffix *oid* comes from the Greek language and means like or in the form of.

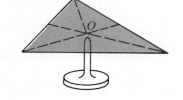

6. Explain why *centroid* is an appropriate name for the point at which the medians of a triangle are concurrent.

Give the meaning of each word. Use a dictionary, if necessary.

7. spheroid   8. colloid   9. centric   10. centrifugal

Written Exercises

1. Draw a right triangle. Construct the median to each side. Label the centroid P.

2. Draw an obtuse triangle. Construct the altitude to each side. Label the orthocenter Q.

3. Construct an isosceles triangle. Construct the centroid and the orthocenter. Where do the two centers appear to lie?

4. Construct an equilateral triangle. Construct the centroid. What is true of the centroid, the orthocenter, the incenter, and the circumcenter?

5. Consider an acute, a right, and an obtuse triangle. Tell whether the orthocenter lies in the interior, on, or in the exterior of each triangle.

6. Repeat Exercise 5, but for the centroid instead of the orthocenter.

Consider $\triangle ABC$ with medians $\overline{AD}$, $\overline{BE}$, and $\overline{CF}$ concurrent at centroid P.

7. If $AD = 18$, find AP.
8. If $CF = 21$, find PF.
9. If $PD = 5$, find PA.
10. If $PE = 12$, find BE.
11. If $CP = 11$, find CF.
12. If $AP = 11$, find PD.
13. If $BP = 4x$ and $BE = 9x - 6$, find BP and BE.
14. If $PF = 3x$ and $PC = 7x - 5$, find PF and PC.
15. If $PD = 2x + 6$ and $AD = 10x$, find PD and AD.

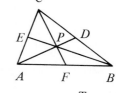

Consider $\triangle RST$ with median $\overline{TM}$, centroid Q, and altitude $\overline{TA}$.

16. If $TA = 15$ and $AM = 8$, find QM.
17. If $TQ = 10$ and $TA = 12$, find AM.
18. If $QM = 2$ and $AM = 3$, find TA.

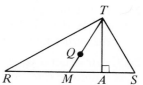

CONCURRENT ALTITUDES AND MEDIANS

B **19.** Supply the missing reasons in the proof of Theorem 14.6 below.

Statements

1. $\triangle ABC$ has medians $\overline{AD}$, $\overline{BE}$, and $\overline{CF}$.
2. $\overline{AD}$ and $\overline{BE}$ meet in a point O.
3. Let H be the midpoint of $\overline{AO}$; let K be the midpoint of $\overline{BO}$.
4. Draw $\overline{HK}$, $\overline{KD}$, $\overline{DE}$, and $\overline{EH}$.
5. In $\triangle ABC$, $\overline{ED} \parallel \overline{AB}$ and $ED = \frac{1}{2}(AB)$.
6. In $\triangle AOB$, $\overline{HK} \parallel \overline{AB}$ and $HK = \frac{1}{2}(AB)$.
7. $\overline{ED} \parallel \overline{HK}$ and $ED = HK$.
8. $HKDE$ is a $\square$.
9. $HO = OD$ and $KO = OE$.
10. $AH = HO$ and $KO = BK$.
11. $AH = HO = OD$ and $BK = KO = OE$
12. $AO = \frac{2}{3}(AD)$; $BO = \frac{2}{3}(BE)$
13. $\overline{AD}$ and $\overline{CF}$ meet in a point P. Let J be the midpoint of $\overline{CP}$. Draw $\square JHFD$. Then $AP = \frac{2}{3}(AD)$; $CP = \frac{2}{3}(CF)$.
14. P is the only point on $\overline{AD}$ such that $AP = \frac{2}{3}(AD)$. So, $O = P$, and $\overline{AD}$, $\overline{BE}$, and $\overline{CF}$ are concurrent.
15. $\therefore CO = \frac{2}{3}(CF)$

Reasons

1.
2. $\overline{AD} \not\parallel \overline{BE}$ by Th. 3.2.
3.
4.
5.
6.
7.
8.
9.
10.
11.
12. Step 11
13. Steps 1–12
14. On a given number line, no two points have the same coordinate. Def. of distance
15. Substitution

20. An isosceles triangle has sides measuring 18 cm, 15 cm, and 15 cm. How far above the base is the centroid?

21. Each side of an equilateral triangle measures 10 mm. Find the lengths of the radius of the incircle and the circumcircle.

C **22.** Given: $\triangle ABC$ with median $\overline{CD}$
Prove: Area $\triangle ADC$ = area $\triangle BDC$

23. Given: $\triangle ABC$ with median $\overline{CD}$, centroid P, and altitudes $\overline{CE}$ and $\overline{PF}$
Prove: $\dfrac{PF}{CE} = \dfrac{1}{3}$, or $PF = \dfrac{1}{3}(CE)$

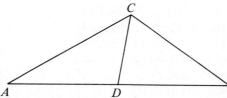

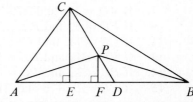

24. Prove that the medians of a triangle divide the triangle into six triangles that are equal in area.

25. Explain why it is logical that the centroid of a triangle is its center of gravity.

26. Construct a triangle given the length of one side and the lengths of the medians to the other two sides.

27. Construct a triangle given the lengths of two sides and the length of the median to the third side.

14.7 Loci in Space

OBJECTIVE ▶ To sketch and describe loci in space

So far the loci that you have studied have involved only coplanar points. In this lesson, you will not be restricted to a single plane. You will be locating points in space and determining loci that are three-dimensional figures.

Recall that the locus of points in a plane at a given distance from a given point is a circle. In Example 1, you will use the same conditions, but you will consider points in space.

Example 1 Sketch and describe the locus of points in space at a given distance d from a given point P.

Start with a
given point P.

Locate several points at a
distance d from point P.

Sketch the figure formed
by all such points.

• P

The locus is a sphere with center P and radius of length d.

Example 2 Sketch and describe the locus of points in space equidistant from two parallel planes.

Start with two
given parallel planes.

Locate several points the same
distance from each plane.

Sketch the figure formed
by all such points

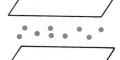

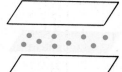

The locus is a plane parallel to each of the given planes and midway between them.

Note that Example 2 is the three-dimensional counterpart of Postulate 29.

LOCI IN SPACE

Example 3 Sketch and describe the locus of points in space equidistant from two given points.

Start with two
given points *A* and *B*.

Locate points the same
distance from *A* as from *B*.

Sketch the figure formed
by all such points.

The locus is a plane that is the perpendicular bisector of $\overline{AB}$.

Note that Example 3 is the three-dimensional counterpart of Theorem 14.1.

Written Exercises

Sketch and describe each locus of points in space.

1. The locus of points in space 5 cm from a given point *Q*

2. The locus of points in space equidistant from two given points *R* and *S*

3. The locus of points equidistant from two given parallel planes *r* and *s* which are 2 m apart

4. The locus of points in space 4 cm from a given line *l*

5. The locus of points in space 3 m from a given plane

6. The locus of points equidistant from the faces of a dihedral angle

7. The locus of points in space equidistant from two given parallel lines

8. The locus of points in space equidistant from the vertices of a given triangle

9. The locus of points in space equidistant from the sides of a given triangle

10. The locus of points in space equidistant from all the points of a given circle

Sketch and describe each locus of points in space.

11. The locus of points in space less than 5 cm from a given point *P*

12. The locus of points in space less than 3 m from a given line *l*

13. The locus of the centers of all circles tangent to a given line *l* at a given point *Q* on *l*

14. The locus of the centers of all circles with a given radius *r* and that pass through a given point *S*

Sketch and describe each locus of points in space.

15. The locus of points in space 2 cm from a given segment $\overline{AB}$

16. The locus of points in space 3 cm from point *A* and 4 cm from point *B*, where *A* and *B* are 5 cm apart

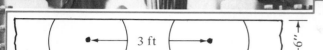

1. In wiring an office, an electrician has been asked to keep intercom wires at least 12 in away from any 120-v electric wires. There are two 120-v wires in the wall where the intercom wires are to be placed. Sketch the wall to show where the intercom wires can be placed.

2. A family is planning to build a house. The city building code states that no part of the house can be closer than 30 ft to the street and 10 ft from all property lines. There is a large tree in the back yard that they do not want to cut down. They must build at least 10 ft away from the trunk of the tree. Draw a plot map of the lot to show where the house can be built.

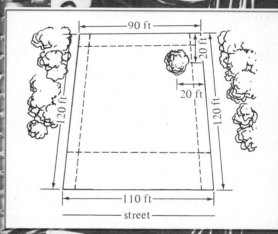

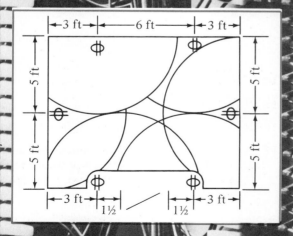

3. In a room, electric outlets are spaced as shown on the left. A lamp has a cord that is 5 ft long. If the lamp should not be closer than 2 ft to the door, sketch the room showing all possible locations of the lamp.

Chapter Fourteen Review

Sketch and describe each locus.

1. The locus of points 1 cm from a given point A [14.1]

2. The locus of points equidistant from the sides of a 30° angle   [14.2]

3. The locus of points less than 2 cm from a given line   [14.3]

4. The locus of points equidistant from two intersecting lines

5. The locus of the centers of all circles tangent to a given line at a given point

6. The locus of points 7 cm from P and 2 cm from Q

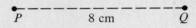

7. The locus of points 4 cm from l and 2 cm from A

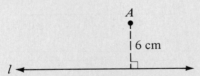

8. The locus of points 3 cm from a circle with a 4-cm radius   [14.4]

Sketch and describe each locus. Show all possible cases. (Ex. 9–10)

∗9. The locus of points x cm from point P and y cm from point Q, where P and Q are d cm apart

∗10. The locus of points equidistant from two given concentric circles and at a given distance from a given line

11. Copy $\triangle ABC$. Locate the incenter of the triangle.   [14.5]

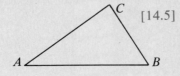

Vocabulary

locus [14.1]
distance from a point to a circle [14.3]
concurrent lines [14.5]
circumcircle [14.5]
circumcenter [14.5]
incircle [14.5]
incenter [14.5]
orthocenter [14.6]
centroid [14.6]

12. Copy $\triangle RST$. Circumscribe a circle about the triangle.   [14.5]

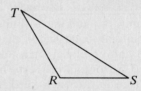

13. Construct a right triangle. Locate the centroid of the triangle.

In $\triangle PQR$, $\overline{PA}$, $\overline{QB}$, and $\overline{RC}$ are medians. Find each indicated measure. (Ex. 14–16)

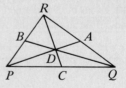

14. If $PA = 18$, find DP.

15. If $DB = 8$, find BQ.

16. If $DC = 2x$ and $DR = 3x + 5$, find RC.

17. An isosceles triangle has sides measuring 10 cm, 10 cm, and 16 cm. How far above the base is the centroid?

494   **CHAPTER FOURTEEN REVIEW**

Chapter Fourteen Test

Sketch and describe each locus.

1. The locus of points equidistant from two given points

2. The locus of points 2 cm from a given line

3. The locus of points less than 3 cm from a given point

4. The locus of the centers of all circles tangent to both sides of a given angle

5. The locus of points equidistant from l and m and 2 cm from A

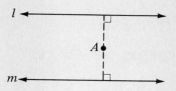

6. The locus of points 4 cm from circle Q

Sketch and describe each locus. Show all possible cases.

*7. The locus of points equidistant from intersecting lines t and u and x units from P, the point of intersection of t and u

*8. The locus of points equidistant from two parallel lines and at a given distance from a given point

Construct.

9. Copy $\triangle XYZ$. Locate the orthocenter of the triangle

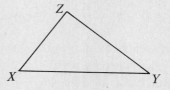

10. Copy $\triangle EFG$. Inscribe a circle in the triangle.

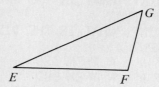

In $\triangle XYZ$, $\overline{XA}$, $\overline{YB}$, and $\overline{ZC}$ are medians. Find each indicated measure.

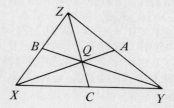

11. If $ZC = 24$, find ZQ.

12. If $BQ = x$ and $QY = 4x - 27$, find BY.

13. Each side of an equilateral triangle measures 12 cm. Find the lengths of a radius of the incircle and a radius of the circumcircle.

Computer Activities

To find the locus of points at a distance D from a circle with radius R, you must consider the following possibilities:

If $D > R$, the radius of the concentric circle is $R + D$

If $D = R$, the radius of the concentric circle is $2 * R$

If $D < R$, the radii of the concentric circles are $R - D$ and $R + D$

See the Computer Section on p. 560 for more information.

PROGRAM

```
10 PRINT "PROGRAM FINDS THE CIRCUMFERENCE OF THE LOCUS OF POINTS"
20 PRINT "AT A GIVEN DISTANCE FROM A CIRCLE"
30 FOR I = 1 TO 3
40 PRINT "WHAT IS THE RADIUS OF THE CIRCLE?"
50 INPUT R
60 PRINT "WHAT IS THE DISTANCE OF THE LOCUS FROM THE CIRCLE?"
70 INPUT D
80 IF D > R THEN 130
90 IF D < R THEN 160
100 LET C2 = 2 * 3.14159 * 2 * R
110 PRINT "RADIUS = 2 * R ="; 2 * R, "CIRCUMFERENCE ="; C2
120 GO TO 200
130 LET C1 = 2 * 3.14159 * {R + D}
140 PRINT "RADIUS = R + D ="; R + D, "CIRCUMFERENCE ="; C1
150 GO TO 200
160 LET C3 = 2 * 3.14159 * {R - D}
170 PRINT "RADIUS = R - D ="; R - D, "CIRCUMFERENCE ="; C3
180 LET C4 = 2 * 3.14159 * {R + D}
190 PRINT "RADIUS = R + D ="; R + D, "CIRCUMFERENCE ="; C4
200 NEXT I
210 END
```

Exercises

Run the program above for the following values. (Ex 1–3)

1. $R = 7$, $D = 3$ 　　　　**2.** $R = 4$, $D = 4$ 　　　　**3.** $R = 5$, $D = 8$

4. Alter the program above to find the area of the locus of points at a given distance from a circle.

College Prep Test

Directions: Choose the one best answer to each question or problem.

1. The locus of points 2 inches from a given line and 3 inches from a point on that line is exactly

   (A) 1 point (B) 2 points (C) 3 points
   (D) 4 points (E) 5 points

2. Which of the following is the equation of the locus of points whose ordinates are equal to −5?

   (A) $x = 5$ (B) $x = -5$ (C) $y = -5$
   (D) $y = 5$ (E) $y = \pm 5$

3. The locus of points in a plane at a given distance d from a given line in the plane is

   (A) one line (B) two lines (C) one circle
   (D) two circles (E) many circles

4. Which of the following is an equation of the locus of points that are at a distance of 5 from the origin?

   (A) $x = 5$ (B) $y = 5$ (C) $x^2 + y^2 = 5$
   (D) $x^2 + y^2 = 25$ (E) $x^2 + y^2 = 0$

5. The locus of points in the plane of a given triangle, equidistant from the 3 vertices of the triangle consists of

   (A) one point (B) one circle (C) one line
   (D) two lines (E) two circles

6. How many points are there that are equidistant from 2 given points A and B and also 2 inches from the line $\overleftrightarrow{AB}$?

   (A) 0 (B) 1 (C) 2 (D) 3 (E) 4

7. The midpoint of the hypotenuse of a right triangle is
   (A) equidistant from all 3 vertices
   (B) the intersection of the 3 angle bisectors
   (C) the intersection of the 3 medians
   (D) the center of the incircle
   (E) the incenter

8. Given $\triangle RST$ with medians $\overline{SL}$, $\overline{RN}$ and $\overline{TM}$ concurrent at P. $SP = 10$ Find PL

   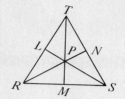

   (A) 10 (B) 5 (C) 15 (D) $3\frac{1}{3}$ (E) $13\frac{1}{3}$

9. Given points A (0, 2) and B (4, 0). What is the equation of the locus of points equidistant from A and B?

   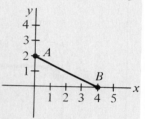

   (A) $y = \dfrac{-1}{2}x + 2$ (B) $y = 2x + 2$

   (C) $y = -\dfrac{1}{2}x + 4$ (D) $y = 2x - 3$

   (E) $y = 2x + 1$

10. Given point P on line l. The number of points that are 3 inches from P and 5 inches from l is

    (A) 0 (B) 1 (C) 2 (D) 3 (D) 4

11. Two concentric circles have radii of 2 in. and 6 in. Line m is tangent to the smaller circle. How many points are equidistant from the circles and 2 inches from m?

    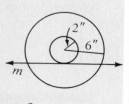

    (A) 0 (B) 1 (C) 2 (D) 3 (E) 4

INEQUALITIES

Mathematics in Design

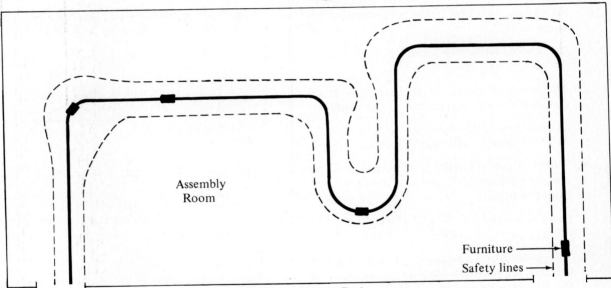

Furniture
Safety lines

Conveyor System Design

Industrial engineers are responsible for designing systems that meet all safety standards. An overhead conveyor system is needed to move furniture through the assembly room of a furniture factory. How should the engineer position the safety lines so that no person or object outside them will be hit by moving furniture? What factors must be considered?

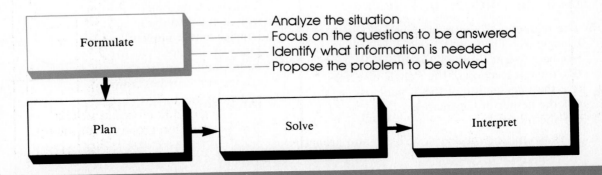

Formulate — — — — Analyze the situation
— — — — Focus on the questions to be answered
— — — — Identify what information is needed
— — — — Propose the problem to be solved

Plan → Solve → Interpret

15.1 Properties of Inequality

OBJECTIVES ► **To apply the properties of inequality to measures of segments and angles**
To prove statements involving inequalities

Recall that the symbol for equality is =. Two symbols for inequality are < (is less than) and > (is greater than).

$b > a$ means that for some positive number c, $b = a + c$. Also, $b > a$ means $a < b$.

In algebra, you used the following properties of inequality. The properties apply for all real numbers, a, b, and c. They are stated for >, but they are also true for <.

Inequality Properties:
Addition

If $a > b$, then $a + c > b + c$.

Subtraction

If $a > b$, then $a - c > b - c$.

Multiplication

If $a > b$ and $c > 0$, then $ac > bc$.

Division

If $a > b$ and $c > 0$, then $\dfrac{a}{c} > \dfrac{b}{c}$.

Since measures in geometric figures are numbers, the properties can be applied to measures of segments and angles, as shown below.

Example 1 Given: $AE > CF$, $EB = FD$
Compare AB and CD. Give the property that applies.

$AE > CF$
$EB = FD$
$AE + EB > CF + FD$ by Addition property of inequality
$AB = AE + EB$ and $CD = CF + FD$ by Def. of between
Thus, $AB > CD$ by the substitution property.

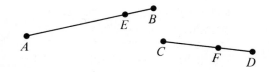

Example 2 Given: m $\angle CBA$ > m $\angle CAB$, m $\angle x$ = m $\angle y$
Compare m $\angle z$ and m $\angle w$. Give the property that applies.

m $\angle CBA$ > m $\angle CAB$
m $\angle x$ = m $\angle y$
m $\angle CBA$ − m $\angle x$ > m $\angle CAB$ − m $\angle y$ by Subtraction property of inequality
m $\angle CBA$ − m $\angle x$ = m $\angle z$ and m $\angle CAB$ − m $\angle y$ = m $\angle w$ by $\begin{cases}\text{Angle addition postulate and}\\\text{subtraction property of equality.}\end{cases}$
Thus, m $\angle z$ > m $\angle w$ by Substitution property.

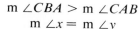

PROPERTIES OF INEQUALITY

When a segment or angle is bisected, the measure of the segment or angle is multiplied by $\frac{1}{2}$. This is used in the next example.

Example 3 Given: $\odot O$ with $AB < CD$, E bisects $\overline{AB}$, F bisects $\overline{CD}$. Compare CF and AE. Give the property that applies.

$$CD > AB$$
$$\frac{1}{2}(CD) > \frac{1}{2}(AB) \text{ by Multiplication property of inequality}$$

Thus, $CF > AE$.

The properties of inequality on page 499 can also be used in proofs, as shown in Example 4.

Example 4 Given: m $\angle x <$ m $\angle z$
Prove: m $\angle ABE <$ m $\angle CBD$

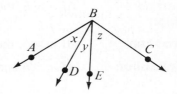

Proof

Statements	Reasons
1. m $\angle x <$ m $\angle z$	1. Given
2. m $\angle z >$ m $\angle x$	2. $a < b$ means $b > a$.
3. m $\angle y =$ m $\angle y$	3. Reflexive property
4. m $\angle z +$ m $\angle y >$ m $\angle x +$ m $\angle y$	4. Add. prop. of inequality
5. m $\angle CBD >$ m $\angle ABE$	5. Angle Add. Post. and Substitution property
6. m $\angle ABE <$ m $\angle CBD$	6. $b > a$ means $a < b$.

Three other properties of inequalities will be useful. These properties also apply to all real numbers a, b, c, and d.

Inequality Properties: Equals-unequals	If $a = b$ and $c > d$, then $a - c < b - d$. If $a = b$ and $c < d$, then $a - c > b - d$.
Transitive	If $a < b$ and $b < c$, then $a < c$. If $a > b$ and $b > c$, then $a > c$.
Trichotomy	For any two real numbers a and b, $a < b$ or $a = b$ or $a > b$.

Example 5 Given: $PR = XZ$, $PQ > XY$
Compare QR and YZ. Give the property that applies.

$$PR = XZ$$
$$PQ > XY$$
$PR - PQ < XZ - XY$ by Subtraction of unequals from equals
$PR - PQ = QR$ and $XZ - XY = YZ$ by Def. of between and Subtraction property
    of equality
Thus, $QR < YZ$ by Substitution property.

Written Exercises

Compare each of the following as indicated. Then give the property that applies.

Ⓐ **1.** Given: $RS < PQ$
M is the midpoint of $\overline{RS}$.
N is the midpoint of $\overline{PQ}$.
Compare RM and PN.

2. Given: m $\angle AEC >$
m $\angle BED$
Compare m $\angle x$ and m $\angle z$.

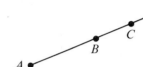

3. Given: $AB > CD$
Compare AC and BD.

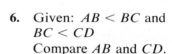

4. Given: $EF = GH$ and
$EX < GY$
Compare XF and YH.

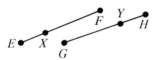

5. Given: $\angle x$ and $\angle y$
Give all possible
relationships between
m $\angle x$ and m $\angle y$.

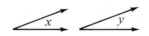

6. Given: $AB < BC$ and
$BC < CD$
Compare AB and CD.

7. Given: m $\angle ABC =$
m $\angle BCD$
m $\angle x >$ m $\angle y$
Compare m $\angle z$ and
m $\angle w$.

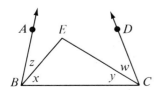

8. Given: m $\angle x =$ m $\angle y$
and m $\angle w <$ m $\angle z$
Compare m $\angle ABC$ and
m $\angle ADC$.

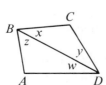

9. Given: $AE < FC$ and
$EB = BF$
Compare AB and BC.

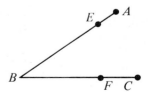

PROPERTIES OF INEQUALITY

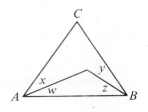

Ⓑ **10.** Given: $\overline{AC} \cong \overline{CB}$ and
m $\angle x >$ m $\angle y$
Prove: m $\angle z >$ m $\angle w$

11. Given: $\odot O$ with
$\overline{AB} > \overline{CD}$, $\overline{OE} \perp \overline{AB}$
$\overline{OF} \perp \overline{CD}$
Prove: $CF < AE$

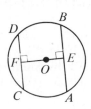

12. Given: $\overline{AB} \cong \overline{BC}$ and
m $\angle DAC <$ m $\angle DCA$
Prove: m $\angle BCD >$
m $\angle BAD$

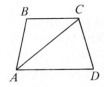

Ⓒ **13.** Given: $ABCD$ is
inscribed in $\odot O$,
m $\angle B >$ m $\angle A$
Prove: m $\angle D <$ m $\angle C$

14. Given: $\triangle ABC$, $\overline{DC} \cong$
$\overline{BC}$, m $\angle y >$ m $\angle z$
Prove: m $\angle x < 2$
m $\angle y$

15. Given: $\overline{AD} \cong \overline{DB}$,
$\overline{BF} \cong \overline{FC}$, m $\angle EAB >$
m $\angle EBA$, m $\angle DBC <$
m $\angle DCB$, m $\angle EBD <$
m $\angle DBF$ Prove:
m $\angle DAE <$ m $\angle FCD$

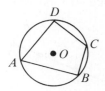

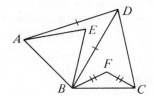

Algebra Review

OBJECTIVE ▶ **To solve inequalities by using the Addition Property and the Division Property**

Inequality properties can be used to solve algebraic inequalities. In the example below, the Addition and Division Properties of Inequality are used.

Example Solve $4x - 5 \leq 19$.

$$4x - 5 \leq 19 \quad (\leq \text{ means "is less than or equal to."})$$
Add 5 to each side. ▶ $\qquad 4x \leq 24$
Divide each side by 4. ▶ $\qquad x \leq 6$

Thus, 6 and all real numbers less than 6 are solutions of $4x - 5 \leq 19$.

Solve.

1. $5x + 2 > -8$
2. $9z - 8 < -17$
3. $3x - 7 \geq -8$
4. $7x - 18 < -7$
5. $3x - 11 \leq 7$
6. $4x + 8 \geq -16$
7. $8z + 8 > 8$
8. $4x - 4 \leq 12$
9. $2y + 13 > 7$
10. $7x - 24 < -3$
11. $3z - 18 > -6$
12. $5y - 17 < 3$

15.2 The Triangle Inequality

OBJECTIVE ►   To apply the Triangle Inequality Theorem

Suppose you are asked to construct a triangle, given the lengths of the three sides. You will find that certain restrictions exist for the lengths of the three segments. Consider the following three cases.

Case I	Case II	Case III
Lengths: 8 cm, 5 cm, 2 cm	Lengths: 9 cm, 5 cm, 14 cm	Lengths: 2 cm, 3 cm, 4 cm

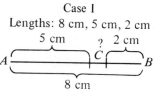   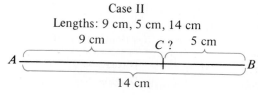   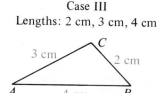

The 5-cm and the 2-cm segments will never meet to form the third vertex C.
$$5 + 2 < 8$$

The 9-cm and the 5-cm segments meet on $\overline{AB}$, so the third vertex C lies on $\overline{AB}$.
$$9 + 5 = 14$$

The 2-cm and the 3-cm segments meet to form the third vertex C, which is not on $\overline{AB}$.
$$2 + 3 > 4$$

These conclusions suggest the following summary and theorem.

Summary	If three segments have lengths such that the sum of any two is greater than the third, then a triangle can be constructed from the segments.

Theorem 15.1   The Triangle Inequality Theorem   In a triangle, the sum of the lengths of any two sides is greater than the length of the third side.

Given: $\triangle ABC$
Prove: $AC + CB > AB$
$\quad\quad\ AB + BC > AC$
$\quad\quad\ AC + AB > BC$

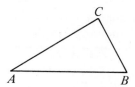

Analysis:
Consider the shortest path between each pair of vertices.

Proof

Statements	Reasons
1. $AC + CB > AB$.	1. The shortest path joining two points is a segment.
2. $AB + BC > AC$.	2. Same as 1
3. $AC + AB > BC$.	3. Same as 1

Example 1 Can a triangle be constructed with segments 6 mm, 11 mm, and 8 mm long?

Check the sum of the
two smallest lengths: $6 + 8 > 11$

Thus, a triangle can be constructed.

Example 1 applies the summary on page 503. If the sum of the two smallest lengths is greater than the third length, it is not necessary to check the other combinations of lengths.

The next example is an application of the Triangle Inequality Theorem.

Example 2 Given: $\odot O$ with segments $\overline{PO}$ and $\overline{PN}$
and radius $\overline{NO}$
Prove: $PN > PM$

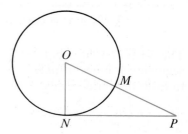

Proof

Statements	Reasons
1. $\odot O$ with radius $\overline{NO}$	1. Given
2. $PN + NO > PO$	2. Triangle Inequality Theorem
3. $PO = PM + MO$	3. Def. of between
4. $PN + NO > PM + MO$	4. Substitution property
5. $NO = MO$	5. Any two radii of a $\odot$ are $\cong$.
6. $PN > PM$	6. Subtraction prop. of inequality

*Subtract NO
and MO from
step 4.* ▶

The following property of inequality is true for all real numbers a, b, c, and d.

**Unequals +
unequals, same
order**

> If $a < b$ and $c < d$, then $a + c < b + d$.
> If $a > b$ and $c > d$, then $a + c > b + d$.

Example 3 Given: $MN < QR$, $NP < RS$
Compare MP and QS. Give
the property that applies.

$$MN < QR$$
$$NP < RS$$

$MN + NP < QR + RS$ by addition of unequals to unequals, same order
$MN + NP = MP$ and $QR + RS = QS$ by Def. of between

Thus, $MP < QS$ by Substitution property.

Oral Exercises

Tell whether a triangle can be constructed with segments having these lengths.

1. 5, 8, 13
4. 4 m, 6 m, 1 m
7. $1\frac{1}{2}$, $2\frac{1}{2}$, $3\frac{1}{2}$

2. 9, 12, 15
5. 12 cm, 9 cm, 4 cm
8. 8.2 m, 6.1 m, 2.1 m

3. 9, 10, 20
6. 16 mm, 11 mm, 6 mm
9. 6 cm, 9 cm, 1 cm

Written Exercises

Explain why each of the following is true. (Ex. 1–4)

  1. People often cut across vacant lots rather than go around a corner.

2. The measure of a diagonal of a rectangle is less than the sum of the measures of two adjacent sides.

3. If the congruent sides of an isosceles triangle each measure 7 cm, then the base measures less than 14 cm.

4. If two sides of a triangle have measures 5 and 7, then the measure of the third side is between 2 and 12.

5. Given: Quadrilateral
   $ABCD$
   Prove: $AB + BC + CD + DA > AC + BD$

6. Given: $\triangle ABC$
   Prove: $AB - BC < AC$

7. Given: $ED = EC$
   Prove: $AB + AD > BC$

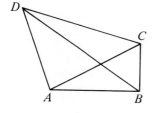
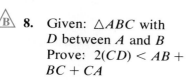

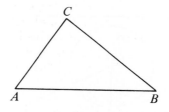
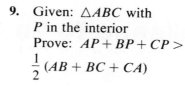

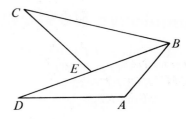
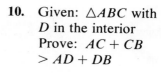

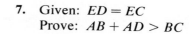 **8.** Given: $\triangle ABC$ with D between A and B
   Prove: $2(CD) < AB + BC + CA$

9. Given: $\triangle ABC$ with P in the interior
   Prove: $AP + BP + CP > \frac{1}{2}(AB + BC + CA)$

10. Given: $\triangle ABC$ with D in the interior
   Prove: $AC + CB > AD + DB$

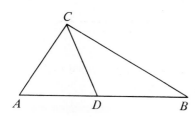

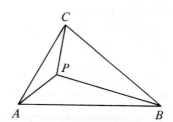

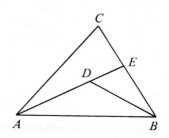

THE TRIANGLE INEQUALITY

11. Given: Quadrilateral $ABCD$
Prove: $AB + AD > DC - CB$

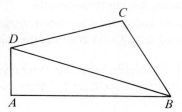

12. Given: $\triangle ABC$ with P in the interior
Prove: $m \angle APB > m \angle C$

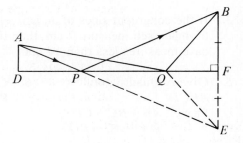

 13. Prove that if P is a point on $\overline{AB}$ of $\triangle ABC$, then CP is less than one half the perimeter of $\triangle ABC$.

14. Prove that the perimeter of a concave quadrilateral is greater than the sum of the lengths of the two diagonals.

15. Light reflected from a mirror surface DF from point A to point B will take the path APB. Show that path APB is shorter than any other path, say path AQB.
$\angle APD \cong \angle BPF$

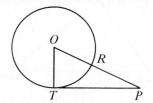

Cumulative Review

1. Given: $\overline{PT}$ is tangent to $\odot O$ at T, $OT = 5$, and $PT = 12$.
Find RP.

2. Given: $\overline{PT}$ is tangent to $\odot O$ at T, $OT = 8$, and $RP = 9$.
Find TP.

→ A Challenge To You

Prove that the length of a median of a triangle is less than one half the sum of the lengths of the two adjacent sides.
[*Hint:* Extend median $\overline{CD}$ to E so that $CD = DE$.]

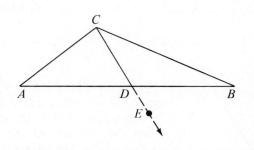

15.3 Inequalities in a Scalene Triangle

OBJECTIVES ▶ **To compare the measures of sides in a scalene triangle**
To compare the measures of angles in a scalene triangle

In this lesson, you will discover relationships that exist among the measures of sides and angles of a scalene triangle. For $\triangle ABC$ below, $AC = 3$ cm and $BC = 5$ cm, so $BC > AC$.

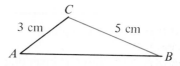

Notice that the measure of the angle opposite $\overline{BC}$ appears to be greater than the measure of the angle opposite $\overline{AC}$, or m $\angle A >$ m $\angle B$. This observation suggests the following theorem.

Theorem 15.2 If one side of a triangle is longer than a second side, then the measure of the angle opposite the first side is greater than the measure of the angle opposite the second side.

Given: $\triangle ABC$ with $BC > AC$
Prove: m $\angle BAC >$ m $\angle B$

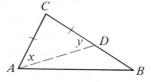

Analysis:
Construct isos. $\triangle ACD$.
Then, m $\angle x =$ m $\angle y$,
m $\angle BAC >$ m $\angle x$, and
m $\angle y >$ m $\angle B$.

Proof

Statements	Reasons
1. $\triangle ABC$ with $BC > AC$	1. Given
2. On $\overline{CB}$, let $CD = AC$.	2. Postulate 6
3. Draw $\overline{AD}$.	3. Two points are contained in exactly one line.
4. m $\angle x =$ m $\angle y$	4. Base $\angle$'s of an isos. $\triangle$ are $\cong$.
5. m $\angle BAC =$ m $\angle DAB +$ m $\angle x$	5. Angle addition postulate
6. m $\angle BAC >$ m $\angle x$	6. $b > a$ means for some $c > 0$, $b = a + c$.
7. m $\angle BAC >$ m $\angle y$	7. Substitution property
8. m $\angle y >$ m $\angle B$	8. An exterior $\angle$ of a $\triangle$ has greater measure than either remote interior $\angle$.
9. ∴ m $BAC >$ m $\angle B$	9. Transitive prop. of inequality

Now consider $\triangle ABC$ with m $\angle A = 40$ and m $\angle B = 70$, or m $\angle B >$ m $\angle A$. It appears that the measure of the side opposite $\angle B$ is greater than the measure of the side opposite $\angle A$, or $AC > BC$. This observation suggests the next theorem.

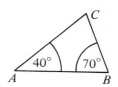

INEQUALITIES IN A SCALENE TRIANGLE

Theorem 15.3

If one angle of a triangle has a greater measure than a second angle, then the side opposite the first angle is longer than the side opposite the second angle.

Given: $\triangle ABC$ with m $\angle A$ > m $\angle B$
Prove: $BC > AC$

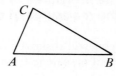

Analysis:
Use an indirect proof. Either $BC < AC$, $BC = AC$, or $BC > AC$. Show that the first two possibilities lead to contradictions.

(See Exercise 12.)

Theorem 15.3 is used in the proof of Example 1.

Example 1

Given: $\triangle ABC$ with $\overline{CD}$ bisecting $\angle ACB$
Prove: $AC > AD$

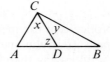

Proof

Statements	Reasons
1. $\overline{CD}$ bisects $\angle ACB$.	1. Given
2. m $\angle x$ = m $\angle y$	2. Def. of $\angle$ bisector and Def. of $\cong$ $\angle$'s
3. m $\angle z$ > m $\angle y$	3. An exterior $\angle$ of a $\triangle$ has greater measure than either remote interior $\angle$.
4. m $\angle z$ > m $\angle x$	4. Substitution property
5. $AC > AD$	5. Theorem 15.3

$\angle z$ is an ext. $\angle$ of $\triangle DBC$. ►

Oral Exercises

Name the angles in order according to their measures, from largest to smallest.

1.
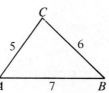

2.
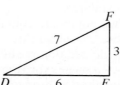

3.

4.

Name the sides in order according to their measures, from largest to smallest.

5.
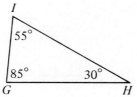

6.

7.

8.
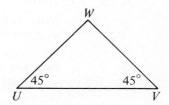

Written Exercises

1. Given: $\triangle ABC$ with $BC > AC$ and m $\angle C > $ m $\angle A$
Prove: m $\angle C > $ m $\angle B$

2. Given: Equilateral $\triangle ABC$
Prove: $AD > CD$

3. Given: $\angle ABC$ is obtuse.
Prove: $AC > AB$ and $AC > BC$

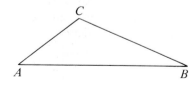
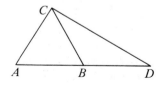
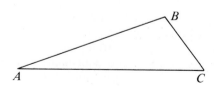

4. Given: $EB > AE$ and $CD > BC$
Prove: m $\angle A > $ m $\angle D$

5. Given: $AC > CB$, $\overrightarrow{AD}$ bisects $\angle CAB$, $\overrightarrow{BD}$ bisects $\angle ABC$.
Prove: $AD > DB$

6. Given: $\triangle ABC$ with m $\angle A < $ m $\angle B$ and $CD < CB$
Prove: m $\angle A < $ m $\angle CDA$

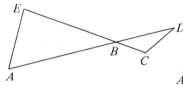
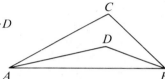
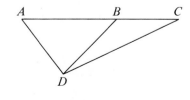

7. Given: m $\angle A > $ m $\angle C$
Prove: $DC > DB$

8. Given: $DB > AC$ and $\overrightarrow{AD}$ bisects $\angle CAB$.
Prove: $DB > DC$

9. Given: $AC = CB$ and $DB > DA$
Prove: m $\angle w < $ m $\angle z$

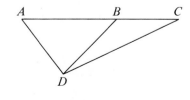
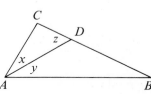
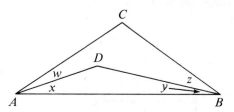

10. Given: $AD < DB$, $DB = DC$
Prove: m $\angle A + $ m $\angle C > $ m $\angle ABC$

11. Given: $BC = BD$, $BD > AB$
Prove: m $\angle ACD < $ m $\angle D + $ m $\angle A$

12. Prove Theorem 15.3.

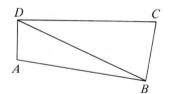
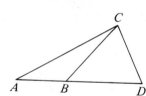

Slides and Coordinates

On graph paper, copy the axes, $\triangle ABC$, $\triangle A'B'C'$, and the slide arrow, TT'.

1. Are the triangles congruent?
2. Give the coordinates of the vertices of $\triangle ABC$ and $\triangle A'B'C'$. Give the coordinates of the tail and the tip of the slide arrow, TT'.
3. Compare the x-coordinates of A and A'; B and B'; C and C'; T and T'.
4. Similarly, compare the y-coordinates.

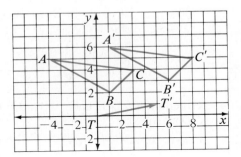

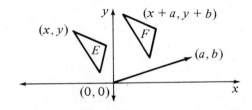

Figure F is a slide image of figure E. The segment from $(0, 0)$ to (a, b) is the slide arrow.

In figure E	In figure F
(x, y)	$\longleftrightarrow$ $(x + a, y + b)$

Copy each figure and the slide arrow on graph paper. Draw the slide image of each.

1. 2. 3.

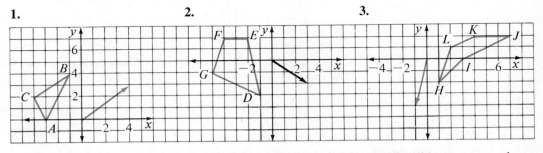

The coordinates of the vertices of a polygon and the tip of a slide arrow are given. Graph and label the polygon, the slide arrow, and the slide image.

4. $A(5, 4)$, $B(3, 1)$, $C(2, 0)$
   tip of slide arrow: $(3, -1)$

5. $D(6, 1)$, $E(4, 3)$, $F(2, -3)$, $G(1, -1)$
   tip of slide arrow: $(-4, 2)$

15.4 Inequalities for Two Triangles

OBJECTIVE ▶ **To apply the Hinge Theorem and its converse to pairs of triangles**

Suppose two sticks are hinged together and connected with an elastic band. The two triangles shown below represent different possibilities for the degree measure of the angle formed by the sticks. Observe the effect on the side opposite that angle as the measure of the angle increases.

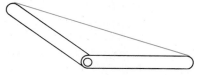

The situation represented above is generalized in Theorem 15.4.

┌ Theorem 15.4   **The Hinge Theorem**   If two sides of one triangle are congruent, respectively, to two sides of another triangle, and the included angle of the first triangle has a greater measure than the included angle of the second triangle, then the third side of the first triangle has a greater measure than the third side of the second triangle.

Given: $\triangle ABC$ and $\triangle DEF$ with
$\overline{AC} \cong \overline{DF}$, $\overline{CB} \cong \overline{FE}$, and
m $\angle ACB >$ m $\angle F$

Prove: $AB > DE$

Analysis: Construct $\triangle ACG \cong \triangle DFE$.
   Let $\overrightarrow{CH}$ bisect $\angle GCB$.
   $AH + HG > AG$
   Prove $\triangle GCH \cong \triangle BCH$
   and substitute
   to show $AB > AG$.

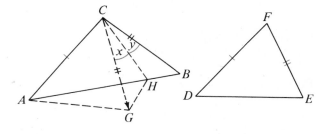

(See Exercise 12.)

You can use the Hinge Theorem to compare lengths of sides in two triangles as shown in Examples 1 and 2.

Example **1** C is the midpoint of $\overline{AD}$, $\overline{AB} \cong \overline{DE}$,
m $\angle A = 65$, m $\angle D = 50$.
Compare CE and BC.

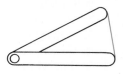

$\overline{AC} \cong \overline{CD}$
$\overline{AB} \cong \overline{DE}$
m $\angle A >$ m $\angle D$
Thus, $BC > CE$, or $CE < BC$ by Theorem 15.4.

INEQUALITIES FOR TWO TRIANGLES

Example **2** Given: $\square ABCD$ with m $\angle ADC >$
m $\angle DCB$
Prove: $AC > BD$

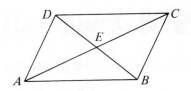

Proof

Statements	Reasons
1. $ABCD$ is a $\square$.	1. Given
2. $\overline{AD} \cong \overline{BC}$	2. Opp. sides of a $\square$ are $\cong$.
3. $\overline{DC} \cong \overline{DC}$	3. Reflexive property
4. m $\angle ADC >$ m $\angle DCB$	4. Given
5. $\therefore AC > BD$	5. The Hinge Theorem

The next theorem is the converse of Theorem 15.4.

Theorem 15.5 **Converse of the Hinge Theorem** If two sides of one triangle are congruent, respectively, to two sides of another
triangle, and the third side of the first has a greater measure than the third side of the second, then the angle opposite the third side of the first triangle has a greater measure than the angle opposite the third side of the second
triangle.

Given: $\triangle ABC$ and $\triangle DEF$ with
$\overline{AC} \cong \overline{DF}$, $\overline{CB} \cong \overline{FE}$, and
$AB > DE$
Prove: m $\angle C >$ m $\angle F$

Analysis: Use an indirect proof.
Either m $\angle C <$ m $\angle F$, m $\angle C =$
m $\angle F$, or m $\angle C >$ m $\angle F$. Show
that the first two cases lead to
contradictions.

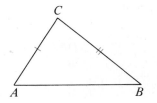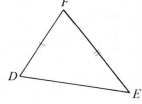

Proof

Statements	Reasons
1. $\overline{AC} \cong \overline{DF}$, $\overline{CB} \cong \overline{FE}$, $AB > DE$	1. Given
2. m $\angle C <$ m $\angle F$ or m $\angle C =$ m $\angle F$ or m $\angle C >$ m $\angle F$	2. Trichotomy property
3. If m $\angle C <$ m $\angle F$, then $AB < DE$.	3. The Hinge Theorem
4. Thus, m $\angle C$ is *not* < m $\angle F$.	4. Given: $AB > DE$
5. If m $\angle C =$ m $\angle F$, then $\triangle ABC \cong \triangle DEF$.	5. SAS for $\cong \triangle$'s
6. Then $AB = DE$	6. CPCTC
7. Thus, m $\angle C \neq$ m $\angle F$	7. Given: $AB > DE$
8. $\therefore$ m $\angle C >$ m $\angle F$	8. Steps 2, 4, and 7

Example 3
Given: $\triangle ABC$ with M the midpoint of
$\overline{AB}$, $\overline{AD} \cong \overline{BE}$, and $DM > EM$
Prove: $BC > AC$

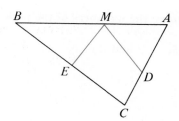

Proof

Statements	Reasons
1. M is the midpoint of $\overline{AB}$.	1. Given
2. $\overline{AM} \cong \overline{MB}$	2. Def. of midpoint
3. $\overline{AD} \cong \overline{BE}$	3. Given
4. $DM > EM$	4. Given
5. m $\angle A >$ m $\angle B$	5. Converse of the Hinge Theorem
6. $\therefore BC > AC$	6. If meas. of 1 $\angle$ of a $\triangle$ is > meas. of a 2nd $\angle$, then side opp. 1 st $\angle$ is longer than side opp. 2nd $\angle$.

Reading in Geometry

Copy and complete each sentence to make a true statement.

1. In a triangle, the sum of the measures of any two sides is ? than the measure of the third side.

2. The length of the ? in a right triangle is greater than the length of either ?.

3. In $\triangle ABC$, if the measure of $\angle A$ is greater than the measure of $\angle B$, then BC is ? than AC.

4. The difference between the lengths of two sides of a triangle is ? than the length of the third side.

5. In $\triangle RST$, if RS is less than ST, then the measure of $\angle R$ is ? than the measure of $\angle T$.

6. In an obtuse triangle, the side opposite the obtuse angle has the ? measure of the three sides.

Oral Exercises

Compare the measures of the indicated segments.

1. $\overline{BC}$ and $\overline{CD}$

2. $\overline{AD}$ and $\overline{DC}$

3. $\overline{CD}$ and $\overline{DB}$

4. $\overline{RV}$ and $\overline{UT}$

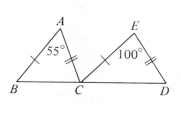
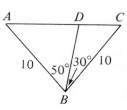
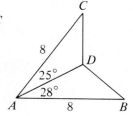
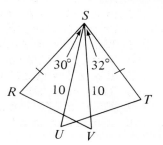

INEQUALITIES FOR TWO TRIANGLES

Compare the measures of the indicated angles.

5. $\angle x$ and $\angle y$

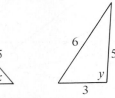

6. $\angle r$ and $\angle s$

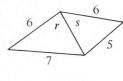

7. $\angle w$ and $\angle z$

8. $\angle p$ and $\angle q$

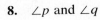
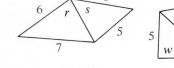

Written Exercises

A **1.** Given: $\square ABCD$ with
m $\angle BAD >$ m $\angle ADC$
Prove: $BD > AC$

2. Given: $\odot O$ with
$AB > CD$
Prove: m $\angle x >$ m $\angle y$

3. Given: $AD = CD$ and
$AB > CB$
Prove: m $\angle ADB >$
m $\angle CDB$

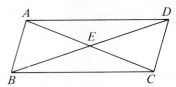

4. Given: $\overline{CD}$ is the
median to $\overline{AB}$ and
$CB < CA$
Prove: m $\angle y <$ m $\angle x$

5. Given: $AC = BC$ and
m $\angle ACD >$ m $\angle DCB$
Prove: $AD > DB$

6. Given: $AB = DC$,
$\overline{AB} \parallel \overline{DC}$, m $\angle AED <$
m $\angle DEC$
Prove: $AD < DC$

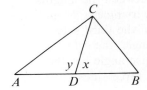

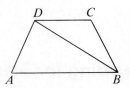

B **7.** Given: $\overline{TU}$ is the median
to $\overline{RS}$ and m $\angle x >$ m $\angle y$
Prove: m $\angle S >$ m $\angle R$

8. Given: $\triangle ABC$ with
m $\angle x <$ m $\angle y$, $\overline{AE} \cong \overline{EB}$
Prove: $AC > CB$

9. Given: $AD = EB$ and
$DB > AE$
Prove: $CB > CA$

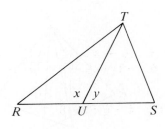
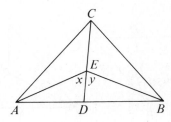
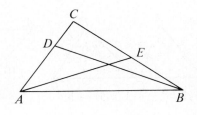

10. Given: m $\angle x$ = m $\angle y$
and $BC > AB$
Prove: m $\angle BDC >$ m $\angle BDA$

11. Given: m $\angle r <$ m $\angle s$
and m $\angle p$ = m $\angle q$
Prove: m $\angle DBC <$ m $\angle ABC$

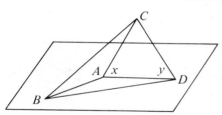

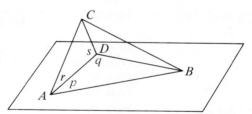

12. Prove Theorem 15.4.

Cumulative **Review** _____

1. Find the area of a rectangle with one side 7 cm long and a diagonal $\sqrt{113}$ cm long.

2. Find the length of a diagonal of a rectangle with one side 6 cm long and an area of 30 cm².

Algebra Review
_____

OBJECTIVE ► **To solve inequalities by using inequality properties**

When negative numbers occur in algebraic inequalities, the two properties below are sometimes necessary.

Inequality Properties: Multiplication, $c < 0$ If $a > b$ and $c < 0$, then $ac < bc$.

Division, $c < 0$ If $a > b$ and $c < 0$, then $\dfrac{a}{c} < \dfrac{b}{c}$.

Example   Solve $2x + 5 > 8x + 23$.

$$2x + 5 > 8x + 23$$

Add −5 to each side. ► $2x > 8x + 18$
Add −8x to each side. ► $-6x > 18$
Divide each side by −6. ► $x < -3$

Thus, all real numbers less than −3 are solutions of $2x + 5 > 8x + 23$.

Solve.

1. $2z + 8 < 8z - 88$
2. $x + 15 > 2x + 10$
3. $9x - 4 > 17x + 28$
4. $2 + x < 5x - 38$
5. $55 + 5x > 12x - 8$
6. $-3x - 8 < 6 + 4x$
7. $-7x + 4 \leq -2x - 6$
8. $6 > -3x - 8 + x$
9. $-x + 8 - 3x < 0$
10. $2x - 3 \geq 5x + 6$
11. $-\dfrac{3}{5}x - 4 \leq 6$
12. $6 - \dfrac{2}{3}x \geq -8$

INEQUALITIES FOR TWO TRIANGLES

515

15.5 Inequalities in Circles

OBJECTIVE ► **To apply inequality relationships to circles**

In a circle there is a relationship between the lengths of chords and their distances from the center. Recall that chords of a given circle that are of the same length are equidistant from the center. For chords $\overline{AB}$ and $\overline{CD}$ at the right, $CD > AB$. Notice that $\overline{CD}$ appears to be nearer to the center of the circle than $\overline{AB}$; that is, $OF < OE$. This observation is generalized in Theorem 15.6.

Theorem 15.6 If two chords of a circle are unequal in length, then the longer chord is nearer to the center of the circle.

Given: $\odot O$ with $AB > BC$,
$\overline{OF} \perp \overline{BC}$, and $\overline{OE} \perp \overline{AB}$
Prove: $OE < OF$

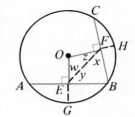

Analysis:
Assume that the two chords have a common endpoint. (If not, construct $\cong$ chords that have a common endpoint.) Use $\triangle OEF$ and $\triangle BEF$.

Proof

Statements	Reasons
1. $\odot O$ with $\overline{OF} \perp \overline{BC}$ and $\overline{OE} \perp \overline{AB}$	1. Given
2. Draw $\overline{EF}$, $\overline{FH}$, and $\overline{EG}$.	2. Two points are contained in exactly one line.
3. $AE = EB$ and $BF = FC$	3. A radius $\perp$ to a chord bisects the chord.
4. $AB = AE + EB$ and $BC = BF + FC$	4. Def. of between
5. $AB = 2(EB)$ and $BC = 2(BF)$	5. Substitution and Distributive properties
6. $AB > BC$	6. Given
7. $EB > BF$	7. Substitution and Division prop. of inequality
8. m $\angle x >$ m $\angle y$	8. Theorem 15.2
9. m $\angle OEB =$ m $\angle OFB$	9. $\perp$ lines form $\cong$ rt. $\angle$'s.
10. m $\angle z +$ m $\angle x =$ m $\angle w +$ m $\angle y$	10. Angle Addition Post.; Substitution
11. m $\angle z <$ m $\angle w$	11. Subtraction of unequals from equals
12. $\therefore OE < OF$	12. Theorem 15.3

Theorem 15.6 is also true for congruent circles. (See Exercise 13.)

Example 1 Compare ON and OM.

$PQ = 12$ and $RS = 10$,
so $PQ > RS$.

Thus $OM < ON$, or $ON > OM$, by Th. 15.6.

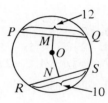

The converse of Theorem 15.6 is also true.

Theorem 15.7 If two chords of a circle are unequally distant from the center, then the chord nearer the center is the longer. (See Exercise 12.)

Theorem 15.7 is also true for congruent circles. (See Exercise 14.)

Example 2

Given: $\odot O$ with $\overline{OE} \perp \overline{AB}$, $\overline{OF} \perp \overline{CD}$, and $OF < OE$
Prove: m $\angle COD >$ m $\angle AOB$

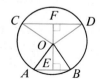

Proof

Statements	Reasons
1. $\overline{DE} \perp \overline{AB}$, $\overline{OF} \perp \overline{CD}$, $OF < OE$	1. Given
2. $CD > AB$	2. Theorem 15.7
3. $\overline{OA} \cong \overline{OC}$ and $\overline{OB} \cong \overline{OD}$	3. Any two radii of a $\odot$ are $\cong$.
4. m $\angle COD >$ m $\angle AOB$	4. Converse of the Hinge Theorem

The proof in Example 3 involves arcs of unequal measure.

Example 3

Given: $\odot O$ with m $\angle x >$ m $\angle y$
Prove: $m\overset{\frown}{AB} > m\overset{\frown}{CD}$

Proof

Statements	Reasons
1. m $\angle x >$ m $\angle y$	1. Given
2. m $\angle x = m\overset{\frown}{AB}$; m $\angle y = m\overset{\frown}{CD}$	2. Meas. of minor arc = meas. of central $\angle$.
3. $\therefore m\overset{\frown}{AB} > m\overset{\frown}{CD}$	3. Substitution property

Oral **Exercises**

Compare the indicated measures.

1. AB and CD, FD and EB

2. AO and CO, $m\overset{\frown}{AB}$ and $m\overset{\frown}{BC}$

3. OP and OR, PN and NR

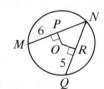

4. RS and TU, WT and VS

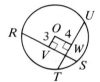

INEQUALITIES IN CIRCLES

Written Exercises _____

1. Given: $\odot O$ with $\overline{OE} \perp \overline{AB}$, $\overline{OF} \perp \overline{CD}$, m $\angle COD <$ m $\angle AOB$
   Prove: $OF > OE$

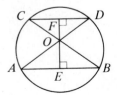

2. Given: $\odot O$ with $m\overset{\frown}{AB} < m\overset{\frown}{CD}$
   Prove: m $\angle x <$ m $\angle y$

3. Given: $\odot O$ with $\overline{OE} \perp \overline{AB}$ and $\overline{OF} \perp \overline{CD}$
   Prove: $AB < CD$

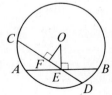

4. Given: $\odot O$ with $\overline{OE} \perp \overline{AB}$, $\overline{OF} \perp \overline{BC}$, $AE > BF$
   Prove: $OE < OF$

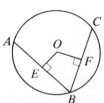

5. Given: $\odot O$ with m $\angle B >$ m $\angle A$
   Prove: $m\overset{\frown}{AC} > m\overset{\frown}{BC}$

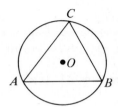

6. Given: $\odot O$ with $AB > CD$, $\overline{OE} \perp \overline{AB}$, $\overline{OF} \perp \overline{CD}$, $\overline{EB} \cong \overline{BF}$
   Prove: m $\angle x >$ m $\angle y$

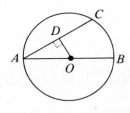

7. Given: $\odot O$ with $m\overset{\frown}{AB} < m\overset{\frown}{BC}$, $\overline{OD} \perp \overline{AB}$, $\overline{OE} \perp \overline{BC}$
   Prove: $OD > OE$

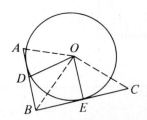

8. Given: $\odot O$ with $\overline{OE} \perp \overline{AB}$, $\overline{OF} \perp \overline{CD}$, m $\angle x >$ m $\angle y$, $\overline{AE} \cong \overline{AF}$
   Prove: $AB > CD$

9. Given: $\odot O$ with diameter $\overline{AOB}$ and chord $\overline{AC}$
   Prove: $AB > AC$
   [Hint: Draw $\overline{OD} \perp \overline{AC}$.]

10. Prove that if a square and an equilateral triangle are inscribed in the same circle, the apothem of the square is longer than the apothem of the triangle.

11. Prove that through any point in the interior of a circle, except the center, the chord that is perpendicular to the radius through this point is shorter than any other chord through the point.

12. Prove Theorem 15.7.

13. Prove Theorem 15.6 for congruent circles.

14. Prove Theorem 15.7 for congruent circles.

Applications

1. Two children wish to fence in a corner of the back yard for their dog. They have 100 ft of fence. They first stretched the fence diagonally across the corner, using 55 ft of fence. What can you predict about the rest of their fencing project? Why?

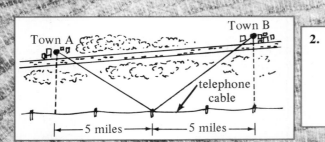

2. Two towns are located on the same highway. The main telephone cable is not parallel to the highway. If the telephone company connects each town to this main cable as shown, will the cable lengths be equal? Why, or why not?

3. A homeowner is cutting an evenly round log to form the largest possible square wooden beam. He will mark the end of the log before beginning to saw. His only measuring device is a carpenter's square, which is not long enough to measure the length of the side of the square beam directly. Assume that the heart of the tree is exactly in the center of the log. How can he use the center to mark the end of the log so that one side of the beam will not be longer than another?

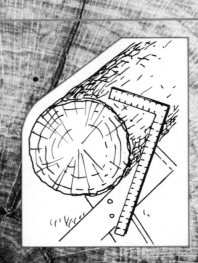

4. The graph shown gives the distribution of tax revenues for Newtown. How can you use a protractor to tell which group receives the largest amount of taxes? the smallest amount?

Chapter Fifteen Review

Compare each of the following as indicated. Then give the property that applies. [15.1]

1. Given: $WY > XZ$
Compare WX and YZ.

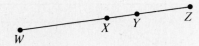

2. Given: m $\angle t <$ m $\angle s$ and m $\angle s <$ m $\angle r$
Compare m $\angle t$ and m $\angle r$.

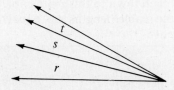

3. Given: $AB > CD$, M is the midpoint of $\overline{AB}$, and N is the midpoint of $\overline{CD}$.
Compare AM and ND.

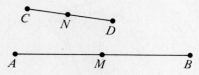

Determine whether a triangle can be constructed with segments having these lengths. [15.2]

4. 7, 9, 15   **5.** 1 m, 3 m, 5 m

Name the angles in order according to their measures, from largest to smallest. [15.3]

6.   **7.**

Name the sides in order according to their measures, from largest to smallest. [15.3]

8.   **9.**

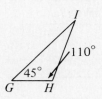   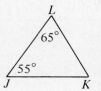

Compare the indicated measures.

10. m $\angle x$ and m $\angle y$ **11.** AB and CD

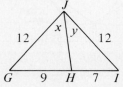

Prove each of the following. [15.4]

12. Given: $ABCD$ is a quadrilateral.
Prove: $AC + BD < AB + BC + CD + DA$

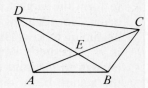

13. Given: $\triangle ABC$ with D in the interior [15.3]
Prove: $AC + BD < AC + CB$

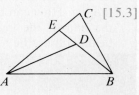

14. Given: $\odot O$ with $\overline{OE} \perp \overline{AB}$, $\overline{OF} \perp \overline{CD}$, and $AE < CF$
Prove: $OE > OF$

*15. Given: m $\angle x >$ m $\angle y$ [15.4]
and m $\angle w =$ m $\angle z$
Prove: m $\angle ABC >$ m $\angle DBC$

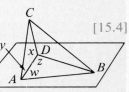

Chapter Fifteen Test

Compare each of the following as indicated. Then give the property that applies.

1. Given: m ∠r > m ∠s
   Compare m ∠ABD and m ∠CBE.

2. Given: PQ = RS, PT < RU
   Compare TQ and US.

Determine whether a triangle can be constructed with segments having these lengths.

3. 6, 2, 4   **4.** 5 m, 6 m, 7 m

Name the angles in order according to their measures, from largest to smallest.

5.   **6.**

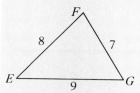

Name the sides in order according to their measures, from largest to smallest.

7.   **8.**

 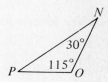

Compare the indicated measures.

9. m ∠x and m ∠y   **10.** OF and OE

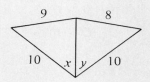

Prove each of the following.

11. Given: ▱PQRS with m ∠SPQ < m ∠PQR
   Prove: SQ < PR

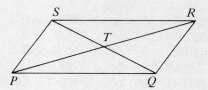

12. Given: AC < CB, $\overrightarrow{AE}$ bisects ∠CAB, $\overrightarrow{BE}$ bisects ∠ABC
   Prove: AE < EB

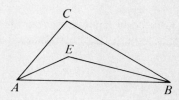

*__13.__ Given: SQ > PS and SQ = SR
   Prove: m ∠P + m ∠R > m ∠PQR

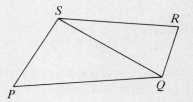

Computer Activities

This activity applies the Triangle Inequality Theorem (15.1) to triangle construction.

You will use the following BASIC inequalities for triangles in the program below.

$$B + C > D$$
$$B + D > C$$
$$C + D > B$$

See the computer section on page 560 for more information.

PROGRAM

```
10 PRINT "PROGRAM DETERMINES IF THREE SEGMENT LENGTHS"
20 PRINT "CAN BE USED TO CONSTRUCT A TRIANGLE"
30 PRINT "ENTER SEGMENT LENGTHS B, C, D"
40 INPUT B, C, D
50 IF B + C < = D THEN 140
60 IF B + D < = C THEN 140
70 IF C + D < = B THEN 140
80 PRINT "B, C, D CAN BE USED TO CONSTRUCT A TRIANGLE"
90 PRINT "DO YOU WANT TO CONTINUE?"
100 PRINT "ANSWER YES OR NO"
110 INPUT N$
120 IF N$ = "YES" THEN 30
130 GO TO 160
140 PRINT "B, C, D CANNOT BE USED TO CONSTRUCT A TRIANGLE"
150 GO TO 90
160 END
```

Exercises

Run this program for the following lengths. (Ex. 1–2)
1. $B = 6$ cm $C = 8$ cm $D = 10$ cm **2.** $B = 16$ mm $C = 11$ m $D = 6$ mm **3.** $B = 5$ m $C = 3$ m $D = 9$ m

4. Add statements to the program above to also check if the given lengths form a right triangle. Use the Pythagorean formula in BASIC: A ↑ 2 + B ↑ 2 = C ↑ 2

5. Write a program to list the sides of scalene triangle ABC from largest to smallest, given the measures of angle A, angle B, and angle C.

College Prep Test

Directions: In each item you are to compare a quantity in Column 1 with a quantity in Column 2. Write the letter of the the correct answer from these choices:

A—The quantity in Column 1 is greater than the quantity in Column 2.
B—The quantity in Column 2 is greater than the quantity in Column 1.
C—The quantity in Column 1 is equal to the quantity in Column 2.
D—The relationship cannot be determined from the given information.

Notes: Information centered over both columns refers to one or both of the quantities to be compared.

A symbol that appears in both columns has the same meaning in each column and all variables represent real numbers.

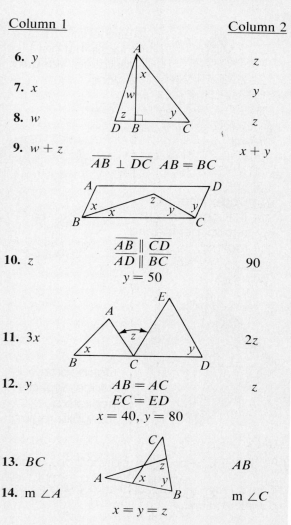

Sample Question and Answer

Column 1	Column 2
$m \angle 4 + m \angle 1$	$m \angle 1 + m \angle 2 + m \angle 3$

Answer: **C** since $m \angle 4 = m \angle 2 + m \angle 3$ by substitution $m \angle 4 + m \angle 1 = m \angle 1 + m \angle 2 + m \angle 3$

Column 1   **Column 2**

1. $2AC$ AB

2. $m \angle B$ In $\triangle ABC$ $AC < AB$ $AC > BC$ $m \angle A$

3. DC $BC + AD$

4. $b - a$ 90

5. BC In $\triangle ABC$ $m \angle A > m \angle B$ $m \angle C = 60$ AB

Column 1   **Column 2**

6. y z

7. x y

8. w z

9. $w + z$ $x + y$

$\overline{AB} \perp \overline{DC} \quad AB = BC$

10. z $\overline{AB} \parallel \overline{CD}$ $\overline{AD} \parallel \overline{BC}$ $y = 50$ 90

11. $3x$ $2z$

12. y $AB = AC$ $EC = ED$ $x = 40, y = 80$ z

13. BC AB

14. $m \angle A$ $x = y = z$ $m \angle C$

16 FIGURES IN SPACE

Regular Polyhedrons

Each of the regular polyhedrons shown below can be constructed from congruent regular polygonal regions. One pattern for construction is shown on the bottom right.

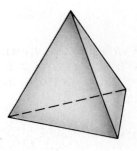

Tetrahedron
4 faces that are
equilateral triangular
regions

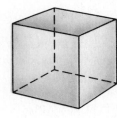

Hexahedron
6 faces that are
square regions

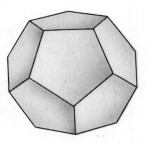

Dodecahedron
12 faces that are
regular pentagonal
regions

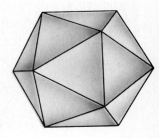

Icosahedron
20 faces that are
equilateral
triangular regions

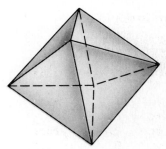

Octahedron
8 faces that are
equilateral
triangular regions

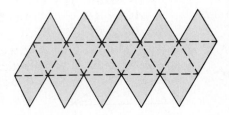

1. For each polyhedron, count the number of faces (*F*), edges (*E*), and vertices (*V*). Find a formula relating *F*, *E*, and *V*.
2. Construct a model of one of these regular polyhedrons. Draw a pattern first.

16.1 Prisms

OBJECTIVES ► **To identify and count the parts of a prism**
To sketch various types of prisms

Recall that all of the points that make up a plane figure lie in the same plane. On the other hand, all of the points that make up a space figure do not lie in the same plane. Space figures are often called **solids.** Several types of solids are shown below.

Prism

Cylinder

Pyramid

Cone

Sphere

A prism is a special type of solid. A prism has two bases which are congruent polygonal regions lying in parallel planes. A prism is named according to its bases. For example, a triangular prism has two bases which are congruent triangular regions.

Triangular Prism

Quadrangular Prism

Pentagonal Prism

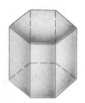
Hexagonal Prism

Example 1 Give the type of base of each prism.

Prism	Type of Base
Quadrangular prism	Quadrilateral region
Pentagonal prism	Pentagonal region
Octagonal prism	Octagonal region

The polygonal regions that make up a prism are called its **faces.** For the sake of simplicity, the faces will be referred to as polygons rather than polygonal regions. The bases of a prism are two of its faces. The faces intersect in segments which are called the **edges** of the prism. The edges intersect in points which are called the **vertices** of the prism. A triangular prism has 5 faces, 9 edges, and 6 vertices.

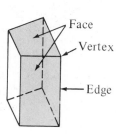
Face
Vertex
Edge

PRISMS

Example 2 Give the number of edges, faces, and vertices of each type of prism.

Prism	Edges	Faces	Vertices
Quadrangular prism	12	6	8
Pentagonal prism	15	7	10
Hexagonal prism	18	8	12

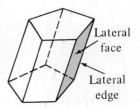

The faces of a prism that are not bases are called the **lateral faces.** The lateral faces of a prism are parallelograms. The edges that are not sides of the bases are called the **lateral edges.** A triangular prism has 3 lateral faces and 3 lateral edges.

Example 3 Give the number of lateral faces and lateral edges for each type of prism.

Prism	Lateral faces	Lateral edges
Quadrangular prism	4	4
Pentagonal prism	5	5
Hexagonal prism	6	6

In a *right prism*, the lateral faces and lateral edges are perpendicular to the bases. The lateral faces of a right prism are rectangles. In an *oblique prism*, the lateral faces and lateral edges are *not* perpendicular to the bases.

Right Prisms 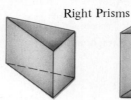 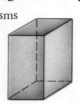　　　Oblique Prisms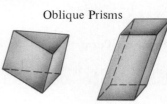

Example 4 Sketch a right pentagonal prism.

Draw 2 congruent pentagons with parallel sides.　　Connect the vertices.　　Be sure that all invisible edges are dashed.

Oral Exercises

1. Explain the difference between a plane figure and a space figure.

2. Name five plane figures. Name five space figures.

Identify each figure as completely as you can.

3.   4.   5.   6.   7.   8.

Written Exercises

Copy and complete the chart. Then sketch each prism.

	Type of Prism	No. of Lateral Edges	No. of Edges	No. of Vertices	No. of Bases	No. of Lateral Faces	No. of Faces	Type of Base
1.	Quadrangular			8				
2.	Pentagonal	5					7	
3.	Hexagonal				2			
4.	Octagonal		24					octagon
5.	Decagonal					10		

Sketch each of the following.

6. A right triangular prism whose bases are right triangles

7. A right triangular prism whose bases are equilateral triangles

8. A right quadrangular prism whose bases are rectangles (a rectangular solid)

9. A rectangular solid with all edges congruent (a cube)

10. A right octagonal prism

11. An oblique hexagonal prism

True or false? Refer to the chart above.

12. A prism has as many bases as lateral faces.

13. A prism has two more lateral edges than faces.

14. A prism has twice as many vertices as lateral faces.

15. A prism has the same number of lateral faces and lateral edges.

16. In a prism, the ratio of the number of vertices to the number of edges is 2:3.

17. A hexagonal prism has twice as many edges as a triangular prism.

PRISMS

527

18. Let V be the number of vertices, F be the number of faces, and E be the number of edges of a prism. What relationship exists between V, F, and E?

19. Suppose a prism has n lateral faces. Represent V, F, and E in terms of n and prove what you discovered in Exercise 18.

20. What is the measure of a dihedral angle formed by two adjacent lateral faces of a right prism whose bases are regular hexagons?

21. What is the measure of a dihedral angle formed by a base and a lateral face of a right prism whose bases are pentagons?

Cumulative Review _____

1. In $\odot O$, m $\angle AOB = 60$ and $AO = 12$. Find the length of $\overparen{AB}$. (Leave answer in terms of π.)

2. The length of the hypotenuse of an isosceles right triangle is 8. Find the length of a leg.

 # A Challenge To You

Inscribed Regular Polyhedrons

A regular tetrahedron is a space figure consisting of 4 faces that are congruent equilateral triangles. (See page 525.) A regular tetrahedron can be inscribed in a larger regular tetrahedron, as shown at the right. Each vertex of the smaller one is the center of a face of the larger one.

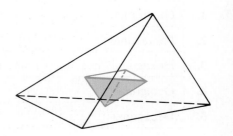

1. Draw a regular octahedron inscribed in a regular hexahedron.
2. Draw a regular hexahedron inscribed in a regular octahedron.
3. Copy and complete the chart. Is there a pattern that tells which polyhedrons can be inscribed in each other? If so, what is the pattern?

Polyhedron	Number of Faces	Number of Vertices
Tetrahedron	4	
Hexahedron		8
Octahedron		
Dodecahedron		20
Icosahedron	20	

16.2 Surface Areas of Prisms

OBJECTIVE ► **To find the lateral area and the total area of a *right* prism**

Since the faces of a prism consist of polygons, you can define the surface area of a prism as the sum of the areas of the faces of the prism. The **lateral area** *(L)* of a prism is the sum of the areas of the lateral faces. The **total area** *(T)* of a prism is the sum of the lateral area and the areas of the two bases. An **altitude** of a prism is a segment perpendicular to the plane of each base with endpoints in the planes of the bases. In a right prism, each lateral edge is also an altitude.

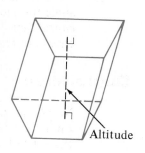
Altitude

For the prism below, two methods for finding the lateral area are shown.

First Method	Second Method
Each lateral face is a rectangle. Find the three areas, A_1, A_2, and A_3, and add.	"Unfold" the lateral faces. Find the area of the large rectangle formed.

Use the formula for the area of a rectangle:

$$A = bh$$
$$A_1 = 5 \cdot 12 = 60$$
$$A_2 = 3 \cdot 12 = 36$$
$$A_3 = 7 \cdot 12 = 84$$
$$A_1 + A_2 + A_3 = 180$$
$$L = 180$$

$$L = ph$$
$$= \begin{pmatrix} \text{perimeter} \\ \text{of} \\ \text{base} \end{pmatrix} \cdot \begin{pmatrix} \text{length of} \\ \text{altitude} \\ \text{of prism} \end{pmatrix}$$
$$= (3 + 5 + 7) \cdot \quad 12$$
$$= 15 \cdot 12$$
$$L = 180$$

Thus, the lateral area is 180 square units.
The second method above suggests the following theorem.

Theorem 16.1 For any right prism, lateral area = perimeter of base × length of an altitude.

$$L = ph$$

(See Exercise 18.)

SURFACE AREA OF PRISMS

529

Example **1** Find the lateral area of the right prism shown.

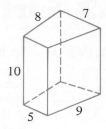

$$L = ph \qquad p = 5 + 9 + 7 + 8 = 29$$
$$L = 29 \cdot 10 \quad h = 10$$
$$L = 290$$

Thus, the lateral area is 290 square units.

Theorem 16.2 follows directly from the definition of total area.

Theorem 16.2 For any prism, total area = lateral area + 2 times base area.

$$T = L + 2B$$

A **rectangular solid** is a right prism whose bases are rectangles. A **cube** is a rectangular solid all of whose edges are congruent. In Examples 2 and 3, you will use Theorem 16.2 to find the total area of a rectangular solid and a right triangular prism, respectively.

Example **2** Find the total area of the rectangular solid shown.

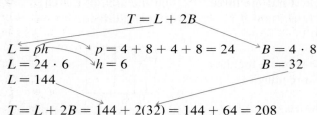

$$T = L + 2B$$

$$L = ph \qquad p = 4 + 8 + 4 + 8 = 24 \qquad B = 4 \cdot 8$$
$$L = 24 \cdot 6 \quad h = 6 \qquad\qquad\qquad B = 32$$
$$L = 144$$

$$T = L + 2B = 144 + 2(32) = 144 + 64 = 208$$
Thus, the total area is 208 square units.

Example **3** Find the total area of a right triangular prism with an altitude measuring 7 cm and whose bases are equilateral triangles with sides measuring 8 cm.

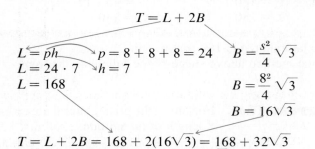

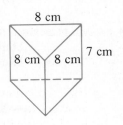

$$T = L + 2B$$

$$L = ph \qquad p = 8 + 8 + 8 = 24 \qquad B = \frac{s^2}{4}\sqrt{3}$$
$$L = 24 \cdot 7 \quad h = 7$$
$$L = 168 \qquad\qquad\qquad\qquad\qquad B = \frac{8^2}{4}\sqrt{3}$$
$$B = 16\sqrt{3}$$

$$T = L + 2B = 168 + 2(16\sqrt{3}) = 168 + 32\sqrt{3}$$
Thus, the total area is $168 + 32\sqrt{3}$ cm².

Written Exercises

Find the lateral area of each right prism. (Ex. 1–4)

A **1.**

2.

3.

4.

5. A lateral edge of a right prism measures 6 cm and the perimeter of a base is 25 cm. Find the lateral area.

7. Find the total area of a right prism whose bases are equilateral triangles with sides measuring 8 cm and with an altitude measuring 10 cm.

9. Find the total area of a rectangular solid whose dimensions are 6 mm, 8 mm, and 11 mm.

6. Find the total area of a cube with each edge 7 cm long.

8. The bases of a prism are regular pentagons with sides measuring 7 mm. An altitude measures 12 mm. Find the lateral area of the prism.

10. The walls and ceiling of a warehouse are to be painted. How many square meters must be covered if the warehouse is 120 m by 96 m with a ceiling 3 m high?

B **11.** An altitude of a right prism measures 14 m, and each base is a right triangle with legs measuring 6 m and 8 m. Find the total area.

13. Find the total area of a prism whose bases are regular hexagons with 8-cm sides and whose altitudes measure 16 cm.

C **15.** In a truncated prism, the bases are not parallel. Find the total area of the truncated right prism shown.

17. A truncated right prism has an equilateral triangular base with 12-unit sides. Two of the lateral edges measure 14 units and the third measures 9 units. Find the total area.

12. A base of a prism is a rhombus with diagonals measuring 10 cm and 24 cm. An altitude measures 16 cm. Find the lateral area.

14. The total area of a right prism is 210 square cm. Each base is a square 5 cm on a side. Find the length of an altitude of the prism.

16. A truncated right prism has a square base with 5-cm sides. Two of the lateral edges measure 8 cm and the other two measure 20 cm. Find the lateral area and the total area.

18. Prove Theorem 16.1.

CALCULATOR ACTIVITIES

Find the volume of each rectangular solid whose three dimensions are given. Give answers to the nearest hundredth.

1. 3.2 cm, 8.6 cm, 9.4 cm

2. 18.5 mm, 12.4 mm, 23.6 mm

3. 4.21 m, 7.93 m, 10.62 m

4. 19.23 cm, 26.35 cm, 31.94 cm

SURFACE AREAS OF PRISMS

16.3 Volumes of Prisms

OBJECTIVE ▶ **To find the volume of a prism**

To find any measure, an appropriate unit must be used. To find the surface area of a solid, a square unit is used. To find the *volume* of a solid, a *cubic unit* is used. A cubic unit of measure is a cube whose edges each measure 1 unit of length. For example, a cube with edges 1 centimeter long is called a *cubic centimeter* (cm³).

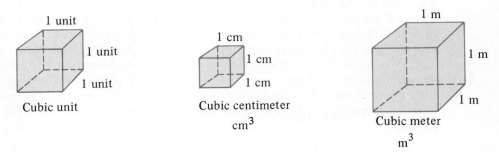

Cubic unit   Cubic centimeter   Cubic meter
                         cm³   m³

Example 1 The *volume* of a solid is the number of cubic units that can be contained in the solid. First, you will consider the volume of a rectangular solid.

Find the volume of the rectangular solid below.

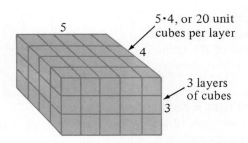

5·4, or 20 unit cubes per layer

3 layers of cubes

$$V = \begin{pmatrix} \text{no. of unit cubes} \\ \text{per layer} \end{pmatrix} \cdot \begin{pmatrix} \text{no. of} \\ \text{layers} \end{pmatrix}$$
$$= \quad \text{Base area} \quad \cdot \quad \text{length of an altitude}$$
$$= \quad\quad 20 \quad\quad \cdot \quad\quad 3$$
$$= \quad\quad 60$$

Thus, the volume is 60 cubic units.

The process used for finding the volume of the prism in Example 1 can be applied to all prisms, both right and oblique. The result is stated in Theorem 16.3, which is given without proof.

┌ **Theorem 16.3** For any prism, volume = base area × length of an ┐
altitude.

$$V = Bh$$

└───┘

The formula $V = Bh$ can be used to find the volume of any prism.

Example 2 Find the volume of the right prism shown below.

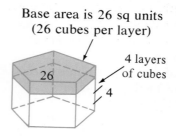

Base area is 26 sq units
(26 cubes per layer)

4 layers of cubes

$V = Bh = 26 \cdot 4 = 104$

Thus, the volume is 104 cubic units.

Example 3 The bases of a prism are equilateral triangles with each side measuring 4 cm. An altitude measures 9 cm. Find the volume of the prism.

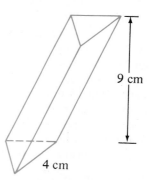

First, find the area of a base.

$$B = \frac{S^2}{4}\sqrt{3}$$

$$= \frac{4^2}{4}\sqrt{3}$$

$$= 4\sqrt{3} \qquad h = 9$$

$$V = Bh = (4\sqrt{3})(9) = 36\sqrt{3}$$

Thus, the volume is $36\sqrt{3}$ cm³.

Oral Exercises _____

1. Let l, w, and h be the dimensions of a rectangular solid. Give a formula for the volume.

2. Let s be the length of an edge of a cube. Give a formula for the volume.

What is the volume of each prism? The area of the base (B) and the altitude length (h) are given.

3. $B = 8$ cm², $h = 3$ cm
6. $B = 9$ m², $h = 6$ m

4. $B = 16$ mm², $h = 4$ mm
7. $B = 9\sqrt{2}$ cm², $h = 5$ cm

5. $B = 10$ cm², $h = 14$ cm
8. $B = 5\sqrt{3}$ m², $h = 4$ m

VOLUMES OF PRISMS

Written Exercises

Find the volume of each right prism. (Ex. 1–5)

1.

2.
25 sq u

3.
63 sq u

4.
10 sq u

5.

6. Find the volume of a cube whose edges each measure 5 cm.

7. Find the volume of a rectangular solid whose dimensions are 4, 7, and 11.

8. A lateral edge of a right prism measures 8 m. The area of the base is 45 m². Find the volume.

9. Find the volume of a prism whose bases are squares, 6 cm on a side, if an altitude measures 11 cm.

10. The bases of a prism are equilateral triangles with sides measuring 8 cm. An altitude measures 5 cm. Find the volume.

11. The bases of a prism are isosceles right triangles with legs measuring 10 m. An altitude measures 16 m. Find the volume.

12. A block is 18 mm wide, 30 mm long, and 9 mm high. Find its volume in cubic centimeters. [1 cm³ = 1,000 mm³]

13. Find the weight of a stone block 1 meter by 1.5 m, by 2 m if the stone weighs 560 kilograms per cubic meter.

14. The total area of a cube is 294 cm². Find the volume.

15. Each base of a rectangular solid measures 7 by 12. Find the length of an altitude if the volume is 504 cubic units.

16. An altitude of a prism measures 9 cm and the base is a right triangle with one leg measuring 5 cm and the hypotenuse measuring 13 cm. Find the volume.

17. How many bricks 20 cm by 10 cm by 5 cm are needed to build a wall 6 m long, 2 m high, and 0.5 m thick, if 10 per cent of the wall is mortar?

18. A cistern in the form of a rectangular solid measures 2 m by 2 m by 3 m. How many liters of water will it hold? [1 m³ = 1,000 L]

19. Find the volume of a prism whose bases are regular hexagons with 10-cm sides and whose altitude measures 12 cm.

20. The volume of a rectangular solid is 432 cubic units. Each side of its square base is $\frac{1}{2}$ the measure of an altitude. Find the area of the base.

21. Each lateral edge of a prism measures 14 cm and makes an angle of 45° with the plane of the base. The area of the base is 62 cm². Find the volume.

22. A diagonal of a face of a cube measures 8 cm. Find the volume of the cube.

23. The dimensions of a rectangular solid are in a ratio of 2:4:5. A diagonal measures $6\sqrt{5}$ cm. Find the volume.

24. If V is the volume of a cube and T is its total area, show that $V = \frac{T}{36}\sqrt{6T}$.

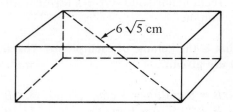

6 √5 cm

16.4 Cylinders

A *cylinder* is a solid that has many properties in common with a prism. A *circular cylinder* has two *bases* which are congruent circular regions lying in parallel planes. The *axis* is the line segment joining the centers of the two circles. An *altitude* is a segment perpendicular to the plane of each base, with endpoints in the planes of the bases.

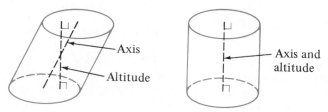

Oblique circular cylinder　　　　　Right circular cylinder

The cylinder on the left above is an *oblique circular cylinder*. Notice that in the cylinder on the right, the axis is also an altitude. When this is true, the cylinder is a *right circular cylinder*. From this point on, when the word "cylinder" is used, it will mean "right circular cylinder."

The lateral area (*L*) of a cylinder can be found in a way similar to the way the lateral area of a prism is found.

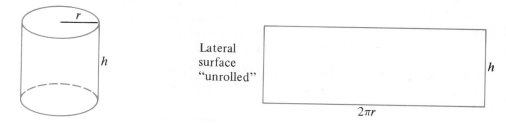

If the lateral surface of a cylinder is "unrolled," it becomes a rectangle. The length of the rectangle is equal to the circumference of a base. The width is equal to the measure of an altitude of the cylinder. Thus, the formula for the lateral area is $L = 2\pi r \cdot h$. Note that this formula is comparable to the formula for the lateral area of a prism, $L = ph$, where $p = 2\pi r$. This argument justifies the following theorem.

> **Theorem 16.4**　For a cylinder, lateral area = circumference of base × length of an altitude.
>
> $$L = 2\pi rh$$

The total area (T) of a cylinder is equal to the lateral area plus the areas of the two bases, as stated in Theorem 16.5.

Theorem 16.5 For a cylinder, total area = lateral area + 2 times base area.

$$T = \quad L \quad + 2B$$
$$T = \quad 2\pi rh \quad + 2\pi r^2$$
$$T = 2\pi r(h + r)$$

The formula $T = 2\pi r(h + r)$ is often the most convenient to use to find total area of a cylinder.

Example 1 The radius of a base of a cylinder is 6 cm long and an altitude is 8 cm long. Find the lateral area and the total area.

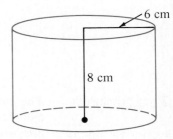

$$L = 2\pi rh \qquad T = 2\pi r(h + r)$$
$$= 2\pi \cdot 6 \cdot 8 \qquad = 2\pi \cdot 6(8 + 6)$$
$$= 96\pi \qquad = 12\pi \cdot 14$$
$$= 168\pi$$

Thus, the lateral area is 96π cm² and the total area is 168π cm².

Recall that the volume of a prism is the product of the area of a base and the length of an altitude. The same formula can be used to find the volume of a cylinder, where the area of a base is πr^2.

Theorem 16.6 For a cylinder, volume = base area × length of an altitude.

$$V = \pi r^2 h$$

Example 2 A water tank is in the shape of a large cylinder. The diameter of the base measures 3 m and an altitude measures 6 m. Find the volume.

$$V = \pi r^2 h \qquad d = 3, \text{ so } r = 1.5.$$
$$V = \pi (1.5)^2 \cdot 6$$
$$V = \pi \cdot 2.25 \cdot 6$$
$$V = 13.5\pi$$

Thus, the volume is 13.5π m³.

A *cylinder of revolution* is formed when a rectangle is revolved about one of its sides as an axis.

Example 3 Find the volume of the cylinder of revolution formed when a rectangle 3 cm by 8 cm is revolved about a 8-cm side.

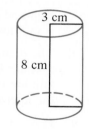

$$V = \pi r^2 h$$
$$= \pi \cdot 3^2 \cdot 8$$
$$= \pi 9 \cdot 8$$
$$= 72\pi$$

Thus, the volume is 72π cm³.

Summary	**Formulas for a Cylinder**

Lateral area: $L = 2\pi rh$
Total area: $T = 2\pi r(h + r)$
Volume: $V = \pi r^2 h$

Reading in Geometry

Replace the question mark with the correct expression from the column at the right.

1. If you unrolled a cylinder, it would look like a ?.
2. The area (A) of a rectangle is ?.
3. The length of an unrolled cylinder is the same as the ? of a circle.
4. The circumference (C) of a circle is ?.
5. The lateral surface (L) of a cylinder is ?.
6. The top of a cylinder is in the shape of a ?.
7. The area of a circle (A) is ?.
8. There are ? circles found on a cylinder.
9. The total area (T) of a cylinder is ?.
10. The ? of the bottom circle is πr^2.
11. The volume (V) of a cylinder is ?.

   a. circumference
   b. circle
   c. 2
   d. $2\pi rh + 2\pi r^2$
   e. $2\pi r$
   f. $2\pi rh$
   g. rectangle
   h. $\pi r^2 h$
   i. layers
   j. length $\times$ width
   k. πr^2
   l. area

Written Exercises

Find the lateral area, total area, and volume of each cylinder. Leave answers in terms of π.

Ⓐ 1.

2.

3.

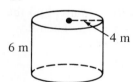

4.

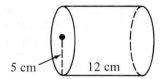

Leave answers in terms of π, whenever possible.

5. A cylindrical oil tank is 20 m high and the radius of its base is m 5 long. Find the volume.

6. Find the total area of a cylinder whose altitude measures 7 m and whose base has a radius 4 m long.

7. The diameter of the base of a cylinder is 16 cm long and its altitude measures 12 cm. Find the lateral area.

8. A cylindrical pail is 10 cm deep and the radius of its base is 5 cm long. Find the volume.

9. How many square cm of tin are required to make the pail in Exercise 8?

10. A concrete roller is 3 m long. Its diameter is 2 m long. How much area will it cover in 400 revolutions?

 11. A diameter of a cylindrical oil tank is 1 m long. The tank is 60 cm long. About how many liters of oil will it hold? [1 L = 1,000 cm³]

12. When a piece of iron is submerged in a cylindrical tank, the water level rises 6 cm. The diameter of the tank is 18 cm long. What is the volume of the piece of iron?

13. Suppose the rectangle in Example 3 is revolved about a 3-cm side. Compare the volume of the resulting cylinder of revolution to the volume of the one in the Example 3. Sketch the figure.

14. Consider the cylinder of revolution in Example 3 and the one in Exercise 13. Compare their lateral areas.

15. The measures of the sides of a rectangle are in the ratio 3:1. It is possible to form two cylinders of revolution with the rectangle. What is the ratio of the lateral areas of the two cylinders? [*Hint:* Let x and $3x$ represent the sides.]

16. Consider the two cylinders of revolution in Exercise 15. What is the ratio of the volumes of the two cylinders?

Refer to the figures at the right for Exercises 17–19.

17. A cylinder may be inscribed in a cube, as shown. What is the ratio of the volume of the cylinder to the volume of the cube?

18. A cylinder may be circumscribed about a cube as shown. What is the ratio of the volume of the cube to the volume of the cylinder?

19. Find the volume of the cylinder and the cube in Exercise 17 if $r = 3$. Then do the same for Exercise 18.

Cylinder inscribed in cube

Cylinder circumscribed about cube

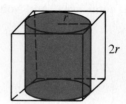
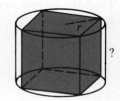

16.5 Pyramids

OBJECTIVES ► **To find the lateral area and the total area of a regular pyramid**
To find the volume of a pyramid

A *pyramid* is a solid whose base is a polygonal region; its *lateral faces* are triangular regions that share a common point called the *vertex*. The lateral faces intersect in segments called the lateral edges of the pyramid. The *altitude* of a pyramid is the segment from the vertex perpendicular to the plane of the base.

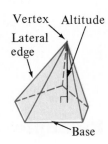

For the sake of simplicity, the faces of a pyramid will be referred to as polygons, even though they are polygonal regions.

A **regular pyramid** is a pyramid with the following special properties:
(1.) The base is a regular polygon.
(2.) The lateral faces are congruent isosceles triangles.
(3.) The altitude meets the base at its center.
The altitude of each lateral face of a regular pyramid is called the **slant height** of the pyramid.

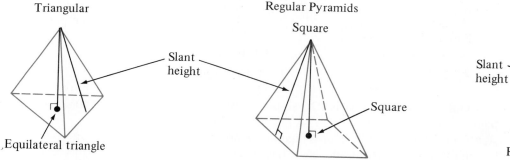

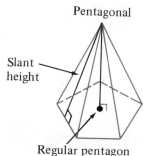

A formula for the lateral area of a regular pyramid can be derived as follows: Suppose the base of a regular pyramid has n sides. Let b be the length of each side of the base and l be the length of the slant height. Then the area of each lateral face is $\frac{1}{2} bl$. Since there are n lateral faces, the lateral area of the pyramid can be found by multiplying the area of a lateral face by n, as shown below.

$$\text{Lateral area} = \left(\begin{array}{c}\text{area of a}\\\text{lateral face}\end{array}\right) \cdot \left(\begin{array}{c}\text{number of sides}\\\text{of the base}\end{array}\right)$$

$$L = \frac{1}{2} bl \qquad \cdot \quad n$$

$$L = \frac{1}{2} l \cdot bn$$

But bn is the perimeter of the base.

So, $\qquad L = \frac{1}{2} lp.$

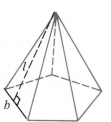

The argument above justifies the next theorem.

> **Theorem 16.7** For a regular pyramid, lateral area $= \frac{1}{2} \times$ length of slant height $\times$ perimeter of base.
> $$L = \frac{1}{2} lp$$
> total area = lateral area + base area.
> $$T = L + B$$

The formula used to find the base area (B) depends upon the type of base that the pyramid has. In Example 1, the base is a regular pentagon, and in Example 2, the base is a square.

Example 1 Find the lateral area and the total area of a regular pyramid whose slant height measures 11 and whose base is a regular pentagon with sides measuring 8 and apothem measuring 6.

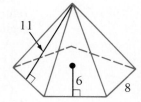

A regular pentagon has 5 congruent sides so $p = 5 \times 8$. ►

$$L = \frac{1}{2} lp \qquad\qquad T = L + B$$

$$= \frac{1}{2} \cdot 11 \cdot (5 \times 8) \qquad B = \frac{1}{2} ap \qquad ◄ \quad \text{\textit{Formula for area of}}$$
$$\text{\textit{a regular polygon}}$$

$$= \frac{1}{2} \cdot 11 \cdot 40 \qquad\qquad = \frac{1}{2} \cdot 6 \cdot 40$$

$$= 220 \qquad\qquad\qquad = 120$$

$$T = 220 + 120 = 340$$

Thus, the lateral area is 220 square units and the total area is 340 square units.

Example 2 Each edge of the base of a regular square pyramid measures 16 m and each lateral edge measures 17 m. Find the total area.

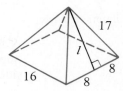

$$T = L + B$$
Find l, the length of the slant height.
Use the Pythagorean Theorem.
$$l^2 + 8^2 = 17^2$$
$$l^2 + 64 = 289$$
$$l^2 = 225$$
$$l = 15$$

A lateral face

$$L = \frac{1}{2} lp \longrightarrow p = 4 \times 16 = 64 \qquad B = s^2$$

$$L = \frac{1}{2} \cdot 15 \cdot 64 \qquad\qquad\qquad = 16^2 \quad ◄ \quad \text{\textit{Formula for area}}$$
$$\text{\textit{of a square}}$$

$$L = 480 \qquad\qquad\qquad\qquad = 256$$

$$T = L + B = 480 + 256 = 736$$
Thus, the total area is 736 m².

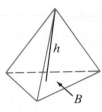
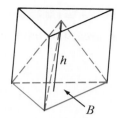

Suppose a pyramid and a prism have the same base and altitude, as shown in the figures above. The volume of the pyramid will be one third the volume of the prism. This leads to the following theorem, which is given without proof.

Theorem 16.8 For any pyramid, volume $= \frac{1}{3} \times$ base area $\times$ length of altitude.

$$V = \frac{1}{3} Bh$$

In Example 3, the formula $V = \frac{1}{3} Bh$ is used to find the volume of a regular triangular pyramid. The base of a regular triangular pyramid is an equilateral triangle.

Example 3

Each edge of the base of a regular triangular pyramid is 6 cm long and the altitude is 5 cm long. Find the volume.

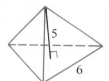

$V = \frac{1}{3} Bh$

$B = \frac{s^2}{4} \sqrt{3}$ ◀ *Formula for area of an equilateral △*

$B = \frac{6^2}{4} \sqrt{3}$

$B = 9\sqrt{3}$

$V = \frac{1}{3} Bh \longrightarrow h = 5$

$V = \frac{1}{3} (9\sqrt{3})\, 5$

$V = 15\sqrt{3}$

Thus, the volume is $15\sqrt{3}$ cm³.

Summary

Formulas for a Pyramid

Lateral Area: $L = \frac{1}{2} lp$ $\begin{cases} \text{Regular} \\ \text{pyramid only} \end{cases}$

Total Area: $T = L + B$

Volume: $V = \frac{1}{3} Bh$

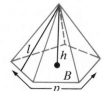

Written Exercises

Find the lateral area, the total area, and the volume of each regular pyramid. (Ex. 1–4)

A 1.
8   9
6
57 sq u

2.
10   8
6

3.
13   12
10

4.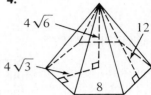
$4\sqrt{6}$ 12
$4\sqrt{3}$ 8

5. Find the lateral area of a regular pyramid whose slant height is 7 cm long and whose base has a perimeter of 20 cm.

6. Find the volume of a pyramid whose base is a square with sides 6 cm long and whose altitude measures 15 cm.

7. Each side of the base of a regular triangular pyramid measures 6 m. Each lateral edge measures 5 m. Find the total area of the pyramid.

8. The altitude of a pyramid measures 12 m. The base is a right triangle with legs measuring 8 m and 11 m. Find the volume.

9. Each side of the base of a regular square pyramid measures 12 cm and each lateral edge measures 10 cm. Find the lateral area and the total area of the pyramid.

10. The base of a pyramid is a rhombus with diagonals measuring 7 and 8. The altitude of the pyramid measures 21. Find the volume.

B 11. The perimeter of the base of a regular pyramid is 56 m and the lateral area is 224 m². How long is the slant height?

12. The lateral area of a regular pyramid is 476 square units and the slant height measures 14 units. Find the perimeter of the base.

13. The slant height of a regular square pyramid measures 26 cm and a side of the base measures 20 cm. Find the lateral area, total area, and volume.

14. Find the lateral area and the total area of a regular hexagonal pyramid whose lateral edges measure 25 cm and whose base has sides measuring 14 cm.

15. The altitude of a regular square pyramid measures 4 cm and a side of the base measures 6 cm. Find the lateral area and the total area.

16. The altitude of a regular triangular pyramid measures 8 cm and each side of the base measures 18 cm. Find the lateral area and the total area.

C 17. Each side of the base of a regular triangular pyramid measures 12 units. The slant height makes an angle of 45° with the altitude. Find the total area and the volume of the pyramid.

18. Derive a formula for the total area of a regular pyramid in terms of its slant height, apothem, and perimeter of the base.

19. The base of a regular square pyramid is inscribed in the base of a cylinder. The two figures have altitudes of the same length. Find the ratio of the volume of the pyramid to the volume of the cylinder. [*Hint:* Express *s* in terms of *r*.]

20. Repeat Exercise 19 for a regular triangular pyramid.

Cumulative Review _____

Find the area of each polygon.

1. An equilateral triangle whose perimeter is 24

2. An equilateral triangle whose altitude measures $5\sqrt{3}$

3. A square whose apothem measures 7

4. A square whose diagonal measures 20

Algebra Review

OBJECTIVE ▶ **To solve systems of equations**

To solve a system of equations:
(1) Get one equation with only one variable;
(2) Solve for the variable;
(3) Substitute the value in one of the original equations and solve for the other variable.

Example   Solve this system. $5x - 3y = 2$
$\qquad\qquad\qquad\qquad\qquad\quad 4x + 2y = 6$

Multiply each side by 2. ▶ $\quad 2(5x - 3y) = 2(2)$
Multiply each side by 3. ▶ $\quad 3(4x + 2y) = 3(6)$
$\qquad\qquad\qquad\qquad\qquad 10x - 6y = \ \ 4$ ◀ *Now the coefficients of y are opposites.*
$\qquad\qquad\qquad\qquad\underline{\quad 12x + 6y = 18}$
Add the equations. ▶ $\qquad 22x \qquad\ = 22$
$\qquad\qquad\qquad\qquad\qquad\qquad x = 1$

$\qquad\qquad\qquad\qquad\qquad\quad 5x - 3y = 2$
Substitute 1 for x. ▶ $\quad 5(1) - 3y = 2$
$\qquad\qquad\qquad\qquad\qquad\quad 5 - 3y = 2$
$\qquad\qquad\qquad\qquad\qquad\quad\ - 3y = -3$
$\qquad\qquad\qquad\qquad\qquad\qquad y = 1$ **Thus, (1, 1) is the solution.**

Solve.

1. $x - y = 7$
$\quad\ x + y = 9$

2. $-2x + y = 6$
$\quad\ \ 2x + 3y = 10$

3. $3x - y = 5$
$\quad\ 2x + y = 5$

4. $3x - 4y = 4$
$\quad\ 2x + 4y = 16$

5. $-x + y = -4$
$\quad\ 3x - 2y = 12$

6. $2x + y = 9$
$\quad\ 3x + 2y = 16$

7. $5x + 2y = 14$
$\quad\ 2x - y = 3$

8. $-12x - y = 14$
$\quad\ \ 5x + 3y = -11$

PYRAMIDS

543

16.6 Cones

OBJECTIVES ► **To find the lateral area, the total area, and the volume of a cone**

A **right circular cone** is a solid that has many properties in common with regular pyramids. The following terms apply to a right circular cone.

1. The **base** is a circular region.
2. The **vertex** is a point that lies on the line perpendicular to the plane of the base at its center.
3. The **altitude** is a segment joining the vertex to the center of the base.
4. A **slant height**, or *element*, is a segment joining the vertex to a point on the circle which bounds the base.
5. The **lateral surface** is the union of all the slant heights. From this point on, the word "cone" will mean "right circular cone." Notice that the regular pyramids below resemble the cone.

Regular pyramids

6 sides

12 sides

24 sides

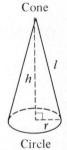

Cone

Circle

A cone is comparable to a regular pyramid with an almost circular base. The circumference of the base of a cone corresponds to the perimeter of the base of a regular pyramid. The table below shows how the formulas for a cone are derived from the formulas for a regular pyramid. The formulas are summarized in Theorem 16.9, which is given without proof.

Formulas	Regular Pyramid	Cone
Lateral area	$L = \frac{1}{2} lp$	$L = \frac{1}{2} lc$ $L = \frac{1}{2} l(2\pi r)$ $L = \pi r l$
Total area	$T = L + B$	$T = L + B$ $T = \pi r l + \pi r^2$ $T = \pi r (l + r)$
Volume	$V = \frac{1}{3} Bh$	$V = \frac{1}{3} Bh$ $V = \frac{1}{3} (\pi r^2) h$ $V = \frac{1}{3} \pi r^2 h$

Note:
$c = 2\pi r$
$B = \pi r^2$
$h = $ length of altitude
$l = $ length of slant height

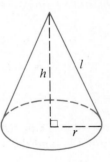

┌ Theorem 16.9 For a cone, lateral area (L) is $\pi r l$, total area (T) is $\pi r(l + r)$, volume (V) is $\frac{1}{3}\pi r^2 h$.

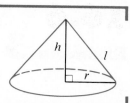

Examples 1 and 2 below are applications of these formulas for a cone.

Example 1 Find the lateral area, the total area, and the volume of the cone shown at the right.

$L = \pi r l$	$T = \pi r(l + r)$	$V = \frac{1}{3}\pi r^2 h$
$= \pi \cdot 9 \cdot 15$	$= \pi \cdot 9(15 + 9)$	$= \frac{1}{3}\pi \cdot 9^2 \cdot 12$
$= 135\pi$	$= \pi \cdot 9 \cdot 24$	$= \frac{1}{3}\pi \cdot 81 \cdot 12$
	$= 216\pi$	$= 324\pi$

Thus, the lateral area is 135π square units, the total area is 216π square units, and the volume is 324π cubic units.

In Example 2, the length of the radius of the base and the length of the slant height of a cone are given. The Pythagorean theorem must be used to find the length of the altitude.

Example 2 The radius of the base of a cone measures 9 cm and the slant height measures 18 cm. Find the lateral area, total area, and volume.

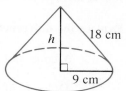

$$\text{Find } h: \quad h^2 + 9^2 = 18^2$$
$$h^2 + 81 = 324$$
$$h^2 = 243$$
$$h = \sqrt{243}, \text{ or } 9\sqrt{3}$$

$L = \pi r l$	$T = \pi r(l + r)$	$V = \frac{1}{3}\pi r^2 h$
$= \pi \cdot 9 \cdot 18$	$= \pi \cdot 9(18 + 9)$	$= \frac{1}{3}\pi \cdot 9^2 \cdot 9\sqrt{3}$
$= 162\pi$	$= \pi \cdot 9 \cdot 27$	$= \frac{1}{3}\pi \cdot 81 \cdot 9\sqrt{3}$
	$= 243\pi$	$= 243\sqrt{3}\pi$

Thus, the lateral area is 162π cm², the total area is 243π cm², and the volume is $243\pi\sqrt{3}$ cm³.

CONES

A **cone of revolution** is formed when a right triangle is revolved about one of its legs as an axis.

Example 3 Find the volume of the cone of revolution formed when a right triangle with legs measuring 4 and 9 are revolved about the 9 = unit leg.

Substitute 4 for r and 9 for h. ► $V = \frac{1}{3}\pi r^2 h$

$= \frac{1}{3}\pi \cdot 4^2 \cdot 9$

$= \frac{1}{3}\pi \cdot 16 \cdot 9$

$= 48\pi$

Thus, the volume is 48π cubic units.

Summary | **Formulas for a Cone**

Lateral area: $L = \pi r l$
Total area: $T = \pi r(l + r)$
Volume: $V = \frac{1}{3}\pi r^2 h$

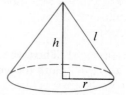

Reading in Geometry _____

Explain the difference between each pair of terms.

1. A cone and a regular pyramid

2. The lateral area and the total area of a cone

3. An element of a cone and the slant height of a cone

4. An element of a cone and the altitude of a cone

Written Exercises _____

Find the lateral area, total area, and volume of each cone. Leave answers in terms of π.

Ⓐ 1.
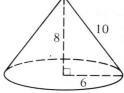

2.

3.
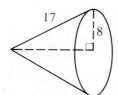

4.

Leave answers in terms of π, wherever possible.

5. The slant height of a cone measures 18 m and the altitude measures 9 m. Find the length of the radius of the base.

6. The slant height of a cone measures 16 cm and the radius of the base measures 5 cm. Find the lateral area and the total area.

7. The altitude of a cone measures 12 cm and the radius of the base measures 6 cm. Find the length of the slant height.

8. The radius of the base of a cone measures 3 units and the altitude measures 7 units. Find the volume.

9. The slant height of a cone measures 20 m and the radius of the base measures 12 m. Find the volume.

10. The altitude of a cone measures 24 units and the slant height measures 26 units. Find the lateral area and the total area.

11. A cone and a cylinder have congruent bases, and their altitudes have the same measure. Compare their volumes.

12. A cone and a cylinder have congruent bases. The altitude of the cone is three times as long as the altitude of the cylinder. Compare their volumes.

B 13. The area of the base of a cone is 49π square units and the slant height measures 20 units. Find the length of the altitude.

14. The volume of a cone is 320π cm³ and the altitude measures 15 cm. Find the length of the radius of the base.

15. Suppose the triangle in Example 3 is revolved about the 4-unit leg. Compare the volume of the resulting cone of revolution with the volume of the cone in Example 3.

16. Consider the cone of revolution in Example 3 and the cone in Exercise 15. Compare their lateral areas.

17. The measures of the legs of a right triangle are in a ratio of $4:1$. It is possible to form two cones of revolution with the right triangle. What is the ratio of the lateral areas of the two cones? [*Hint:* Let x and $4x$ represent the legs.]

18. Consider the two cones of revolution in Exercise 17. What is the ratio of the volumes of the two cones?

C 19. Suppose a square with 6-cm sides is revolved about a diagonal as an axis. Find the volume.

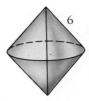

6

20. Find the surface area of the figure in Exercise 19.

21. Suppose a 3-4-5 right triangle is revolved about its hypotenuse as an axis. Find the volume.

22. Find the surface area of the figure in Exercise 21.

23. In the figure shown, the length of the altitude is twice the length of the radius of the base. Find the ratio of the volume of the cone to the volume of the cylinder.

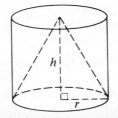

24. For the cone and cylinder in Exercise 23, what is the ratio of their lateral areas?

25. What is the ratio of their total areas?

CALCULATOR ACTIVITIES

A calculator can be useful in obtaining approximations of areas and volumes where π is involved. The formulas for a cone can be rewritten in the "language" of the calculator as follows:

$$L = rl\pi \qquad T = (l + r)r\pi \qquad V = \frac{r \cdot r \cdot h}{3}\pi$$

If your calculator does not have a π button, you may omit the part of each exercise which requires a π button.

Example Find three *different* approximations for the volume of a cone if $r = 7.5$ and $h = 6.3$. Use 3.14, 3.1416, and the π button on your calculator.

$$V = \frac{r \cdot r \cdot h}{3}\pi = \frac{(7.5)(7.5)(6.3)}{3}\pi$$

Press   → 7.5 ⊗ 7.5 ⊗ 6.3 ⊕ 3 ⊜
Display → 118.125   ← Write down.
Press   → ⊗ 3.14 ⊜
Display → 370.9125   ← Write down and clear.

Press   → 118.125 ⊗ 3.1416 ⊜
Display → 371.1015   ← Write down and clear.

Press   → 118.125 ⊗ π ⊜
Display → 371.10064   ← Write down and clear.

Thus, approximations for the volume are
     370.9125 if $\pi \doteq 3.14$,
     371.1015 if $\pi \doteq 3.1416$ ◄
     371.10064 if the π button is pressed.

Notice that the π button approximation lies between the other two.

Find three different approximations for the lateral area, total area, and volume of each cone.

	Find	r	l	h	3.14 for π	3.1416 for π	π button
1.	Lateral Area	3.2	6.5	—			
2.	Total Area	5.8	4.5	—			
3.	Volume	7.6	—	8.3			

16.7 Spheres

OBJECTIVES ► **To find the area and the volume of a sphere**

Recall that a circle is the set of all points in a plane at a given distance from a fixed point called the center. By removing the restriction "in a plane" and moving into space, you can define a sphere in a similar manner. A **sphere** is the set of *all* points at a given distance from a given point called the **center.** Most terms defined for circles also apply to spheres. For example, a **radius** of a sphere is a segment that joins the center and any point on the sphere.

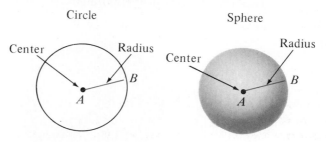

A **great circle of a sphere** is the intersection of the sphere and any plane that contains the center of the sphere. **Thus,** a radius of a great circle is also a radius of the sphere.

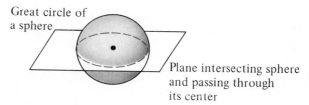

Plane intersecting sphere and passing through its center

Example 1 Find the area of a great circle of a sphere whose radius measures 7.

$$A = \pi r^2$$
$$A = \pi 7^2$$
$$A = 49\pi \text{ square units}$$

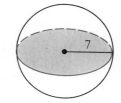

Two intersecting great circles formed by perpendicular planes divide a sphere into four quadrants. It can be proved in advanced geometry that the surface area of a quadrant is equal to the area of a great circle. Thus, the area of a quadrant is πr^2. This suggests the next theorem.

One quadrant ($\frac{1}{4}$) of a sphere

Two intersecting great circles formed by perpendicular planes

SPHERES

⌐ Theorem 16.10 For a sphere, area = 4 × area of great circle. ¬
$$A = 4\pi r^2$$

Example 2 Find the area of a sphere with a 5-cm radius.

$A = 4\pi r^2 = 4\pi \cdot 5^2 = 4\pi \cdot 25 = 100\pi$

Thus, the area is 100π cm².

Suppose you cut a solid sphere into pyramidlike figures. Use enough "pyramids" to cover the entire sphere. (Only 3 are shown.) Let B_1, B_2, B_3, . . ., B_n be the areas of the bases of the pyramids.

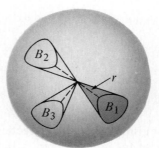

Volume of a pyramid $= \frac{1}{3}Bh$
Volume of shaded pyramid $= \frac{1}{3}B_1 r$

The volume of each "pyramid" is $\frac{1}{3}Bh$, where h is the length of the radius of the sphere.

Volume of sphere = Sum of volumes of pyramids
$$V = \frac{1}{3}B_1 r + \frac{1}{3}B_2 r + \frac{1}{3}B_3 r + \cdots + \frac{1}{3}B_n r$$
$$= \frac{1}{3}r(B_1 + B_2 + B_3 + \cdots + B_n)$$
$$= \frac{1}{3}r \text{ (area of sphere)}$$
$$= \frac{1}{3}r(4\pi r^2)$$
$$= \frac{4}{3}\pi r^3$$

Thus, you have derived a formula for the volume of a sphere, as stated in Theorem 16.11.

⌐ Theorem 16.11 For a sphere, the volume is $\frac{4}{3}\pi r^3$. ¬

$$V = \frac{4}{3}\pi r^3$$

CHAPTER SIXTEEN

Example **3** Find the volume of a sphere with a 9-cm radius.

$$V = \frac{4}{3}\pi r^3 = \frac{4}{3}\pi \cdot 9^3 = \frac{4}{3}\pi \; 729 = 972\pi$$

Thus, the volume is 972π cm³.

Summary

Formulas for a Sphere

Area: $A = 4\pi r^2$

Volume: $V = \frac{4}{3}\pi r^3$

Written Exercises

Find the area and volume of each sphere. Leave answers in terms of π. (Ex. 1–4)

 1.

 2.

 3.

 4.

Leave answers in terms of π, whenever possible

5. A baseball has a radius 7 cm long. Find its surface area.
7. The area of a great circle of a sphere is 54π cm². Find the area of the sphere.
9. The diameter of a sphere is 8 m long. Find the area and the volume.

 11. Find the length of a radius of a sphere whose area is 196π cm².
13. Find the length of a radius of a sphere whose volume is 972π cm³.

15. If the number of square units in the area of a sphere is equal to the number of cubic units in its volume, find the length of a radius of the sphere.

6. Find the volume of a sphere with a radius 3 cm long.
8. How much air can be pumped into a basketball if its maximum diameter measures 20 cm?
10. Two spheres have radii of lengths 1 mm and 4 mm. What is the ratio of their surface areas?

12. A great circle of a sphere has an area of 64π square units. Find the volume.
14. If the length of the radius of a sphere is doubled, what happens to the area of the sphere? to the volume?
16. Find the volume of metal in a hollow metal ball if its outside diameter measures 12 cm and its inside diameter measures 10 cm.

17. The radius of a sphere is 13 cm long. How far from the center of the sphere should a plane be passed so as to intersect the sphere in a circle whose area is 144π cm²?

18. Two spheres resting on a table touch each other. One sphere has a radius that is 5 cm long and the other has a radius that is 8 cm long. How far apart are the centers of the spheres.

19. If a sphere with radius of length r is inscribed in a cube, what is the ratio of the volume of the sphere to the volume of the cube? [*Hint:* The height of the cube equals the length of a diameter of the sphere.]

20. If a sphere with radius of length r is inscribed in a cylinder, what is the ratio of the volume of the sphere to the volume of the cylinder? [*Hint:* The height of the cylinder equals the length of a diameter of the sphere.]

→ A Challenge To You

It can be shown that in the picture below, the volume of the cylinder is equal to the volume of the sphere plus the volume of the cone. In the mobile shown, the cylinder will balance the sphere and the cone combined if all are solid figures constructed from the same material.

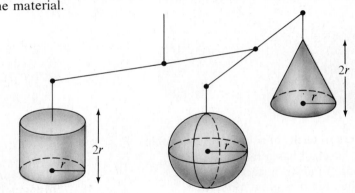

Volume of cylinder	=	Volume of sphere	+	Volume of cone

$$V = \pi r^2 h \longleftarrow h = 2r \qquad V = \frac{4}{3}\pi r^3 \qquad V = \frac{1}{3}\pi r^2 h \longleftarrow h = 2r$$

$$V = \pi r^2(2r) \qquad\qquad\qquad V = \frac{1}{3}\pi r^2(2r)$$

$$V = 2\pi r^3 \qquad\qquad\qquad\qquad V = \frac{2}{3}\pi r^3$$

$$2\pi r^3 = \frac{4}{3}\pi r^3 + \frac{2}{3}\pi r^3$$

Construct a mobile with figures similar to the ones shown. Why might the balance system need to be adjusted?

1. Concrete is usually sold by the yard. A yard of concrete is really one-cubic yard in volume. How many yards of concrete must be ordered to pour the rectangular section shown?

2. A number $2\frac{1}{2}$ can of peaches is 10.0 cm in diameter and 11.0 cm tall. A number 10 can is 15.3 cm in diameter and 17.7 cm tall. How many times more peaches should the number 10 can hold? If a number $2\frac{1}{2}$ can sells for $0.50, then what is the most you should expect to pay for the large can?

3. "Fancy pack" treats containing nuts and dried fruit are packed in cones 12 cm tall and 6 cm in diameter or in cylinders 7 cm in diameter and 4 cm deep. Which contains more? How much more?

4. A restaurant owner wishes to use cups for her expensive desserts that look large but contain a small amount. Which of the cups pictured should she use for the expensive dessert? Use your calculator to find the difference.

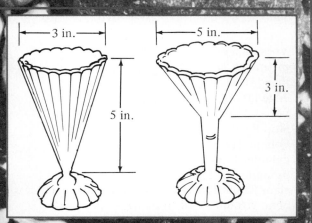

Chapter Sixteen Review

Sketch each of the following. Then state how many edges, vertices, and faces each has. [16.1]

1. a cube

2. a right hexagonal prism

Find the lateral area, total area, and volume. Leave answers in terms of π. [16.2, 16.3]

3. rectangular solid

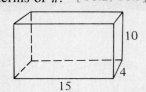

4. right prism

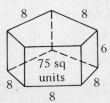

5. right prism

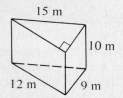

6. [16.4]

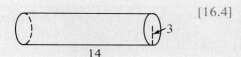

Vocabulary
prism [16.1]
face [16.1]
edge [16.1]
vertex [16.1]
altitude [16.2]
volume [16.3]
cylinder [16.4]
pyramid [16.5]
slant height [16.5]
cone [16.6]
sphere [16.7]

7. regular pyramid [16.5]

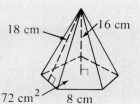

8. regular pyramid

9. cone [16.6]

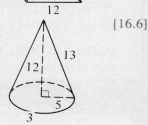

10. cone

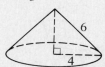

Leave answers in terms of π.

11. The radius of a sphere measures 6 cm. Find [16.7]

12. The diameter of a sphere measures 4 cm. Find the volume.

13. The volume of a rectangular solid is 300 m³. The base is a rectangle 4 m by 15 m. Find the length of an altitude. [16.3]

14. A rectangle 7 cm by 9 cm is revolved about a 9-cm side as an axis. Find the total area of the cylinder of revolution formed. [16.4]

***15.** Each side of the base of a regular triangular pyramid is 12 cm long. A slant height makes an angle of 60° with the altitude. Find the total area and volume of the pyramid. [16.5]

***16.** Suppose a square with 8-cm sides is revolved about a diagonal as an axis. Find the volume of the figure formed. [16.6]

Chapter Sixteen Test

Sketch each of the following. Then state how many edges, faces, and vertices each has.

1. a rectangular solid

2. a right pentagonal prism

Find the lateral area, total area, and volume. Leave answers in terms of π.

3. rectangular solid

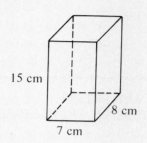

15 cm

8 cm

7 cm

4. right prism

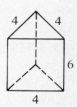

4   4

6

4

5. cylinder

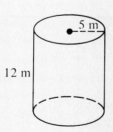

5 m

12 m

6. regular pyramid

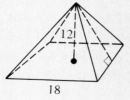

12

18

7. cone

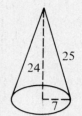

24   25

7

8. cone

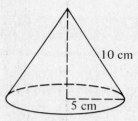

10 cm

5 cm

Leave answers in terms of π.

9. The diameter of a sphere measures 4 cm. Find the area.

10. The radius of a sphere measures 3 cm. Find the volume.

11. Find the volume of a prism whose bases are regular hexagons with 4-cm sides and whose altitude measures 10 cm.

*12. Each side of the base of a regular square pyramid is 8 cm long. A slant height makes an angle of 45° with the altitude. Find the volume of the pyramid.

*13. Suppose a square with 12-cm sides is revolved about a diagonal as an axis. Find the area of the figure formed.

Computer Activities

You often need to find the surface area of a solid figure when you wrap a package, paint, or wallpaper. You can use the program below to find the total area of any prism. Use the BASIC formula:

$$T = L + 2 * B$$

where **T** is total area
L is lateral area (**L = P * H**)
B is base area
P is perimeter of base
H is measure of altitude of prism

See the computer section on page 560 for more information.

PROGRAM

```
10 PRINT "PROGRAM FINDS THE TOTAL AREA OF ANY PRISM"
20 PRINT "TYPE IN PERIMETER OF BASE, ALTITUDE OF PRISM, BASE AREA"
30 INPUT P, H, B
40 LET L = P * H
50 LET T = L + {2 * B}
60 PRINT "TOTAL AREA ="; T
70 PRINT "DO YOU WANT THE TOTAL AREA FOR ANOTHER PRISM?"
80 PRINT "ENTER YES OR NO"
90 INPUT N$
100 IF N$ = "YES" THEN 20
110 END
```

Exercises

Run the program above for the following values. (Ex. 1–2)
1. $P = 10$, $H = 4$, $B = 6$
2. $P = 4$, $H = 1$, $B = 1$
3. Alter the program above to compute the base area for rectangular, triangular, or regular hexagonal bases. The type of base is given as input instead of **B**. Start the program with the following statements.

```
10 PRINT "PROGRAM FINDS THE TOTAL AREA OF ANY RIGHT PRISM"
20 PRINT "TYPE IN PERIMETER OF BASE, ALTITUDE OF PRISM"
30 INPUT P, H
40 PRINT "ENTER TYPE OF BASE"
50 PRINT "ENTER 1 FOR RECTANGLE"
60 PRINT "ENTER 2 FOR TRIANGLE"
70 PRINT "ENTER 3 FOR REGULAR HEXAGON"
```

4. Write a program to find the volume of a cone, pyramid, sphere, or cylinder.

College Prep Test

Directions: In each item you are to compare a quantity in Column 1 with a quantity in Column 2. Write the letter of the correct answer from these choices:

    A—The quantity in Column 1 is greater than the quantity in Column 2.
    B—The quantity in Column 2 is greater than the quantity in Column 1.
    C—The quantity in Column 1 is equal to the quantity in Column 2.
    D—The relationship cannot be determined from the given information.

Notes: Information centered over both columns refers to one or both of the quantities to be compared.

    A symbol that appears in both columns has the same meaning in each column and all variables represent real numbers.

Sample Question and Answer.

Column 1		Column 2
Area $\odot O$		25π

$$DO \perp OC$$
$$\text{Area } \triangle DOC = 12.5$$

Answer: C. Since $\overline{DO} \perp \overline{OC}$, Area $\triangle DOC = \frac{1}{2} DO \cdot OC = 12.5$ and $DO \cdot OC = 25$

$$\text{Area } \odot O = \pi r^2 = \pi(DO \cdot OC) = 25\pi$$

Column 1   **Column 2**

1. Volume of cylinder A Volume of cylinder B

2. Total Area of A Total Area of B

3. Volume of Cone

$$\frac{\text{height of Cone}}{\text{height of Cylinder}} = \frac{3}{1}$$
$$\frac{\text{base of Cone}}{\text{base of Cylinder}} = 1$$

   Volume of Cylinder

4. No. of edges in a triangular prism.   No. of vertices in a hexagonal prism.

Column 1   **Column 2**

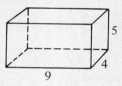

5. Volume of above Prism   Volume of above Prism

6. Volume of cylinder   Volume of sphere

7. Lateral area of cylinder   Area of sphere

8. Area of $ABCD$ Area of Circle O

$$BC = 25\pi$$
$$DC = 10$$

9. Perimeter of $ABCD$ 20

10. Area of shaded portion $25\pi - 20$

$$AB = BC = CD = AD = OD$$
$$\text{Perimeter } \triangle ODC = 15$$

Cumulative Review (Chapters 1–16)

Write the letter that indicates the best answer.

1. If the measure of an angle is 10° more than the measure of its supplement, then the measure of the angle is

   (A) 85° (B) 95°
   (C) 170° (D) none of these

2. It is possible for a triangle to be

   (A) both scalene and obtuse
   (B) both equilateral and acute
   (C) both of these
   (D) neither of these

3. Each interior angle of a regular polygon with nine sides measures

   (A) 120° (B) 144°
   (C) $147\frac{3}{11}$° (D) none of these

4. 8 is the geometric mean of 2 and

   (A) 16 (B) 32
   (C) 64 (D) none of these

5. If the hypotenuse of a 45°–45° right triangle is 10 m long, then the length of a leg is

   (A) 5 (B) $5\sqrt{2}$ m
   (C) 10 (D) $10\sqrt{2}$

6. A central angle and an inscribed angle of a circle intercept the same arc. If the inscribed angle measures 35°, then the central angle measures

   (A) $17\frac{1}{2}$° (B) 35°
   (C) 70° (D) none of these

7. For points $P(-5, 2)$ and $Q(3, -4)$, PQ is equal to

   (A) $2\sqrt{2}$ (B) 10
   (C) 100 (D) none of these

8. An equation in Standard Form for the line through $A(3, 1)$ and $B(-2, 5)$ is

   (A) $4x + 5y = 17$ (B) $-4x + 5y = 7$
   (C) $y - 1 = -\frac{4}{5}(x - 3)$ (D) none of these

9. The locus of points equidistant from the sides of an angle is

   (A) a point (B) a line
   (C) a circle (D) none of these

10. In $\triangle ABC$, $\overline{AC} \cong \overline{BC}$, AC is 10 cm, and AB is 16 cm. The centroid of $\triangle ABC$ is _____ from $\overline{AB}$.

    (A) 2 cm (B) 3 cm
    (C) 6 cm (D) none of these

11. In $\odot O$, if $OF < OE$, then

    (A) $AB < CD$
    (B) $<COD > \angle AOB$
    (C) $CF > EB$
    (D) all of these

12. If a radius of a sphere measures 6 cm, then the volume is

    (A) 72π (B) 144π
    (C) 288π (D) none of these

13. The total area of the figure shown is

    (A) 50π
    (B) 75π
    (C) $50\sqrt{3}\pi$
    (D) $25(\pi + \sqrt{3})$

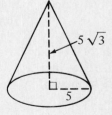

True or false

14. The distance between two points on a number line is the absolute value of the difference of the coordinates of the two points.

15. A postulate is a statement to be proved.

16. If two lines are parallel, then they are not skew.

17. A concave polygon cannot be equiangular.

18. The diagonals of a rhombus are congruent.

19. If the measure of a base of a trapezoid is 3 units longer than the measure of the median, then the measure of the other base is 3 units shorter than the measure of the median.

Find each indicated measure.

20. Given: $\overline{ST} \parallel \overline{PQ}$, $PS = 5$, $SR = 4$, and $ST = 6$. Find PQ.

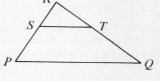

21. The angle of elevation from a spot on the ground to the top of a tree measures 48°. The spot is 5 m from the base of the tree. How tall is the tree, to the nearest tenth of a meter?

22. Given: $\odot O$ with $m\widehat{QR} = 100$, $m\widehat{QS} = 30$, and $m\widehat{ST} = 136$. Find $m \angle P$.

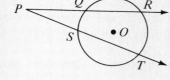

23. Each side of an equilateral triangle measures 9. Find the area.

24. Give the slope of the line perpendicular to $\overleftrightarrow{AB}$ for $A(-3, 4)$, $B(-2, -1)$.

25. Find the coordinates of the center and the length of a radius of a circle with the equation $x^2 + y^2 - 6x + 10y = 15$

Sketch and describe each locus. Show all possible cases.

26. The locus of points 4 cm from a given line

27. The locus of points less than 2 cm from a given point.

28. The locus of points equidistant from two given points and at a given distance from a given point

Prove the following:

29. Given: $\overline{WX} \cong \overline{ZY}$, $\overline{WX} \subset \overline{ZY}$, and $m \angle ZVW < m \angle ZVY$
    Prove: $ZW < ZY$

Leave answers in terms of π.

30. Find the lateral area, the total area, and the volume of the cylinder shown.

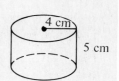

31. Find the lateral area of the regular pyramid shown.

32. Suppose a rhombus with 5-cm sides is revolved about a diagonal which is 6 cm long. Find the volume of the figure formed.

Computer Section

COMPUTERS AND THEIR USES

OBJECTIVES:

To discover the uses of computers
To describe their effects on society

Computers are playing an ever increasing role in our lives. Grocers use computerized checkout registers. Bankers use computers to process checks and to keep records. Teachers use computers for grading and scheduling, and as an aid to teaching. Airlines provide reservations and information through computer networks. Subway and train systems are controlled and maintained by computers. Physicians use computers to diagnose illness and for research. Engineers and designers use computer graphics to assist them with their projects. Computers play a vital role in the space program and in forecasting the weather. Computers have even become part of our recreation through video games and computer-assisted amusement parks and sporting events. Computers can be programmed to play music or speak. Computers are useful in solving crimes, in gathering scientific statistics for research, and in providing security for your credit and financial transactions. Computers are being used widely because they are faster, cheaper and more reliable than any other method.

In education, computers are changing what is taught and how it is taught. These changes may have an effect on your career choice and the courses you take in school. With microcomputers, you have many opportunities to learn about computers and programming.

A "micro" consists of an entire computer on one small chip. A chip is a small rectangular piece of silicon on which several thousand transistors have been integrated. Input to the computer can be done with an ordinary cassette recorder and a keyboard typewriter. Output can be on a television screen. Microprocessors can also be designed to perform specific tasks in microwave ovens, cameras, programmable calculators, and automobiles. New careers and additional on-the-job training programs in computer science are opening up everyday.

The computer is a powerful tool for exploring all kinds of new ideas.

EXERCISES:

1. Describe a personal experience in which the computer played a role.

2. Discuss some ways you might use a computer.

3. Describe how a computer might be helpful in solving a crime.

4. A computer can multiply two four-digit numbers in one hundred nanoseconds (a nanosecond is a billionth of a second). How does the speed of the calculator compare to this? Experiment by timing the multiplication on the calculator.

5. One output device is a high-speed line printer that prints 1000 lines per minute. How long will it take for the computer to print a document that con-contains 756,830 lines?

RUNNING A PROGRAM

OBJECTIVES:

To run a BASIC program
To debug a BASIC program
A program is a set of step by step instructions to the computer. To run a BASIC program there are certain commands that are referred to as *system commands.* These words have a special meaning to the computer.

EXAMPLE:

RUN   Tells the computer to run the program
LIST   Tells the computer to print in order a list of all statements in the current program. This listing helps you to debug programs.

To run the program below, type in all the lines exactly as they are written. Be sure to press the correct button after each line so that the line or statement is entered into the computer's memory. Find the correct button by consulting the operator's manual for your computer. *Enter* will be used here.

```
10 PRINT "Type your name"      ◄ Press enter.
20 INPUT N$
30 PRINT "Welcome to the World of Computers"; N$      ◄ Press enter.
40 PRINT "Programming a computer requires a special language"      ◄ Press enter.
50 PRINT "Some languages are BASIC, COBAL, and PASCAL"      ◄ Press enter.
60 PRINT "BASIC is the language used here"      ◄ Press enter.
70 PRINT "Good Luck"; N$      ◄ Press enter.
80 END
```

Type in LIST and press enter. The program you typed in should appear on the screen. Check that each line has been typed correctly. Correct a typing error or incorrect format by retyping the entire line. To remove a line that is causing an error and does not need to be in the program, type in the statement number and *Press enter.* Some common errors to avoid in writing programs are missing statements or statement numbers, improper ordering of statements, incorrect statement format, and unacceptable variable names. You can also debug or correct a BASIC program by responding to the error messages that may appear when running the program.

Type in RUN and press enter. Type in your name after the question mark. What you see on the screen is the output. Be sure to check that the output of a program is correct and reasonable. As you run the programs given in this book, you may find that reserved words or symbols for your computer may be different than the ones given here. If necessary, check the operator's manual for your computer and substitute the correct symbol.

WHAT IS A COMPUTER?

OBJECTIVES: To identify the parts of a computer
To explain what each part does

Most computers have components for input, control, memory, and output.

INPUT:
The input part of the computer provides a means of entering information and data. Some examples of input devices are a keyboard similar to a typewriter, punched cards, magnetic tape, and a telephone.

MEMORY:
This portion of the computer saves information to be processed along with the program. The program is a set of rules for processing the information and controlling the parts of the computer. There are two kinds of memory: primary and secondary. The primary memory has the fastest recall and is used to save the programs to run the system. The secondary memory has more capacity but is usually slower. It consists of devices like magnetic tape cassettes and floppy disks.

CENTRAL PROCESSING UNIT:
The CPU consists of two main parts. One is the control unit, which interprets your programs and directs the flow of information in the machine. The other part is the arithmetic/logic unit where the calculations and processing take place.

OUTPUT:
The output devices transmit the results of programs out of the computer. Output devices include cathode ray tube (CTR) displays and printers.

Here is a diagram that shows the main components of a computer:

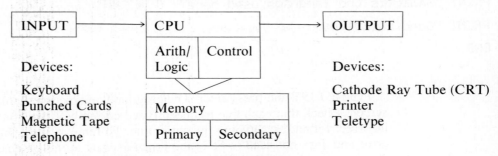

EXERCISES: Which are components of a digital computer?

1. CPU   2. logic unit   3. programs

4. printers   5. disks   6. flow charts

7. magnetic tape   8. calculators

9. Floppy disks are a form of secondary storage for the computer. An 8 in floppy disk can store approximately 256,000 characters on one side of a single density disk. How many five letter words can it store? Could it store the words in a pocket dictionary?

PROBLEM SOLVING WITH THE COMPUTER

OBJECTIVE:

To apply problem solving steps in writing a computer program

You can use the computer to solve the same problem repeatedly once you have written the computer program. You will find that the computer is especially useful in solving problems that require a repeated process called *iteration*, logical comparison between numbers, or long computational procedures. There are several steps to follow when solving a problem with the aid of the computer.

ANALYZE the problem:

This step requires that you state the problem clearly and completely. You make a flow chart in this step.

CODE the program:

Translate your flow chart into a program language. In this book you will use BASIC (Beginners All Purpose Symbolic Instruction Code).

SIMULATE the program:

Follow the program through with the aid of a flow chart. Use sample data that you can easily check by hand.

RUN the program:

Enter the program into the computer at the terminal and run it with test data.

CORRECT the errors:

Study the results of the program and determine if the output is accurate and reasonable. Sometimes you get output that looks correct but because of an error in the program, it is really incorrect. Correct or "debug" the program and rerun it.

EXAMPLE 1:

Apply the first three problem-solving steps for the following math problem: Find the sum of three numbers.

ANALYZE

How many numbers are you going to add?
What is the mathematical operation?
What will be the result of the problem?
What are the steps necessary to solve the problem?
Each shape in a flow chart has a special meaning.

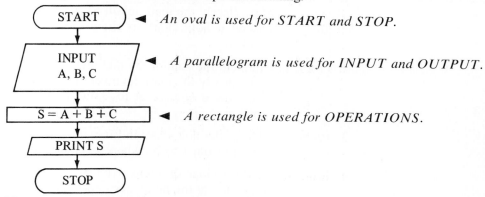

◄ *An oval is used for START and STOP.*

◄ *A parallelogram is used for INPUT and OUTPUT.*

◄ *A rectangle is used for OPERATIONS.*

CODE

You will learn BASIC statements to code this problem later in the chapter.

SIMULATE

Follow the steps on the flow chart with the numbers 4, 5, and 10.
Add the three numbers 4, 5, and 10. Replace S with 19. Print S.

EXAMPLE 2:   Design a flow chart to compute the sum of the integers from 1 to 100. Print the sum.

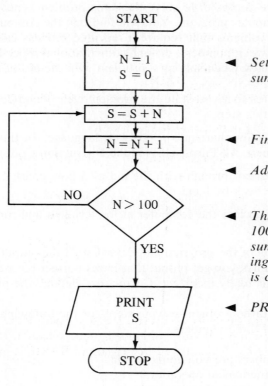

▸ *Set the counter, N, equal to 1 and the sum, S, equal to 0.*

▸ *Find the sum.*

▸ *Add to the counter, N.*

▸ *This shape is used for decisions. If N > 100, you fall through and PRINT the sum. Otherwise, this process of executing a set of instructions again and again is called a* loop.

▸ *PRINT the sum S.*

EXERCISES:

1. Problem: Change fractions to decimals.
   State clearly the math involved in solving this problem.
   Design a flow chart to show the steps necessary to solve the problem.

2. Problem: Compute the sum of the odd integers from 1 through 99.
   State clearly the math involved in solving the problem.
   Construct a flow chart to show the steps necessary to solve the problem.

3. Problem: Change the flow chart in Problem 2 to compute the sum of the odd integers from 1 to N, where N is any odd integer.

*4. Problem: Find the slope of a line given two points.
   State clearly the math steps necessary to solve the problem.

564

NUMERICAL EXPRESSIONS IN BASIC

OBJECTIVES:

To write numbers in BASIC
To write numerical expressions using BASIC symbols
To evaluate BASIC numerical expressions

To use the five steps in problem solving on the computer and to write other programs, you need to be able to communicate with the computer. BASIC is one of many programming languages you can use. Two other popular languages used today are FORTRAN and COBOL.

You write numbers in BASIC as decimals or decimal approximations.

EXAMPLE 1:

Write the following numbers in BASIC form.

Numeric form	BASIC form
3	3
-71	-71
$\dfrac{7}{8}$	.875
$\sqrt{3}$	1.732051
π	3.141593
$3\dfrac{1}{4}$	3.25

For mathematical calculations, BASIC has five operations. The five arithmetic symbols are: addition ($+$), subtraction ($-$), multiplication ($*$), division ($/$), and raise to a power ($\uparrow$). A numerical expression in BASIC can be a single number or a phrase.

EXAMPLE 2:

Write each of the following numerical expressions using BASIC arithmetic symbols.

Numerical expression	BASIC arithmetic symbol
$88 + 6$	$88 + 6$
$10 - 7$	$10 - 7$
6×8	$6 * 8$
$12 \div 4$	$12 / 4$
3^2	$3 \uparrow 2$

BASIC performs operations in this order.

1. Raise a number to a power.
2. Multiplication and division from left to right.
3. Addition and subtraction from left to right.
4. When parentheses are present, do the operations within the parentheses first, following the above order.

565

EXAMPLE 3:   Evaluate each BASIC numerical expression.

BASIC expression	Value
$(4 + 2) + 5$	11
$8 - 7$	1
$7 - 8$	-1
$(10 - 7) + 4$	7
$16/4 * 3$	12
$35 / (2 + 3)$	7
$4 + 2 \uparrow 3 - 5$	$4 + 8 - 5$ or 7
$(4 + 2) \uparrow 3 - 5$	$216 - 5$ or 211

EXAMPLE 4:   Evaluate the BASIC numerical expression.
$$(35 * 4) + (6 + 9) / 3$$

Think ▶   First perform operations in parentheses.
$$35 * 4 = 140$$
$$6 + 9 = 15$$
New problem: $140 + 15/3$

Think ▶   Perform division before addition.
$$15/3 = 5$$
New problem: $140 + 5 = 145$

EXERCISES: Write the following numbers in BASIC form.

1. $3\dfrac{1}{2}$ 2. 6   3. $\dfrac{11}{12}$

4. $\dfrac{2}{3}$ 5. $6\dfrac{3}{4}$ 6. 3.76

Write each expression using BASIC arithmetic symbols.

7. $5 (3 + 4)$ 10. $12 - 2^3$

8. 4^2 11. $\dfrac{3}{5} + 6$

9. $\dfrac{16 - 8}{2}$ 12. $\dfrac{14 \cdot 2 + 6}{(3^2) + 4}$

Evaluate each BASIC numerical expression.

13. $6 + 12$ 16. $3 \uparrow 2 * 8 + 2$

14. $(3 * 4) /6$ 17. $36/6 * 4 + 3 \uparrow 2$

15. $12 - 7 * 8 + 6/3$ 18. $2 \uparrow 3 /4 * 10 \uparrow 3 - 7$

566

VARIABLE EXPRESSIONS IN BASIC

OBJECTIVES:
To write BASIC variables
To write variable expressions using BASIC variables
To write equations and inequalities in BASIC form

A variable in BASIC is a quantity whose value can be assigned and changed during a computer program. The variable can be referred to by name. Each program variable is stored in the computer's memory.

A BASIC variable is a single letter or a letter followed by a single digit.

EXAMPLE 1:
Tell if each of the following is an acceptable BASIC variable:
A, X, 3, Y, 4A, A1, XYZ, NEW, A2, X9, NEW1, A344.

Acceptable BASIC Variables	Unacceptable BASIC Variables
A	3
X	4A
Y	XYZ
A1	NEW
A2	NEW1
X9	A344

A variable in BASIC can be a single variable or an expression.

EXAMPLE 2:
Write the following algebraic expressions in BASIC and indicate the variable.

	BASIC Expression	Variable
6 increased by Y	$6 + Y$	Y
10 more than 3 times A	$3 * A + 10$	A
M decreased by 7	$M - 7$	M
One-third of the sum of X, Y, and Z	$(X + Y + Z)/3$	X, Y, Z
B raised to the power of 2	$B \uparrow 2$	B

You can use variables in equations.

EXAMPLE 3:
Write a BASIC equation for the area of a rectangle.

$$A = L * W$$

where
$A = $ area
$L = $ length
$W = $ width

Write a BASIC equation for a line.

$$Y = M * X + B$$

where (X, Y) is a point on the line, M is the slope of the line, and B is the y-intercept.

You can write variables when comparing quantities.

EXAMPLE 4: Write the given algebraic expression in BASIC form.

Variable Expression	BASIC Expression
$x - 2x > 20 + 3x$	$X - 2 * X > 20 + 3 * X$
$y \geq 2x + 3$	$Y >= 2 * X + 3$
$x^2 + 6 < y^2 - 3$	$X \uparrow 2 + 6 < Y \uparrow 2 - 3$
$(x + y)^2 \neq x^2 + y^2$	$(X + Y) \uparrow 2 <> X \uparrow 2 + Y \uparrow 2$
$x + y \leq 3$	$x + y <= 3$

EXERCISES: Write BASIC variables for the following:

1. number of angles in a polygon
2. length of the side of a square
3. value of median of triangle
4. circumference of a circle
5. volume of a cylinder
6. point of intersection of two lines

Tell if each of these BASIC expressions has acceptable variables.

7. $Z = X + Y$
8. $A = BONE + BTWO$
9. $OLD = NEW + S$
10. $A = (B + H) / 2$
11. $X1 + 3 * X2 + 6$
12. $Y = M * X + 1B$

Write in BASIC form.

13. $C = \pi d$ (use 3.14 for π)
14. $a > \frac{1}{2}b + c + 23$
15. $X \geq 3X - 8$
16. $a \leq \pi r^2$
17. $L < \frac{1}{2}p$
18. $\frac{1}{3}BH \neq \frac{1}{2}BH$

Write a BASIC equation for the following:
19. the area of a trapezoid where A = area and
    S = sum of the bases

20. the perimeter of a square where P = perimeter and
    S = length of a side

21. the area of a triangle where A = area, B = length of the base, and H = length
    of the altitude

SIMPLE BASIC STATEMENTS

OBJECTIVES:

To number statements in a BASIC program
To write LET statements
To write PRINT statements
To write END statements

    A program is a set of instructions to the computer. Each instruction contains a BASIC command and is numbered so that the computer will execute each statement in the correct order. The last statement is always the END statement. The END statement tells the computer the program is finished.

EXAMPLE 1:

Indicate possible numbers for the following BASIC program.

```
10 LET A = 6
20 PRINT A
30 END
```
◄ *Lines are not numbered consecutively so that instructions may be added later, if needed.*

The LET command assigns a value or expression to a variable.

EXAMPLE 2:

What is the value of the variable in each statement?

a. `LET X = 8`   Assigns the value of 8 to the variable X.

   `LET Y = −7`   Assigns the value of −7 to Y.

b. `LET A = 3`   The computer performs A + B and stores
   `LET B = 5`   the result, 8, in memory at a place
   `LET C = A + B` called C.

You can also use the LET statement to increase the value of a variable.

EXAMPLE 3:

What is the effect on C of the following statement?

`LET C = C + 1`   This instruction increases the value of C by 1.

    The PRINT statement causes the computer to print what follows the PRINT word. You can use the print statement to print numerical constants and expressions.

EXAMPLE 4:

What will the computer print after each statement?

Numeric Constants and Expressions	Computer PRINTS
`PRINT 16`	16
`PRINT (3 + 2) * 6`	30
`PRINT 7, 8, 8 − 7, 8 + 7`	7, 8, 1, 15

You can use the PRINT statement to print characters or strings of characters. To do this write the PRINT statement and enclose the character or string of characters inside quotation marks. You can vary the spacing on each line of output, too. If you use a comma, you will get wide spacing. If you use a semicolon, you will get close spacing. To skip a line in the output, use a PRINT statement by itself.

569

EXAMPLE 5:   What is the output of the following PRINT statements?

```
10 PRINT "THE ANSWER IS NO"        THE ANSWER IS NO

20 PRINT                           (one line of space)

30 LET X = 3

40 LET Y = 2

50 PRINT "SUM ="; X + Y            SUM = 5

60 PRINT "6/12"                    6/12

70 PRINT "X ="; X; "Y ="; Y        X = 3  Y = 2
```

EXERCISES: What is the value of the variable X in each statement?
The phrases in the boxes give information needed to find X.
They are not part of the program statement.

1. LET X = 6   2. LET X = 3 + Y if Y = 2

3. LET X = {3 * 6} /9 + 2 ↑ 3   4. LET X = S + R $\boxed{where\ S = -5}$

5. LET X = M * M1 + B $\boxed{where\ M = 2,}$ $\boxed{and\ R = -4}$

   $\boxed{M1 = 3,\ B = 4}$ 6. LET X = 3

What will the computer print after each of the following PRINT statements?

7. PRINT −11   8. PRINT "THE AREA IS"; X *when x = 12*

9. PRINT {6 * 8} /12   10. PRINT X + Y *When X = 20 and Y = 10*

11. PRINT "{X, Y} ="; X; Y,   12. PRINT "THE TRIANGLES ARE CONGRUENT"
    when X = 20 and Y = 10

13. PRINT 6, 3 * 4, "THE VOLUME
    IS"; X *when X = 7*

What will the computer print at the end of each program?

14. 10 LET N = 5   15. 10 LET B = 5
    20 LET A = 2   20 LET H = 10
    30 LET B = 3   30 LET A1 = {1/2} * B * H
    40 LET X = A ↑ N + B * 3   40 PRINT "AREA OF TRIANGLE IS";
    50 END   A1; "CM ↑ 2"
                                        50 END

570

BASIC STATEMENTS FOR INPUTTING DATA

OBJECTIVES:
To use INPUT statements
To use READ/DATA statements

The INPUT command is used to enter data into the computer. This instruction prompts the computer to type a "?" and to wait for you to enter a number for each variable in the command. The numbers and variables are separated by commas.

EXAMPLE 1:

```
10 INPUT A          A is assigned the value 3.
 ? 3

10 INPUT X, Y, Z    X is assigned the value 5.
 ? 5, 10, 15        Y is assigned the value 10.
                    Z is assigned the value 15.
```

EXAMPLE 2:

What is the output if you assign B, the value of 7 and H, the value of 4?

```
10 INPUT B, H

20 LET A = .5 * B * H

30 PRINT "THE AREA OF THE TRIANGLE IS"; A

40 END
```

OUTPUT
Computer prints: ?
You enter two numbers separated by a comma: ? 7, 4
Computer prints: THE AREA OF THE TRIANGLE IS 14

The *READ* and *DATA* statements are used to enter data into the program. They are used together as a pair.

EXAMPLE 3:

What values are assigned to A, B, and C with the following statements?

```
20 READ A, B, C

40 DATA 4, 6, 8
```

When the READ command is read by the computer, the variable A is assigned 4, the variable B is assigned 6, and the variable C is assigned 8. Some computers will then print OUT OF DATA IN LINE 20.

EXAMPLE 4:

What is the computer output for the following program?

```
10 READ L, B

20 LET T = L + 2 * B

30 PRINT "THE TOTAL AREA OF A CYLINDER IS"; T

40 DATA 7, 8

50 END
```

OUTPUT: The total area of a cylinder is 23

571

The DATA statement can be located anywhere in the program before the END statement.

EXAMPLE 5:   What is the computer output for the following program?

```
10 READ M, R
20 LET L = {M/360} * {2 * 3. 14 * R}
30 PRINT "THE LENGTH OF THE ARC IS"; L
40 DATA 90, 4
50 END
OUTPUT
THE LENGTH OF THE ARC IS 6.28
```

The next lesson gives examples of the DATA statement used with IF THEN and GO TO statements.

EXERCISES   What is the computer output for each program?

1.
```
10 LET A = 2
20 LET B = 6
30 LET C = A + B
40 PRINT C

50 END
```

2.
```
10 LET X = 25
20 LET Y = 35
30 PRINT X * Y

40 END
```

3.
```
10 INPUT A1, A2
20 LET A3 = A1/A2
30 PRINT A3
40 END
? 35, 7
```

4.
```
10 INPUT X1, Y1
20 INPUT X2, Y2
30 LET S = {Y2 − Y1}/{X2 − X1}
40 PRINT "SLOPE ="; S
50 END
? 1, 4
? 3, 12
```

5.
```
10 READ A, B
20 LET C = A ↑ B
30 PRINT C
40 DATA 5, 4
50 END
```

6.
```
5 READ X, Y, Z
10 PRINT X, Y, Z, X + Y + Z
40 DATA −2, −4, −6
50 END
```

7. Write a program that will find the equation of a line given the slope and the y-intercept. Use an input statement for M, B and a PRINT statement to print out Y = MX + B.

8. Write a program to find the measure of the third angle of a triangle given the measures of angles A and B in a DATA statement. Use a READ statement to assign the measures to angles A and B. Use a PRINT statement to print "THE MEASURE OF ANGLE C IS", followed by the measure of angle C.

BASIC CONDITIONALS

OBJECTIVES: To use GO TO statements.
To use IF THEN statements.

The GO TO statement causes the computer to go to a new statement and continue the program from there.

EXAMPLE 1:   What statement is executed after statement 40?

```
10 READ A, B
20 LET C = A + B
30 PRINT "C="; C
40 GO TO 10                    ◄   The computer goes back to line 10.
50 DATA 2, 4, 6, 8, 10, 12     ◄   Assigns 2 to A and 4 to B first time.
                                   Assigns 6 to A and 8 to B second time.
60 END                             Assigns 10 to A and 12 to B third time.
```

The IF THEN statement is a conditional command. If the given condition is true, the computer will branch to the given statement. If it is false the computer will execute the next statement.

EXAMPLE 2:   Write a program to compute the square of numbers less than or equal to 10.

```
10 INPUT X
20 IF X > 10 THEN 50           ◄   If the variable is greater than 10 the
30 LET C = X ↑ 2                   program ends; otherwise it continues.
40 PRINT C
50 END
```

EXAMPLE 3:   Tell which path the computer would take for the given set of data. This program will print only positive numbers from a given set of data.

```
10 READ X
20 IF X < 0 THEN 10
30 PRINT X
40 GO TO 10
50 DATA 2, −2, −3, 3, −1, 7, −7, 8
60 END
```

$$\underrightarrow{\text{IF } 2 < 0 \text{ THEN } 10} \quad \text{True? No}$$
$$\downarrow \text{false? Yes}$$

PRINT 2

$$\underrightarrow{\text{IF } -2 < 0 \text{ THEN } 10} \quad \text{True? Yes}$$
$$\downarrow \text{false? No}$$

Program goes to 10 and continues until all numbers have been read.

573

Write the IF THEN statements for the following conditions.

1. If the value of X equals Y, then go to line 30.

2. If the value of 24 divided by C is greater than 24 divided by D, then go to line 90.

3. If the value of A is less than or equal to zero, then go to line 50. (Use <= for less than or equal to)

4. If the value X is not equal to Y, then go to 100. (Use <> for not equal to)

Give the output for each program.

```
5. 10 READ X, Y
   15 DATA 2, -7, 3, 6, 5, 4
   20 IF X > Y THEN 10
   25 PRINT X, Y
   30 GO TO 10

   35 END
```

```
6. 3 INPUT R, S, T,
   6 LET T = R + S + T
   9 IF T <> 180 THEN 18
   12 PRINT T

   15 GO TO 21
   18 PRINT "NOT A TRIANGLE"

   21 END
   ? 30, 45, 85
```

```
7. 10 LET X = 2
   20 PRINT X/2
   30 LET X = X + 2
   40 IF X > 12 THEN 60
   50 GO TO 20
   60 END
```

```
8. 5 READ A, B, C
   10 LET S1 = A ↑ 2 + B ↑ 2
   15 LET S2 = C ↑ 2
   20 IF S1 <> S2 THEN 5
   25 PRINT "RIGHT TRIANGLE FOR"; A; B; C
   30 GO TO 5
   35 DATA 3, 4, 5, 6, 7, 8, 2, 3, 0
   40 END
```

9. Write a program to determine if a given line is parallel to the X-axis. Use an INPUT statement to obtain the slope.

10. Write a program to find the smallest volume of three volumes. (Use READ/DATA statements.)

11. Write a program to find the values for which the area of a parallelogram is the same as the area of a trapezoid. Use as INPUT the height and base lengths.

ITERATION IN BASIC

OBJECTIVE: To use the FOR NEXT loop

The FOR and NEXT statements go together. The same variable is used in both the FOR command and NEXT command. Use the FOR NEXT loop to repeat a group of instructions.

EXAMPLE 1: What values are assigned to N in the program below?

N is assigned values of 1, 2, 3, 4, 5

After N has been assigned 5, the program will drop out of the loop to line 60 and continue.

```
10 FOR N = 1 to 5          ◄ Any number
    .                        of instructions
    .
50 NEXT N
60 INSTRUCTION
```

EXAMPLE 2: Write a program to find the cube of numbers from 1 to 4.

```
10 FOR X = 1 to 4          OUTPUT
20 LET Y = X ↑ 3           CUBE IS 1
30 PRINT "CUBE IS"; Y      CUBE IS 8
40 NEXT X                  CUBE IS 27
50 END                     CUBE IS 64
```

Sometimes, you will have a set of instructions that you want to repeat again and again. Each pass through the loop is called an *iteration*. Recall that there are several statements in BASIC that you can use for loops. You can use the IF THEN and GO TO statements, or you can use the FOR NEXT statements.

EXAMPLE 3: Write programs to find the value of the expression $\dfrac{2 * X + X \uparrow 2}{X - 5}$ for values of X from 1 to 4. Use the IF THEN statement in Program A and the FOR NEXT statement in Program B.

Program A (IF THEN)

```
10 LET X = 1
20 PRINT {2 * X + X ↑ 2}/{X - 5}
30 LET X = X + 1
40 IF X > 4 THEN 60
50 GO TO 20
60 END
```

Program B (FOR NEXT)

```
10 FOR X = 1 TO 4
20 PRINT {2 * X + X ↑ 2}
         /{X - 5}
30 NEXT X
40 END
```

OUTPUT From Both A and B
```
-.75
-2.6666666
-7.5
-24
```

FOR NEXT

575

The FOR NEXT loop can be incremented by numbers other than 1 with the step option: FOR X = 1 to N STEP N where N is any number.

EXAMPLE 4:   Give the output for the following program.

```
10 FOR X = 2 to 10 STEP 2        [OUTPUT]        2
20 PRINT X                                       4
30 NEXT X                                        6
40 END                                           8
                                                10
```

EXERCISES   Give the output for each program.

1.
```
10 FOR A = 0 TO 15 STEP 3
20 LET S = A + 1
30 PRINT S
40 NEXT A
50 END
```

2.
```
5 FOR T = 4 TO 8 STEP 2
10 PRINT 3 * T + T
15 NEXT T
20 END
```

3.
```
2 LET X = 0
4 FOR Y = 1 TO 4
6 LET T = X ↑ Y
8 LET X = X + 1
10 PRINT T
12 NEXT Y
14 END
```

4.
```
5 LET T = .5
10 FOR R = 70 TO 40 STEP 5
20 LET D = R * T
30 PRINT "DISTANCE COVERED
          IN .5 HRS. IS"; D
40 PRINT "RATE IS"; R
50 NEXT R
60 END
```

*5.
```
10 FOR X = 1 TO 5 STEP 2
20 FOR Y = 2 TO 6 STEP 2
30 LET Z = X ↑ 2 + Y ↑ 2
40 PRINT Z
50 NEXT X
60 NEXT Y
70 END
```

6. Write a program to find the circumferences of different circles as R, the radius, increases from 1 to 10 in steps of 0.5. Use a FOR NEXT loop.

7. Write a program to find the measure of angle A given the measures of angles B and C. Use a FOR NEXT loop to generate values of angles B and C from 5° to 45° in increments of 5°.

ADVANCED BASIC STATEMENTS

OBJECTIVES:

To use REM statements
To use BASIC functions
To use character strings
To use arrays and dimension statements

The REM statement allows the programmer to enter comments into the program listing that do not effect the output but provide documentation about what is happening in the program.

EXAMPLE 1:

Use a REM statement to indicate what the variables are and what the program does.

```
5 REM INPUT THE STOPPING POINT, A; THE NUMBER B, FOR FINDING
7 REM MULTIPLES OF 4
10 INPUT A, B
20 REM THIS LOOP WILL PRINT THE MULTIPLES OF A NUMBER
30 FOR X = 1 TO A
40 LET Y = B * X
50 PRINT Y
60 NEXT X
70 END
? 4, 3
```

OUTPUT   3   6   9   12

These REM statements give information but do not change the output. It is very important to document your program for finding errors later on.

BASIC functions are computer programs that are already written and stored in the computer for use within BASIC programs.
Some BASIC functions you may want to use are:

1. SQR(X)   ◄ *finds square root of X.*

2. INT(X)   ◄ *gives the greatest integer less than or equal to X.*

3. SIN(X)┐   ◄ *gives the sine, cosine or tangent of X where X is in radian*
   COS(X)│   *measure.*
   TAN(X)┘

4. RND(X)   ◄ *finds a random number between 0 and 1.*

EXAMPLE 2: Write a program to find the square root of X using a BASIC function.

```
10 INPUT X
20 LET Y = SQR(X)    ◄ SQR is BASIC Function name and call to
                        square root program.
30 PRINT Y
40 END
   ? 4         OUTPUT: 2
   ? 11        OUTPUT: 3.317
```

> *Note:* This is correct, but the computer actually gives the answer 3.31663.

A character string variable allows you to use alphabetic characters for a variable in BASIC. A character variable is represented by a letter followed by a dollar sign.

$$A\$$$
$$R\$$$

EXAMPLE 3: You can use a character string variable to ask a question, make a choice, or represent a name.

Use a character string variable to answer "YES" or "NO."

```
. ⎫
. ⎬ other statements
. ⎭
50 PRINT "DO YOU WANT TO CONTINUE?"
60 PRINT "ANSWER YES OR NO"
70 INPUT A$
80 IF A$ = "YES" THEN 10    ◄ Quotation marks are
                               needed for computer to
90 END                         process characters.
```

BASIC also provides a means for storing a list of items in the computer's memory. This is done with an *array* and a *dimension statement*.
DIM A(4) creates an array with 4 spaces. Each space is given a subscript from 1 to 4.

EXAMPLE 4:
```
10 DIM A(5)
20 FOR X = 1 TO 5
30 LET A(X) = X ↑ 2    ◄ Sets each array position equal to the square of X.
                       ◄ Prints the value of the array position.
40 PRINT A(X)
50 NEXT X
60 END
```

ARRAY	OUTPUT	MEMORY	
A(1)	1		A(1)
A(2)	4		A(2)
A(3)	9		A(3)
A(4)	16		A(4)

EXERCISES: Write a BASIC program to evaluate and print the following expressions.

1. $T = 3 \pi r(h + r)$
2. $D = \sqrt{(X2 - X1)^2 + (Y2 - Y1)^2}$
3. $\sqrt{(a + b)^3}$
4. $V = 1/3 \pi r^2 h$
5. Write a BASIC program to compute the area and the circumference of a circle given its radius.

Give the output for each program.

```
6. 10 INPUT X
   20 LET Y = INT{X}
   30 PRINT Y
   40 GO TO 10
   50 END
    ? 9.76
```

```
7. 10 FOR T = 1 TO 9
   20 PRINT SQR{T}
   30 NEXT T
   40 END
```

```
8. 10 DIM T{10}
   20 REM THIS LOOP FILLS THE ARRAY T
   30 FOR X = 1 TO 10
   40 LET T{X} = —1 * X
   50 NEXT X
   60 REM THIS LOOP PRINTS OUT ARRAY
   70 FOR Y = 1 TO 10
   80 PRINT T{Y}
   90 NEXT Y
  100 END
```

```
9. 10 LET A$ = "TRY"
   20 LET B$ = "AGAIN"
   30 INPUT X, Y
   40 IF X ≥ Y THEN 60
   50 PRINT A$; B$
   60 END
    ? 3, 4
```

```
10. 10 PRINT "EQUATION OF CIRCLE FOR CENTER {H, K} AND RADIUS R"
    20 PRINT "R = SQR{{     } ↑ 2 + {Y — K} ↑ 2}"
    30 PRINT "WHAT IS THE MISSING TERM?"
    40 INPUT T$
    50 IF T$ = "X — H" THEN 80
    60 PRINT "NO, THE FORMULA R = SQR{{X — H} ↑ 2 + {Y — K} ↑ 2}"
    70 GO TO 90
    80 PRINT "RIGHT"
    90 END
     ? XH
```

Resources

Albrecht, et al., Robert. *BASIC*. New York: John Wiley & Sons, 1973.

Cassell, Dan & Richard Swanson. *BASIC Made Easy: A Guide to Programming Microcomputers and Minicomputers*. Englewood Cliffs, N. J.: Prentice-Hall, 1980.

Coan, James S. *BASIC BASIC*, 2nd ed. Rochelle Park, N. J.: Hayden Book Company, 1978.

Dwyer, Thomas & Margot Critchfield. *BASIC and the Personal Computer*. Reading, Mass.: Addison-Wesley Publishing Company, 1979.

Dwyer, Thomas & Michael Kaufman. *A Guided Tour of Computer Programming in BASIC*. Boston: Houghton Mifflin Company, 1973.

Moursund, David. *BASIC Programming for Computer Literacy*. New York: McGraw-Hill, 1978.

Wu, Margaret S. *Introduction to Computer Data Processing with BASIC*. New York: Harcourt Brace Jovanovich, 1980.

Postulates, Theorems, and Corollaries

Postulate 1	For any two points, there is exactly one line containing them. *(38)*
Theorem 2.1	Two lines intersect in, at most, one point. *(38)*
Postulate 2	Three noncollinear points are contained in exactly one plane. *(38)*
Postulate 3	If two points of a line are in a given plane, then the line itself is in the plane. *(39)*
Postulate 4	If two planes intersect, then they intersect in exactly one line. *(39)*
Postulate 5	Space contains an infinite number of points, not all coplanar. A plane contains an infinite number of points, not all collinear. A line contains an infinite number of points. *(39)*
Theorem 2.2	A line and a point not on the line are contained in exactly one plane. *(40)*
Theorem 2.3	If a line intersects a plane but is not contained in the plane, then the intersection is exactly one point. *(40)*
Theorem 2.4	Two intersecting lines are contained in exactly one plane. *(40)*
Postulate 6	On every line, there is a segment with a given point as an endpoint congruent to any given segment. *(42)*
Postulate 7	For every ray, there is an angle with the given ray as a side congruent to any given angle. *(42)*
Postulate 8	Every segment has exactly one midpoint. *(42)*
Postulate 9	Every angle, except a straight angle, has exactly one bisector. *(42)*
Postulate 10	Angle Addition Postulate: If D is in the interior of $\angle ABC$ then m $\angle ABC =$ m $\angle ABD +$ m $\angle DBC$. *(43)*
Postulate 11	The sum of the measures of the angles with the same vertex on one side of a line and no interior points in common is 180°. The sum of the measures of all angles around a common vertex and with no interior points in common is 360°. *(47)*

Theorem 2.5	All right angles are congruent. *(47)*
Theorem 2.6	Two perpendicular lines form four congruent right angles. *(47)*
Postulate 12	For a given point and a line in a plane, there is exactly one line through the point that is perpendicular to the given line. *(49)*
Theorem 2.7	If two lines form congruent adjacent angles, then the lines are perpendicular. *(50)*
Theorem 2.8	Supplements of congruent angles are congruent. *(53)*
Corollary	Supplements of the same angle are congruent. *(53)*
Theorem 2.9	Complements of congruent angles are congruent. *(54)*
Corollary	Complements of the same angle are congruent. *(54)*
Theorem 2.10	Vertical angles are congruent. *(55)*
Theorem 2.11	Any two plane angles of a dihedral angle are congruent. *(60)*
Postulate 13	Alternate Interior Angle Postulate: If two parallel lines are intersected by a transversal, then the alternate interior angles are congruent. *(74)*
Theorem 3.1	If two parallel lines are intersected by a transversal, then the corresponding angles are congruent. *(75)*
Theorem 3.2	If two parallel lines are intersected by a transversal, then the interior angles on the same side of the transversal are supplementary. *(76)*
Postulate 14	If two lines are intersected by a transversal so that the alternate interior angles are congruent, then the lines are parallel. *(79)*
Theorem 3.3	If two lines are intersected by a transversal so that the corresponding angles are congruent, then the lines are parallel. *(80)*
Corollary	If two coplanar lines are perpendicular to the same line, then they are parallel. *(80)*
Theorem 3.4	If two lines are intersected by a transversal so that the interior angles on the same side of the transversal are supplementary, then the lines are parallel. *(80)*

Postulate 15	The Parallel Postulate: Through a point not on a line, there is exactly one line parallel to the given line. *(84)*
Theorem 3.5	The sum of the measures of the angles of a triangle is 180. *(86)*
Theorem 3.6	If two angles of one triangle are congruent to two angles of a second triangle, then the third angles are congruent. *(87)*
Theorem 3.7	In a plane, two lines parallel to the same line are parallel to each other. *(90)*
Theorem 3.8	If two parallel planes are intersected by a third plane, then the lines of intersection are parallel. *(95)*
Theorem 4.1	The measure of an exterior angle of a triangle is equal to the sum of the measures of its two remote interior angles. *(108)*
Corollary	The measure of an exterior angle of a triangle is greater than the measure of either of its remote interior angles. *(108)*
Postulate 16	SSS for ≅ △'s: Two triangles are congruent if the three sides of one are congruent to the corresponding sides of the other. *(114)*
Postulate 17	SAS for ≅ △'s: Two triangles are congruent if two sides and the included angle of one are congruent to the corresponding two sides and included angle of the other. *(118)*
Postulate 18	ASA for ≅ △'s: Two triangles are congruent if two angles and the included side of one are congruent to the corresponding two angles and included side of the other. *(120)*
Theorem 4.2	(AAS): Two triangles are congruent if two angles and the side opposite one of them are congruent to the corresponding two angles and side of the other. *(124)*
Theorem 5.1	If two sides of a triangle are congruent, then the angles opposite those sides are congruent. *(139)*
Corollary 1	An equilateral triangle is also equiangular. *(140)*
Corollary 2	The measure of each angle of an equilateral, or equiangular triangle is 60°. *(140)*
Theorem 5.2	If two angles of a triangle are congruent, then the sides opposite those angles are congruent. *(140)*
Corollary	An equiangular triangle is also equilateral. *(141)*

Theorem 5.3	Leg-Leg (LL): Two right triangles are congruent if the two legs of one are congruent to the corresponding legs of the other. *(157)*
Theorem 5.4	Leg-Acute Angle (LA): Two right triangles are congruent if a leg and an acute angle of one are congruent to the corresponding leg and acute angle of the other. *(158)*
Theorem 5.5	Hypotenuse-Acute Angle (HA): Two right triangles are congruent if the hypotenuse and an acute angle of one are congruent to the hypotenuse and the corresponding acute angle of the other. *(158)*
Theorem 5.6	Hypotenuse Leg: Two right triangles are congruent if the hypotenuse and a leg of one are congruent to the hypotenuse and corresponding leg of the other. *(159)*
Theorem 5.7	Perpendicular Bisector Theorem: A point on the perpendicular bisector of a segment is equidistant from the end points of the segment. *(166)*
Theorem 5.8	A line containing two points, each equidistant from the end points of a segment is the perpendicular bisector. *(167)*
Theorem 5.9	Corresponding medians of congruent triangles are $\cong$. *(171)*
Theorem 5.10	Corresponding altitudes of congruent triangles are $\cong$. *(171)*
Theorem 6.1	The sum of the measures of the angles of a convex quadrilateral is 360°. *(188)*
Theorem 6.2	The sum of the measures of the angles of a convex polygon with n sides is $(n-2)\,180°$. *(189)*
Corollary	The measure of an angle of a regular polygon with insides is $\dfrac{(n-2)\,180°}{n}$. *(196)*
Theorem 6.3	The sum of the measures of the exterior angles, one at each vertex, of any convex quadrilateral is 360°. *(193)*
Theorem 6.4	The sum of the measures of the exterior angles, one at each vertex, of any convex polygon is 360°. *(194)*
Corollary	The measures of an exterior angle of a regular polygon with n sides is $\dfrac{360°}{n}$. *(194)*
Theorem 7.1	A diagonal of a parallelogram separates the parallelogram into two congruent triangles. *(211)*
Corollary 1	Opposite sides of a parallelogram are congruent. *(212)*

584

Theorem 8.6	SASAS for ≅ quadrilaterals: Two quadrilaterals are congruent if any three sides and the included angles of one are congruent, respectively, to three sides and the included angles of the other. *(251)*
Theorem 8.7	ASASA for ≅ quadrilaterals: Two quadrilaterals are congruent if any three angles and the included sides of one are congruent, respectively, to three angles and the included sides of the other. *(251)*
Theorem 8.8	Corresponding sides of a symmetric polygon are ≅. *(257)*
Theorem 8.9	Corresponding angles of a symmetric polygon are ≅. *(257)*
Theorem 8.10	If two triangles are reflections, they are congruent. *(260)*
Corollary	If two quadrilaterals are reflections, then they are congruent. *(260)*
Postulate 21	A line of symmetry of a symmetric polygon is the perpendicular bisector of any segment joining a pair of corresponding points of the polygon. *(256)*
Postulate 22	AA for ~ △'s: If two angles of a triangle are congruent to two angles of a second triangle, then the two triangles are similar. *(278)*
Theorem 9.1	If a line is parallel to one side of a triangle and intersects the other two sides, then it divides the two sides proportionally. *(282)*
Theorem 9.2	If a line divides two sides of a triangle proportionally, then it is parallel to the third side of the triangle. *(283)*
Theorem 9.3	SAS for ~ △'s: If an angle of one triangle is congruent to an angle of another triangle and the lengths of the corresponding sides including these angles are proportional, then the triangles are similar. *(285)*
Theorem 9.4	SSS for ~ △'s: If the corresponding sides of two triangles are proportional, then the triangles are similar. *(286)*
Theorem 9.5	Corresponding medians of similar triangles are proportional to corresponding sides. *(290)*
Theorem 9.6	Corresponding altitudes of similar triangles are proportional to corresponding sides. *(291)*
Theorem 9.7	The bisector of an angle of a triangle divides the opposite side into segments proportional to the other sides of the triangle. *(291)*

Theorem 9.8	If a tetrahedron is intersected by a plane parallel to its base, then the triangle formed by the intersection is similar to the base. *(298)*
Theorem 10.1	In a right triangle, the altitude to the hypotenuse forms two triangles, each similar to the original triangle, and each similar to the other. *(306)*
Corollary 1	In a right triangle, the length of the altitude to the hypotenuse is the geometric mean of the lengths of the segments of the hypotenuse that are formed. *(306)*
Corollary 2	If the altitude is drawn to the hypotenuse of a right triangle, then the length of either leg is the geometric mean of the length of the hypotenuse, and the length of the segment of the hypotenuse adjacent to that leg. *(307)*
Theorem 10.2	Pythagorean Theorem: In any right triangle, the square of the length of the hypotenuse is equal to the sum of the squares of the lengths of the two legs. *(310)*
Theorem 10.3	Converse of the Pythagorean Theorem: If the sum of the squares of the lengths of two sides of a triangle is equal to the square of the length of the third side, then the triangle is a right angle. *(315)*
Theorem 10.4	In a 45°–45° (isosceles) right triangle, the length of the hypotenuse is equal to the length of a leg times $\sqrt{2}$. *(318)*
Theorem 10.5	In a 30°–60° right triangle, 1. The hypotenuse is twice as long as the leg opposite the 30° angle, and 2. The leg opposite the 60° angle is $\sqrt{3}$ times as long as the leg opposite the 30° angle. *(319)*
Theorem 11.1	All radii of a circle are congruent. *(338)*
Theorem 11.2	In a circle, a radius perpendicular to a chord bisects the chord. *(339)*
Theorem 11.3	If chords of a circle or congruent circles are congruent, then the chords are equidistant from the center(s). *(342)*
Theorem 11.4	If chords of a circle or congruent circles are equidistant from the center(s), then the chords are congruent. *(343)*
Theorem 11.5	If a line is tangent to a circle, then it is perpendicular to the radius drawn to the point of tangency. *(345)*
Theorem 11.6	If a line is perpendicular to a radius at its endpoint on the circle, then it is tangent to the circle. *(345)*

Theorem 11.7	Tangent segments to a circle from the same point are congruent. *(346)*
Postulate 23	Arc Addition Postulate: If P is a point on $\overset{\frown}{AB}$, then $m\overset{\frown}{AP} + m\overset{\frown}{PB} = m\overset{\frown}{APB}$. *(352)*
Theorem 11.8	In a circle or in congruent circles, congruent arcs determine congruent central angles and congruent chords. *(356)*
Theorem 11.9	In a circle or in congruent circles, congruent chords determine congruent central angles and congruent arcs. *(356)*
Theorem 11.10	In a circle or in congruent circles, congruent central angles determine congruent arcs and congruent chords. *(356)*
Theorem 11.11	The measure of an inscribed angle is one-half the measure of its intercepted arc. *(359)*
Corollary 1	If two inscribed angles intercept the same arc (or congruent arcs), the angles are congruent. *(360)*
Corollary 2	An angle inscribed in a semicircle is a right angle. *(360)*
Corollary 3	If two arcs of a circle are included between parallel secants, then the arcs are congruent. *(360)*
Corollary 4	Opposite angles of a quadrilateral are supplementary. *(361)*
Theorem 11.12	The measure of an angle formed by two secants intersecting in the interior of a circle is one-half the sum of the measures of the arcs intercepted by the angle and its vertical angle. *(364)*
Theorem 11.13	The measure of an angle formed by two secants intersecting in the exterior of a circle is one-half the difference of the measures of the intercepted arcs. *(365)*
Theorem 11.14	The measure of an angle formed by a secant and a tangent intersecting at the point of tangency is one-half the measure of the intercepted arc. *(368)*
Theorem 11.15	The measure of an angle formed by a secant and a tangent intersecting in the exterior of a circle is one-half the difference of the measures of the intercepted arcs. *(369)*
Theorem 11.16	The measure of an angle formed by two tangents to the same circle is one-half the difference of the measures of the intercepted arcs. *(369)*

Theorem 11.17	If two chords of a circle intersect, then the product of the lengths of the segments of one chord equals the product of the lengths of the segments of the other. *(373)*
Theorem 11.18	If two secants intersect in the exterior of a circle, then the product of the lengths of one secant segment and its external secant segment equals the product of the lengths of the other secant segment and its external secant segment. *(374)*
Theorem 11.19	If a tangent and a secant intersect in the exterior of a circle, then the square of the length of the tangent segment equals the product of the lengths of the secant segment and its external secant segment. *(374)*
Postulate 24	The area of a rectangle is the product of the length of a base and the length of a corresponding altitude. *(388)*
Corollary	The area of a square is the square of the length of a side. *(388)*
Postulate 25	Area Addition Postulate: If a region is the union of two or more nonoverlapping regions, then its area is the sum of the areas of these nonoverlapping regions. *(388)*
Postulate 26	Congruent figures have the same area. *(391)*
Theorem 12.1	Area rt. $\triangle = \frac{1}{2}\,bh$: The area of a right triangle is one-half the product of the lengths of the two legs. *(391)*
Theorem 12.2	Area $\triangle = \frac{1}{2}\,bh$: The area of any triangle is one-half the product of the length of a base and the length of a corresponding altitude. *(391)*
Theorem 12.3	The area of a rhombus is one-half the product of the lengths of the diagonals. *(392)*
Theorem 12.4	Area $\triangle = \frac{s^2}{4}\sqrt{3}$: If s is the length of a side of an equilateral triangle, then the altitude is $\frac{s}{2}\sqrt{3}$ and the area is $\frac{s^2}{4}\sqrt{3}$. *(393)*
Theorem 12.5	Area $\square = bh$: The area of any parallelogram is the product of the length of a base and the length of a corresponding altitude. *(395)*
Theorem 12.6	The area of a trapezoid is one-half the product of the length of the altitude and the sum of the lengths of the two bases. *(398)*
Theorem 12.7	The ratio of the areas of two similar triangles is the square of the ratio of the lengths of any two corresponding sides. *(402)*

Theorem 12.8	The ratio of the perimeters of two similar polygons is the same as the ratio of the lengths of any two corresponding sides. *(403)*
Theorem 12.9	The area of a regular polygon is one-half the product of the length of an apothem and the perimeter. *(407)*
Theorem 12.10	For all circles, the ratio of the circumference to the length of a diameter is the same. *(410)*
Corollary	If c is the circumference of a circle with a diameter of length d and a radius of length r, then $c = \pi d$ or $c = 2\pi r$. *(410)*
Theorem 12.11	Area $\odot = \pi r^2$: The area of a circle with a radius of length r is πr^2. *(412)*
Theorem 12.12	$l = \dfrac{m}{360} \cdot 2\pi r$: If the degree measure of an arc is m and the length of a radius of the circle is r, then the length l of the arc is given by the formula $l = \dfrac{m}{360} \cdot 2\pi r$. *(415)*
Theorem 12.13	Area sector $= \dfrac{m}{360} \cdot 2\pi r$: In a circle, the area of a sector bounded by an arc of measure m and radii of length r is given by the formula Area $= \dfrac{m}{360} \cdot \pi r^2$. *(418)*
Theorem 13.1	The Distance Formula: The distance d between $P(x_1, y_1)$ and $Q(x_2, y_2)$ is given by the formula $d = \sqrt{(x_2 - x_1)^2 + (y_2 - y_1)^2}$. *(433)*
Theorem 13.2	The Midpoint Formula: Let $P(x_1, y_1)$ and $Q(x_2, y_2)$ be any two points in a coordinate plane. Then the midpoint m of $\overline{PQ}$ has the coordinates $\left(\dfrac{x_1 + x_2}{2}, \dfrac{y_1 + y_2}{2}\right)$. *(435)*
Theorem 13.3	Standard Form: The graph of an equation that can be written in the form $ax + by = c$ (a and b not both equal to 0) is a line. *(442)*
Theorem 13.4	Point-slope Form: If a line passes through $P(x_1, y_1)$ and has slope m, then an equation of the line is $y - y_1 = m(x - x_1)$. *(443)*
Theorem 13.5	Slope-intercept Form: If a line has slope m and y-intercept b, then an equation of the line is $y = mx + b$. *(446)*
Theorem 13.6	If two nonvertical lines have the same slope, then the lines are parallel. *(449)*
Theorem 13.7	If two nonvertical lines are parallel, then the lines have the same slope. *(449)*

Theorem 13.8	If the slopes of two nonvertical lines are negative reciprocals, then the lines are perpendicular. *(450)*
Theorem 13.9	If two nonvertical lines are perpendicular, then their slopes are negative reciprocals. *(450)*
Theorem 13.10	The equation of a circle with (h, k) the coordinates of the center and a radius of length r is $(x - h)^2 + (y - k)^2 = r^2$. *(456)*
Theorem 13.11	If d is the distance between points $A(x_1, y_1, z_1)$ and $B(x_2, y_2, z_2)$, then $d = \sqrt{(x_2 - x_1)^2 + (y_2 - y_1)^2 + (z_2 - z_1)^2}$. *(459)*
Postulate 27	The locus of points at a given distance d from a given point P is a circle with center P and d the length of a radius. *(468)*
Postulate 28	The locus of points a given distance d from a given line l is a pair of lines each parallel to l and at the distance d from l. *(468)*
Postulate 29	The locus of points equidistant from two given parallel lines is a line parallel to each of the given lines and midway between them. *(469)*
Theorem 14.1	The locus of points equidistant from two given points is the perpendicular bisector of the segment joining the points. *(471)*
Theorem 14.2	The locus of points equidistant from the sides of an angle is the angle bisector. *(472)*
Theorem 14.3	The perpendicular bisectors of the sides of a triangle are concurrent at a point that is equidistant from the vertices of the triangle. *(484)*
Theorem 14.4	The bisectors of the angles of a triangle are concurrent at a point that is equidistant from the sides of the triangle. *(485)*
Theorem 14.5	The lines containing the altitudes of a triangle are concurrent. *(488)*
Theorem 14.6	The medians of a triangle are concurrent at a point that is two-thirds of the distance from each vertex to the midpoint of the opposite side. *(489)*
Theorem 15.1	The Triangle Inequality Theorem: In a triangle, the sum of the lengths of any two sides is greater than the length of the third side. *(503)*
Theorem 15.2	If one side of a triangle is longer than a second side, then the measure of the angle opposite the first side is greater than the measure of the angle opposite the second side. *(507)*
Theorem 15.3	If one angle of a triangle has a greater measure than a second angle, then the side opposite the first angle is longer than the side opposite the second angle. *(508)*

Theorem 15.4	The Hinge Theorem: If two sides of one triangle are congruent, respectively, to two sides of another triangle, and the included angle of the first triangle has a greater measure than the included angle of the second triangle, then the third side of the first triangle has a greater measure than the third of the second triangle. *(511)*
Theorem 15.5	Converse of the Hinge Theorem: If two sides of one triangle are congruent, respectively, to two sides of another triangle, and the third side of the first triangle has a greater measure than the third side of the second triangle, then the angle opposite the third side of the first triangle has a greater measure than the angle opposite the third side of the second triangle. *(512)*
Theorem 15.6	If two chords of a circle are unequal in length, then the longer chord is nearer to the center of the circle. *(516)*
Theorem 15.7	If two chords of a circle are unequally distant from the center, then the chord nearer the center is the longer. *(517)*
Theorem 16.1	For any right prism, lateral area = perimeter of base × length of an altitude. $L = ph$ *(529)*
Theorem 16.2	For any prism, total area = lateral area + 2 × base area. $T = L + 2B$ *(530)*
Theorem 16.3	For any prism, volume = base area × length of an altitude. $V = Bh$ *(533)*
Theorem 16.4	For a cylinder, lateral area = circumference of base × length of an altitude. $L = 2\pi rh$ *(535)*
Theorem 16.5	For a cylinder, total area = lateral area + 2 × base area. $I = L + 2B; I = 2\pi rh + 2\pi r^2; I = 2\pi r(h + r)$ *(536)*
Theorem 16.6	For a cylinder, volume = base area × length of an altitude. $V = \pi r^2 h.$ *(536)*
Theorem 16.7	For a regular pyramid, lateral area = ½ × length of slant height × perimeter of base. $L = \frac{1}{2}\, lp$ total area = lateral area + base area. $T = L + B$ *(540)*
Theorem 16.8	For any pyramid, volume = ⅓ × base area × length of altitude. $V = \frac{1}{3}\, BH$ *(541)*
Theorem 16.9	For a cone, lateral area (L) is πrd; total area (I) is $\pi r(l + r)$; volume (V) is $\frac{1}{3}\, \pi r^2 h.$ *(545)*
Theorem 16.10	For a sphere, area = 4 × area of great circle. $A = 4\pi r^2$ *(550)*

Trigonometric Ratios

Angle Measure	Sin	Cos	Tan	Angle Measure	Sin	Cos	Tan
0°	0.000	1.000	0.000	46°	.7193	.6947	1.036
1°	.0175	.9998	.0175	47°	.7314	.6820	1.072
2°	.0349	.9994	.0349	48°	.7431	.6691	1.111
3°	.0523	.9986	.0524	49°	.7547	.6561	1.150
4°	.0698	.9976	.0699	50°	.7660	.6428	1.192
5°	.0872	.9962	.0875	51°	.7771	.6293	1.235
6°	.1045	.9945	.1051	52°	.7880	.6157	1.280
7°	.1219	.9925	.1228	53°	.7986	.6018	1.327
8°	.1392	.9903	.1405	54°	.8090	.5878	1.376
9°	.1564	.9877	.1584	55°	.8192	.5736	1.428
10°	.1736	.9848	.1763	56°	.8290	.5592	1.483
11°	.1908	.9816	.1944	57°	.8387	.5446	1.540
12°	.2079	.9781	.2126	58°	.8480	.5299	1.600
13°.	.2250	.9744	.2309	59°	.8572	.5150	1.664
14°	.2419	.9703	.2493	60°	.8660	.5000	1.732
15°	.2588	.9659	.2679	61°	.8746	.4848	1.804
16°	.2756	.9613	.2867	62°	.8829	.4695	1.881
17°	.2924	.9563	.3057	63°	.8910	.4540	1.963
18°	.3090	.9511	.3249	64°	.8988	.4384	2.050
19°	.3256	.9455	.3443	65°	.9063	.4226	2.145
20°	.3420	.9397	.3640	66°	.9135	.4067	2.246
21°	.3584	.9336	.3839	67°	.9205	.3907	2.356
22°	.3746	.9272	.4040	68°	.9272	.3746	2.475
23°	.3907	.9205	.4245	69°	.9336	.3584	2.605
24°	.4067	.9135	.4452	70°	.9397	.3420	2.747
25°	.4226	.9063	.4663	71°	.9455	.3256	2.904
26°	.4384	.8988	.4877	72°	.9511	.3090	3.077
27°	.4540	.8910	.5095	73°	.9563	.2924	3.270
28°	.4695	.8829	.5317	74°	.9613	.2756	3.487
29°	.4848	.8746	.5543	75°	.9659	.2588	3.732
30°	.5000	.8660	.5774	76°	.9703	.2419	4.010
31°	.5150	.8572	.6009	77°	.9744	.2250	4.331
32°	.5299	.8480	.6249	78°	.9781	.2079	4.704
33°	.5446	.8387	.6494	79°	.9816	.1908	5.145
34°	.5592	.8290	.6745	80°	.9848	.1736	5.671
35°	.5736	.8192	.7002	81°	.9877	.1564	6.314
36°	.5878	.8090	.7265	82°	.9903	.1392	7.115
37°	.6018	.7986	.7536	83°	.9925	.1219	8.144
38°	.6157	.7880	.7813	84°	.9945	.1045	9.514
39°	.6293	.7771	.8098	85°	.9962	.0872	11.43
40°	.6428	.7660	.8391	86°	.9976	.0698	14.30
41°	.6561	.7547	.8693	87°	.9986	.0523	19.08
42°	.6691	.7431	.9004	88°	.9994	.0349	28.64
43°	.6820	.7314	.9325	89°	.9998	.0175	57.29
44°	.6947	.7193	.9657	90°	1.000	0.000	
45°	.7071	.7071	1.000				

Table of Roots and Powers

No.	Sq.	Sq. Root	Cube	Cu. Root	No.	Sq.	Sq. Root	Cube	Cu. Root
1	1	1.000	1	1.000	51	2,601	7.141	132,651	3.708
2	4	1.414	8	1.260	52	2,704	7.211	140,608	3.733
3	9	1.732	27	1.442	53	2,809	7.280	148,877	3.756
4	16	2.000	64	1.587	54	2,916	7.348	157,564	3.780
5	25	2.236	125	1.710	55	3,025	7.416	166,375	3.803
6	36	2.449	216	1.817	56	3,136	7.483	175,616	3.826
7	49	2.646	343	1.913	57	3,249	7.550	185,193	3.849
8	64	2.828	512	2.000	58	3,364	7.616	195,112	3.871
9	81	3.000	729	2.080	59	3,481	7.681	205,379	3.893
10	100	3.162	1,000	2.154	60	3,600	7.746	216,000	3.915
11	121	3.317	1,331	2.224	61	3,721	7.810	226,981	3.936
12	144	3.464	1,728	2.289	62	3,844	7.874	238,328	3.958
13	169	3.606	2,197	2.351	63	3,969	7.937	250,047	3.979
14	196	3.742	2,744	2.410	64	4,096	8.000	262,144	4.000
15	225	3.875	3,373	2.466	65	4,225	8.062	274,625	4.021
16	256	4.000	4,096	2.520	66	4,356	8.124	287,496	4.041
17	289	4.123	4,913	2.571	67	4,489	8.185	300,763	4.062
18	324	4.243	5,832	2.621	68	4,624	8.246	314,432	4.082
19	361	4.359	6,859	2.668	69	4,761	8.307	328,509	4.102
20	400	4.472	8,000	2.714	70	4,900	8.357	343,000	4.121
21	441	4.583	9,261	2.759	71	5,041	8.426	357,911	4.141
22	484	4.690	10,648	2.802	72	5,184	8.485	373,248	4.160
23	529	4.796	12,167	2.844	73	5,329	8.544	389,017	4.179
24	576	4.899	13,824	2.884	74	5,476	8.602	405,224	4.198
25	625	5.000	15,625	2.924	75	5,625	8.660	421,875	4.217
26	676	5.099	17,576	2.962	76	5,776	8.718	438,976	4.236
27	729	5.196	19,683	3.000	77	5,929	8.775	456,533	4.254
28	784	5.292	21,952	3.037	78	6,084	8.832	474,552	4.273
29	841	5.385	24,389	3.072	79	6,241	8.888	493,039	4.291
30	900	5.477	27,000	3.107	80	6,400	8.944	512,000	4.309
31	961	5.568	29,791	3.141	81	6,561	9.000	531,441	4.327
32	1,024	5.657	32,768	3.175	82	6,724	9.055	551,368	4.344
33	1,089	5.745	35,937	3.208	83	6,889	9.110	571,787	4.362
34	1,156	5.831	39,304	3.240	84	7,056	9.165	592,704	4.380
35	1,225	5.916	42,875	3.271	85	7,225	9.220	614,125	4.397
36	1,296	6.000	46,656	3.302	86	7,396	9.274	636,056	4.414
37	1,369	6.083	50,653	3.332	87	7,569	9.327	658,503	4.431
38	1,444	6.164	54,872	3.362	88	7,744	9.381	681,472	4.448
39	1,521	6.245	59,319	3.391	89	7,921	9.434	704,969	4.465
40	1,600	6.325	64,000	3.420	90	8,100	9.487	729,000	4.481
41	1,681	6.403	68,921	3.448	91	8,281	9.539	753,571	4.498
42	1,764	6.481	74,088	3.476	92	8,464	9.592	778,688	4.514
43	1,849	6.557	79,507	3.503	93	8,649	9.644	804,357	4.531
44	1,936	6.633	85,184	3.530	94	8,836	9.695	830,584	4.547
45	2,025	6.708	91,125	3.557	95	9,025	9.747	857,375	4.563
46	2,116	6.782	97,336	3.583	96	9,216	9.798	884,736	4.579
47	2,209	6.856	103,823	3.609	97	9,409	9.849	912,673	4.595
48	2,304	6.928	110,592	3.634	98	9,604	9.899	941,192	4.610
49	2,401	7.000	117,649	3.659	99	9,801	9.950	970,299	4.626
50	2,500	7.071	125,000	3.684	100	10,000	10.000	1,000,000	4.642

Glossary

acute angle: An angle with a measure m such that $0 < m < 90$. An acute angle is a sharp angle. *(p. 23)*

acute triangle: An acute triangle has no obtuse or right angles. All three angles are acute angles. Each angle has a measure less than 90°. *(p. 103)*

adjacent angles: Two angles in a plane that have a common vertex and a common side but no common interior points. *(p. 24)*

alternate exterior angles: Alternate exterior angles are formed on opposite sides of a transversal crossing two lines. If the two lines are parallel, then the alternate exterior angles are congruent. *(p. 72)*

alternate interior angles: Alternate interior angles are formed on opposite sides of a transversal crossing two lines. If the two lines are parallel, then the alternate interior angles are congruent. *(p. 72)*

altitude: An altitude of a triangle is a segment from a vertex of the triangle perpendicular to the line containing the opposite side of the triangle. An altitude of a trapezoid or parallelogram is any segment from a point on one of the bases perpendicular to a point on the line containing the other base. *(p. 169)*

altitude of a cone: *See* cone.

altitude of a cylinder: *See* cylinder.

altitude of a prism: A segment that is perpendicular to the plane of each base. *(p. 529)*

altitude of a pyramid: *See* pyramid.

angle: An angle consists of two rays with a common endpoint. The rays are the sides of the angle; the common endpoint is the vertex. *(p. 12)*

angle of depression: The angle through which a line of vision must be depressed from the horizontal to sight an object. *(p. 329)*

angle of elevation: The angle through which a line of vision must be elevated from the horizontal to sight an object. *(p. 329)*

apothem of a regular polygon: A segment from the center of the polygon perpendicular to a side of the polygon. *(p. 406)*

auxiliary line: A line used in a proof that is not part of the original figure. An auxiliary line should be drawn to satisfy only one set of conditions. *(p. 86)*

base angles: The angles of an isosceles triangle opposite the legs or congruent sides. *(p. 139)*

base of a cone: *See* cone.

base of a cylinder: *See* cylinder.

base of a prism: *See* prism.

base of a pyramid: *See* pyramid.

bisector of a segment: A bisector of a segment is any figure that intersects the segment at its midpoint. *(p. 8)*

bisector of an angle: A ray $\overrightarrow{OP}$ is the bisector of an angle $\angle AOB$ if it is in the interior of the angle and if $\angle AOP = \angle POB$. *(p. 14)*

center of a circle: *See* circle.

center of a regular polygon: The common center of its inscribed and circumscribed circles.

center of a sphere: *See* sphere.

central angle of a circle: An angle whose vertex is the center of a circle. *(p. 355)*

centroid of a triangle: The point at which the medians are concurrent. *(p. 488)*

chord of a circle: A segment whose endpoints lie on the circle. *(p. 338)*

circle: The set of all points in a plane that are a given distance from a given point. The given point is the *center* of the circle. *(p. 337)*

circular region: The union of a circle and its interior. *(p. 387)*

circumcenter of a triangle: The center of the circumcircle of the triangle. *(p. 485)*

circumcircle of a triangle: The circle that is circumscribed about a triangle. *(p. 485)*

circumference of a circle: The limit of the perimeters of inscribed regular polygons of the circle as the number of sides of the polygons increases indefinitely. *(p. 409)*

circumscribed circle: A circle in which a polygon is inscribed. *(p. 343)*

circumscribed polygon: A polygon whose sides are tangent to a circle. *(p. 346)*

collinear points: Collinear points are points that are all in the same line. *(p. 2)*

common external tangent: A common tangent that does not intersect the segment that joins the centers of the two circles. *(p. 347)*

common internal tangent: A common tangent that intersects the segment that joins the centers of the two circles. *(p. 347)*

common tangent: A line that is tangent to each of two coplanar circles. *(p. 347)*

complementary: Two angles are complementary if the sum of their measures is 90°. *(p. 27)*

concentric circles: Coplanar circles with a common center. *(p. 352)*

congruent: Congruent figures have exactly the same size and shape. *(p. 123)*

congruent angles: Two angles are congruent if they have equal measures. *(p. 13)*

congruent arcs: Arcs of the same circle or congruent circles that have the same measure. *(p. 355)*

congruent circles: Circles with congruent radii. *(p. 342)*

congruent triangles: Congruent triangles have the same size and shape. Triangles can be proved congruent by SAS, SSS, ASA, and SAA patterns. *(p. 102)*

construction: A geometric construction is drawn with compass and straightedge. The compass is used to transfer equal distances. The straightedge is used to draw straight lines.

converse: The converse of a statement in "If . . ., then . . ." form is a statement formed by interchanging the "if" and the "then" parts of the sentence. The converse of a true statement is not necessarily true itself. *(p. 79)*

convex: A convex region is a region that has the special property that the segment connecting any two points of the region will be completely in the region. If a figure is not convex, it is concave. *(p. 188)*

coordinate(s) of a point: On a number line, the coordinate of a point is the number that corresponds to the point. In a coordinate plane, the coordinates of a point make up the ordered pair that corresponds to the point. *(p. 5)*

coordinate plane: A plane containing two perpendicular number lines that intersect at 0. *(p. 429)*

cone: A right circular cone is a solid with the following properties: The base is a circular region; the vertex is a point that lies on the line perpendicular to the plane of the base at its center; the altitude is a segment joining the vertex to the center of the base.

coplanar points: Coplanar points are points that are in the same plane. *(p. 2)*

corresponding angles: Corresponding angles are formed on the same side of a transversal. If the lines are parallel, then the corresponding angles are congruent. *(p. 72)*

corollary: A corollary of a theorem is a theorem whose proof requires only a few simple steps in addition to the proof of the original theorem. *(p. 53)*

cosine: The cosine of an acute angle of a right triangle is the ratio of the length of the leg adjacent to the angle to the length of the hypotenuse. *(p. 321)*

cylinder: A circular cylinder has two bases that are congruent circular regions. The axis is the line segment joining the centers of the two circles. An altitude is a segment that is perpendicular to the plane of each base. In the right circular cylinder on the right, the axis is also an altitude. In the oblique circular cylinder on the left, the axis is not an altitude. *(p. 535)*

diagonal: A diagonal of a polygon is a segment that connects any two nonconsecutive sides of the polygon. *(p. 184)*

diameter of a circle: A chord that contains the center of a circle. *(p. 338)*

dihedral angles: Dihedral angles are formed by intersecting planes. The measure of a dihedral angle is that of one of its plane angles. *(p. 59)*

distance from a point to a circle: The distance from point P to circle O is measured along $\overleftrightarrow{PO}$ and is the length of the shortest segment joining P and circle O. *(p. 475)*

equiangular triangle: All three angles of an equiangular triangle are congruent. *(p. 103)*

equidistant: A point is equidistant from two other points if the distances from this point to the two points are equal. *(p. 9)*

equilateral triangle: An equilateral triangle has three congruent sides. *(p. 103)*

exterior angle: An exterior angle of a triangle is an angle that is adjacent and supplementary to one of the angles of the triangle. *(p. 14)*

extremes: *See* proportion. *(p. 270)*

face of a prism: *See* prism.

geometric mean: The positive number m is the *geometric mean of* two positive numbers a and b if $\dfrac{a}{m} = \dfrac{m}{b}$. *(p. 271)*

great circle of a sphere: The intersection of a sphere and any plane that contains the center of the sphere. *(p. 515)*

hypotenuse: The hypotenuse of a right triangle is the side opposite the right angle. *(p. 157)*

indirect proof: An indirect proof assumes that the desired conclusion is not true and shows that this assumption leads to some contradiction. *(p. 90)*

inscribed angle: An angle whose vertex lies on a circle and whose sides are secants of the circle. *(p. 359)*

inscribed circle: A circle about which a polygon is circumscribed. *(p. 346)*

inscribed polygon: A polygon whose sides are chords of a circle. *(p. 343)*

intersection: The intersection of two geometric figures is all of the points that the figures have in common. The intersection of two planes is a line or no points at all. *(p. 47)*

isosceles trapezoid: An isosceles trapezoid is a trapezoid with congruent legs. *(p. 246)*

isosceles triangle: An isosceles triangle has at least two congruent sides. *(p. 103)*

lateral area of a prism: The sum of the areas of the lateral faces.

lateral edge of a pyramid: *See* pyramid.

lateral face of a prism: *See* prism.

lateral face of a pyramid: *See* pyramid.

lateral surface of a cone: *See* cone.

line of symmetry: The reflection line of a reflection transformation. *(p. 145)*

locus: A geometric figure containing all points that satisfy given conditions. *(p. 466)*

measure of a major arc: 360 minus the measure of the central angle whose sides determine the arc. *(p. 351)*

measure of a minor arc: The measure of the central angle that intercepts the arc. *(p. 351)*

median: A median of a triangle is a segment from a vertex to the midpoint of the opposite side. The median of a trapezoid is the segment that connects the midpoints of the two legs of the trapezoid. *(p. 170, p. 243)*

midpoint of a segment: The midpoint of a segment is the point on the segment that determines two congruent segments. *(p. 8)*

noncollinear points: Noncollinear points are points that are not in the same line. *(p. 2)*

noncoplanar points: Noncoplanar points are points that are not in the same plane. *(p. 2)*

oblique circular cylinder: *See* cylinder.

oblique prism: *See* prism.

obtuse angle: An angle is obtuse if it has a measure m such that $90 < m < 180$. *(p. 23)*

obtuse triangle: An obtuse triangle has exactly one obtuse angle. *(p. 103)* Two angles must be acute angles. *(p. 103)*

ordinate: The second number in an ordered pair is called the *ordinate,* the *y-coordinate,* or the *second coordinate.* *(p. 429)*

origin: The point of intersection of the axes in a coordinate plane. *(p. 429)*

orthocenter of a triangle: The point at which the altitudes are concurrent. *(p. 488)*

parallel lines: Parallel lines are coplanar lines that do not intersect. *(p. 68)*

parallel planes: Two planes are parallel if they do not intersect. *(p. 94)*

parallelogram: A quadrilateral with two pairs of parallel sides is a parallelogram. *(p. 211)*

perimeter: The perimeter of any polygon is the sum of the lengths of the sides of the polygon. *(p. 403)*

perpendicular: Perpendicular lines are lines that intersect to form right angles. Perpendicular segments or rays are contained in perpendicular lines. A line is perpendicular to a plane if it is perpendicular to every line in the plane through the point of intersection of the line and the plane. *(p. 47)*

perpendicular bisector: A perpendicular bisector of a segment is a line or other figure that is both a bisector of the segment and perpendicular to it. *(p. 166)*

perpendicular planes: Two planes are perpendicular if they form a right dihedral angle. *(p. 61)*

plane angle: A plane angle of a dihedral angle is made up of two rays, one in each face of the dihedral angle, each perpendicular to the edge of the dihedral angle at the same point. *(p. 60)*

polygon: A polygon is composed of three or more coplanar segments that intersect only at the endpoints. Each endpoint is shared by exactly two of the segments. *(p. 182)*

postulate: A postulate is a statement of a geometric property that is accepted without proof. *(p. 30)*

prism: The polygonal regions that make up prisms are called *faces*. The bases are two faces that are congruent polygonal regions lying in parallel planes. The other faces are the *lateral faces*. The faces intersect in segments which are *edges*. The lateral faces intersect in *lateral edges*. The edges intersect in points which are *vertices*. *(p. 525)*

proof: A proof is a formal argument that shows that a conclusion follows logically from other statements. *(p. 22)*

proportion: A *proportion* is an equation of the form $\frac{a}{b} = \frac{c}{d}(b \neq 0, d \neq 0)$, a and d are the extremes of the proportion; b and c are the means of the proportion. *(p. 270)*

pyramid: A solid whose *base* is a polygonal region. Its *lateral faces* are triangular regions that share a common point called the *vertex*. The lateral faces intersect in segments called the *lateral edges* of the pyramid. The *altitude* of a pyramid is the segment from the vertex perpendicular to the plane of the base. *(p. 539)*

quadrilateral: A quadrilateral is a polygon with four sides. *(p. 208)*

radius of a circle: A segment that joins the center and any point on the circle. *(p. 338)*

radius of a sphere: A segment that joins the center and any point on the sphere.

ratio: The ratio of two numbers a and b is the number $\frac{a}{b}(b \neq 0)$.

ray: A ray $\overrightarrow{AB}$ is the set of points that includes segment $\overline{AB}$ and all points P such that B is between A and P. A ray has one endpoint but extends indefinitely in the other direction. *(p. 6)*

rectangle: A rectangle is a parallelogram with four right angles. This means that all of the angles are congruent. The diagonals of a rectangle are congruent. *(p. 226)*

reflection: One special geometric transformation is the reflection. The reflection is always congruent to the original figure. The line of reflection is the perpendicular bisector of the segment joining corresponding points of the original figure and its image. *(p. 144)*

regular polygon: A regular polygon is a polygon that is both equiangular and equilateral.

regular pyramid: The base is a regular polygon; the lateral faces are congruent isosceles triangles; the altitude meets the base at its center. A slant height is the altitude of a lateral face.

remote exterior angle: It is an exterior angle that is not adjacent to the given exterior angle. *(p. 107)*

rhombus: A rhombus is a parallelogram with all four sides congruent. *(p. 226)*

right angle: A right angle has a measure of 90°. *(p. 23)*

right circular cone: *See* cone.

right circular cylinder: *See* cylinder.

right prism: *See* prism.

right triangle: A right triangle has exactly one right or 90° angle. *(p. 306)*

scalene triangle: A scalene triangle has no congruent sides or angles. *(p. 103)*

secant of a circle: A line that intersects a circle at two points. *(p. 338)*

sector of a circle: A region bounded by two radii of a circle and an arc determined by the radii. *(p. 418)*

segment: A segment $\overline{AB}$ is the set of points A, B and all points between A and B. A segment is named by its endpoints. A segment is straight and has a definite length. *(p. 6)*

semicircle: Consists of the endpoints of a diameter of a circle and all points of the circle that lie on one side of the diameter. *(p. 351)*

similar polygons: Two polygons are similar if corresponding angles are congruent and corresponding sides are proportional. *(p. 275)*

sine: The sine of an acute angle of a right triangle is the ratio of the length of the leg opposite the angle to the length of the hypotenuse. *(p. 321)*

skew lines: Skew lines are lines that are noncoplanar. They cannot intersect. *(p. 68)*

slant height of a cone: *See* cone.

slant height of a regular pyramid: *See* regular pyramid.

slope of a line: The slope m of a line passing through $P(x_1, y_1)$ and $Q(x_2, y_2)$ is defined as follows: $m = \dfrac{y_2 - y_1}{x_2 - x_1}$ $(x_2 \neq x_1)$. *(p. 438)*

space: Space is the set of all points. *(p. 2)*

sphere: The set of all points at a given distance from a given point called the *center*. *(p. 549)*

square: A rectangle with four congruent sides. It also is a rhombus with four congruent right angles. *(p. 226)*

straight angle: A straight angle has a degree measure of 180. A straight angle can also be thought of as a line. *(p. 23)*

supplementary angles: Two angles are supplementary if the sum of their measures is 180°. *(p. 27)*

tangent circles: Two coplanar circles that are tangent to the same line in the same point. *(p. 347)*

tangent to a circle: A line that is coplanar with a circle and intersects the circle at exactly one point. The point is called the *point of tangency*. *(p. 338)*

theorem: A statement that can be proved to be true, as opposed to a postulate that is assumed to be true without proof. *(p. 38)*

total area of a prism: The sum of the lateral area and the areas of the two bases. *(p. 529)*

transformation: A geometric transformation is a way of relating the points of a figure with the points of a second figure, called the *image*.

transversal: A transversal is a line that intersects two or more coplanar lines in different points. *(p. 71)*

trapezoid: A trapezoid is a quadrilateral with exactly one pair of parallel sides. *(p. 239)*

triangle: A triangle is a polygon with three sides. It consists of three segments that have three noncollinear points as their endpoints. *(p. 86)*

vertex: The vertex of an angle is the common endpoint of the two rays that make up the angle. *(p. 429)*

vertex of a cone: *See* cone.

vertex of a prism: *See* prism.

vertex of a pyramid: *See* pyramid.

vertical angles: The congruent nonadjacent angles formed by two intersecting lines. *(p. 25)*

Index

SELECTED ANSWERS

(Included are odd answers to written exercises, chapter reviews, and all answers to cumulative and algebra reviews.)

Page 3
1. collinear   3. coplanar but noncollinear
5. collinear   7. True   9. False   11. True
13. False   15. True   17, 19, 21. Answers
may vary.   23. At most only 2 pts can be
collinear since the 4 pts given are noncoplanar.

Algebra Review
1. 2   2. 5   3. 8   4. 6   5. 4   6. 22
7. 2   8. 8   9. 25   10. 10   11. 0

Page 7
1. −3   3. −0.8   5. 1.8   7. 7   9. 5
11. 15   13. $\overline{ST}$ 15. $\overline{US}$ 17. $\overrightarrow{RS}$; $\overrightarrow{RT}$
19. 3 cm; 28 mm   21. 1 cm; 12 mm   23. C
25. B 27. 1; −7   29. 4.4; −11.2   31. $\overline{PR}$ +
$\overline{RQ} \neq \overline{PQ}$

Pages 10–11
1. ≠   3. ≅   5. ≅   7. ≠   9. ≅   11. ≅
13. ≅   15. Follow constr on p 9, then ex 3.
17. Follow constr on p 9, then constr on p 10.
19. 11   21. 6   23. −7   25. $2\frac{7}{8}$ 27. $-5\frac{7}{16}$
29. Constr $\overline{MX} \cong \overline{AB}$ constr $\overline{MA} \cong \overline{CD}$ with A
between M and X.   31. Constr seg $\cong \overline{PQ}$.
Constr midpt, p 10, and repeat.   33. $q = 2m - p$
35. $r = p + \frac{3}{4}(q - p)$, or $r = \frac{1}{4}p + \frac{3}{4}q$

Pages 15–16
1. 30°   3. 76°   5. 110°   7. 20°   9. 138°
11. ≅   13. ≅   15, 17. Follow ex 2 on p 13,
then constr on p 14.   19. Follow constr on
p 13.   21. Follow ex 2 on p 13, constr on
p 14, and repeat.   23. Repeat ex 21. The
required $\angle$ is $\frac{1m}{2}\angle + \frac{1m}{4}\angle$.   25. Yes, def.
of $\angle$ bisector.   27. 27°   29. No. There is no
interior.

Page 18
1. $\overrightarrow{AB}$; $\overrightarrow{AC}$ 3. collinear   5. coplanar but
noncollinear   7. coplanar but noncollinear
9. 4   11. 6   13. −3   15. Yes   17. 135°
19. Follow constr on p 9.   21. Follow constr
on p 13.   23. 38

Page 26
1. $\angle AEB$; 25° or $\angle BEC$; 65°   3. $\angle AEC$ or
$\angle CED$; 90°.   5. not adj; no common side
7. adj   9. adj.   11. adj   13, 15. Answers may
vary.   17. False   19. True   21. True
23. False   1. No   2. point, line, and plane   3. 7

Page 29
1. 60°; 150°   3. 85°; 175°   5. not poss; 52°
7. not poss; 40°   9. 67.5°; 157.5°   11. 95 − m;
185 − m   13. 70°   15. 80°   17. 60°   19. 45°
21. 60°   23. 52°   25. 61°   27. 52°   29. 38°

Page 32
1. m $\angle AOB$ = m $\angle DOC$; m $\angle AOB$ =
m $\angle BOC$; m $\angle AOD$ = m $\angle BOC$ 3. $\angle JKL \cong$
$\angle LKM$; def. of $\angle$ bis   5. $\overrightarrow{TU}$ bis $\angle STV$; def of
$\angle$ bis   7. E is the midpt of $\overline{DF}$; def of midpt.
9. m $\angle b$ = 42; def of comp $\angle$'s   11. m $\angle f$ =
76; def of supp $\angle$'s   13. m $\angle C$ = m $\angle D$ = 90;
def of supp $\angle$'s   15. No; pt Z not in interior
of $\angle XYW$.   17. Yes; def of comp $\angle$'s and
$\cong \angle$'s, subst and subtr props.   1. 110°
2. 90°   3. Segments that have the same length.

Pages 36–37
1. $\overline{CD}$; $\overline{AB} \cong \overline{CD}$ 3. Given; def of $\cong$ seg;
given; subst prop   5. m $\angle A$ = m $\angle C$, (trans
prop); $\angle A \cong \angle C$ (def of $\cong \angle$'s)   7. m $\angle XOY$ =
m $\angle ZOY$ (reflex prop); m $\angle WOX$ = m $\angle ZOY$
(subtr prop); $\angle WOX \cong \angle ZOY$ (def of $\cong \angle$'s)
9. m $\angle A$ + m $\angle B$ = m $\angle B$ + m $\angle C$ (trans prop)
m $\angle B$ = m $\angle B$ (reflex prop); m $\angle A$ = m $\angle C$
(subtr prop)   11. m $\angle H$ = 70 (subst prop);
m $\angle H$ = m $\angle I$ (trans prop) $\angle H \cong \angle I$ (def of $\cong$
$\angle$'s)   13. $NO - RS = PQ - RS$ (trans prop);
$RS = RS$ (reflex prop); $NO = PQ$ (add prop)
15. $\frac{1}{2}$(m $\angle WYZ$) = $\frac{1}{2}$(m $\angle QST$) (div prop);
m $\angle XYZ$ = m $\angle RST$ (trans prop); $\angle XYZ \cong$
$\angle RST$ (def of $\cong \angle$'s)

Page 41
1. T   3. F   5. T   7. F   9. F   11. F
13. T   15. Yes   17. No   19. 4   21. No
23. $\overleftrightarrow{AB}$, $\overleftrightarrow{AC}$ intersect (given); A, B, C are 3
noncollinear points in plane S (Post 2); $\overleftrightarrow{AB}$, $\overleftrightarrow{AC}$
in plane S (Post 3); $\overleftrightarrow{AB}$, $\overleftrightarrow{AC}$ intersect in 1 pt.

Algebra Review

1. 7   **2.** 52   **3.** 4   **4.** 5   **5.** -12 **6.** 25

Pages 45–46

1. $\angle AOB$ **3.** $\angle DOE$ **5.** 11 cm   **7.** 8 m
9. 100   **11.** 62   **13.** 78   **15.** 20 mm
17. Given; def of betw; $TU + UV = TV$; subst prop; $ST = UV$ **19.** $BC = BC$ (reflex prop); $AC - BC = BD - BC$ (subtr prop); $AC = AB + BC$ and $BD = BC + CD$ (def of betw) $AB = AC - BC$ and $CD = BD - BC$ (subtr prop); $AB = CD$ (subst prop)   **21.** m $\angle AOC =$ m $\angle OOB$ (def of $\cong$ $\angle$'s); m $\angle AOC =$ m $\angle 1 +$ m $\angle 2$ and m $\angle DOB =$ m $\angle 2 +$ m $\angle 3$ (Post 10 $\angle$ add post); m $\angle 1 +$ m $\angle 2 =$ m $\angle 2 +$ m $\angle 3$ (subst prop); m $\angle 2 =$ m $\angle 2$ (reflex prop); m $\angle 1 =$ m $\angle 3$ (subtr prop); $\angle 1 \cong \angle 3$ (def of $\cong$ $\angle$'s   **23.** $EG = FG$ and $EH = FI$ (def of $\cong$ seg); $EG = EH + HG$ and $FG = FI + IG$ (def of betw); $EH + HG = FI + IG$ (subst prop); $HG = IG$ (subtr prop); $\overline{HG} \cong \overline{IG}$ (def of $\cong$ seg)   **25.** $JK = NM$ (def of $\cong$ seg); $\frac{1}{2}(JL) = \frac{1}{2}(NL)$ (subst); $JL = NL$ (mult prop); $\overline{JL} \cong \overline{NL}$ (def of $\cong$ seg)   **27.** $OQ = QP$, $OQ = RT$ and $OP = RS$ (def of $\cong$ seg); $OP = OQ + QP$ and $RS = RT + TS$ (def of between); $OQ + QP = RT + TS$ (subst prop); $QP = TS$ (subtr prop); $RT = TS$ (subst prop); T bisects RS (def of bis)

Algebra Review

1. $3x + 12$ **2.** $12a^3 + 18a^2$ **3.** $8x^5 - 10x^2$
4. $-15t + 105$ **5.** $-24x^5 + 16x^4$ **6.** $2z^2 - 5z - 3$ **7.** $6x^2 + x - 15$ **8.** $4r^2 + 12r + 9$
9. $p^2 - q^2$ **10.** $9c^2 - 16$ **11.** $16c^4 - 9b^2$
12. $25x^2 + 30xy^2 + 9y^4$

Page 51

1. $\overline{QA} \perp \overline{OD}$; $\overline{OD} \perp \overline{OG}$; $\overline{OC} \perp \overline{OF}$; $\overrightarrow{OA}$ and $\overrightarrow{OG}$ form a st $\angle$.   **3.** Follow constr p 48.   **5.** Constr midpt of seg, then follow constr top of p. 49.   **7.** m $\angle XYT +$ m $\angle WZV = 180$ (def of suppl $\angle$'s), m $\angle XYT =$ m $\angle WZV$ (def of $\cong$ $\angle$'s); m $\angle WZV +$ m $\angle WZV = 180$, or 2 m $\angle WZV = 180$ (subst prop); m $\angle WZV = 90$ (div prop); $\overrightarrow{ZV} \perp \overrightarrow{XW}$ (def of $\perp$)   **9.** Follow ex 2 p 49. Meas of desired $\angle$ is $(90° + 45°)$.   **11.** $\angle AEC \cong \angle AED$ (Th 2.6: two lines form 4 $\cong$ rt $\angle$'s.)

Pages 55–56

1. 50   **3.** 72   **5.** $\angle 2 \cong \angle 3$ **7.** $\angle 2 \cong \angle 3$
9. Given; given; given; def of compl $\angle$'s; def of compl $\angle$'s; comp of $\cong$ $\angle$'s are $\cong$ **11.** m $\angle 1 +$ m $\angle 2 = 180$ (Post 11); $\angle Z$ is suppl to $\angle 1$ (def of suppl $\angle$'s); $\angle 5$ is suppl to $\angle 1$ (subst prop)

Cumulative Review

1. Answers may vary.   **2.** acute   **3.** 90°

Page 58

1. Given: $\angle DOC \cong \angle COB$; $\angle AOB \cong COB$. Prove: $\angle DOC \cong \angle AOB$ **3.** Given: $\overleftrightarrow{AB}$ and $\overleftrightarrow{CD}$ intersect at E, forming vert $\angle$s $\angle 1$ and $\angle 2$; $\angle 3$ is suppl to $\angle 1$; $\angle 4$ is suppl to $\angle 2$. Prove: $\angle 3 \cong \angle 4$ **5.** Given: $\angle 3$ and is adj and suppl to $\angle 1$; $\angle 2$ is adj and suppl to $\angle 1$. Prove: $\angle 3$ and $\angle 2$ are vert $\angle$'s.   **7.** Given: $\angle 2$ is compl to $\angle 1$; $\angle 5$ is compl to $\angle 4$; $\angle 2 \cong \angle 5$; $\angle 3 + 2$ is suppl to $\angle 1$; $\angle 6 + 5$ is suppl to $\angle 4$. Prove: $\angle 3 + 2 \cong \angle 6 + 5$; $\angle 1 \cong \angle 4$ (Th 2.9: compl of $\cong$ $\angle$'s are $\cong$); $\angle 3 + 2 \cong \angle 6 + 5$ (Th 2.8: suppl of $\cong$ $\angle$'s are $\cong$).   **9.** Given: $\angle 1$ and $\angle 2$ are compl; $\angle 1 \cong \angle 2$. Prove: m $\angle 1 = 45$; m $\angle 2 = 45$; m $\angle 1 +$ m $\angle 2 = 90$ (def of comp $\angle$'s); m $\angle 1 =$ m $\angle 2$ (def of $\cong$ $\angle$'s); 2 m $\angle 1 = 90$ and 2 m $\angle 2$; $= 90$ (subst prop); m $\angle 1 = 45$ and m $\angle 2 = 45$ (div prop).

Cumulative Review

1. 4   **2.** Yes   **3.** True

Pages 61–62

1. 82   **3.** 81   **5.** 111   **7.** 53   **9.** False
11. True   **13.** False   **15.** Too little info; $\angle WOZ$ is a plane.   **17.** 90   **19.** 150
21. 90   **23.** Given: $\overleftrightarrow{AB} \perp q$. Prove: $p \perp q$, where p is any plane containing $\overleftrightarrow{AB}$; p and q intersect at some line $\overleftrightarrow{CD}$ (Post 4); there is $\overrightarrow{FB}$ in $q \perp \overleftrightarrow{CD}$ (Post 12); $\overrightarrow{FB} \perp \overleftrightarrow{AB}$ (def of 1 $\perp$ pl); $\angle A - \overleftrightarrow{CD} - F$ is a rt $\angle$ (def of d. h $\angle$); $p \perp q$ (def of $\perp$ pl)

Algebra Review

1. $8x^2 - x + 3$ **2.** $6x^3 + 8x^2 - 4x + 7$
3. $4x^4 + 5x^3 + 2x^2$ **4.** $2x^4 + 2x^3 + x^2 + x$
5. $3 + 7x + x^2 + x^3$ **6.** $4 - 2x - 2x^2$
7. $4x^4 - 12x^3 + 7x^2$ **8.** $3x^3 - 2x^2 + 5x + 4$

Page 64

1. acute   **3.** right   **5.** neither   **7.** comp
9. 110°,   **11.** F   **13.** T   **15.** 154
17. Post 11; Post 11; def supp $\angle$'s; def supp $\angle$'s; given; supp of $\cong$ $\angle$'s are $\cong$ **19.** Follow constr top p 49, then ex 2.   **21.** Given: $\overleftrightarrow{AB}$ and $\overleftrightarrow{CD}$ intersect at E. Prove: $\overleftrightarrow{AB}$ and $\overleftrightarrow{CD}$ are coplanar.   **23.** m $\angle 1 =$ m $\angle 2$, and m $\angle 2 =$ m $\angle 3$ (def of $\cong$ $\angle$'s); m $\angle 1 =$ m $\angle 3$ (trans prop); $\angle 1 \cong \angle 3$ (def of $\cong$ $\angle$'s)

Page 70

1., 3. Answers may vary.   **5.** T   **7.** T   **9.** T
11. F   **13.** sometimes T   **15.** always T
17. See answers ex 6, 7 p. 69; no; yes.

Cumulative Review

1. an angle   2. See constr. p 10   3. Yes, if the rays form a straight $\angle$.

Pages 72–73

1. $\overleftrightarrow{AE}$; $\overleftrightarrow{CG}$; $\overleftrightarrow{FI}$ 3. none of these   5. alt int
7. none of these   9. corr   11. corr   13. corr
15. alt int   17. alt ext   19. alt int   21. none of these   23. alt ext   25. A, E, F, H, M, N, W, Z   27. E, F, H, M, N, W, Z

Algebra Review

1. 5   2. $^-$10   3. 11   4. -8 5. 2   6. 1
7. $\frac{5}{4}$ 8. $\frac{3}{2}$ 9. $-\frac{1}{2}$ 10. $-\frac{7}{2}$ 11. -2
12. -4

Pages 77–78

1. 63°, 63°   3. 71°, 71°   5. 70°, 70°   7. 22°, n.e.i, n.e.i   9. Given; corr $\angle$'s of $\parallel$ lines are $\cong$; $\angle EIJ$; $\angle ABC \cong \angle EIJ$; trans prop
11. m $\angle 1$ + m $\angle 2$ = 180 and m $\angle 3$ + m $\angle 4$ = 180 (Th 3.2); m $\angle 1$ + m $\angle 2$ + m $\angle 3$ + m $\angle 4$ = 360 (add prop)   13. m $\angle 1$ + m $\angle 2$ = 180 (Post 11); $\angle 1$ and $\angle 2$ are supp (def of supp $\angle$'s); $\angle 2 \cong \angle 3$ (Post 13); $\angle 1$ and $\angle 3$ are supp (subst prop)   15. Given: $\overleftrightarrow{AB} \parallel \overleftrightarrow{CD}$; $\overrightarrow{EF} \perp \overrightarrow{AB}$. Prove: $\overrightarrow{EF} \perp \overleftrightarrow{CD}$; $\angle 1$ is a rt $\angle$ (Th 2.6); $\angle 1 \cong \angle 2$ (Post 13); $\angle 2$ is a rt $\angle$ (subst prop); $\overrightarrow{EF} \perp \overleftrightarrow{CD}$ (def of $\perp$ lines)
17. meas of n, k, w, z = 76; meas of 1, m, x, y = 104; meas of p, t, q, u = 59; meas of r, o, s, v = 121   19. $\angle AED$ is a comp of $\angle JHM$
21. m $\angle 3$ = 42

Page 82

1. True   3. False   5. $\overrightarrow{BC} \parallel \overrightarrow{EG}$; all $\angle$'s are $\cong$ (All rt $\angle$s are $\cong$.)   7. $\angle 1 \cong \angle 2$ (Vert $\angle$'s are $\cong$.); $\angle 2 \cong \angle 4$ (trans prop); $\angle 2$ supp to $\angle 3$ (Th 3.2); $\angle 4$ supp to $\angle 3$ (subst prop); $t \parallel s$ (Th 3.4)   9. $l \nparallel m$ 11. $r \nparallel s$ 13. $r \nparallel s$
15. $\angle ADC$ supp to $\angle A$ (Th 3.2); $\angle ABC$ supp $\angle A$ (subst prop); $\overleftrightarrow{BC} \parallel \overleftrightarrow{AD}$ (Th 3.4)
17. m $\angle 2$ + m $\angle 3$ = 180 (Post 11); $\angle 2$ and $\angle 3$ are supp (def of supp $\angle$'s); $\angle 1 \cong \angle 3$ (cor supp of the same $\angle$ are $\cong$); $\overleftrightarrow{AB} \parallel \overleftrightarrow{CD}$ (Th 3.3)
19. Given: $\overleftrightarrow{AB} \parallel \overleftrightarrow{CD}$, $\overrightarrow{EG}$ bisects $\angle IEB$, $\overrightarrow{FH}$ bisects $\angle EFD$. Prove: $\overrightarrow{EG} \parallel \overrightarrow{FH}$; $\angle IEB \cong \angle EFD$ (Th 3.2); m $\angle IEB$ = m $\angle EFD$ (def of $\cong$ $\angle$'s); $\frac{1}{2}$ m $\angle IEB = \frac{1}{2}$ m $\angle EFD$ (div prop);

m $\angle 1 = \frac{1}{2}$ m $\angle IEB$ and m $\angle 2 = \frac{1}{2}$ m $\angle EFD$

(def of bis); m $\angle 1$ = m $\angle 2$ (subst prop); $\angle 1 \cong \angle 2$ (def of $\cong$ $\angle$'s) $\overrightarrow{EG} \parallel \overrightarrow{FH}$ (Th 3.3)
21. Given: $\overrightarrow{EH} \parallel \overrightarrow{FG}$, $\overrightarrow{EH}$ bisects $\angle BEF$, $\overrightarrow{FG}$ bisects $\angle CFE$. Prove: $\overleftrightarrow{AB} \parallel \overleftrightarrow{CD}$; $\angle 1 \cong \angle 2$ (Post 13); m $\angle 1$ = m $\angle 2$ (def of $\cong$ $\angle$'s);

m $\angle 1 = \frac{1}{2}$ m $\angle BEF$ and m $\angle 2 = \frac{1}{2}$ $\angle CFE$

(def of bis); $\frac{1}{2}$ m $\angle BEF = \frac{1}{2}$ m $\angle CFE$ (subst prop); m $\angle BEF$ = m $\angle CFE$ (mult prop); $\angle BEF \cong \angle CFE$ (def of $\cong$ $\angle$'s); $\overleftrightarrow{AB} \parallel \overleftrightarrow{CD}$ (post 14)

Cumulative Review

1. Measures are equal.   2. 148°   3. 34°

Page 85

1. cannot tell   3. $\neq$ 5. cannot tell   7. cannot tell   9. cannot tell   11. $\parallel$ 13. $\nparallel$
15. Given: $\overleftrightarrow{AB} \parallel \overleftrightarrow{CD}$, $\overleftrightarrow{GH}$ inters $\overleftrightarrow{AB}$ at F. Prove: $\overleftrightarrow{GH}$ inters $\overleftrightarrow{CD}$, if $\overleftrightarrow{GH}$ does not inters $\overleftrightarrow{CD}$, $\overleftrightarrow{GH} \parallel \overleftrightarrow{CD}$. This contradicts post 15.

Pages 88–89

1. 45°; 45°; 90°   3. 50°; 60°; 70°   5. 30
7. $\angle C$ is a rt $\angle$ (def of $\perp$ lines); m $\angle C$ = 90 (def of a rt $\angle$); m $\angle A$ + m $\angle B$ + m $\angle C$ = 180 (Th 3.5); m $\angle A$ + m $\angle B$ = 90 (subst prop)
9. $\angle DBA \cong \angle CBE$ (vert $\angle$'s are $\cong$); $\angle A \cong \angle E$ (Th 3.6)   11. m $\angle C$ + m $\angle CDE$ + m $\angle CED$ = 180 and m $\angle C$ + m $\angle A$ + m $\angle B$ = 180 (Th 3.5); m $\angle C$ + m $\angle CDE$ + m $\angle CED$ = m $\angle C$ + m $\angle A$ + m $\angle B$ (trans prop); m $\angle CDE$ + m $\angle CED$ = m $\angle A$ + m $\angle B$ (subt prop); 2 m $\angle CDE$ = 2 m $\angle A$ (subst prop); m $\angle CDE$ = m $\angle A$ (div prop); $\angle CDE \cong A$ (def of $\cong$ $\angle$'s); $\overline{DE} \parallel \overline{AB}$ (Th 3.3)   13. 67
15. too little info   17. 76   19. $\angle ABH \cong \angle EGJ$ contradicts $\overleftrightarrow{AC} \nparallel \overleftrightarrow{FJ}$.

Page 91

1. Suppose $\angle 1 \cong \angle 2$. Then $l \parallel m$ (Post 14); This contradicts the given. $\therefore \angle 1 \ncong \angle 2$.   3. Suppose $t \perp s$. Then $\angle 3 \cong \angle 4$. ($\perp$ lines form $\cong$ rt $\angle$'s). This contradicts the given. $\therefore t \not\perp s$
5. Suppose $r \parallel s$. Then $\angle 2 \cong \angle 3$ (Post 13); $\angle 2$ is a rt $\angle$ (Th 2.6); $\angle 3$ is a rt $\angle$ (subst prop); $s \perp t$ (def of $\perp$ lines). This contradicts the given. $\therefore r \nparallel s$.   7. Suppose $l \parallel m$. Then $\angle 1$ and $\angle 2$ are suppl (Th 3.2); m $\angle 1$ + m $\angle 2$ = 180 (def of supp $\angle$'s). This contradicts the given. $\therefore l \nparallel m$
9. Given: $\triangle ABC$. Prove: $\angle A$ and $\angle B$ cannot both be obtuse $\angle$'s. Suppose $\angle A$ and $\angle B$ are both obtuse $\angle$'s. Then m $\angle A$ + m $\angle B$ > 180 and m $\angle A$ + m $\angle B$ + m $\angle C$ > 180. This contradicts Th 3.5. $\therefore \angle A$ and $\angle B$ cannot be obtuse.   11. Given: $\triangle ABC$. Prove: $\overleftrightarrow{AC} \nparallel \overleftrightarrow{BC}$. Suppose $\overleftrightarrow{AC} \parallel \overleftrightarrow{BC}$. Then $\overleftrightarrow{AC}$ and $\overleftrightarrow{BC}$ are intersected by a transv; $\angle A$ and $\angle B$ are supp. ($\angle$s on the same side of the transv are supp); m $\angle A$ + m $\angle B$ = 180 (def of supp $\angle$s) m $\angle A$ + m $\angle B$ + m $\angle C$ > 180. This contradicts Th 3.5. $\overleftrightarrow{AC} \nparallel \overleftrightarrow{BC}$ 13. Suppose $r \parallel t$. Then $s \parallel t$ (Th 3.7). This contradicts the given. $\therefore r \nparallel t$.

15. Suppose $\angle C \neq \angle F$. Then m $\angle A$ + m $\angle B$ + m $\angle C \neq$ m $\angle D$ + m $\angle E$ + m $\angle F$ (add prop of ineq). This contradicts m $\angle A$ + m $\angle B$ + m $\angle C$ = 180 and m $\angle D$ + m $\angle E$ + m $\angle F$ = 180 (Th 3.5). $\therefore \angle C \cong \angle F$

Page 93

1. Follow constr p 92.   3. Follow ex 1 p 92.
5. Follow constr p 10 and constr p 92.

Page 96

1. F   3. T   5. T   7. T   9. $m \parallel l$ and $p \parallel l$, but $m \not\parallel p$ 11. $p \parallel q$, but $l \not\parallel m$ 13. p and q have no pt in common (def of $\parallel$ planes); $l \parallel p$ (l and p have no pt in common) (def of line $\parallel$ to plane)   15. Given: l intersects plane p at pt X; m is on p. Prove: $l \not\parallel m$. Assume $l \parallel m$. Then l and m are coplanar; but only pt X on l is contained in p; therefore $l \not\parallel m$.   17. Given: $p \parallel q$; t intersects p. Prove: t intersects q. Assume t does not intersect q. Then $t \parallel p$, which contradicts the given. $\therefore t$ intersects q.
19. No. Planes are parallel, or they intersect.

Page 98

1. m $\angle 9$ = 60; m $\angle 8$ = 120   3. 40   5. None
7. If lines do not intersect, then they are $\parallel$.
9. Follow instructions on p 92.   11. F
13. $\overleftrightarrow{AD} \not\parallel \overleftrightarrow{HI}$ 15. Refer to ex 9, 10 on p 91.

Pages 105–106

1. Must have an obtuse $\angle$ and no sides $\cong$.
3. Must have 3 acute angles and two sides $\cong$.
5. Must have 3 acute angles and no sides $\cong$.
7. AT 9. NT 11. NT 13. ST 15. ST
17. 1SOS rt $\triangle$'s   19. U; A; B; D;   23. Given: ABC is equiangular. Prove: ABC is not obtuse. Assume $\triangle ABC$ is obtuse (one of 2 possibilities); $\angle A$ is obtuse (def of obtuse $\triangle$); $\angle A$, $\angle B$, $\angle C$ are obtuse $\angle$'s (def of equian $\triangle$); m $\angle A$ + m $\angle B$ + m $\angle C$ > 180 (This contradicts Th 3.5); $\triangle ABC$ is not obtuse (only other possibility).

Page 109

1. 120   3. 62   5. $\angle 2 \cong \angle 3$ (Th 3.6); $\angle 1 \cong \angle 4$ (Th 2.8)   7. Given: $\triangle ABC$, exterior $\angle 2$. Prove: m $\angle 2$ = m $\angle A$ + m $\angle B$. m $\angle A$ + m $\angle B$ + m $\angle 1$ = 180 (Th 3.5); m $\angle 1$ + m $\angle 2$ = 180 (Post 11); m $\angle A$ + m $\angle B$ + m $\angle 1$ = m $\angle 1$ + m $\angle 2$ (trans prop); m $\angle 2$ = m $\angle A$ + m $\angle B$ (subtr prop).

Pages 112–113

1. $\triangle DEF$ 3. $\triangle QPR$ 5. $\triangle DBC$
13, 15. Answers may vary.   17. 31°

Algebra Review

1. $3x(2x^2 - 3)$ 2. $5y^2(y^2 - 3y + 5)$
3. $4(2z^3 + 3z^2 + 5)$ 4. $9a(3a^4 + 4a^2 - 2a + 5)$

Pages 116–117

1. $\triangle ABC \cong \triangle DEF$ 3. $\triangle MNO \cong \triangle HFG$
5. $\neq$ 7. Given; given; $\overline{MO} \cong \overline{MO}$; $\triangle OPM$ (SSS)   9. Follow constr p 115.   11. Follow constr p 115. Use 3 seg $AS \cong$ sides of given $\triangle$'s.   13. Follow constr p 115. Use 3 seg $\cong$ $\overline{MN}$. 15. $\overline{AB} \cong \overline{BC} \cong \overline{CA}$ and $\overline{DE} \cong \overline{EF} \cong \overline{FD}$ (def of equila $\triangle$'s); $\overline{AB} \cong \overline{BC} \cong \overline{CA} \cong \overline{DE} \cong \overline{EF} \cong \overline{FD}$ (subst prop); $\triangle ABC \cong \triangle DEF$ (SSS)   17. $\overline{KL} \cong \overline{NM}$ (given); $\overline{LM} \cong \overline{LM}$ (reflex prop); $\overline{KL} + \overline{LM} \cong \overline{LM} + \overline{NM}$ or $\overline{KM} \cong \overline{LN}$ (add prop); $\overline{KQ} \cong \overline{NO}$ and $\overline{QM} \cong \overline{OL}$ (given); $\triangle KMQ \cong \triangle NLO$ (SSS)
19. $\overline{AB} \cong \overline{BC}$ (def of bis); $\overline{DB} \cong \overline{DB}$ (reflex prop); $\overline{AD} \cong \overline{CD}$ (given); $\triangle ADB \cong \triangle CBD$ (SSS)   21. $\overline{XZ} \cong \overline{XY} \cong \overline{YZ}$ and $\overline{XZ} \cong \overline{XW} \cong \overline{ZW}$ and $\overline{YZ} \cong \overline{ZW} \cong \overline{YW}$ and $\overline{XW} \cong \overline{YW} \cong \overline{XY}$ (def of equila $\triangle$'s); $\overline{XZ} \cong \overline{XY} \cong \overline{YZ} \cong \overline{ZW} \cong \overline{XW} \cong \overline{YW}$ (Subst prop); $\overline{XZ} \cong \overline{XZ}$, $\overline{XY} \cong \overline{XY}$, $\overline{YZ} \cong \overline{YZ}$, $\overline{ZW} \cong \overline{ZW}$, $\overline{XW} \cong \overline{XW}$, $\overline{YW} \cong \overline{YW}$ (reflex prop); $\triangle XYZ \cong \triangle XYW \cong \triangle XWZ \cong \triangle YZW$ (SSS)   23. No. The sum of the lengths of any 2 seg. must be > length of the 3rd seg.

Pages 121–122

1. Follow constr. p 118 for SAS and ex 3 p 119 for ASA 3. $\overline{RA}$; $<A$; $\overline{AE}$ 5. Yes, $\triangle ABC \cong \triangle DEF$ 7. Yes, $\triangle MNO \cong \triangle QPR$ 9. SAS
11. Yes, SAS   13. Yes ASA   15. $\overline{FJ} \cong \overline{JG}$ (def of bis); $\angle FJH \cong \angle IJG$ (vert $\angle$'s); $\overline{HJ} \cong \overline{JI}$ (def of bis); $\triangle FJH \cong \triangle GJF$ (SAS)
17. $\overline{AC} \cong \overline{BC}$ (given); $\angle ACD \cong \angle BCD$ (def of bis); $\overline{CD} \cong \overline{CD}$ (reflex prop); $\triangle ADC \cong \triangle BDC$ (SAS)   19. $\angle LKI \cong \angle JIK$ and $\angle LIK \cong \angle JKI$ (Post 13); $\overline{IK} \cong \overline{IK}$ (reflex prop); $\triangle LKI \cong \triangle JIK$ (ASA)   21. Follow constr p 119, ex 3.   23. m $\angle UST$ = m $\angle UTS$ = m $\angle SUT$ = 60, m $\angle SUV$ = m $\angle UVS$ = m $\angle VSU$ = 60, m $\angle VUT$ = m $\angle UTV$ = m $\angle TVU$ = 60, m $\angle SVT$ = m $\angle VTS$ = m $\angle TSV$ = 60 (def of equian $\triangle$'s); $\angle UST \cong \angle UTS \cong \angle SUT \cong \angle SUV \cong \angle UVS \cong \angle VSU \cong \angle VUT \cong \angle UTV \cong \angle TVU \cong \angle SVT \cong \angle VTS \cong \angle TSV$ (def of $\cong \angle$'s and subst prop); $\overline{SU} \cong \overline{SU}$, $\overline{UT} \cong \overline{UT}$, $\overline{ST} \cong \overline{ST}$, $\overline{UV} \cong \overline{UV}$, $\overline{SV} \cong \overline{SV}$; $\overline{TV} \cong \overline{TV}$ (reflex prop); $\triangle STU \cong \triangle SVU \cong \triangle TVU \cong \triangle STV$ (ASA)

Page 126

1. SAS; yes   3. SSA; no   5. ASA; yes
7. Given; given; alt int $\angle$s of parallel lines are

≅; reflex prop; AAS   **9.** ∠M ≅ ∠K (given); $\overline{MN}$ ≅ $\overline{KN}$ (given); ∠MNJ ≅ ∠KNL (vert ∠'s); △JNM ≅ △LNK (ASA)   **11.** ∠B ≅ ∠E (given); $\overline{EC}$ ≅ $\overline{CB}$ (def of midpt); ∠ACB ≅ ∠DCE (vert ∠'s); △ABC ≅ △DEC (ASA)   **13.** $\overline{ML}$ ≅ $\overline{KJ}$ and $\overline{KL}$ ≅ $\overline{MJ}$ (given); $\overline{KM}$ ≅ $\overline{KM}$ (reflex prop); △MLK ≅ △KJM (SSS)   **15.** $\overline{UV}$ ≅ $\overline{VS}$ (def of bis); ∠UVT ≅ ∠SVT (Th 2.6); $\overline{VT}$ ≅ $\overline{VT}$ (reflex prop); △UVT ≅ △SVT (SAS)   **17.** ∠A ≅ ∠D (given); ∠DEC ≅ ∠ECB (Post 13); ∠ECB ≅ ∠FBA (Th 3.1); ∠DEC ≅ ∠FBA (subst prop); $\overline{BF}$ ≅ $\overline{EC}$ (given); △ABF ≅ △DEC (AAS)   **19.** ∠C ≅ ∠C' (Th 3.6); $\overline{BC}$ ≅ $\overline{B'C'}$ and ∠B ≅ ∠B' (given); △ABC ≅ △A'B'C' (ASA)   **21.** $\overline{GH}$ ≅ $\overline{JH}$ (trans prop); ∠IHG ≅ ∠IHJ (Th 2.6 and Th 2.5); $\overline{IH}$ ≅ $\overline{IH}$ (reflex prop); △GHI ≅ △JHI (SAS)

Page 130

1. equilat; equiang, acute   **3.** 105°   **5.** See ex 1 p. 104   **7.** 100°   **9.** Yes, ASA   **11.** See constr p. 115   **13.** $\overline{RS}$; ∠S; $\overline{ST}$ **15.** Yes, SSS   **17.** No, SSA not ≅ pattern   **19.** AAS

Cumulative Review

1. B   **2.** B   **3.** B   **4.** A   **5.** c   **6.** A
7. D   **8.** c   **9.** b   **10.** A   **11.** c   **12.** c
13. D   **14.** 62°   **15.** 115°   **17.** 11, −3
18. −5.3, 2.1   **19.** Follow midpt constr p 10.
20. Follow angle bis constr p 14.   **21.** F
22. F   **23.** T   **24.** T   **25.** F   **26.** F
27. T   **28.** m < 1 = 122; m < 4 = 58
29. m ∠1 = 113; m ∠10 = 49   **30.** m < 7 = 48; m < 8 = 48   **31.** m ∠7 = 70   **32.** ∠1 ≅ ∠2 (given); l ∥ m (Post 14); ∠3 ≅ ∠4 (Post 13)
33. DC = DC (reflex prop); AD + DC = DC + CF (add prop); △ACB ≅ △FDE (SAS for ≅ △'s)   **34.** $\overline{AB}$ ≅ $\overline{AB}$ (reflex prop); ∠CBA ≅ ∠DBA (Th 2.6); △ABC ≅ △ABD

Page 138

1. ∠A ≅ ∠D; ∠B ≅ ∠E; ∠C ≅ ∠F; $\overline{AB}$ ≅ $\overline{DE}$; $\overline{BC}$ ≅ $\overline{EF}$; $\overline{CA}$ ≅ $\overline{FD}$ **3.** ∠P ≅ ∠Q; ∠T ≅ ∠U; ∠L ≅ ∠M; $\overline{PT}$ ≅ $\overline{QU}$; $\overline{TL}$ ≅ $\overline{UM}$; $\overline{LP}$ ≅ $\overline{MQ}$ **5.** OQ = 9 cm   **7.** $\overline{AD}$ ≅ $\overline{CB}$ and $\overline{CD}$ ≅ $\overline{AB}$ (given); $\overline{AC}$ ≅ $\overline{AC}$ (reflex prop); △ADC ≅ △CBA (SSS); ∠D ≅ ∠B (CPCTC)   **9.** 56   **11.** $\overline{WZ}$ ≅ $\overline{YX}$ and ∠2 ≅ ∠4 (given); $\overline{XZ}$ ≅ $\overline{XZ}$ (reflex prop); △WXZ ≅ △YZX (SAS); ∠1 ≅ ∠3 (CPCTC); $\overline{XW}$ ∥ $\overline{YZ}$ (Post 14)   **13.** $\overline{CD}$ ≅ $\overline{CD}$ (reflex prop); ∠CDA ≅ ∠CDB (Th 2.6); $\overline{AD}$ ≅ $\overline{BD}$ (given); △ACDA ≅ △CDB (SAS); $\overline{AC}$ ≅ $\overline{BC}$ (CPCTC); △ABC is isos (def of isos △)   **15.** $\overline{LK}$ ≅ $\overline{JK}$ and $\overline{LI}$ ≅ $\overline{JI}$ (given); $\overline{IK}$ ≅ $\overline{IK}$ (reflex prop); △KLI ≅ △KJI (SSS); ∠LKI is a rt ∠ (def of ⊥ lines); ∠JKI ≅

∠LKI (CPCTC); ∠JKI is a rt ∠ (subst prop); $\overline{JK}$ ⊥ $\overline{IK}$ (def of ⊥ lines)

Page 142

1. m ∠B = 70; m ∠C = 40   **3.** m ∠H = m ∠I = 60   **5.** m ∠X = m ∠Y = m ∠Z = 60   **7.** m ∠X = m ∠Y = 82; m ∠Z = 16   **9.** m ∠D = m ∠F = 45   **11.** 20 cm   **13.** ∠B ≅ ∠1 (Th 5.1); ∠1 ≅ ∠2 (Th 2.10); ∠B ≅ ∠2 (subst prop)   **15.** ∠D ≅ ∠E (Th 5.1); ∠2 ≅ ∠D (Post 13); ∠1 ≅ ∠E (Th 3.1); ∠1 ≅ ∠2 (Trans prop)   **17.** m ∠1 + m ∠ROP = 180; m ∠2 + m ∠RPO = 180 (Post 11); ∠1 and ∠ROP are supp, ∠2 and ∠RPO are supp (def of supp ∠'s); ∠ROP ≅ ∠RPO (Th 2.8); $\overline{RO}$ ≅ $\overline{RP}$ (Th 5.2); △OPR is isos (def of isos △'s)   **19.** ∠A ≅ ∠B ≅ ∠C (def of equian △'s); $\overline{AC}$ ≅ $\overline{CB}$, $\overline{AC}$ ≅ $\overline{AB}$, $\overline{AB}$ ≅ $\overline{CB}$ (Th 5.2); $\overline{AC}$ ≅ $\overline{AB}$ ≅ $\overline{CB}$ (subst prop); △ABC is equila (def of equila △'s)   **21.** ∠1 ≅ ∠4 (Th 5.1); ∠1 ≅ ∠S, ∠4 ≅ ∠T (Th 3.1); ∠S ≅ ∠T (subst prop); $\overline{SV}$ ≅ $\overline{TV}$ (Th 5.2); $\overline{SV}$ − $\overline{VW}$ ≅ $\overline{TV}$ − $\overline{VU}$ or $\overline{SW}$ ≅ $\overline{TU}$ (subst prop)   **23.** 31   **25.** $\overline{PY}$ ≅ $\overline{PZ}$ (Th 5.2); $\overline{PX}$ ≅ $\overline{PX}$ (reflex prop); △PXZ ≅ △PXY (SAS); $\overline{XZ}$ ≅ $\overline{XY}$ (CPCTC); △XYZ is isos (def of isos △'s)

Algebra Review

1. 4   **2.** 4√2   **3.** 3√5   **4.** 7√3   **5.** 11√2
6. 10   **7.** 6√5   **8.** −24√3   **9.** 2x√2
10. 12x√x

Page 155

1, 3. Answers may vary.   **5.** $\overline{SU}$ ≅ $\overline{VT}$ and ∠S ≅ ∠V (given); $\overline{SW}$ ≅ $\overline{VW}$ (Th 5.2); △SUW ≅ △VTW (SAS)   **7.** $\overline{AX}$ ≅ $\overline{BY}$ and ∠ZXY ≅ ∠ZYX (given); $\overline{XY}$ ≅ $\overline{XY}$ (reflex prop); △AYX ≅ △BXY (SAS); ∠AYX ≅ ∠BXY (CPCTC)   **9.** ∠EDC ≅ ∠GCD (Th 3.6); ∠GCD is a rt ∠ (def of ⊥ lines); ∠EDC is a rt ∠ (subst prop); $\overline{ED}$ ⊥ $\overline{CD}$ (def of ⊥ lines)   **11.** m ∠5 + m ∠3 = 180, m ∠6 + m ∠4 = 180 (Post 11); ∠5 and ∠3 are supp, ∠6 and ∠4 are supp (def of supp ∠'s); ∠5 ≅ ∠6 (Th 2.8); $\overline{SR}$ ≅ $\overline{SR}$ (reflex prop); $\overline{OR}$ ≅ $\overline{QS}$ (add prop); △OPR ≅ △QPS (ASA)   **13.** R△GEC   **15.** R△DGC   **17.** R△AGF   **19.** pt O   **21.** R△SOC   **23.** R△BCD   **25.** $\overline{AE}$ **27.** R△HDC

Algebra Review

1. (x − 4)(x − 2)   **2.** (x + 5)(x − 3)   **3.** (x + 4)(x + 5)   **4.** (x − 1)(x + 1)   **5.** (x − 9)(x + 9)   **6.** (3x − 6)(3x + 6)   **7.** (2x + 1)(3x − 2)   **8.** (x + 5)(2x − 3)   **9.** (3x − 2)(2x − 3)

Page 160

1. $\angle Y$, $\angle S$ are rt $\angle$'s (def of $\perp$ lines); $\triangle XYZ$, $\triangle RST$ are rt $\triangle$'s (def of rt $\triangle$'s); $\overline{XY} \cong \overline{RS}$ and $\overline{ZY} \cong \overline{TS}$ (given); $\triangle XYZ \cong \triangle RST$ (LL)
3. $\angle Y$, $\angle S$ are rt $\angle$'s (def of $\perp$ lines); $\triangle XYZ$, $\triangle RST$ are rt $\triangle$'s (def of rt $\triangle$'s); $\overline{XY} \cong \overline{RS}$, $\angle Z \cong \angle T$ (given); $\triangle XYZ \cong \triangle RST$ (LA)
5. $\angle ADB$, $\angle BEA$ are rt $\angle$'s (def of $\perp$ lines); $\overline{AB} \cong \overline{AB}$ (reflex prop); $\triangle ABE$, $\triangle BAD$ are rt $\triangle$'s (def of rt $\triangle$'s); $\triangle ABE \cong \triangle BAD$ (HL)
7. $\angle ADB$, $\angle BEA$ are rt $\angle$'s (def of $\perp$ lines); $\triangle AFD$, $\triangle BFE$ are rt $\triangle$'s (def of rt $\triangle$'s); $\angle DFA \cong \angle EFB$ (Th 2.10); $\triangle AFD \cong \triangle BFE$ (HA)   9. $\angle IJG$, $\angle IJH$ are rt $\angle$'s (def of $\perp$ lines); $\triangle IJG$, $\triangle IJH$ are rt $\triangle$'s $\overline{GJ} \cong \overline{JH}$ (def of bis); $\overline{IJ} \cong \overline{IJ}$ (reflex prop); $\triangle IJG \cong \triangle IJH$ (LL) $\overline{IG} \cong \overline{IH}$ (CPCTC); $\triangle GHI$ is isos (def of isos $\triangle$'s)   11. $\angle MOK$, $\angle LNK$ are rt $\angle$'s (def of $\perp$ lines); $\triangle MOK$, $\triangle LNK$ are rt $\triangle$'s (def of rt $\triangle$); $\angle K \cong \angle K$ (reflex prop); $\triangle MOK \cong \triangle LNK$ (HA); $\overline{MO} \cong \overline{LN}$ (CPCTC)   13. $\angle RSP$, $\angle VWT$ are rt $\angle$'s (def of $\perp$ lines); $\triangle RSP$, $\triangle VWT$ are rt $\triangle$'s (def of rt $\triangle$'s); $\angle P \cong \angle T$, $\overline{PR} \cong \overline{TV}$ (CPCTC); $\triangle RSP \cong \triangle VWT$ (HA) $\overline{RS} \cong \overline{VW}$ (CPCTC)   15. $\angle ZAX$, $\angle ZAY$ are rt $\angle$'s (def of $\perp$ lines); $\triangle ZAX$, $\triangle ZAY$ are rt $\triangle$'s (def of rt $\triangle$'s); $\overline{ZA} \cong \overline{ZA}$ (reflex prop); $\triangle XAZ \cong \triangle YAZ$ (HL)   17. $\angle ZAX$, $\angle ZAY$ are rt $\angle$'s (def of $\perp$ lines); $\triangle ZAX$, $\angle ZAY$ are rt $\triangle$'s (def of rt $\triangle$'s); $\overline{ZA} \cong \overline{ZA}$ (reflex prop); $\triangle XAZ \cong \triangle YAZ$ (HL); $\angle ZXY \cong \angle ZYX$ (Th 5.1); $\angle ZXA \cong \angle ZYA$ (CPCTC); $\angle AXY \cong \angle AYX$ (subt prop)   19. $\angle ZAX$, $\angle ZAY$ are rt $\angle$'s (def of $\perp$ lines); $\triangle ZAX$, $\triangle ZAY$ are rt $\triangle$'s (def of rt $\triangle$'s); $\overline{ZA} \cong \overline{ZA}$ (reflex prop); $\triangle XAZ \cong \triangle YAZ$ (LL); $\overline{ZX} \cong \overline{ZY}$ (CPCTC); $\angle ZXY \cong \angle ZYX$ (Th 5.1)

Cumulative Review

1. Answers may vary.   2. Answers may vary.
3. No, No

Page 163

1. $\overline{AB} \cong \overline{CD}$; $\overline{AC} \cong \overline{CA}$; $\angle BAC \cong \angle DCA$; $\triangle DCE$ and $\triangle BAE$ 3. $\overline{KL} \cong \overline{MN}$; $\angle LOK \cong \angle NOM$; $\angle OKL \cong \angle OMN$; $\triangle KLM$ and $\triangle MNK$ 5. $\angle FIG$, $\angle GJF$ are rt $\angle$'s (def of $\perp$ lines); $\triangle FIG$, $\triangle GJF$, $\triangle FKI$, $\triangle GKJ$ are rt $\triangle$'s (def of rt $\triangle$'s); $\overline{FG} \cong \overline{FG}$ (reflex prop); $\triangle FIG \cong \triangle GJF$ (HL); $\overline{FI} \cong \overline{GJ}$ (CPCTC); $\angle IKF \cong \angle JKG$ (Th 2.10); $\triangle FKI \cong \triangle GKJ$ (LA)
7. $\overline{AC}$ and $\overline{BD}$ bisect each other at E (def of bis); $\overline{DE}$ (def of bis); Th 2.10; $\triangle CDE$ (CPCTC); $\angle 1 \cong \angle 2$; $\overline{CA}$; reflex prop; (SAS)   9. $\angle LGF$, $\angle KIH$ are rt $\angle$'s (def $\perp$ lines); $\triangle FGL$, $\triangle HIK$ are rt $\triangle$'s (def of rt $\triangle$'s); $\overline{LF} \cong \overline{KH}$, $\angle LFG \cong \angle KHI$ (CPCTC); $\triangle FGL \cong \triangle HIK$ (HA)
11. $\overline{FL} \cong \overline{KJ}$, $\angle F \cong \angle J$ (CPCTC); $\overline{FH} \cong \overline{JH}$ (add; betweeness; subst); $\triangle FHL \cong \triangle JHK$ (SAS)

13. $\angle QNM$, $\angle QNO$, $\angle RNQ$, $\angle PNQ$ are rt $\angle$'s (def of $\perp$ lines); $\triangle QNM$, $\triangle QNO$, $\triangle RNQ$, $\triangle PNQ$ are rt $\triangle$'s (def of rt $\triangle$'s); $\overline{QN} \cong \overline{QN}$ (reflex prop), $\triangle QNR \cong \triangle QNP$ (HL); $\angle RQN \cong \angle PQN$ (CPCTC); $\triangle QNM \cong \triangle QNO$ (LA); $\overline{NM} \cong \overline{NO}$ (CPCTC)   15. $\angle DEB$, $\angle CFA$ are rt $\angle$'s (def of $\perp$ lines); $\triangle DEB$, $\triangle CFA$ are rt $\triangle$'s (def of rt $\triangle$'s); $\triangle DEB \cong \triangle CFA$ (HL); $\overline{AB} \cong \overline{AB}$ (reflex prop); $\angle CAB \cong \angle DBA$ (CPCTC); $\triangle CAB \cong \triangle DBA$ (SAS); $\overline{AD} \cong \overline{BC}$ (CPCTC)   17. 66   19. $\angle DAB$, $\angle CBA$ are rt $\angle$'s (def of $\perp$ lines); $\triangle DAB$, $\triangle CBA$ are rt $\triangle$'s (def of rt $\triangle$'s); $\overline{AB} \cong \overline{AB}$ (reflex prop); $\triangle DAB \cong \triangle CBA$ (LL); $\overline{AC} \cong \overline{BD}$ (CPCTC)
21. $\triangle ADC \cong \triangle BCD$ (HL); $\angle DCA \cong \angle CDB$ (CPCTC); $\overline{ED} \cong \overline{EC}$. (Th 5.2)   23. $AD \parallel BC$ (2 lines $\perp$ to same line are $\parallel$); $\angle ABC$ is a rt $\angle$ (def of $\perp$ lines); m$\angle ABC$ + m$\angle DCB$ = 180 (def of supp $\angle$'s); m$\angle DCB$ = 90 (subt); $BC \perp DC$ (def $\perp$ lines); $\angle BAD$ is a rt $\angle$ (def of $\perp$ lines); m$\angle BAD$ + m$\angle ADC$ = 180 (def of $\perp$ lines); m$\angle BAD$ = 90 (subt); $AD \perp DC$ (def of $\perp$ lines)   25. Proof 23; $\overline{DA} \cong \overline{DA}$ (reflex prop); $\triangle DAB \cong \triangle ADC$ (HL); $\overline{DC} \cong \overline{AB}$ (CPCTC); $\angle CDB \cong \angle DBA$, $\angle DCA \cong \angle CAB$ (Post 13); $\triangle AEB \cong \triangle CED$ (ASA); $\overline{AE} \cong \overline{CE}$, $\overline{DE} \cong \overline{BE}$ (CPCTC); $\overline{AE} \cong \overline{CE}$ $\overline{DE} \cong \overline{BE}$ (subst prop)
27. $\angle QRP \cong \angle MRN$ (Th 2.10); $\triangle QRP \cong \triangle MRN$ (SAS); $\angle PMO \cong \angle NQO$ (CPCTC); $\angle O \cong \angle O$ (reflex prop); $\overline{QN} \cong \overline{MP}$ (add prop); $\triangle PMO \cong \triangle NQO$ (AAS); $\overline{OQ} \cong \overline{OM}$ (CPCTC)
29. $\overline{XA} \cong \overline{XA}$ (reflex prop); $\triangle XAZ \cong \triangle XAY$ (SSS); $\angle ZXB \cong \angle YXB$ (CPCTC); $\overline{XB} \cong \overline{XB}$ (reflex prop); $\triangle ZXB \cong \triangle YXB$ (SAS); $\overline{ZB} \cong \overline{YB}$ (CPCTC)

Page 168

1. $\angle XZW \cong \angle YZW$ 3. all corresponding parts of $\triangle XZW$ and $\triangle YZW$ 5. $\angle CDE \cong \angle ECB$ 7. Given: isos $\triangle ABC$, $\overline{AC} \cong \overline{BC}$, CD bis $\angle ACB$. Prove: $\overline{CD}$ bis $\overline{AB}$; $\angle ACD \cong \angle DCB$ (def of bis); $\overline{CD} \cong \overline{CD}$ (reflex prop); $\triangle ACD \cong \triangle BCD$ (SAS); $\overline{AD} \cong \overline{DB}$ (CPCTC); $\overline{CD}$ bis $\overline{AB}$ (def of bis)   9. Given: isos $\triangle ABC$, $\overline{AC} \cong \overline{BC}$, CD bis $\angle ACB$. Prove: $\overline{CD}$ is the $\perp$ bis of $\overline{AB}$; $\angle ACD \cong \angle DCB$ (def of bis); $\overline{CD} \cong \overline{CD}$ (reflex prop); $\triangle ADC \cong \triangle BDC$ (SAS); $\overline{AD} \cong \overline{DB}$ (CPCTC); CD is $\perp$ bis of AB (Th 5.8)   11. Given: $\angle ACB$, $\overleftrightarrow{CP}$ bis $\angle ACB$, $PA \perp CA$, $PB \perp CB$. Prove: $\overline{PA} \cong \overline{PB}$; $\angle ACP \cong \angle BCP$ (def of bis); $\overline{CP} \cong \overline{CP}$ (reflex prop); $\angle CPA \cong \angle CBP$ (Th 2.6); $\triangle ACD \cong \triangle BDC$ (AAS); $\overline{PA} \cong \overline{PB}$ (CPCTC)
13. Given; given; reflex prop; SSS; CPCTC; SAS; CPCTC; CPCTC; Post 11; def of supp $\angle$'s; Th 2.7; def of $\perp$ bis   15. $\overline{DC} \cong \overline{DA}$, $\overline{BA} \cong \overline{BC}$ (Th 5.7); $\overline{DB} \cong \overline{DB}$ (reflex

609

prop); $\triangle DCB \cong \triangle DAB$ (SSS); $\angle BAD \cong \angle BCD$ (CPCTC) **17.** $\angle 2 \cong \angle 4$ (subt prop); $\overline{FI} \cong \overline{FG}$, $\overline{HI} \cong \overline{HG}$ (Th 5.2); $\overline{FH}$ is $\perp$ bis of $\overline{GI}$ (Th. 5.8); $\overline{IJ} \cong \overline{JG}$ (def of bis); $\triangle HIJ \cong \triangle HGI$ (SAS); $\angle IHJ \cong \angle HGJ$ (CPCTC); $\overline{FH}$ bis $\angle IHG$ (def of bis) **19.** $\overline{MO} \cong \overline{MO}$ (reflex prop); $\angle NMO \cong \angle KMO$ (def of bis); $\triangle NMO \cong \triangle KMO$ (SAS); $\overline{NO} \cong \overline{KO}$ (CPCTC); $\overline{ML} \cong ML$ (reflex prop); $\angle MLN$, $\angle MLK$ are rt $\angle$'s (def of $\perp$ lines); $\triangle MLN$, $\triangle MLK$ are rt $\triangle$'s (def of rt $\triangle$'s); $\triangle MLN \cong \triangle MLK$ (HL); $\overline{KL} \cong \overline{NL}$ (CPCTC); $\angle LNO \cong \angle LKO$ (Th 5.1); $\triangle LNO \cong \triangle LKO$ (SAS); $\angle NLO \cong \angle KLO$ (CPCTC); $\overline{LO}$ bis $\angle NLK$ (def of bis)

Cumulative Review

1. ASA; SAS; AAS; SSS **2.** HL; HA; LL; LA **3.** Follow constr p 14.

Page 172

1. $\overline{CD} \perp \overline{AB}$ (def of alt); $\angle CDA$, $\angle CDB$ are rt $\angle$'s (def of $\perp$ lines); $\triangle ADC$, $\triangle BDC$ are rt $\triangle$'s (def of rt $\triangle$'s); $\overline{CD} \cong \overline{CD}$ (reflex prop); $\triangle ADC \cong \triangle BDC$ (LL) **3.** 50 **5.** 16 **7.** $\overline{ZW} \perp \overline{XY}$ (def of alt); $\angle ZWX$, $\angle ZWY$ are rt $\triangle$'s (def of $\perp$ lines); $\triangle ZWX$, $\triangle ZWY$ are rt $\triangle$'s (def of rt $\triangle$'s); $\overline{ZW} \cong \overline{ZW}$ (reflex prop); $\angle XZW \cong \angle YZW$ (def of bis); $\triangle ZWX \cong \triangle ZWY$ (LA); $\overline{XZ} \cong \overline{YZ}$ (CPCTC); $\triangle XYZ$ is isos (def of isos $\triangle$'s) **9.** $\angle ACB$ is a rt $\angle$ (def of $\perp$ lines); $\angle 4 \cong \angle 4$ (reflex prop); $\angle CDB \cong \angle ACB$ (Th 3.6); $\angle CDB$ is a rt $\angle$ (subst prop); $\overline{CD} \perp \overline{AB}$ (def $\perp$ lines); $\overline{CD}$ is an alt of $\triangle ABC$ (def of alt) **11.** $\angle O \cong \angle T$, $\overline{OP} \cong \overline{ST}$, $\angle OPQ \cong \angle TSV$ (CPCTC); $2 \angle OPR \cong \angle OPQ$, $2 \angle TSU \cong \angle TSV$ (def of bis); $2 \angle OPR \cong 2 \angle TSU$ (subst prop); $\angle OPR \cong \angle TSU$ (div prop); $\triangle OPR \cong \triangle TSU$ (ASA); $\overline{PR} \cong \overline{SU}$ (CPCTC) **13.** Given; CPCTC; def of $\cong$ seg; given; def of median; subst prop; def of $\cong$ seg; CPCTC; CPCTC; SAS; CPCTC **15.** Given: $\triangle ABC$ is equilat; $\overline{AE}$ alt. to $\overline{CB} \cdot \overline{CD}$ alt to $\overline{AB}$. Prove: $\overline{AE} \cong \overline{CD}$; $\overline{AE} \perp \overline{CB}$, $\overline{CD} \perp \overline{AB}$ (def of alt); $\angle AEB$, $\angle CDB$ are rt $\angle$'s (def of $\perp$ lines); $\triangle AEB$, $\triangle CDB$ are rt $\triangle$'s (def of rt $\triangle$'s); $\angle B \cong \angle B$ (reflex prop); $\overline{BC} \cong \overline{AB}$ (def of equil $\triangle$'s) $\triangle AEB \cong \triangle CDB$ (HA); $\overline{AE} \cong \overline{CD}$ (CPCTC) **17.** Given: isos $\triangle ABC$, $\overline{AC} \cong \overline{BC}$, $\overline{CD}$ alt. to $\overline{AB}$. Prove: $\overline{CD}$ is median to $\overline{AB}$; $\angle A \cong \angle B$ (Th 5.1); $\overline{CD} \perp \overline{AB}$ (def of alt); $\angle CDA \cong \angle CDB$ (Th 2.6); $\overline{CD} \cong \overline{CD}$ (reflex prop); $\triangle ACD \cong \triangle BCD$ (AAS); $\overline{AD} \cong \overline{DB}$ (CPCTC); D is the midpt of $\overline{AB}$ (def of midpt); $\overline{AD} \cong \overline{DB}$ (def of median) **19.** Given: isos $\triangle ABC$, $\overline{AC} \cong \overline{BC}$, $\overline{CD}$ median to $\overline{AB}$. Prove: $\overline{CD}$ bis $\angle ACB$; D is midpt. of $\overline{AB}$ (def of median); $\overline{AD} \cong \overline{DB}$ (def of midpt); $\overline{CD} \cong \overline{CD}$ (reflex prop); $\triangle ADC \cong \triangle BDC$ (SSS); $\angle ACD \cong \angle DCB$ (CPCTC); $\overline{CD}$ bis $\angle ACB$

(def of bis) **21.** Given: $\triangle ABC$, $\overline{CD}$ median to $\overline{AB}$, $\overline{CD} \perp \overline{AB}$. Prove: $\triangle ABC$ is isos; D is midpt of $\overline{AB}$ (def of median); $\overline{AD} \cong \overline{DB}$ (def of midpt); $\angle ADC \cong \angle BDC$ (Th 2.6); $\overline{CD} \cong \overline{CD}$ (reflex prop); $\triangle ADC \cong \triangle BDC$ (SAS); $\overline{AC} \cong \overline{BC}$ (CPCTC); $\triangle ABC$ is isos (def of isos $\triangle$) **23.** Given: $\triangle ABC$, $\overline{CD}$ median to $\overline{AB}$, $\overline{CD}$ bis $\angle ACB$. Prove: $\triangle ABC$ is isos. Draw $\overline{DM} \perp \overline{AC}$, $\overline{DN} \perp \overline{BC}$ (Post 12); $\angle AMD$, $\angle CMD$, $\angle CND$, $\angle BND$ are rt $\angle$'s (def of $\perp$ lines); $\triangle CMD$, $\triangle CND$, $\triangle AMD$, $\triangle BND$ are rt $\triangle$'s (def of rt $\triangle$'s); $\angle MCD \cong \angle NCD$ (def of bis); $\overline{CD} \cong \overline{CD}$ (reflex prop); $\triangle CDM \cong \triangle CDN$ (HA); $\overline{MD} \cong \overline{ND}$ (CPCTC); D is midpt of $\overline{AB}$ (def of med); $\overline{AD} \cong \overline{DB}$ (def of midpt); $\triangle AMD \cong \triangle BND$ (HL for $\cong$ rt $\triangle$'s) $\angle A \cong \angle B$ (CPCTC); $\overline{AC} \cong \overline{BC}$ (Th 5.2); $\triangle ABC$ is isos (def of isos $\triangle$'s) **25.** $\angle CDE \cong \angle ADE$ (def of bis); $\overline{ED} \cong \overline{ED}$ (reflex prop); $\triangle CDE \cong \triangle ADE$ (SAS); $\overline{CE} \cong \overline{EA}$ (CPCTC); $\angle DBC$, $\angle DBA$ are rt $\angle$'s (def of $\perp$ lines); $\triangle DBC$, $\triangle DBA$ are rt $\triangle$'s (def of rt $\triangle$'s); $\overline{DB} \cong \overline{DB}$ (reflex prop); $\triangle DBC \cong \triangle DBA$ (HL); $\overline{BC} \cong \overline{BA}$ (CPCTC); $\overline{BE} \cong \overline{BE}$ (reflex prop); $\triangle BCE \cong \triangle BAE$ (SSS); $\angle CBE \cong \angle ABE$ (CPCTC); $\overline{BE}$ bis $\angle CBA$ (def of bis) **27.** $\overline{JF} \cong \overline{HF}$, $\angle JFG \cong \angle HFG$ (CPCTC); $\overline{FI} \cong \overline{FI}$ (reflex prop); $\triangle JFI \cong \triangle HFI$ (SAS); $\angle JIF \cong \angle HIF$ (CPCTC); $\overline{JI} \perp \overline{FG}$ (def of alt); $\angle JIF$ is a rt $\angle$ (def of $\perp$ lines); $\angle HIF$ is a rt $\angle$ (subst prop); $\overline{HI} \perp \overline{FG}$ (def of $\perp$ lines); $\overline{HI}$ is alt of $\triangle FHG$ (def of alt) **29.** $\angle NML$, $\angle OML$ are rt $\angle$'s (def of $\perp$ lines); $\triangle NML$, $\triangle OML$ are rt $\triangle$'s (def of rt $\triangle$'s); $\overline{LM} \cong \overline{LM}$ (reflex prop); $\overline{NM} \cong \overline{MO}$ (def of bis); $\triangle OLM \cong \triangle NLM$ (LL) **31.** $\overline{NM} \cong \overline{NM}$ (reflex prop); $\angle KMN$, $\angle LMN$ are rt $\angle$'s (def of $\perp$ lines); $\triangle KMN$, $\triangle LMN$ are rt $\triangle$'s (def of rt $\triangle$'s); $\triangle KMN \cong \triangle LMN$ (HL); $\overline{LM} \cong \overline{KM}$ (CPCTC)

Pages 175–176

1. Follow constr p. 174, ex. 3. **3.** Follow constr p 49, ex. 5. **5.** Follow constr p 174, ex. 2. **7.** T **9.** T **11.** F **13.** F **15.** Follow constr p 174, ex. 2. **17.** Follow constr p 174, ex. 3.

Cumulative Review

1. Yes; obtuse $\triangle$ **2.** No **3.** Yes; the third line could be a transversal.

Algebra Review

1. $\dfrac{x-2}{8}$ **2.** $\dfrac{6x+10}{x+4}$ **3.** $\dfrac{y-1}{y+7}$ **4.** $\dfrac{6+2y}{3}$ **5.** $\dfrac{2z-2}{z+6}$ **6.** 1

Page 178

1. $\overline{AB} \cong \overline{FD}$; $\overline{BC} \cong \overline{FE}$; $\overline{CA} \cong \overline{ED}$ **3.** $\overline{DE}$

5. ≅ (LL)　**7.** ≅ (HL)　**9.** altitude　**11.** ∠1 ≅ ∠2 (def of bis); $\overline{AC} \cong \overline{AC}$ (reflex prop); △ADC ≅ △ABC (SAS) $\overline{CD} \cong \overline{CB}$ (CPCTC)　**13.** $\overline{GE} \cong \overline{GF}$, $\overline{GH} \cong \overline{GI}$ (CPCTC); $\overline{HE} \cong \overline{IF}$ (subtr prop);　**15.** 55°　**17.** Follow constr p 174, ex 2.

Page 187

1. Yes　**3.** No; segments intersect at pts that are not endpts.　**5.** No; not a union of seg.　**7.** No; not a union of seg.　**9.** $\overline{AB}$, $\overline{BC}$, $\overline{CD}$, $\overline{DA}$: A, B, C, D; quadrilateral; 2　**11.** $\overline{KL}$, $\overline{LM}$, $\overline{MN}$, $\overline{NO}$, $\overline{OP}$, $\overline{PQ}$, $\overline{QR}$, $\overline{RK}$: K, L, M, N, O, P, Q, R; octagon; 20　**13.** No; $\overline{XY}$ not always part of figure.　**15.** Convex; $\overline{XY}$ is always part of figure.　**17, 19, 21.** Answers may vary.　**23.** 11　**25.** 12

Cumulative Review

1. See Theorem 5.1, p. 139.　**2.** Answers will vary.　**3.** See ex 2, p 49.

Pages 190–192

1. 118°　**3.** 90°　**5.** 80°　**7.** 80°, 80°, 100°, 100°　**9.** 65°, 73°, 113°, 109°　**11.** 1080°　**13.** 6840°　**15.** 17640°　**18.** 1080°　**19.** 5　**21.** 12　**23.** 15　**25.** 18　**27.** cannot　**29.** can　**31.** 120°　**33.** 80°, 80°, 80°, 160°, 160°, 160°　**35.** Given: convex pentagon $ABCDE$. Prove: m ∠A + m ∠B + m ∠C + m ∠D + m ∠E = 540. Draw AC, AD (Post 1); m ∠BAE = m ∠1 + m ∠2 + m ∠3, m ∠BCD = m ∠4 + m ∠5 (Post 10); m ∠EDC = m ∠6 + m ∠7; m ∠1 + m ∠B + m ∠4 = 180, m ∠2 + m ∠5 + m ∠6 = 180, m ∠3 + m ∠E + m ∠7 = 180 (Th 3.5); m ∠A + m ∠B + m ∠C + m ∠D + m ∠E = 540 (subst and add prop)　**37.** Given: convex quad $ABCD$. Prove: m ∠A + m ∠B + m ∠C + m ∠D = 360. m ∠BAD = m ∠1 + m ∠8, m ∠ABC = m ∠2 + m ∠3, m ∠BCD = m ∠4 + m ∠5, m ∠CDA = m ∠6 + m ∠7 (Post 10); m ∠1 + m ∠10 + m ∠2 = 180, m ∠3 + m ∠4 + m ∠11 = 180, m ∠6 + m ∠5 + m ∠12 = 180, m ∠7 + m ∠9 + m ∠8 = 180 (Th 3.5); m ∠1 + m ∠2 + m ∠3 + m ∠4 + m ∠5 + m ∠6 + m ∠7 + m ∠8 + m ∠9 + m ∠10 + m ∠11 + m ∠12 = 720 (add prop); m ∠9 + m ∠10 + m ∠11 + m ∠12 = 30 (Post 11); m ∠1 + m ∠2 + m ∠3 + m ∠4 + m ∠5 + m ∠6 + m ∠7 + m ∠8 = 360 (subst prop); m ∠A + m ∠B + m ∠C + m ∠D = 360 (subst prop)　**39.** Given: convex hexagon $ABCDEF$. Prove: m ∠A + m ∠B + m ∠C + m ∠D + m ∠E + m ∠F = 720. m ∠FAB = m ∠12 + m ∠1, m ∠ABC = m ∠2 + m ∠3, m ∠BCD = m ∠4 + m ∠5, m ∠CDE = m ∠6 + m ∠7, m ∠DEF = m ∠8 + m ∠9, m ∠EFA = m ∠10 + m ∠11 (Post 10); m ∠1 +

m ∠2 + m ∠13 = 180, m ∠3 + m ∠4 + m ∠14 = 180, m ∠5 + m ∠6 + m ∠15 = 180, m ∠7 + m ∠8 + m ∠16 = 180, m ∠9 + m ∠10 + m ∠17 = 180, m ∠11 + m ∠12 + m ∠18 = 180 (Th 3.5); m ∠1 + m ∠2 + m ∠3 + m ∠4 + m ∠5 + m ∠6 + m ∠7 + m ∠8 + m ∠9 + m ∠10 + m ∠11 + m ∠12 + m ∠13 + m ∠14 + m ∠15 + m ∠16 + m ∠17 + m ∠18 = 1080 (add prop); m ∠13 + m ∠14 + m ∠15 + m ∠16 + m ∠17 + m ∠18 = 360 (Post 11); m ∠1 + m ∠2 + m ∠3 + m ∠4 + m ∠5 + m ∠6 + m ∠7 + m ∠8 + m ∠9 + m ∠10 + m ∠11 + m ∠12 = 720 (subtr prop); m ∠A + m ∠B + m ∠C + m ∠D + m ∠E + m ∠F = 720 (subst prop).　**41.** The sum of the ∠'s is 360. Th 6.1 applies.　**43, 45.** The sum of the measures of the angles is $(n - 2)180$. Th 6.2 applies.

Page 195

1–3. 360°; yes　**5.** 41°, 72°, 58°, 60°, 39°, 90°　**7.** Given: convex pentagon $ABCDE$, ext ∠s 1, 2, 3, 4, 5. Prove: m ∠1 + m ∠2 + m ∠3 + m ∠4 + m ∠5 = 360. m ∠1 + m ∠6 = 180, m ∠2 + m ∠7 = 180, m ∠3 + m ∠8 = 180, m ∠4 + m ∠9 = 180, m ∠5 + m ∠10 = 180 (Post 11); m ∠1 + m ∠2 + m ∠3 + m ∠4 + m ∠5 + m ∠6 + m ∠7 + m ∠8 + m ∠9 + m ∠10 = 900 (add prop); m ∠6 + m ∠7 + m ∠8 + m ∠9 + m ∠10 = 540 (Th 6.2); m ∠1 + m ∠2 + m ∠3 + m ∠4 + m ∠5 = 360 (subtr prop)　**9.** 1260, 900, 360

Algebra Review

1. 2　**2.** −4　**3.** −7　**4.** 1　**5.** $\dfrac{-31}{26}$　**6.** $\dfrac{-9}{22}$

Pages 197–198

1. equilateral triangle　**3.** regular hexagon　**5.** 60°　**7.** 108°　**9.** 140°　**11.** 168°　**13.** 120°　**15.** 72°　**17.** 36°　**19.** 7.2°　**21.** 3　**23.** 12　**25.** 5　**27.** 12　**29.** poss, 4　**31.** not poss　**33.** poss, 12　**35.** not poss　**37.** poss, 3　**39.** not poss　**41.** False; rectangle　**43.** No

Page 201

1. Follow constr top of p 199.　**3.** Follow constr top of p 200.　**5.** Constr a ⊥ to a given line; 90° ∠s are formed.　**7.** Follow steps of ex 1, p 199.　**9.** Constr 30° ∠; ∠ forming linear pr with this 30° ∠ is 150°.　**11.** Constr 15° ∠; at vertex constr ⊥ to one of rays of 15° ∠; compl of 15° ∠ is the 75° ∠.　**13.** Constr a 75° ∠; bis it; one of its parts is $37\frac{1}{2}°$ ∠.

15. Constr a 45° ∠; bis it; that gives two $22\frac{1}{2}°$ ∠s; the ∠ that forms a linear pr with either of these is a $157\frac{1}{2}°$ $\angle$.   **17.** Bisect the given seg; using this new length, follow steps of constr 6.2 p 200.   **19.** Follow same steps as ex 18, except constr 150° $\angle$s instead of 135° $\angle$s and a reg dodecagon is constr.   **21.** Follow steps as in ex. 18, except constr $157\frac{1}{2}°$ $\angle$s instead of 135 $\angle$s and a reg. 16-sided figure is constr.   **23.** Draw a seg $4\frac{2}{3}$ cm; divide by 3; follow steps of constr 6.1 p 199, using seg $\cong$ to seg of $1\frac{5}{9}$ cm.   **25.** Follow steps to constr a reg pentagon on p 201; constr $\perp$ bis of each side, which also bis each of 5 $\cong$ arcs of $\odot$; connect the 10 $\cong$ arcs with seg to form a reg decagon.

Cumulative Review
1. 18   **2.** 900°   **3.** SSA (HL for rt $\triangle$'s)

Page 204
1. Yes   **3.** No, more than 2 seg with same endpt.   **5.** convex   **7.** concave   **9.** 540   **11.** 360   **13.** 108   **15.** See Ex 35, p 190.   **17.** T   **19.** F   **21.** T   **23.** 52°, 64°, 88°, 79°, 77°   **25.** 25   **27.** Follow steps of constr 6.1, p 199, drawing only the $\angle$, not the $\triangle$.   **29.** Constr a 60° $\angle$, bis it, then bis one of the 30° $\angle$'s thus formed.

Page 210
1. $\overline{AC}$, $\overline{BD}$; yes   **3.** $\overline{IK}$, $\overline{JL}$; no   **5, 7.** Answers will vary.   **9.** Yes   **11.** No   **13.** not necess   **15.** opp. seg are $\parallel$

Page 214
1. 60, 120, 60   **3.** 135, 45   **5.** 13   **7.** 17   **9.** $\cong$; SAS   **11.** $\cong$; SAS   **13.** not necess   **15.** Given: $\square ABCD$. Prove: $\angle A$ and $\angle B$ supp, $\angle B$ and $\angle C$ supp, $\angle C$ and $\angle D$ supp, $\angle D$ and $\angle A$ supp; $\overline{AB} \parallel \overline{DC}$, $\overline{AD} \parallel \overline{BC}$ (def of $\square$) $\angle A$ and $\angle B$ supp, $\angle B$ and $\angle C$ supp, $\angle C$ and $\angle D$ supp, $\angle D$ and $\angle A$ supp (Th. 3.2)   **17.** Given: $\square ABCD$, diag $\overline{BD}$ and $\overline{AC}$. Prove: $\angle A \cong \angle C$, $\angle D \cong \angle B$; $\triangle ABD \cong \triangle CDB$, $\triangle DAC \cong \triangle BCA$ (Th 7.1); $\angle A \cong \angle C$, $\angle D \cong \angle B$ (CPCTC); $\overline{AB} \cong \overline{CD}$, $\overline{AD} \cong \overline{BC}$ (CPCTC)   **19.** $\overline{WZ} \parallel \overline{XY}$ (def of $\square$); $\angle VXU \cong \angle VZT$, $\angle ZTV \cong \angle VUX$ (Post 13); $\overline{WZ} \cong \overline{XY}$ (Cor 7.1); $\overline{WZ} \cong 2\overline{TZ}$, $\overline{XY} \cong 2\overline{XU}$ (def of midpt); $2\overline{TZ} \cong 2\overline{XU}$ (subst prop); $\overline{TZ} \cong \overline{XU}$ (div prop); $\triangle TVZ \cong \triangle UVX$ (ASA); $\overline{TV} \cong \overline{VU}$, $\overline{ZV} \cong \overline{VX}$ (CPCTC); V is the midpt of $\overline{TU}$ and $\overline{XZ}$ (def of midpt)

Cumulative Review
1. $\frac{360}{6}$; 60   **2.** $\frac{(12-2)180}{12}$; 150   **3.** convex

Page 218
1. Yes   **3.** No   **5.** No   **7.** No   **9.** Yes; Th 7.5   **11.** Yes; def of $\square$ **13.** Yes; def of $\square$ **15.** Yes; Th 7.6   **17.** Given: $\angle A \cong \angle C$, $\angle B \cong \angle D$. Prove: $ABCD$ is $\square$; m $\angle A$ + m $\angle B$ + m $\angle C$ + m $\angle D$ = 360 (Th 6.1); 2 m $\angle A$ + 2 m $\angle B$ = 360, 2 m $\angle C$ + 2 m $\angle B$ = 360; (subst prop); m $\angle A$ + m $\angle B$ = 180, m $\angle C$ + m $\angle B$ = 180 (div prop); $\angle A$ and $\angle B$ are supp, $\angle C$ and $\angle B$ are supp (def of supp); $\overline{AD} \parallel \overline{BC}$, $\overline{AB} \parallel \overline{DC}$ (Th 3.4)   **19.** $\overline{XU} \cong \overline{VZ}$ (CPCTC); $UXVZ$ is a $\square$ (Th 7.4)   **21.** $\overline{AD} \cong \overline{AB} \cong \overline{DB}$, $\overline{DC} \cong \overline{BC} \cong \overline{DB}$ (def of equila $\triangle$'s); $\overline{AD} \cong \overline{BC}$, $\overline{AB} \cong \overline{DC}$ (subst prop); $ABCD$ is a $\square$ (Th 7.4)   **23.** Given: $\angle A$ and $\angle B$ supp, $\angle B$ and $\angle C$ supp, $\angle C$ and $\angle D$ supp, $\angle D$ and $\angle A$ supp. Prove: $ABCD$ is a $\square$; $\overline{AD} \parallel \overline{BC}$, $\overline{AB} \parallel \overline{DC}$ (Th 3.4); $ABCD$ is a $\square$ (def of $\square$)   **25.** Answers may vary.   **27.** Given: $\overline{AE}$ bis $\angle A$, $\overline{CF}$ bis $\angle C$, $AFCE$ is a $\square$. Prove: $ABCD$ is a $\square$; $\angle 1 \cong \angle 3$ (Th 7.1); $\overline{AE} \cong \overline{FC}$ (Th 7.1); $\angle 1 \cong \angle 2$, $\angle 3 \cong \angle 4$ (def of bis); $\angle 2 \cong \angle 4$ (subst prop); $\overline{EC} \parallel \overline{AF}$ (def of $\square$); $\angle 5 \cong \angle 1$, $\angle 6 \cong \angle 3$ (Post 13); $\angle 5 \cong \angle 6$ (subst prop); $\triangle ADE \cong \triangle CBF$ (ASA); $\overline{AD} \cong \overline{BC}$, $\overline{DE} \cong \overline{FB}$ (CPCTC); $\overline{EC} \cong \overline{AF}$ (Th 7.1); $\overline{DC} \cong \overline{AB}$ (add prop); $ABCD$ is a $\square$ (Th 7.3)

Page 221
1. 5   **3.** $\overline{XZ}$ **5.** 2   **7.** 7   **9.** $\overline{ST} \parallel \overline{RQ}$, $\overline{ST} = \frac{1}{2} \overline{RQ}$ (Th 7.7); $\overline{RU} = \frac{1}{2} \overline{RQ}$ (def of a midpt); $\overline{ST} \cong \overline{RU}$ (subst prop); $RSTU$ is a $\square$ (Th 7.5)   **11.** $\overline{DE} \cong \overline{EA}$, $\overline{DF} \cong \overline{FB}$ (def of midpt); $\angle DFE \cong \angle CFB$ (Th 2.10); $\triangle DEF \cong \triangle BCF$ (SAS); $\overline{BC} \cong \overline{DE}$, $\angle FBC \cong \angle EDF$ (CPCTC); $\overline{EA} \cong \overline{BC}$ (subst prop); $\overline{AD} \parallel \overline{BC}$ (Post 14); $EABC$ is a $\square$ (Th 7.5)   **13.** $\overline{KM} \parallel \overline{GH}$, $\overline{KL} = \frac{1}{2} \overline{GH}$, $\overline{KM} \parallel \overline{JI}$, $\overline{LM} = \frac{1}{2} \overline{JI}$ (Th 7.7); $\overline{JI} \parallel \overline{GH}$ (Th 3.7); $\overline{KL} \cong \overline{LM}$ (def of midpt); $\frac{1}{2} \overline{GH} \cong \frac{1}{2} \overline{JI}$ (subst prop); $\overline{GH} \cong \overline{JI}$ (mult prop); $GHIJ$ is $\square$ (Th 7.5)   **15.** Given: quad $WXYZ$, A, B, C, D are the midpts of $\overline{WX}$, $\overline{WZ}$, $\overline{YZ}$, $\overline{XY}$, respectively. Prove: $\overline{AC}$ and $\overline{BD}$ bis each other. Draw $\overline{AB}$, $\overline{BC}$, $\overline{CD}$, $\overline{DA}$, $\overline{XZ}$ (Post 1); $\overline{AB} \parallel \overline{XZ}$, $\overline{AB} = \frac{1}{2} \overline{XZ}$, $\overline{DC} \parallel \overline{XZ}$, $\overline{DC} = \frac{1}{2} \overline{XZ}$ (Th 7.7); $\overline{AB} \parallel \overline{DC}$ (Th 3.6); $\overline{AB} \cong \overline{DC}$ (subst prop); $ABCD$ is a $\square$ (Th 7.5); $\overline{AC}$

and $\overline{BD}$ bis each other (Th 7.2)   **17.** $\overline{RS} =$
$\frac{1}{2} \overline{NO}$, $\overline{TS} = \frac{1}{2} \overline{QP}$ (Th 7.7); $\overline{RS} + \overline{TS} =$
$\frac{1}{2}(\overline{QP} + \overline{NO})$ (add prop); $\overline{RT} = \frac{1}{2}(\overline{QP} + \overline{NO})$
(subst prop)

Page 225

1. 4   **3.** 12   **5.** 12   **7.** 9   **9.** $7\frac{1}{2}$ **11.** 9
13. 34   **15.** $\overleftrightarrow{AD} \parallel \overleftrightarrow{BE} \parallel \overleftrightarrow{CF}$ (Th 3.3); $\overline{DE} \cong \overline{EF}$
(Th 7.8)   **17.** $\overleftrightarrow{AD} \parallel \overleftrightarrow{BE}$ (Th 3.3); $\overleftrightarrow{AD} \parallel \overleftrightarrow{BE} \parallel$
$\overleftrightarrow{CF}$ (Th 3.7); $\overline{AB} \cong \overline{BC}$ (Th 7.8)   **19.** Follow
constr p 223.   **21.** Follow constr p 223.
23. Follow constr p 223, div seg into 5 $\cong$ seg,
constr a seg $\cong$ to 4 of the 5 seg.   **25.** $\overline{PX} \parallel$
$\overline{QY}$ (Cor 3.3); $PXYQ$ is a $\square$ (def of $\square$); $\overline{PX} \cong$
$\overline{QY}$ (Cor 7.1)   **27.** Give counter example.
29. Given: $\overline{PX} \perp$ m, $\overline{QY} \perp$ m, $\overline{PX} \cong \overline{QY}$.
Prove: 1 $\parallel$ m; $\overline{PX} \parallel \overline{QY}$ (Cor 3.3); $PXYQ$ is a
$\square$ (Th 7.5); $l \parallel$ m (def of $\square$)

Page 229

1. T   **3.** T   **5.** F   **7.** P, Rh, R, S   **9.** R,
Rh, R, S   **11.** R, S   **13.** P, Rh, R, S
15. R, S   **17.** 105; 75   **19.** 8   **21.** Given:
rect $ABCD$, diag. $\overline{AC}$ and $\overline{DB}$. Prove: $\overline{AC} \cong$
$\overline{DB}$; $\overline{AD} \cong \overline{CB}$ (Cor 7.1); $\overline{AB} \cong \overline{AB}$ (reflex
prop); $\angle DAB$, $\angle CBA$ are rt $\angle$'s (def of rect);
$\angle DAB \cong \angle CBA$ (Th 2.5); $\triangle DAB \cong \triangle CBA$
(SAS); $\overline{AC} \cong \overline{DB}$ (CPCTC)   **23.** Given: Rh
$ABCD$, diag $\overline{AC}$ and $\overline{DB}$ intersect at E. Prove:
$\overline{AC}$ bis $\angle DAB$, $\angle DCB$, and $\overline{DB}$ bis $\angle ADC$,
$\angle ABC$; $\overline{AD} \cong \overline{DC} \cong \overline{CB} \cong \overline{BA}$ (def of Rh);
$\overline{DB} \cong \overline{DB}$, $\overline{AC} \cong \overline{AC}$ (reflex prop); $\triangle ADC \cong$
$\triangle ABC$, $\triangle DAB \cong \triangle DCB$ (SSS); $\angle 1 \cong \angle 2$,
$\angle 3 \cong \angle 4$, $\angle 5 \cong \angle 6$, $\angle 7 \cong \angle 8$ (CPCTC);
$\overline{AC}$ bis $\angle DAB$ and $\angle DCB$, $\overline{DB}$ bis $\angle ADC$ and
$\angle ABC$ (def of bis)   **25.** Given: square $ABCD$,
diag $\overline{AC}$ and $\overline{DB}$. Prove: $\overline{AC} \cong \overline{DB}$. Same proof
as ex 21.

Cumulative Review

1. 25   **2.** No, not $\triangle$s in general. Yes, if $\triangle$ is
a rt $\triangle$.   **3.** A median of a $\triangle$ is a seg drawn
from a vertex to the midpoint of the opposite
side.

Page 232

1. T   **3.** F   **5.** rect.   **7.** rect   **9.** cannot
tell   **11.** rect.   **13.** rhombus   **15.** $EFGH$
is a $\square$ (Th 7.5); $EFGH$ is a rect. (If a $\square$ has $\cong$
diag, then it is a rect.)   **17.** Given $\square ABCD$
with $\overline{DA} \cong \overline{AB}$. Prove: $ABCD$ is a rhombus;
$\overline{DA} \cong CB$, $\overline{AB} \cong \overline{DC}$ (Cor 7.1); $\overline{AB} \cong \overline{CB} \cong$
$\overline{DC} \cong DA$ (subst prop) $ABCD$ is rh (def of rh).
19. Given: rhombus $ABCD$, E, F, G, H are

midpts of $\overline{AB}$, $\overline{BC}$, $\overline{CD}$, $\overline{DA}$, respectively.
Prove: $EFGH$ is a rect. Draw $\overline{AC}$, $\overline{DB}$ (Post 1);
$\overline{HG} \parallel \overline{AC}$, $HG = \frac{1}{2} AC$; $\overline{EF} \parallel \overline{AC}$, $EF = \frac{1}{2} AC$
(Th 7.7); $\overline{HG} \parallel \overline{EF}$ (Th 3.7); $\overline{HG} \cong \overline{EF}$
(subst prop); $EFGH$ is a $\square$ (Th 7.5); $\overline{DB} \perp \overline{AC}$
(diag of rh are $\perp$); $\overline{HE} \parallel \overline{DB}$ (Th 7.7); $\overline{AC} \perp$
$\overline{EF}$, $\overline{EF} \perp \overline{EH}$ (Ex. 15, p. 78); $\angle DEF$ is a rt $\angle$
(def $\perp$ lines); $EFGH$ is rect (a $\square$ with 1 rt $\angle$ is
a rect)   **21.** True, $EFGH$ is a $\square$ (Th 7.3);
$EFGH$ is a rh (def of a rh).   **23.** Give counter
example.

Page 234

1. none of these   **3.** parallelogram   **5.** cannot
tell   **7.** rectangle   **9.** cannot tell   **11.** F
13. F   **15.** T   **17.** F   **19.** Follow constr
p 223, div seg into 5 $\cong$ seg, constr a seg $\cong$
to 3 of the 5 seg.   **21.** 7   **23.** 12   **25.** Same
proof as ex 15, p 214.

Pages 240–241

1. $\overline{DE} \parallel \overline{AB}$ (Th 7.7); $ABED$ is a trap (def of
trap)   **3.** $\overline{LM} \parallel \overline{ON}$ (def of a trap); $\overline{LP} \cong \overline{MQ}$
(Th 7.9); $\angle OPL$, $\angle NQM$ are rt $\angle$'s (def of $\perp$
lines); $\triangle OPL$, $\triangle NQM$ are rt $\triangle$'s (def of rt $\triangle$'s);
$\triangle OPL \cong \triangle NQM$ (LA); $\overline{LO} \cong \overline{MN}$ (CPCTC)
5. Yes   **7.** No   **9.** Yes   **11.** No
13. False   **15.** False   **17.** True. Given: trap
$ABCD$, E, H, G, F are midpts of $\overline{AD}$, $\overline{DC}$,
$\overline{CB}$, $\overline{BA}$, respectively. Prove $\overline{EG}$ and $\overline{FH}$
bisect each other. Draw $\overline{EF}$, $\overline{FG}$, $\overline{GH}$, $\overline{HE}$, $\overline{DB}$
(Post 1); $\overline{EF} \parallel \overline{DB}$, $EF = \frac{1}{2} DB$; $\overline{HG} \parallel \overline{DB}$,
$HG = \frac{1}{2} DB$ (Th 7.7); $\overline{EF} \parallel \overline{HG}$ (Th 3.7); $\overline{EF} \cong$
$\overline{HG}$ (subst); $EFGH$ is a $\square$ (Th 7.5); $\overline{EG}$ and
$\overline{FH}$ bis each other (Th 7.2).   **19.** False, a
rectangle

Cumulative Review

1. A rt $\triangle$ with $\cong$ legs.   **2.** A post. is accepted;
a th. is proved.   **3.** The side whose endpts are
vertices of the two angles.

Algebra Review

1. $\dfrac{9a + 10}{a^2 - 9}$ **2.** $\dfrac{-x - 7}{x^2 - 4}$ **3.** $\dfrac{y + 18}{y^2 + 6y}$

4. $\dfrac{10 + 6c}{3}$ **5.** $\dfrac{17z + 17}{5z + 3}$ **6.** $\dfrac{12f^2 + 12f + 1}{4f^2 - 1}$

7. $\dfrac{3w^2 + 7w + 1}{w + 2}$ **8.** $\dfrac{4b^2 - b - 2}{4b^3 - b}$

Pages 244–245

1. 7 cm   **3.** 15 cm   **5.** 10   **7.** $11\frac{1}{2}$ **9.** 15

11. 8   13. 7   15. 14   17. $\overline{QM} \cong \overline{QP}$;
$\angle POM \cong \angle NMO$; others are possible
19. Given: trap $ABCD$ with med $\overline{EF}$, alt $\overline{HG}$;
Prove: $\overline{EF}$ bis $\overline{HG}$; $\overline{EF} \parallel \overline{DC} \parallel \overline{AB}$ (Th 8.1);
$\overline{DE} \cong \overline{EA}$ (def of med of trap); $\overline{HI} \cong \overline{IG}$
(Th 7.8)   21. F   23. F. Draw UA and AV
2 cm, XA and WV 1 cm. $\triangle UAX$ is not isos.
25. No; they can have various lengths.
27. Yes; all 3 seg are of same length; $a =$
$\frac{1}{2}(a + a)$ and the 3 seg are $\parallel$.

Pages 248–249

1. 83°   3. 109°, 42°   5. 70°, 16°   7. $BCDE$
is a trap (def of trap); $\angle C \cong \angle B$ (Th 5.1);
$BCDE$ is an isos trap (Th 8.3)   9. $\overline{DA} \cong \overline{CB}$
(def of isos trap); $\overline{AB} \cong \overline{AB}$ (reflex prop);
$\angle DAB \cong \angle CBA$ (Th 8.2); $\triangle ABD \cong \triangle BAC$
(SAS)   11. True. Given: isos trap $ABCD$ with
$\overline{AB} \parallel DC$. Prove: $\angle A$ and $\angle C$ are supp, $\angle B$ and
$\angle D$ are supp; $\angle A \cong \angle B$, $\angle C \cong \angle D$ (Th 8.2);
$\angle A$ and $\angle D$ are supp, $\angle B$ and $\angle C$ are supp
(Th 3.2); $\angle A$ and $\angle C$ are supp, $\angle B$ and $\angle D$ are
supp (subst prop)   13. True. Given: trap
$ABCD$ with $\overline{AB} \parallel \overline{CD}$, $\angle A$ and $\angle C$ supp, $\angle B$
and $\angle D$ supp. Prove: $ABCD$ is isos trap; $\angle A$
and $\angle D$ are supp, $\angle B$ and $\angle C$ are supp (Th 3.2);
$\angle A \cong \angle B$, $\angle D \cong \angle C$ (Th 2.8); $ABCD$ is isos
trap (Th. 8.3).   15. Given: trap $ABCD$ with
$\overline{DC} \parallel \overline{AB}$, $\angle A \cong \angle B$, $\angle C \cong \angle D$. Prove: trap
$ABCD$ is isos. Draw $\overline{DF} \perp \overline{AB}$, $\overline{CE} \perp \overline{AB}$ (Post
12) $\overline{DF} \cong \overline{CE}$ (Th 7.9); $\angle DFA$, $\angle CEB$ are rt
$\angle$'s (def of $\perp$ lines); $\triangle DFA \cong \triangle CEB$ (LA);
$\overline{DA} \cong \overline{CB}$ (CPCTC); Trap $ABCD$ is isos (def
of isos trap).   17. $\angle ABF$, $\angle CBF$ are rt $\angle$'s
(def of $\perp$ lines); $\triangle ABF$, $\triangle CBF$ are ft $\triangle$'s (def
of rt $\triangle$'s); $\overline{FB} \cong \overline{FB}$ (reflex); $\triangle ABF \cong \triangle CBF$
(LL); $\overline{AF} \cong \overline{FC}$ (CPCTC); 2 $\overline{AM} = AF$,
2 $\overline{NC} = FC$ (def of midpt); 2 $\overline{AM} \cong$ 2 $\overline{NC}$
(subst); $\overline{AM} \cong \overline{NC}$ (div prop); $\overline{MN} \parallel \overline{AC}$ (Th
7.7); $ACNM$ is an isos trap (def of isos trap).

Cumulative Review

2. Th 3.2   3. Follow steps constr p 14.

Pages 252–253

1. $\overline{AB} \cong \overline{JK}$, $\overline{BC} \cong \overline{KL}$, $\overline{CD} \cong \overline{LM}$, $\overline{DA} \cong \overline{MJ}$,
$\angle A \cong \angle J$, $\angle B \cong \angle K$, $\angle C \cong \angle L$, $\angle D \cong \angle M$
3. quad $ABCD \cong$ quad $EFGH$ 5. quad
$TQRS \cong$ quad $UXWV$ 7. $\angle DFE \cong \angle CFE$
(def of bis); $\overline{FE} \cong \overline{FE}$ (reflex); $\angle FEA \cong \angle FEB$
(Th 2.6); $\overline{AE} \cong \overline{EB}$ (def of bis); quad $AEFD \cong$
quad $BEFC$ (SASAS for $\cong$ quad's)   9. $\overline{AB} \cong$
$\overline{BC} \cong \overline{FE} \cong \overline{AF} \cong \overline{CD} \cong \overline{BE} \cong \overline{DE}$ (subst);
$\angle 3 \cong \angle 4$ (Th 2.8); $\angle 2$, $\angle 4$ suppl (Th 3.2); $\angle 1 \cong$
$\angle 2$ (Th 2.8); rh $ABEF \cong$ rh $CBED$ (SASAS)
11. $DE \cong FC$, $EG \cong GF$, $DG = GC$; $\angle D \cong$

$\angle C$, $\angle DEG \cong \angle CFG$ (CPCTC); $\overline{AD} \cong \overline{BC}$,
$\overline{DF} \cong \overline{CE}$ (add prop); m $\angle AEG +$ m $\angle DEG = 180$,
m $\angle BFD +$ m $\angle CFG = 180$ (Post 11); $\angle AEG$
and $\angle DEG$ are supp, $\angle BFD$ and $\angle CFG$ are
supp (def of supp $\angle$'s); $\angle AEG \cong \angle BFD$ (Th
2.8); quad $EABC \cong$ quad $FBAD$ (SASAS)
13. $\overline{HM} \cong \overline{JK}$, $\angle M \cong \angle K$, $\overline{ML} \cong \overline{KL}$
(CPCTC); $\angle MLI \cong \angle M$. $\angle KLI \cong \angle K$ (Th 8.2);
$\angle MLI \cong \angle KLI$ (subst prop); $\overline{LI} \cong \overline{LI}$ (reflex)
trap $HILM \cong$ trap $JILK$ (SASAS)   15. $\angle A \cong$
$\angle D$, $\angle ABE \cong \angle DEB$, $\overline{AB} \cong \overline{ED}$ (CPCTC);
$\angle EGC \cong \angle FGB$ (Th 2.10); quad $ABGF \cong$
quad $DEGC$ (ASASA)   17. $\angle 3 \cong \angle 7$ (substr.
prop); $\angle ADC \cong \angle EHG$ (add prop)   19. No.
Consider a square with sides K units long and
rhombus that is not a square with sides K units
long. The two are not $\cong$.

Algebra Review

1. 11   2. -26 3. -7 4. -2 5. $\frac{5}{3}$ 6. $\frac{17}{10}$

Page 255

1. Draw $AB = 7$ cm. At each endpt const a $\perp$.
Make $\overline{CA} \cong \overline{DB} \cong \overline{AB}$. Draw $\overline{CD}$ to complete
sq.   3. Follow steps of ex 1, p 254.
5. Follow steps of ex 2, p 254.   7. Let $\overline{XY} =$
10 cm. Bis $\overline{XY}$. Using half $\overline{XY}$, call it $\overline{AB}$ as a
side of rect. At A and B constr $\perp$'s. Using A
as a center and $\overline{XY}$ as a radius, constr an arc
intersecting $\perp$ at B. Similarly using B as a
center and $\overline{XY}$ as a radius, constr an arc
intersecting $\perp$ at A. Connect these 2 pts of
intersection for required rect.   9. Using a
base $\overline{AB} = s$, at A as center and s as radius
constr an arc. Similarly, at B as center and s as
radius draw another arc. Again using A as
center and d as radius draw an arc, and using B
as center and d as radius draw an arc. Pts of
intersection of these arcs can be used to
complete required trap.   11. Constr $AB = b$,
$AD = e$, m $\angle DAB = 45$; constr $\overline{DC} \parallel \overline{AB}$,
$DC = b$. Connect C to B.   13. See proof of
Th. 8.6, p. 251.   15. No

Page 258

1. 3   3. 2   5. $\overline{AD} \cong \overline{CD}$, $\overline{AB} \cong \overline{CB}$, $\angle A \cong$
$\angle C$ 7. $\overline{QP} \cong \overline{KL}$, $\overline{PO} \cong \overline{LM}$, $\angle K \cong \angle Q$,
$\angle L \cong \angle P$, $\angle M \cong \angle O$ 9. Yes   11. No
13. Yes; no; if 2, then pentagon is regular and
there will be 10; no; no; yes   15. No; no
17. Yes   19. Given: Oct $ABCDEFGH$ with
$\overleftrightarrow{AE}$ line of symmetry. Prove: $\angle B \cong \angle H$,
$\angle C \cong G$, $\angle F \cong \angle D$. Draw $\overline{BH}$, $\overline{GC}$, $\overline{DF}$ inter
$\overleftrightarrow{AE}$ at M, I, J (Post 1); $\overline{AH} \cong \overline{AB}$, $\overline{ED} \cong \overline{EF}$
(Th 8.8); $\overleftrightarrow{AE}$ bis $\overline{BH}$, $\overleftrightarrow{AE}$ bis $\overline{CG}$, $\overleftrightarrow{AE}$ bis $\overline{DF}$
(Post 21); $\overline{BM} \cong \overline{MH}$, $\overline{CI} \cong \overline{IG}$, $\overline{DJ} \cong \overline{JF}$
(def of bis); $\overline{AM} \cong \overline{AM}$, $\overline{JE} \cong \overline{JE}$ (reflex);

△ABM ≅ △AHM, △EDJ ≅ △EFJ (SSS); ∠BAM ≅ ∠HAM, ∠DEJ ≅ ∠FEJ (CPCTC); $\overline{AI} \cong \overline{AI}$, $\overline{EI} \cong \overline{EI}$ (reflex); ∠AIC ≅ ∠AIG, ∠EIC ≅ ∠EIG (Th 2.6); quad ABCI ≅ quad AHGI, quad EDCI ≅ quad EFGI (SASAS); ∠B ≅ ∠H, ∠BCI ≅ ∠HGI, ∠D ≅ ∠F, ∠DCI ≅ ∠FGI (def ≅ quads); ∠C ≅ ∠G (add prop) **21.** Given: Sept ABCDEFG with $\overleftrightarrow{AH}$ line of symmetry. Prove: $\overline{AG} \cong \overline{AB}$, $\overline{GF} \cong \overline{BC}$, $\overline{FE} \cong \overline{DC}$. Draw $\overleftrightarrow{GB}, \overleftrightarrow{FC}$ inters $\overleftrightarrow{AH}$ at I, J (Post 1); $\overleftrightarrow{AH}$ bis $\overline{GB}$, $\overleftrightarrow{AH}$ bis $\overline{FC}$, $\overleftrightarrow{AH}$ bis $\overline{ED}$ (Post 21); $\overline{AG} \cong \overline{AB}$ (Th 5.7); $\overline{GI} \cong \overline{IB}$, $\overline{FJ} \cong \overline{JC}$, $\overline{EH} \cong \overline{HD}$ (def of bis); $\overline{IJ} \cong \overline{IJ}$, $\overline{JH} \cong \overline{JH}$ (reflex); ∠GIJ ≅ ∠BIJ, ∠IJF ≅ ∠IJC, ∠FJH ≅ ∠CJH, ∠JHE ≅ ∠JHD (Th 2.6); quad GIJF ≅ quad BIJC, quad FJHE ≅ quad CJHD (SASAS); $\overline{GF} \cong \overline{BC}$, $\overline{FE} \cong \overline{DC}$ (def of ≅ quad)

Page 261

1. reflection **3.** reflection **5.** not reflection **7.** $\overline{AC} \cong \overline{EF}$; $\overline{AB} \cong \overline{DE}$; $\overline{CB} \cong \overline{FD}$, ∠C ≅ ∠F, ∠B ≅ ∠D, ∠A ≅ ∠E **9.** $\overline{YS} \cong \overline{VU}$, $\overline{SW} \cong \overline{UX}$, $\overline{YW} \cong \overline{VX}$, ∠S ≅ ∠U, ∠Y ≅ ∠V, ∠W ≅ ∠X **11.** It is the common bis of $\overline{GL}$, $\overline{HK}$, $\overline{IN}$, and $\overline{JM}$. **13.** T **15.** F **17.** Given: quad ABCD and A'B'C'D' are reflections; ℓ is the line of symmetry. Prove: quad ABCD ≅ quad A'B'C'D'. Draw $\overline{AC}, \overline{A'C'}, \overline{DB}, \overline{D'B'}$ (Post 1); ℓ is ⊥ bis of $\overline{AA'}, \overline{BB'}, \overline{CC'}, \overline{DD'}$ (def of reflec); △ADC and △A'D'C' are refl, △DCB and △D'C'B' are refl (def of reflec); △ADC ≅ △A'D'C', △DCB ≅ △D'C'B' (Th 8.10); $\overline{AD} \cong \overline{A'D'}$, ∠ADC ≅ ∠A'D'C', $\overline{DC} \cong \overline{D'C'}$, ∠DCB ≅ ∠D'C'B', $\overline{BC} \cong \overline{B'C'}$ (CPCTC); quad ABCD ≅ quad A'B'C'D' (SASAS) **19.** Connect any two corresponding pts; then construct the ⊥ bis of that seg.

Page 264

1. $\overline{EF}$ **3.** $\overline{AB}, \overline{DC}$ **5.** Isos **7.** F **9.** F **11.** T **13.** F **15.** T **17.** On line ℓ lay off $\overline{AB} \cong A$. At A constr a ⊥. Lay off $\overline{AC} \cong b$. At C constr $\overleftrightarrow{CD} \parallel \overleftrightarrow{AB}$. Using A and B as centers and C as a radius, constr arcs intersecting $\overleftrightarrow{CD}$. Join these pts of intersection to complete the required trap. **19.** ∥ $\overline{FC} \cong \overline{CB}$, $\overline{DC} \cong \overline{CG}$ (def of bis); ∠FCD ≅ ∠GCB (Th 2.10); ∠F ≅ ∠B, ∠D ≅ ∠G (Post 13); CGAB ≅ CDEF (SASAS)

Cumulative Review

1. c **2.** b **3.** c **4.** a **5.** d **6.** c **7.** d **8.** d **9.** a **10.** b **11.** b **12.** a **13.** c **14.** CB **15.** AC, AD **16.** F **17.** T **18.** F **19.** F **20.** T **21.** F **22.** T **23.** T **24.** T **25.** T **26.** F **27.** F **28.** 75, 105 **29.** 12 **30.** 15 **31.** See page 49, ex. 2

32. See constr p 223. **33.** See p 114, ex 2. **34.** ∠A ≅ ∠A (reflex); △ACD ≅ △ABE (ASA); $\overline{EB} \cong \overline{DC}$ (CPCTC) **35.** $\overline{RS} \parallel \overline{UT}$ (def of ▱); $\overline{UV} \parallel \overline{WS}$ (Th 3.3); VSWU is a ▱ (def of ▱)

Pages 273–274

1. T **3.** T **5.** F **7.** T **9.** 3, 10; 2, x; 15 **11.** 9, 4; x, 12; 3 **13.** 8, 9; 12, x; 6 **15.** 9, 6; 4, x; $13\frac{1}{2}$ **17.** $\frac{2}{3} = \frac{4}{6}, \frac{3}{2} = \frac{6}{4}, \frac{4}{2} = \frac{6}{3}$ **19.** $\frac{4}{2} = \frac{8}{4}$; $\frac{2}{4} = \frac{4}{8}, \frac{8}{4} = \frac{4}{2}$ **21.** $\frac{10}{5} = \frac{y}{3}, \frac{10}{x} = \frac{5}{3}, \frac{5}{10} = \frac{3}{x}$ **23.** $\frac{4}{3} = \frac{x}{z}, \frac{z}{3} = \frac{x}{y}, \frac{y}{x} = \frac{3}{z}$ **25.** 2 **27.** 10 **29.** $\sqrt{21}$ **31.** $\sqrt{77}$ **33.** F **35.** T **37.** $\frac{9}{7}$ **39.** $\frac{5}{7}$ **41.** $\frac{21}{14}$ **43.** $\frac{b}{a}$ **45.** 36°, 54° **47.** 110, 132 **49.** 6 cm, 4 cm **51.** 10, 12 **53.** T; $ad = bc$ (mult prop); $\frac{a}{c} = \frac{b}{d}$ (div prop) **55.** T; $\frac{a}{b} + \frac{b}{b} = \frac{c}{d} + \frac{d}{d}, \frac{a+b}{b} = \frac{c+d}{d}$ (add prop) **57.** T; $\frac{a}{b} = \frac{c}{d}, \frac{b}{a} = \frac{d}{c}$ (recip prop); $\frac{a}{a} + \frac{b}{a} = \frac{c}{c} + \frac{d}{c}$; $\frac{a+b}{a} = \frac{c+d}{c}$ (add prop); $\frac{a}{a+b} = \frac{c}{c+d}$ (recip prop) **59.** T; $\frac{a}{b} \cdot \frac{n}{n} = \frac{c}{d} \cdot \frac{m}{m}$ (prop of 1) **61.** $\frac{a}{b} \cdot bd = bd \cdot \frac{c}{d}$; $ad = bc$ (mult prop)

Pages 276–277

1. No; corr S's not prop. **3.** Yes; corr ∠s ≅ and corr S's prop. **5.** $\frac{AB}{EF} = \frac{BC}{FG} = \frac{CD}{GH} = \frac{AD}{EH}$ **7.** $y = 10$; $x = 12$ **9.** $z = 8\frac{1}{3}$; $y = 6\frac{2}{3}$; $x = 3\frac{1}{3}$ **11.** $x = 6\frac{1}{4}$; $y = 6\frac{2}{5}$; $z = 4\frac{4}{5}$ **13.** 2; 1 **15.** 8; 12 **17.** 91; 68; 177 **19.** No; corres S's may not be prop. **21.** Given: sq ABCD and sq XYZW. Prove: sq ABCD ~ sq XYZW. $\overline{AB} \cong \overline{BC} \cong \overline{CD} \cong \overline{DE}$; $\overline{XY} \cong \overline{YZ} \cong \overline{ZW} \cong \overline{WX}$ (prop of sq); AB = BC = CD = DE; XY = YZ = ZW = WZ (def of ≅); $\frac{AB}{XY} = \frac{BC}{YZ} = \frac{CD}{ZW} = \frac{DE}{WX}$ (div prop); ∠s A, B, C, D, X, Y, Z, W are rt ∠s (prop of sq); ∠A ≅ ∠X, ∠B ≅ ∠Y, ∠C ≅ Z, ∠D ≅ ∠W (all rt ∠s are ≅); ABCD ~ XYZW (def of ~ poly)

Pages 280–281

1. No; corr. ∠s ≢ **3.** Yes; (Post 22)

5. Yes; (Post 22)　　**7.** $\angle D \cong \angle D$ (reflex prop); $\triangle ABD \sim \triangle CED$ (Post 22)　　**9.** $\angle O \cong \angle M$ (Post 13); $\angle K \cong \angle N$ (Post 13); $\triangle OKL \sim \triangle MNL$ (Post 22)　　**11.** 10　　**13.** No
15. $\angle GJI \cong \angle KHI$ ($\perp$s form $\cong$ rt $\angle$s); $\angle I \cong \angle I$ (reflex prop); $\triangle HKI \sim \triangle JGI$ (Post 22);
17. $\angle V \cong \angle V$ (reflex prop); $\overline{WT} \parallel \overline{RS}$ (def of $\square$); $\angle VTW \cong \angle S$ (Th 3.1); $\triangle RSV \sim \triangle WVT$ (Post 22)　　**19.** $\angle LMN \cong \angle JKN$ and $\angle MLN \cong \angle KJN$ (Post 13) $\triangle LMN \sim \triangle JKN$ (Post 22); $\dfrac{MN}{NK} = \dfrac{LN}{NJ}$ (def of $\sim$ poly)　　**21.** F　　**23.** F
25. $XYZW$ is a $\square$ (Th 7.5); $\overline{WX} \parallel \overline{ZY}$ (def of $\square$); $\angle XWV \cong \angle ZTW$ (Post 13); $\angle WXV \cong \angle TZW$ (Th 7.3); $\triangle WTZ \sim \triangle VWX$ (Post 22)
27. $\angle DEA$ a rt $\angle$ (def of $\perp$); $\angle DEA \cong \angle BCA$ (all rt $\angle$s $\cong$); $\angle A \cong \angle A$ (reflex prop); $\triangle ABC \sim \triangle ADE$ (Post 22) $\dfrac{AD}{AB} = \dfrac{DE}{BC}$ (def $\sim$ poly); $\overline{BC} \perp \overline{AC}$ (def $\perp$ L's); $\overline{BC} \parallel \overline{DE}$ (Cor 3.3); $\angle BCD \cong \angle CDE$ (Post 13); $\angle BCD \cong \angle DCE$ (def $\angle$ bis); $\angle CDE \cong \angle DCE$ (subst); $\overline{DE} \cong \overline{EC}$ (Th 5.2); $\dfrac{AD}{AB} = \dfrac{EC}{BC}$ (subst)

Cumulative Review
1. 70　　**2.** 79

Page 284
1. T　　**3.** T　　**5.** F　　**7.** $2\frac{2}{3}$　　**9.** $8\frac{3}{4}$　　**11.** $5\frac{3}{5}$
13. 26　　**15.** 12　　**17.** $\overline{AC} \parallel \overline{ED}$ (Th 3.3); $\dfrac{BD}{DC} = \dfrac{BE}{EA}$ (Th 9.1)　　**19.** $\dfrac{AE}{EB} = \dfrac{DG}{GB}$ (Th 9.1) $\overline{DA} \parallel \overline{CB}$ (def $\square$); $\overline{EF} \parallel \overline{CB}$ (Th 3.7); $\dfrac{DG}{GB} = \dfrac{DF}{FC}$ (Th 9.1); $\dfrac{AE}{EB} = \dfrac{DF}{FC}$ (subst)
21. Given $AB \parallel CD \parallel EF$. Prove: $\dfrac{AC}{CE} = \dfrac{BD}{DF}$.

Draw $\overleftrightarrow{AF}$ (Post 1); $\dfrac{AC}{CE} = \dfrac{AG}{GF}$ (Th 9.1); $\dfrac{BD}{DF} = \dfrac{AG}{GF}$ (Th 9.1); $\dfrac{AC}{CE} = \dfrac{BD}{DF}$ (trans prop)

Cumulative Review
1. 12　　**2.** Follow constr steps p 14.
3. Corres $\angle$'s $\cong$ and corres s's propor.

Pages 288–289
1. Yes; SSS　　**3.** Yes; AA　　**5.** No; $\cong$ $\angle$s are not included $\angle$s.　　**7.** No; only 1 pr $\cong$ $\angle$s
9. Yes; SAS　　**11.** Yes　　**13.** No　　**15.** No
17. $\nsim$　　**19.** $\nsim$　　**21.** $\nsim$　　**23.** $\angle ZTS \cong \angle ZXY$ (corr $\angle$s are $\cong$); $\angle STR \cong \angle Y$ (opp $\angle$s of $\square$ are $\cong$); $\angle TSZ \cong \angle Y$ (corr $\angle$s are $\cong$); $\angle STR \cong \angle XRT$ (Post 13) $\angle TSZ \cong \angle XRT$ (subst);

$\triangle XRT \approx \triangle TSZ$ (Post 22)　　**25.** $\angle NPM \cong \angle NRQ$ ($\perp$s form $\cong$ rt $\angle$s); $\angle RNQ \cong \angle RNQ$ (reflex prop); $\triangle NQR \sim \triangle NMP$ (Post 22)
27. $\angle LRN \cong \angle LRM$ ($\perp$s form $\cong$ rt $\angle$s); $\triangle LNR \sim \triangle LMR$ (Post 22)　　**29.** $\angle R \cong \angle WUV$, $\angle S \cong \angle WVU$ (Th 3.1); $\triangle UVW \sim \triangle RST$ (Post 22)　　**31.** $\overline{TU} \cong \overline{TV}$, $\overline{TR} \cong \overline{TS}$ (CPCTC); $\dfrac{TU}{TR} = \dfrac{TV}{TS}$ (div)　　**33.** $\angle CTQ \cong \angle RJV$ ($\perp$s form $\cong$ rt $\angle$s); $\angle CQT \cong \angle CUT$ (Th 5.1); $\triangle CTQ \sim \triangle RJV$ (Post 22); $\dfrac{CQ}{RV} = \dfrac{QT}{JV}$ (def $\sim$ poly)
35. Case I—Given: $\triangle$s ABC, DEF, $\angle B \cong \angle E$, $\overline{AB} \cong \overline{BC}$, $\overline{DE} \cong \overline{EF}$. Prove: $\triangle ABC \sim \triangle DEF$. $\dfrac{AB}{DE} = \dfrac{BC}{EF}$ (div prop); $\triangle ABC \sim \triangle DEF$ (Th 9.3) Case II—Given: $\triangle$s ABC, DEF, $\overline{AB} \cong \overline{BC}$, $\overline{DE} \cong \overline{EF}$, $\angle A \cong \angle D$. Prove: $\triangle ABC \sim \triangle DEF$. $\angle A \cong \angle C$, $\angle D \cong \angle F$ (Th 5.1); $\angle C \cong \angle F$ (subst); $\triangle ABC \sim \triangle DEF$ (Post 22)
37. Given: $\triangle$s ABC, DEF, $\dfrac{AB}{DE} = \dfrac{BC}{EF} = \dfrac{AC}{DF}$. Prove: $\triangle ABC \sim \triangle DEF$. Constr $\overline{DB'} \cong \overline{AB}$, then draw $\overline{B'C'} \parallel \overline{EF}$ (Post 15); $\angle B' \cong \angle E$, $\angle C' \cong \angle F$ (Th 3.1); $\triangle DB'C' \sim \triangle DEF$ (Post 22); $\dfrac{DB'}{DE} = \dfrac{DC'}{DF} = \dfrac{B'C'}{EF}$ (def $\sim$ poly); $\dfrac{BC}{EF} = \dfrac{B'C'}{EF}$, $\dfrac{DC'}{DF} = \dfrac{AC}{DF}$ (subst, trans prop); $\overline{AC} \cong \overline{DC'}$, $\overline{BC} \cong \overline{B'C'}$ (mult prop); $\triangle ABC \cong \triangle DB'C'$ (Post 16); $\angle B' \cong \angle B$; $\angle C \cong \angle C'$ (CPCTC); $\triangle ABC \sim \triangle DEF$ (Post 22)
39. The $\perp$'s to each side of a $\triangle$ form a $\triangle \sim$ to the given $\triangle$. See ex. 24, pp 280, 281.

Page 293
1. $8\frac{2}{5}$　　**3.** 4; 8　　**5.** 6　　**7.** 12; 8
11. $\dfrac{AD}{AB} = \dfrac{DE}{EB}$, $\dfrac{DC}{CB} = \dfrac{DE}{EB}$ (Th 9.7); $\dfrac{AD}{AB} = \dfrac{DC}{CB}$ (subst)　　**13.** $\angle s \cong \angle w$ (def $\sim$ poly); $\angle TUS \cong \angle XYW$ ($\perp$s form $\cong$ rt $\angle$s); $\triangle TUS \sim \triangle XYW$ (Post 21); $\dfrac{TU}{XY} = \dfrac{US}{YW}$ (def $\sim$ poly)　　**15.** Follow constr 9.1, p 292.　　**17.** Given: $\triangle ABC \sim \triangle EFG$, with corr alts $\overline{AD}$ and $\overline{EH}$. Prove: $\dfrac{AC}{EG} = \dfrac{AD}{EH}$. $\angle C \cong \angle G$ (def $\sim$ poly); $\angle ADC \cong \angle EHG$ ($\perp$s form $\cong$ rt $\angle$'s); $\triangle ADC \sim \triangle EHG$ (Post 21); $\dfrac{AC}{EG} = \dfrac{AD}{EH}$ (def $\sim$ poly)　　**19.** Given: $\triangle ABC \sim \triangle DEF$, $\overline{BG}$, $\overline{EJ}$ alts, $\overline{BH}$, $\overline{EK}$ meds. Prove: $\dfrac{BH}{EK} = \dfrac{BG}{EJ}$. $\dfrac{BH}{EK} = \dfrac{AB}{ED}$ (Th 9.5); $\dfrac{BG}{EJ} = \dfrac{AB}{ED}$ (Th 9.6); $\dfrac{BH}{EK} = \dfrac{BG}{EJ}$ (subst)

Pages 295–296

(Answers may vary 1–3.)

1. $\dfrac{XY}{AB} = \dfrac{CD}{ZW}$; $\dfrac{AB}{XY} = \dfrac{ZW}{CD}$ **3.** $\dfrac{RP}{AJ} = \dfrac{WF}{RP}$;

$\dfrac{AJ}{RP} = \dfrac{RP}{WF}$ **5.** 558 **7.** $\angle F \cong \angle I$, $\angle G \cong \angle J$

(Post 13); $\triangle FHG \sim \triangle IHJ$ (Post 22); $\dfrac{GH}{FH} = \dfrac{JH}{IH}$

(def $\sim$ poly); $GH \cdot IH = FH \cdot JH$ **9.** $\angle Y \cong$

$\angle X$ ($\perp$s form $\cong$ rt $\angle$s); $\angle YVU \cong \angle XVW$ (Th

2.10); $\triangle YVU \sim \triangle XUW$ (Post 22) $\dfrac{VY}{VX} = \dfrac{VU}{VW}$

(def $\sim$ poly); $VY \cdot VW = VX \cdot VU$ (prop of

propor) **11.** $\overline{CA}$ bisects $\angle ZCB$ (def $\angle$

bisector); $\dfrac{ZA}{AB} = \dfrac{ZC}{BC}$ (Th 9.7); $ZA \cdot BC =$

$ZC \cdot AB$ (prop of propor) **13.** $DC = 6$;

$FB \cdot FC = 63$

17. $\angle JKY \cong \angle b$ (Post 13); $\angle JKY$

$\cong \angle a$ (trans prop); $\overline{JY} \cong \overline{JK}$ (Th 5.2); $\dfrac{XK}{KZ} = \dfrac{XJ}{JY}$

(Th 9.3); $\dfrac{XK}{KZ} = \dfrac{XJ}{JK}$ (subst); $XK \cdot JK = KZ \cdot XJ$

(prop of propor) **19.** $\dfrac{ED}{DA} = \dfrac{EF}{FB}$ (Th 9.3);

$\overline{FB} \cong \overline{CB}$ (Th 5.2); $\dfrac{ED}{DA} = \dfrac{EF}{CB}$ (subst); $ED \cdot CB$

$= DA \cdot EF$ (prop of propor)

Algebra Review

1. $6\sqrt{2}$ **2.** $8\sqrt{3}$ **3.** $\sqrt{2}$ **4.** $3\sqrt{5}$
5. $-\sqrt{3}$ **6.** $23\sqrt{2}$ **7.** 5 **8.** 8 **9.** $70\sqrt{6}$
10. 8 **11.** 2 **12.** $10\sqrt{3}$

Page 299

1. $10\dfrac{2}{7}$ **3.** 6; 9 **5.** 18 **7.** $\dfrac{BX}{BA} = \dfrac{BZ}{BF}$;

$\dfrac{BY}{BC} = \dfrac{BZ}{BF}$ (def of $\sim$ poly); $\dfrac{BX}{BA} = \dfrac{BY}{BC}$ (subst);

$\angle XBY \cong \angle XBY$ (reflex prop); $\triangle XBY \sim \triangle ABC$
(Th 9.3) **9.** $\angle TAS \cong \angle ZAY$ (Th 2.10); $\triangle ATS$
$\sim \triangle AZY$ (Th 9.3) **11.** $\overline{EF} \parallel \overline{AB}$ (Th 3.8);

$\dfrac{DF}{DB} = \dfrac{DE}{DA}$ (Th 9.1); $\angle EDF \cong \angle EDF$ (reflex);

$\triangle DEF \sim \triangle DAB$ (Th 9.3); similarly, show
$\triangle DFG \sim \triangle DBC$ and $\triangle DEG \sim \triangle DAC$; then,
$\dfrac{EF}{AB} = \dfrac{DF}{DB} = \dfrac{DE}{DA}$, $\dfrac{FG}{BC} = \dfrac{DF}{DB} = \dfrac{DG}{DC}$, and
$\dfrac{GE}{CA} = \dfrac{DG}{DC} = \dfrac{DE}{DA}$ (def $\sim$ poly); $\dfrac{EF}{AB} = \dfrac{FG}{BC} = \dfrac{GE}{CA}$
(subst); $\triangle EFG \sim \triangle ABC$ (Th 9.4)

Page 302

1. $\dfrac{8}{12} = \dfrac{x}{15}$; $12x = 120$; $x = 10$ **3.** $\dfrac{x}{y} = \dfrac{8}{3}$

5. $\dfrac{9}{x} = \dfrac{x}{16}$; $x^2 = 144$ $x = 12$ **7.** $\dfrac{7}{4} = \dfrac{x}{\frac{252}{x}}$; $4x^2 =$

1764, $x^2 = 441$; $x = 21$; 21, 12 **9.** No, sides
are not proportional. **11.** $\dfrac{4}{6} = \dfrac{12}{x}$; $x = 18$

13. $\angle DCB \cong \angle DCB$ (reflex prop); $\angle CEA \cong$
$\angle CBA$ (all rt $\angle$s are $\cong$); $\triangle CPE \sim \triangle CBD$

(Post 22) **15.** $DF = \dfrac{1}{2}CB$ and $DE = \dfrac{1}{2}AB$

(Th 7.7); $\dfrac{DF}{CB} = \dfrac{1}{2} = \dfrac{DE}{AB}$; $DE \cdot CB = DF \cdot AB$
(prop of propor)

Page 309

1. 2 **3.** 9 **5.** 4 **7.** 3 **9.** 8 **11.** 9
13. $8\sqrt{2}$ **15.** 10 **17.** $\triangle BEC \sim \triangle CEA$ and
$\triangle CDE \sim \triangle CEA$ (Th 10.1); $\triangle CDE \sim \triangle BEC$
(trans prop) **19.** Given: $\triangle ABC$, $\angle C$ a rt $\angle$,
alt $\overline{CD}$. Prove: $\dfrac{AD}{CD} = \dfrac{CD}{BD}$. $\triangle ACD \sim \triangle CBD$

(Th 10.1); $\dfrac{AD}{CD} = \dfrac{CD}{BD}$ (def $\sim$ poly) **21.** Yes;

$20(16) = KZ^2$; $8\sqrt{5}$; **23.** Yes; $6^2 = 9(\overline{HY})$;

$HY = 4$; $\dfrac{XY}{ZY} = \dfrac{ZY}{HY}$; $ZY = 2\sqrt{13}$ **25.** No

27. Given: rt $\triangle ABC$, $\overline{CD}$ alt to hypot. Prove:
$\dfrac{AC}{AD} \neq \dfrac{CB}{DB}$. $\triangle ACD \sim \triangle BCD$ (Th 10.1);

$\dfrac{AC}{CB} = \dfrac{AD}{CD}$; (def of $\sim$ polys); $\dfrac{AC}{AD} = \dfrac{CB}{CD}$

(propor prop); If Th true, then $DB = CD$, not

always true. Thus, false. **29.** $\dfrac{r}{h} = \dfrac{h}{s}$ (Th. 10.1);

$\dfrac{u}{h} = \dfrac{h}{u + v}$ (Th. 10.1); $h^2 = r \cdot s$ and $h^2 = u(u + v)$
(prop of propor); $r \cdot s = u(u + v)$ (trans prop)

31. $\dfrac{r}{h} = \dfrac{h}{s}$ (Th. 10.1); $h^2 = r \cdot s$ (prop of propor);

Pages 312–313

1. 10 **3.** 12 **5.** 8 **7.** 7 **9.** 5 **11.** 9
13. 7 **15.** $\sqrt{2}$ **17.** 10 mm **19.** 36 cm
21. $d = s\sqrt{2}$ **23.** $9\dfrac{3}{13}$ **25.** $12\dfrac{1}{2}$ **27.** $5\sqrt{3}$
29. $(AD)^2 = (AE)^2 + (DE)^2$, $(BC)^2 = (EB)^2 +$
$(EC)^2$ (Th 10.2); $(AD)^2 + (BC)^2 = (AE)^2 +$
$(DE)^2 + (EB)^2 + (EC)^2$ (add'n); $(AE)^2 + (EB)^2 =$
$(AB)^2$, $(DE)^2 + (EC)^2 = (DC)^2$ (Th 10.2); $(AD)^2$
$+ (BC)^2 = (AB)^2 + (DC)^2$ (subst) **31.** $RU^2 =$
$RT^2 + TU^2$ (Th 10.2); $TS^2 = SR^2 + RT^2$;
$RU^2 - TU^2 = RT^2$ (subst); $TS^2 - RS^2 = RT^2$
(subst); $RU^2 - TU^2 = TS^2 - RS^2$ (trans)
33. 26 cm **35.** $d = s\sqrt{3}$ **37.** $\dfrac{\sqrt{1,463}}{18}$

617

Pages 316–317

1. No **3.** No **5.** Yes; $\angle B$ **7.** No

9. Yes; $\angle B$ **11.** Yes **13.** Yes **15.** $\frac{a^2 b^2}{a^2} +$
$\frac{a^2 b^2}{b^2} = c^2$ (mult); $b^2 + a^2 = c^2$ (alg); $\triangle ABC$ is a
rt $\triangle$ (Th 10.3). **17.** No **19.** No **21.** No
23. $\frac{AD}{AC} = \frac{AC}{AB}$ (def geom mean); $(AC)^2 = (AD)$
(AB) (prop of propor); $(AD)^2 + (CD)^2 = (AC)^2$
(Th 10.2); $(AD)^2 + (CD)^2 = (AD)(AB)$ (subst);
$(CD)^2 = (AD)(AB) - (AD)^2$ (subt); $(CD)^2 =$
$(AD)(AB - AD)$ (distr prop); $(CD)^2 = (AD)(DB)$
(subst); $\frac{AD}{CD} = \frac{CD}{DB}$ (div); $\triangle ABC$ is a rt $\triangle$
(ex. 22). **25.** $a^2 + b^2 = c^2$ or $a^2 + b^2 \neq c$;
if $a^2 + b^2 = c^2$, then $\triangle ABC$ is a rt $\triangle$ (Th 10.3);
this contradicts the given, so $a^2 + b^2 \neq c^2$

Cumulative Review
1. 70°, 40° **2.** 30°, 60°

Algebra Review
1. $15\sqrt{2}$ **2.** $6\sqrt{2}$ **3.** $8\sqrt{3}$ **4.** $\sqrt{2}$
5. $3\sqrt{5}$ **6.** $6\sqrt{2}$ **7.** $8\sqrt{5}$ **8.** $-\sqrt{3}$
9. $23\sqrt{2}$ **10.** 5 **11.** 8 **12.** $70\sqrt{6}$ **13.** 8
14. 2 **15.** $10\sqrt{3}$

Page 320
1. $BC = 4$, $AC = 4\sqrt{3}$ **3.** $LK = 6$, $JK = 6\sqrt{2}$
5. $XZ = YZ = 6\sqrt{2}$ **7.** $XY = 6$, $YZ = 3\sqrt{2}$
9. $XY = 4\sqrt{2}$ $YZ = 4$ **11.** $BC = 18$, $CA =$
$18\sqrt{3}$ **13.** $AB = 18$, $CA = 9\sqrt{3}$ **15.** $AB =$
12, $BC = 6$ **17.** $9\sqrt{3}$ **19.** $JK = 16\sqrt{2}$,
$LM = 8\sqrt{2}$ **21.** Given: rt $\triangle ABC$, m $\angle B =$
45, m $\angle C = 45$, $\overline{AB} = \ell$. Prove: $BC = \ell\sqrt{2}$.
$\overline{AB} \cong \overline{AC}$ (Th 5.2); $AC = \ell$ (def $\cong$); $(BC)^2 =$
$\ell^2 + \ell^2$ (Th 10.2); $(BC)^2 = 2\ell^2$ (alg); $BC = \ell\sqrt{2}$
(alg) **23.** $d^2 = s^2 + s^2$ (Th 10.2); $d^2 = 2s^2$ (alg);
$d = s\sqrt{2}$ (alg) **25.** m $\angle FGH = 30$ (diag of
$\square$ bis $\angle$s); $\angle FHG$ is a rt $\angle$ (diag of rhomb $\perp$
each other); m $\angle GFD = 60$ (ac $\angle$s of rt $\triangle$ are
comp) If $FH = s$, $GF = 2s$, $GH = s\sqrt{3}$ (Th
10.5); $DG = DE = EF = FG = 2s$ (rhomb is
equilat); $GE = 2s\sqrt{3}$, $DF = 2s$ (diag $\square$ bis ea
other) $\frac{GD + DE + EF + FG}{(GE) \cdot (DF)} = \frac{8s}{(2s\sqrt{3})(2s)} =$
$\frac{2}{s\sqrt{3}} \neq \frac{1}{2\sqrt{3}}$ (subst and alg)

Pages 322–323
1. 1.333, 0.800, 0.600, 0.750, 0.600, 0.800
3. 0.343, 0.324, 0.946, 2.917, 0.946, 0.324
5. 1.118, 0.745, 0.667, 0.894, 0.667, 0.745
7. 1.732 **9.** 0.500 **11.** 0.707 **13.** 0.436,
0.400, 0.917, 2.291, 0.917, 0.400 **15.** 0.354,
0.333, 0.943, 2.828, 0.943, 0.333 **17.** 0.333,
0.316, 0.949, 3.000, 0.949, 0.316 **19.** sin $B =$

$\frac{b}{c}$; cos $A = \frac{b}{c}$; sin $B = \cos A$ **21.** tan $B = \frac{b}{a}$;
tan $A = \frac{a}{b}$; $\frac{1}{\tan A} = \frac{b}{a}$; tan $B = \frac{1}{\tan A}$ **23.** tan
$A = \frac{a}{b}$; tan $(90 - A) = \tan B = \frac{b}{a}$; tan $A =$
$\frac{1}{\tan B}$; tan $A = \frac{1}{\tan (90 - A)}$

Page 325
1. 41° **3.** 65° **5.** 54° **7.** 32° **9.** 15° **11.** 30°
13. T **15.** F **17.** T **19.** F **21.** F **23.** T
25. T **27.** sin $A = \frac{a}{c}$; $c > a$; $\frac{a}{c} < 1$;

29. tan $A = \frac{\sin A}{\cos A}$; $\frac{\sin A}{\cos A} = \frac{\frac{a}{c}}{\frac{b}{c}} = \frac{a}{b}$; tan A

Pages 327–328
1. sin 40° $= \frac{7}{c}$; 10.9 **3.** tan $A = \frac{12}{7}$; 60°

5. sin 75° $= \frac{b}{20}$; 19.3 **7.** cos 24° $= \frac{12}{c}$; 13.1

9. tan 18° $= \frac{b}{c}$; 1.9 **11.** sin $B = \frac{9}{15}$; 37°

13. cos $A = \frac{15}{20}$; 41° **15.** cos 40° $= \frac{a}{18}$; 13.8

17. sin 49° $= \frac{17}{c}$; 22.5 **19.** sin 38° $= \frac{a}{10}$; 6.2

21. sin $A = \frac{3}{5}$; 37° **23.** tan $A = \frac{14}{17}$; 39°

25. m $\angle A = 90 - 35 = 55$; tan 35° $= \frac{AC}{18}$;

$AC = 12.6$; cos 35° $= \frac{18}{AB}$; $AB = 22.0$

27. m $\angle B = 90 - 27 = 63$; tan 27° $= \frac{BC}{15}$;

$BC = 7.6$; cos 27° $= \frac{15}{AB}$; $AB = 16.8$

29. m $\angle B = 90 - 56° = 34$; sin 56 $= \frac{BC}{32}$; $BC =$

26.5; cos 56 $= \frac{AC}{32}$; $AC = 17.9$ **31.** tan $A = \frac{1}{4}$;

m $\angle A = 14$; m $\angle B = 76$ **33.** tan 27° $= \frac{10}{AC}$;

$AC = 19.6$; sin 27° $= \frac{10}{AB}$; $AB = 22.0$; $p = 10 +$

$19.6 + 22.0 = 51.6$ **35.** sin 28° $= \frac{ST}{20}$;

$ST = 9.39$; sin 51° $= \frac{9.39}{SU}$; $SU = 12.1$

Pages 330–331
1. tan 25° $= \frac{x}{100}$; 46.6 m **3.** sin 10° $= \frac{1}{x}$;

5.8 m   **5.** $\tan 38° = \dfrac{x}{30}$; 23.4 m   **7.** $\sin 73 = \dfrac{x}{5}$; 4.8 cm   **9.** $\sin 55° = \dfrac{L}{6}$; $L = 4.9$ cm; $\cos 55° = \dfrac{w}{6}$; $w = 3.4$ cm   **11.** $\tan 26° = \dfrac{35}{d}$; 71.8 m   **13.** $\sin 75° = \dfrac{h}{150}$; 144.9 m   **15.** $\sin 34° = \dfrac{h}{8}$; 4.5 mm   **17.** $\cos 52° = \dfrac{EB}{9}$; $EB = 5.5$; $AB = 17.5$ **19.** $\tan \frac{1}{2} A = \dfrac{9}{12}$; $\frac{1}{2} A = 37$; m $\angle A = 74$; m $\angle C = 74$; m $\angle B = 106 =$ m $\angle D$ **21.** $\cos 20° = \dfrac{h}{10}$; 9.4 cm   **23.** $\cos A = \dfrac{9}{14}$; m $\angle A = 50° =$ m $\angle B$; m $\angle C = 80$ **25.** $\cos A = \dfrac{9}{12}$; 41°, 41°, 98°   **27.** $\cos A = \dfrac{4.5}{12}$; 68°, 68°, 112°, 112°

Page 334

1. $\triangle ABC \sim \triangle ACD \sim \triangle CBD$ 90   **3.** $8^2 + 5^2 = 89$; $\sqrt{89}$ **5.** Yes   **7.** No   **9.** $\sqrt{6^2 + 6^2 + 6^2} = 6\sqrt{3}$ **11.** $6^2 + 6^2 = 72$; $6\sqrt{2}$; 6   **13.** $\tan = \dfrac{opp}{adj} = \dfrac{3}{}$ **15.** 0.5299   **17.** 28°   **19.** $\dfrac{LJ}{10} = 0.5543$; 5.543; 48°   **21.** $\tan 42 = \dfrac{x}{20}$; 13.4 m   **23.** $\dfrac{4}{y} = \cos 52$; $\dfrac{4}{.6157}$; 6.5

Pages 340–341

1. rad: $\overline{OA}, \overline{OD}, \overline{OC}, \overline{OB}$; diam: $\overline{AB}, \overline{CD}$ **3.** ch: AB; no secs or tans   **5.** $\triangle AOB \cong \triangle COB$ (SSS)   **7.** 6   **9.** 12; $12\sqrt{3}$ **11.** $7\sqrt{2}$; 14   **13.** 9; $9\sqrt{2}$ **15.** 26   **17.** $\overline{OA} \cong \overline{OB}$ (Th 11.1); $\angle OAB \cong \angle OBA$ (Th 5.1)   **19.** Given: $\odot O$, radii $\overline{OA}, \overline{OB}$. Prove: $\overline{OA} \cong \overline{OB}$. $OA = OB$ (def of $\odot$); $\overline{OA} \cong \overline{OB}$ (def of $\cong$ seg)   **21.** $\angle DOA \cong \angle BOC$ (Th 2.10); $\overline{OD} \cong \overline{OB} \cong \overline{OA} \cong \overline{OC}$ (Th 11.1); $\triangle DOA \cong \triangle BOC$; (Post 17); $\overline{AD} \cong \overline{BC}$ (CPCTC)   **23.** Draw $\overline{OR}, \overline{OS}$; $\overline{OR} \cong \overline{OS}$ (Th 11.1); $\overline{OM} \cong \overline{OM}$ (reflex prop); $\triangle OMR \cong \triangle OMS$ (Post 16); $\angle OMR \cong \angle OMS$ (CPCTC); $\overline{XY} \perp \overline{RS}$ (Th 2.5); $\angle TNO \cong \angle OMS$ (Post 13); $\angle OMS$ a rt $\angle$ ($\perp$s form rt $\angle$'s); $\angle TNO$ is a rt $\angle$ (subst); $\overline{OY} \perp \overline{TU}$ (def $\perp$); $\overline{OY}$ bis $\overline{TU}$ (Th 11.2); N is the midpt of $\overline{TU}$ (def of midpt)   **25.** Draw rad $\overline{OC}, \overline{OF}, \overline{OD}, \overline{OG}$; $\overline{OH} \cong \overline{OH}$ (reflex); $\overline{OF} \cong \overline{OG}$ (Th 11.1); $\overline{FH} \cong \overline{HG}$ (def bis); $\triangle OFH \cong \triangle OGH$ (Post 16); $\angle OHF \cong \angle OHG$ (CPCTC); $\overline{AB} \perp \overline{FG}$ (Th 2.5); $\overline{OE} \cong \overline{OE}$ (reflex); $\overline{OC} \cong \overline{OD}$ (Th 11.1); $\overline{CE} \cong \overline{ED}$ (def bis); $\triangle OCE \cong \triangle ODE$ (Post

16); $\angle CEO \cong \angle DEO$ (CPCTC); $\overline{AB} \perp \overline{CD}$ (Th 2.5); $\angle OHF \cong \angle DEO$ ($\perp$s form $\cong$ rt $\angle$'s); $\overline{CD} \parallel \overline{FG}$ (Post 14)   **27.** Given: $\odot O$, chord $\overline{AB}$, $\overrightarrow{DE} \perp$ bis of $\overline{AB}$ at D. Prove: O lies on $\overrightarrow{DE}$. Draw $\overline{OA}, \overline{OB}$; $\overline{OA} \cong \overline{OB}$ (Th 11.1); $\overline{AD} \cong \overline{DB}$ (def of bis); $\overline{OD}$ is $\perp$ bis of $\overline{AB}$ (Th 5.8) O lies on $\overline{DE}$ (Post 12).   **29.** Given: $\odot O$, $\overline{AD} \cong \overline{AC}$, $\overline{BC} \cong \overline{BD}$. Prove: $\overline{AB}$ is a diam of $\odot O$. $\overline{AB} \perp$ bis of $\overline{CD}$ (Th 5.8); O is on $\overline{AB}$ (ex 27) $\overline{AB}$ is a diam of $\odot O$ (def of diam)

Cumulative Review

1. $\angle SUT, \angle SVR$ are rt $\angle$'s ($\perp$s form rt $\angle$'s); $\angle SUT \cong \angle SVR$ (all rt $\angle$'s $\cong$); $\angle S \cong \angle S$ (reflex) $\triangle RSV \sim \triangle TSV$ (Post 22)   **2.** $\angle ZWY \cong \angle XYW$, $\angle WZX \cong \angle ZXY$ (Post 13); $\triangle ZWP \sim \triangle XYP$ (Post 22)

Pages 343–344

1. $\cong$ **3.** $\neq$ **5.** $\neq$ **7.** $\neq$ **9.** $BC = 16$ **11.** 70, 70   **13.** $WX = 6$ **15.** $VY = 4$ **17.** $\overline{AM} \cong \overline{BN}$, $\overline{RM} \cong \overline{MS} \cong \overline{UN} \cong \overline{NT}$ **19.** $\overline{OA} \cong \overline{OB} \cong \overline{QC} \cong \overline{QD}$; $\overline{AE} \cong \overline{EB}$; $\overline{CF} \cong \overline{FD}$ **21.** $\overline{OX} \cong \overline{OY} \cong \overline{OW} \cong \overline{OZ}$ (Th 11.1); $\triangle XOY \cong \triangle ZOW$ (Post 17); $\overline{XY} \cong ZW$ (CPCTC); $\overline{OT} \cong \overline{OU}$ (Th 11.3)   **23.** $\angle XTO \cong \angle ZUO$ ($\perp$s form $\cong$ rt $\angle$'s); $\overline{OX} \cong \overline{OZ}$ (Th 11.1); $\triangle XOT \cong \triangle ZOU$ (Th 4.2); $\overline{OT} \cong \overline{OU}$ (CPCTC); $\overline{XY} \cong \overline{WZ}$ (Th 11.4)   **25.** Given: $\odot O$, $\odot P$, Ch. $\overline{AB} \cong$ Ch. $\overline{DE}$, $\overline{OC} \perp \overline{AB}$, $\overline{PF} \perp \overline{DE}$, $\overline{OC} \cong \overline{PF}$. Prove: $\odot O \cong \odot P$. Draw $\overline{AO}, \overline{DP}$; $\angle ACO \cong \angle DFP$ ($\perp$s form $\cong$ rt $\angle$'s) $\overline{OC}$ bis $\overline{AB}$ and $\overline{PF}$ bis $\overline{DE}$ (Th 11.2); $AC = \frac{1}{2} AB$, $DF = \frac{1}{2} DE$ (def bis); $AC = DF$ (trans prop); $\triangle ACO \cong \triangle DFP$ (Post 17); $\overline{OA} \cong \overline{DP}$ (CPCTC) $\odot O \cong \odot P$ (def $\cong \odot$)   **27.** Given: $\triangle ABC$ inscr in $\odot O$, $\overline{OD} \perp \overline{AB}$, $\overline{OE} \perp \overline{BC}$, $\overline{OF} \perp \overline{AC}$, $\overline{OD} \cong \overline{OE} \cong \overline{OF}$; Prove: $\triangle ABC$ is equilateral. $\overline{AB} \cong \overline{BC} \cong \overline{AC}$ (Th 11.4); $\triangle ABC$ is equilat (def).

Pages 349–350

1. 11   **3.** 17   **5.** 28   **7.** $\overline{QP} \cong \overline{RP} \cong \overline{SP}$ **9.** $\overline{FO} \cong \overline{IO}$; $\angle EFO \cong \angle GFO \cong \angle HIO \cong \angle JIO$ **11.** Draw $\overline{OX}$; $\overline{OX} \perp \overline{AB}$ (Th 11.5); $\overline{OX}$ bis $\overline{AB}$ (Th 11.2); $\overline{AX} \cong \overline{BX}$ (def of seg bis)   **13.** $\overline{AP} \cong \overline{BP}$ (Th 11.7); $\angle PAB \cong \angle PBA$ (Th 5.1); $\overline{OA} \cong \overline{OB}$ (Th 11.1); $\angle OAB \cong \angle OBA$ (Th 5.1); $\overline{OA} \perp \overline{AP}$, $\overline{OB} \perp \overline{BP}$ (Th 11.5); $\angle OAP, \angle OBP$ are rt $\angle$'s ($\perp$s form rt $\angle$'s); m $\angle OAB +$ m $\angle PAB = 90$, m $\angle OBA +$ m $\angle PBA = 90$ ($\angle$ add, subst); m $\angle OAB +$ m $\angle OBA +$ m $\angle PAB +$ m $\angle PBA = 180$ (add); m $\angle P +$ m $\angle PAB +$ m $\angle PBA = 180$ (Th 3.5); m $\angle OAB +$ m $\angle OBA +$ m $\angle PAB +$ m $\angle PBA =$ m $\angle P +$ m $\angle PAB +$ m $\angle PBA$ (trans); m $\angle P =$

m $\angle OAB$ + m $\angle OBA$ (subtr); m $\angle P$ = 2 m $\angle OAB$ (subst) **15.** $\overline{OA} \cong \overline{OD}$ (Th 11.1); $\angle OAC \cong \angle ODC$ (Th 5.1); $\overline{OD} \perp \overline{DE}$ (Th 11.5); $\angle ODE$ is a rt $\angle$ ($\perp$s form rt $\angle$'s); $\angle ODC$ comp of $\angle EDO$ (def of comp $\angle$'s); $\angle OAC$ comp of $\angle ACO$ (ac $\angle$'s of rt $\triangle$'s are comp); $\angle ACO \cong \angle EDC$ (Th 2.9); $\angle ACO \cong \angle ECD$ (Th 2.10); $\angle EDC \cong \angle ECD$ (subst) **17.** $AX = 2$; $BY = 5$; $CZ = 3$ **19.** 24

Cumulative Review

1. $b + \frac{1}{2}a$ **2.** $\frac{b+d}{2}$

Pages 353–354

1. Yes **3.** No **5.** 60 **7.** 120 **9.** 50 **11.** 30 **13.** $\overline{AB}, \overline{BC}, \overline{DC}, \overline{DA}$ **15.** $\overset{\frown}{DCB}, \overset{\frown}{DAB}$ **17.** $\overline{UX}; \overline{TW}$ **19.** 79 **21.** 101 **23.** 143 **25.** 71.5 **27.** circle cannot have $370°$ **29.** Draw $\overline{OC}, \overline{OD}; OC \perp CP, OD \perp DP$ (Th 11.5); $\angle OCP, \angle ODP$ are rt $\angle$'s ($\perp$s form rt $\angle$'s); m $\angle COD + x + 90 + 90 = 360$ (Th 6.1); m $\angle COD = 180 - x$ (subt); m $\angle COD = m\overset{\frown}{CD}$; m$\overset{\frown}{CD} = 180 - x$ (subst)

31. $\tan 66° = \frac{BC}{8}$ 18.0 **33.** m$\overset{\frown}{TSQ}$ = 180 (meas semi $\odot$ = 180); m$\overset{\frown}{TSQ}$ = m$\overset{\frown}{TS}$ + m$\overset{\frown}{SQ}$ (Post 23); m$\overset{\frown}{SQ}$ = 180 - m $\angle P$ (ex 29); m$\overset{\frown}{TS}$ + $180 - m \angle P = 180$ (subst); m$\overset{\frown}{TS}$ = m $\angle P$ (add) **35.** m$\overset{\frown}{RS}$ = $180 - m \angle RPS$, m$\overset{\frown}{ST}$ = $180 - m \angle TPS$ (ex 29); m $\angle RPT$ = m $\angle RPS$ + m $\angle TPS$ (Post 9); m$\overset{\frown}{RS}$ + m$\overset{\frown}{ST}$ = $360 -$ m $\angle RPT$ (add, subst)

Cumulative Review

1. $5\sqrt{2}$ **2.** $7\sqrt{2}$

Pages 357–358

1. No **3.** No **5.** $\overset{\frown}{CD}, \overset{\frown}{AB}; \overset{\frown}{AD}, \overset{\frown}{CB}, \overset{\frown}{DBC}, \overset{\frown}{BDA}$ **7.** None **9.** $\overset{\frown}{BC} \cong \overset{\frown}{HI}$ **11.** $\overline{RS} \cong \overline{RT}$ (Th 11.8); $\angle RST$ is isos (def) **13.** $\overline{XZ} \cong \overline{YZ}$ (Th 5.2); $\overset{\frown}{XZ} \cong \overset{\frown}{YZ}$ (Th 11.9) **15.** $\overline{KL} \cong \overline{LM}$ (Th 11.8) $\angle KOL \cong \angle MOL$ (Th 11.8); m $\angle KOL$ + m $\angle NOK$ = 180, m $\angle NDM$ + m $\angle MOL$ = 180 (Post 11); $\angle KOL$ suppl to $\angle NOK$, $\angle MOL$ suppl to $\angle NOM$ (def); $\angle NOK \cong \angle NOM$ (Th 26); $\overline{NK} \cong \overline{NM}$ (Th 11.10); $\triangle NKL \cong \triangle NML$ (Post 16); $\angle KNL \cong \angle MNL$ (CPCTC) **17.** Given: $\odot O \cong \odot P$, cord $\overline{AB} \cong$ cord $\overline{CD}$. Prove: $\angle O \cong \angle P$, $\overset{\frown}{AB} \cong \overset{\frown}{CD}$. $\overline{AO} \cong \overline{CP} \cong \overline{OB} \cong \overline{PD}$ (def $\odot$); $\triangle OAB \cong \triangle CPD$ (Post 16); $\angle O \cong \angle P$ (CPCTC); m$\overset{\frown}{AB}$ = m $\angle O$, m$\overset{\frown}{CD}$ = m $\angle P$ (meas of cent $\angle$ = meas its int arc); m$\overset{\frown}{AB}$ $\cong$ m$\overset{\frown}{CD}$ (subst); $\overset{\frown}{AB} \cong \overset{\frown}{CD}$ (def $\cong$ $\overset{\frown}{s}$) **19.** Draw $\overline{OS}$; $\angle SUO \cong \angle SVO$ ($\perp$ form $\cong$ rt $\angle$'s); $\angle ROS \cong \angle TOS$ (Th

11.8); $\overline{OS} \cong \overline{OS}$ (reflex); $\triangle OSU \cong \triangle OSV$ (Th 4.2); $\overline{SU} \cong \overline{SV}$ (CPCTC) **21.** $x\sqrt{3}$ **23.** Draw $\overline{AD}, \overline{BC}$; m$\overset{\frown}{AD}$ = m$\overset{\frown}{AC}$ + m$\overset{\frown}{CD}$, m$\overset{\frown}{CB}$ = m$\overset{\frown}{CD}$ + m$\overset{\frown}{DB}$ (Post 23) m$\overset{\frown}{AC}$ + m$\overset{\frown}{CD}$ = m$\overset{\frown}{DB}$ + m$\overset{\frown}{CD}$ (add); m$\overset{\frown}{AD}$ = m$\overset{\frown}{CB}$ (subst); $\overline{AD} \cong \overline{CB}$, $\overline{AC} \cong \overline{BD}$ (Th 11.8); $\overline{CD} \cong \overline{CD}$ (reflex); $\triangle ACD \cong \triangle BDC$ (Post 16); $\angle ACD \cong \angle BDC$ (CPCTC) **25.** Draw $\overline{DO}$; $\angle EOD \cong \angle D$ (Post 13); $\angle ADE \cong \angle B$ (Th 3.1); $\overline{DO} \cong \overline{BO}$ (Th 11.1); $\angle D \cong \angle B$ (Th 5.1); $\angle AOE \cong \angle EOD$ (subst); $\overline{AE} \cong \overline{ED}$ (Th 11.10)

Pages 362–363

1. 90 **3.** m $\angle I$ = m $\angle J$ = 56 **5.** m $\angle J$ = 67; m $\angle K$ = 94 **7.** m $\angle ACD$ = 32; m$\overset{\frown}{BC}$ = 64 **9.** 43 **11.** 12 **13.** 156 **15.** 66 **17.** 122 **19.** 142 **21.** 38 **23.** m $\angle PNO$ = 16.25; m $\angle ONM$ = 57.5 **25.** $\overline{OQ} \cong \overline{OR}$ (Th 11.1); $\angle PRQ \cong \angle SQR$ (Th 5.1) **27.** $\overset{\frown}{RU} \cong \overset{\frown}{ST}$ (Th 11.11, Cor 3); $\overset{\frown}{UT} \cong \overset{\frown}{UT}$ (reflex); m$\overset{\frown}{RU}$ + m$\overset{\frown}{UT}$ = m$\overset{\frown}{RT}$, m$\overset{\frown}{ST}$ + m$\overset{\frown}{TU}$ = m$\overset{\frown}{SU}$ (Post 23); m$\overset{\frown}{RU}$ + m$\overset{\frown}{UT}$ = m$\overset{\frown}{ST}$ + m$\overset{\frown}{TU}$ (add); m$\overset{\frown}{RT}$ = m$\overset{\frown}{SU}$ (subst); $\overset{\frown}{RT} \cong \overset{\frown}{SU}$ (def $\overset{\frown}{s}$); $\overline{RT} \cong \overline{SU}$ (Th 11.8) **29.** Follow ex. 28; then $\frac{AD}{AC} = \frac{CD}{CB}$ (def $\sim$ poly); $AD \cdot CB = AC \cdot CD$ (prop of propor) **31.** Draw diam $\overline{PC}$; m $\angle CPB$ = $\frac{1}{2}$m$\overset{\frown}{CB}$, m $\angle APC = \frac{1}{2}$m$\overset{\frown}{CA}$ (case I); m $\angle CPB -$ m $\angle APC = \frac{1}{2}$m$\overset{\frown}{CB} - \frac{1}{2}m\overset{\frown}{CA}$ (subtr); m $\angle CPB -$ m $\angle APC$ = m $\angle APB$ (Post 10); m $\angle APB$ = $\frac{1}{2}$(m$\overset{\frown}{CB}$ $-$ m$\overset{\frown}{CA}$) (subst); m$\overset{\frown}{CB}$ $-$ m$\overset{\frown}{CA}$ = m$\overset{\frown}{AB}$ (Post 23); m $\angle APB = \frac{1}{2}$m$\overset{\frown}{AB}$ (subst)

33. m $\angle ABC = \frac{1}{2}$m$\overset{\frown}{AC}$ (Th 11.11); m$\overset{\frown}{AC}$ = 180 (semi $\odot$ meas 180); m $\angle ABC = \frac{1}{2}$ (180) or 90 (subst); $\angle ABC$ is a rt $\angle$ (an $\angle$ of 90° is rt $\angle$) **35.** Given: $\odot O$, $\angle ABC$ inscr in maj $\overset{\frown}{ABC}$; Prove: m $\angle ABC$ < 90. m$\overset{\frown}{ABC}$ > 180 (def maj); m$\overset{\frown}{ABC}$ + m$\overset{\frown}{AC}$ = 360 ($\odot$ contains 360°); m$\overset{\frown}{AC}$ < 180 (subtr); m $\angle ABC = \frac{1}{2}$m$\overset{\frown}{AC}$ (Th 11.11); m $\angle ABC$ < 90 (subst) **37.** Given: $\odot O \cong \odot P$, $\triangle ABC$ inscr in $\odot O$, $\triangle DEF$ inscr in $\odot P$, $\angle A \cong \angle D$, $\angle B \cong \angle E$. Prove: $\triangle ABC \cong \triangle DEF$. m $\angle B = \frac{1}{2}$m$\overset{\frown}{AC}$, m $\angle E = \frac{1}{2}$m$\overset{\frown}{DF}$ (Th 11.11); $\frac{1}{2}$m$\overset{\frown}{AC}$ = $\frac{1}{2}$m$\overset{\frown}{DF}$ (subst); m$\overset{\frown}{AC}$ = m$\overset{\frown}{DF}$ (mult); $\overset{\frown}{AC} \cong \overset{\frown}{DF}$ (def $\cong$ $\overset{\frown}{s}$); $\overline{AC} \cong \overline{DF}$ (Th 11.8); $\triangle ABC \cong \triangle DEF$ (Th 4.2) **39.** false; rectangle

Cumulative Review

1. F 2. T 3. T 4. T 5. T 6. T

Pages 366–367

1. 50 3. 60 5. 50 7. 30 9. 11
11. 84 13. 6; 109 15. 62; 45 17. T
19. 24 21. m $\angle STQ$ = 90 ($\perp$s form rt $\angle$'s);
m $\angle STQ = \frac{1}{2}$(m$\widehat{PR}$ + m$\widehat{QS}$) (Th 11.12); 90 =
$\frac{1}{2}$(m$\widehat{PR}$ + m$\widehat{QS}$) (subst); m$\widehat{PR}$ + m$\widehat{QS}$ = 180
(mult) 23. $\angle N \cong \angle Q$ (Th 11.11, Cor 1);
$\angle L \cong \angle L$ (reflex); $\triangle LQM \sim \triangle LNP$ (Post 22)
25. 100 27. Given: $\odot O$ and $\odot P$ tang at T, O
lies on $\odot P$, chord $\overline{AT}$ int $\odot P$ at B. Prove: $\overline{TB} \cong$
$\overline{AB}$. OT is diam of $\odot P$ (Th 11.5) Draw $\overline{OB}$;
$\angle OBT$ is a rt $\angle$ (Th 11.11, Cor 2); $\overline{OB} \perp \overline{AT}$
(sides of a rt $\angle$ are $\perp$); $\overline{OB}$ bis $\overline{AT}$ (Th 11.2);
$\overline{TB} \cong \overline{AB}$ (def)

Pages 370–372

1. 76 3. 48 5. 71 7. 55 9. 32
11. 141 13. 90 15. 99 17. 72 19. 50
21. 60; 30 23. 10.75; 79.25 25. Draw $\overline{AB}$;
m $\angle z$ = m $\angle x$ + m $\angle y$ (Th 4.2); m $\angle x$ =
m $\angle z$ − m $\angle y$ (subtr); m $\angle z = \frac{1}{2}$m$\widehat{ACB}$, m $\angle y$
$= \frac{1}{2}\widehat{AB}$ (Th 11.14); m $\angle x = \frac{1}{2}$m$\widehat{ACB} - \frac{1}{2}m\widehat{AB}$
(subst); m $\angle x = \frac{1}{2}$(m$\widehat{ACB}$ − m$\widehat{AB}$) (distr prop)
27. $\angle UVS \cong \angle VST$ (Post 13); m $\angle UVS$ =
m $\angle VST$ (def $\cong \angle$'s); m $\angle UVS = \frac{1}{2}$m$\widehat{US}$ (Th
11.11); m $\angle VST = \frac{1}{2}$m$\widehat{US}$ (Th 11.14); $\frac{1}{2}$m$\widehat{SU}$ =
$\frac{1}{2}$m$\widehat{SV}$ (subst); m$\widehat{US}$ = m$\widehat{SV}$ (mult); $\overline{US} \cong \overline{SV}$
(Th 11.8) 29. Given: $\odot O$, $\odot Q$ internally tan
at P, $\overrightarrow{PE}$ the common tan, $\overrightarrow{PA}$ int $\odot Q$ at B.
Prove: m$\widehat{PA}$ = m$\widehat{PB}$. m $\angle APE \cong$ m $\angle BPE$
(reflex); m $\angle APE = \frac{1}{2}$m$\widehat{PA}$, m $\angle BPE = \frac{1}{2}\widehat{PB}$
(Th 11.14); $\frac{1}{2}$m$\widehat{PA} = \frac{1}{2}m\widehat{PB}$ (subst); m$\widehat{PA}$ =
m$\widehat{PB}$ (mult) 31. $\angle LMS \cong \angle RMN$ (Th 2.10);
m $\angle LMS = \frac{1}{2}$m$\widehat{LM}$, m $\angle RMN = \frac{1}{2}$m$\widehat{NM}$ (Th
11.14); $\frac{1}{2}$m$\widehat{LM} = \frac{1}{2}m\widehat{NM}$ (subst); m$\widehat{LM}$ = m$\widehat{NM}$
(mult) 33. Given: $ABCD$ insc in $\odot O$, $\angle EAD$
is an ext $\angle$ of $ABCD$. Prove: $\angle EAD \cong \angle C$.
$\angle BCD$ suppl to $\angle BAD$ (Th 11.11, Cor 4);
m $\angle EAD$ + m $\angle BAD$ = 180 (Post 12); $\angle EAD$
supp to $\angle BAD$ (def supp $\angle$'s); $\angle EAD \cong \angle C$
(Th 2.8) 35. Given: $\odot O$, $\odot q$ ext. tang. at P,
$\overleftrightarrow{PT}$ tan to $\odot O$ and $\odot Q$ at P, $\overleftrightarrow{AB}$ a common ext

tang to $\odot O$ and $\odot Q$, chs $\overline{AP}$, $\overline{PB}$. Prove: $\angle APB$
is a rt $\angle$. $\overline{TA} \cong \overline{TP}$, $\overline{TB} \cong \overline{TP}$ (Th 11.7);
$\overline{TA} \cong \overline{TP} \cong \overline{TB}$ (trans); T is center of a $\odot$ with
rad $\overline{AT}$, $\overline{PT}$, $\overline{BT}$ (def of $\odot$); $\angle APB$ is a rt $\angle$
($\angle$ inscr in semi $\odot$ is a rt $\angle$)

Pages 375–376

1. 3 3. 18 5. 12 7. 6 9. 12 11. $13\frac{1}{3}$;
11 13. $7\frac{1}{3}$; $6\frac{2}{3}$ 15. 12 17. Draw $\overline{AB}$, $\overline{AC}$;
$\angle P \cong \angle P$ (reflex); m $\angle PAC = \frac{1}{2}$m$\widehat{AC}$ (Th
11.14); m $\angle B = \frac{1}{2}$m$\widehat{AC}$ (Th 11.11); m $\angle PAC$ =
m $\angle B$ (subst); $\angle PAC \cong \angle B$ (def $\cong \angle$'s); $\triangle PAC \sim$
$\triangle PCA$ (Post 21); $\frac{PA}{PB} = \frac{PC}{PA}$ (def $\sim$ poly); $(PA)^2$
$= PB \cdot PC$ (prop of propor) 19. $\angle T \cong \angle T$
(reflex); $\angle K \cong \angle M$ (Th 11.11, Cor 1); $\triangle KLT$
$\sim \triangle MJT$ (Post 21); $\frac{KL}{MJ} = \frac{TL}{TJ}$ (def $\sim$ poly);
$KL \cdot TJ = TL \cdot MJ$ (prop of propor)
21. $(TM)^2 = MS \cdot MP$, $(TM)^2 = MR \cdot MQ$ (Th
11.19); $MS \cdot MP = MR \cdot MQ$ (subst)
23. Draw $\overline{AB}$; m $\angle DGE = \frac{1}{2}$(m$\widehat{ED}$ + m$\widehat{BC}$);
m $\angle ABD = \frac{1}{2}$m$\widehat{AED}$ (Th 11.11); m$\widehat{AED}$ = m$\widehat{AE}$
+ m$\widehat{ED}$ (Post 23); m $\angle ABD = \frac{1}{2}$(m$\widehat{AE}$ + m$\widehat{ED}$)
(subst); m $\angle ABD = \frac{1}{2}$(m$\widehat{BC}$ + m$\widehat{ED}$) (subst);
m $\angle DGE$ = m $\angle ABD$ (subst); $\angle DGE \cong \angle ABD$
(def); $\angle D \cong \angle D$ (reflex); $\triangle DGF \sim \triangle DBA$
(Post 21); $\frac{AD}{BD} = \frac{GD}{FD}$ (def $\sim$ poly); $AD \cdot FD =$
$BD \cdot GD$ (prop of propor)

Cumulative Review

1. 10cm 2. 3

Page 379

1. Open compass to measure the 2-cm seg; use
this rad and constr a $\odot$. 3. Use rad 3 cm;
draw $\odot$; draw a rad of $\odot$ and extend it; constr
$\perp$ to rad at its endpt on $\odot$. 5. (a) Constr a $\odot$;
with same rad, mark off 6 consec $\cong$ arcs; from
each pt as ctr, with same rad, draw the 6 arcs in
$\odot$. (b) Constr a $\odot$ and mark off 6 $\cong$ $\widehat{s}$ as in 5(a);
draw 3 diams (use alternate pts); bisect a rad;
use $\frac{1}{2}r$ as rad and midpts of radii as ctrs; draw
3 $\odot$. 7. Constr $\perp$ to seg at given pt; measure
given seg with compass; mark off this length on
$\perp$; use this pt as ctr and same rad to draw $\odot$.
9. Constr $\perp$ bis of 2 nonadj sides of sq; use pt of

int as ctr, $\frac{1}{2}s$ as rad, and draw $\odot$. **11.** Follow constr on p 377. Let R be int of $\overleftrightarrow{OP}$ with $\odot O$. Constr $\overleftrightarrow{RQ} \perp \overleftrightarrow{OP}$, int $\overleftrightarrow{TP}$ at Q. Bis $\angle RQP$, with $\overrightarrow{QU}$ int $\overleftrightarrow{OP}$ at U. With $\overrightarrow{RU}$ as rad, draw $\odot U$. **13.** Draw a circle. Constr $\perp$ bis of diam. Connect intersect with endpt of diam. Constr $\perp$ bis of four sides. Connect Intersects with Endpt of each side. **15.** Inscr reg hex; constr $\perp$ bis of each side; where these int $\odot$, connect pts to vert of hex. **17.** P, D, F non coll, draw $\overrightarrow{PD}$ and $\overrightarrow{PF}$; on $\overrightarrow{PD}$, mark $PA = a$, $AB = b$; on $\overrightarrow{PF}$, mark $PC = c$; draw $\overrightarrow{AC}$; constr $\overleftrightarrow{BE} \parallel \overleftrightarrow{AC}$, to int $\overrightarrow{PF}$ at E; $CE = x$. **19.** Follow steps on p 378; $x = \sqrt{ab}$ **21.** ex 19 with a replaced by $4a$ **23.** ex 19 with b replaced by $\frac{1}{2}a$

Page 382
1. $\overline{OF}, \overline{OE}, \overline{GO}$ **3.** $\overline{EG}$ **5.** $\overrightarrow{BA}$ **7.** $\overline{AD} \perp$ bis $\overline{BC}$ (Th 11.2); $AC = AB$ (Th 5.7); $\overline{AC} \cong \overline{AB}$ (def); $\angle C \cong \angle B$ (Th 5.1); **9.** 64 **11.** 97 $= \frac{1}{2}(91 \tan \overset{\frown}{BD})$; 103 **13.** $47 = \frac{1}{2}(m\overset{\frown}{AD} - 21)$; 115 **15.** 40 **17.** 14 **19.** Follow steps p 377. **21.** $\odot O \cong \odot P$ (def); $\overline{OA} \cong \overline{OB}$; $\overline{PC} \cong \overline{PD}$ (Th 11.11); $\angle A \cong \angle B$, $\angle C \cong \angle D$ (Th 5.1); $\angle B \cong \angle D$ (subst); $\angle O \cong \angle P$ (Th 3.6); $\overset{\frown}{AB} \cong \overset{\frown}{CD}$ (Th 11.10)

Pages 389–390
1. 22.75m² **3.** 24.51 cm² **5.** $7\sqrt{5}$m²
7. 25 cm² **9.** $(x + y)^2$ or $x^2 + 2xy + y^2$
11. $x^2 + 2xy + y^2$ **13.** 52 cm **15.** $\sqrt{5}$ m
17. $x + 1$ **19.** 48 **21.** $6\sqrt{10}$ **23.** $36\sqrt{3}$ cm²
25. 128 cm² **27.** 60 mm² **29.** 76 m²
31. 256 cm² **33.** $A = bh$, $A' = b'h'$ (Post 24); $A' = b'h$ (subst); $\frac{A}{A'} = \frac{bh}{b'h}$ (div); $\frac{A}{A'} = \frac{b}{b'}$ (alg)
35. $A = 5^2$, $A' = (25)^2$ (area of sq is s^2), $A' = 4 \cdot 5^2$ (alg); $A' = 4A$ (subst). The statement is disproved.

Algebra Review
1. $\frac{b}{3}$ **2.** $k - 4$ **3.** $\frac{t - s}{r}$ **4.** $6a$ **5.** b
6. $\frac{3}{rx - 2}$ **7.** $3 - x$ **8.** $8 - 2x$ **9.** $3x - 12$
10. $\frac{-2c}{4b - 3}$ **11.** $\frac{4z}{6y + 3}$ **12.** $\frac{3t}{5r - 7}$
13. $\frac{3p}{-6p + 2}$ **14.** $\frac{-2h}{bc - 4}$ **15.** $\frac{2yz}{3 + 5yz}$

Pages 393–394
1. 12 m² **3.** 8 cm² **5.** 9.69 km² **7.** 2.5 cm²
9. 16 cm **11.** 1.6 km **13.** 5 cm **15.** $6\sqrt{3}$

cm; $36\sqrt{3}$ cm² **17.** $11\frac{1}{4}$ **19.** 18 **21.** 6
23. $\overline{DE} \perp \overline{AC}$, $DE = \frac{1}{2}DB$ (diags of rh $\perp$ bis of each other); Area $\triangle ADC = \frac{1}{2}DE \cdot d_2$ (Th 12.2); Area $\triangle ADC = \frac{1}{2}\left(\frac{1}{2}d_1\right)d_2$, or $\frac{1}{4}d_1d_2$ (subst); $\triangle ADC \cong \triangle CBA$ (Th 7.1); Area $\triangle ADC =$ Area $\triangle CBA$ (Post 26); Area $ABCD =$ Area $ADC +$ Area CBA (Post 27); Area $ABCD = 2$ Area ADC (subst); Area $ABCD = 2 \cdot \frac{1}{4}d_1d_2$ (subst); Area $ABCD = \frac{1}{2}d_1d_2$ (alg)
25. Given: sq $ABCD$, $AC = d$. Prove: Area $ABCD = \frac{1}{2}d^2$. $\overline{AC} \cong \overline{DB}$ (diags of sq $\cong$); $DB = d$ (subst); $ABCD$ is a rhombus (def); Area $ABCD = \frac{1}{2}AC \cdot DB$ (Th 12.3); Area $ABCD = \frac{1}{2}d^2$ (subst) **27.** $\frac{15\sqrt{7}m^2}{4}$ **29.** Given: $\triangle ACB$, base b, alt h. Prove: Area $\triangle ACB = \frac{1}{2}bh$. Area $\triangle ACB +$ Area $\triangle CDA =$ Area $\triangle ADB$ (Post 27); Area $\triangle ADC = \frac{1}{2}xh$, Area $\triangle ADB = \frac{1}{2}h(b + x)$ (Th 12.1); Area $\triangle ACB + \frac{1}{2}xh = \frac{1}{2}(b + x) \cdot h$ (subst); Area $\triangle ACB = \frac{1}{2}(b + x)h - \frac{1}{2}xh$ (subt); Area $\triangle ACB = \frac{1}{2}bh$ (alg)
31. Given: $\triangle ABC \sim \triangle A'B'C'$. Prove: $\frac{\text{Area } ABC}{\text{Area } A'B'C'} = \frac{h^2}{h'^2}$. Area $ABC = \frac{1}{2}bh$, Area $A'B'C' = \frac{1}{2}b'h'$ (Th 12.2); $\frac{b}{b'} = \frac{h}{h'}$ (Th 9.6); $\frac{\text{Area } ABC}{\text{Area } A'B'C'} = \frac{\frac{1}{2}bh}{\frac{1}{2}b'h'}$ (div prop); $\frac{\text{Area } ABC}{\text{Area } A'B'C'} = \frac{h}{h'} \cdot \frac{h}{h'} = \frac{h^2}{h'^2}$ (subst) **33.** Given: $\triangle ABC$, alt h, base b; $\triangle A'B'C'$; alt h', base b', $b \cong b'$. Prove: $\frac{\text{Area } ABC}{\text{Area } A'B'C'} = \frac{h}{h'}$. Area $ABC = \frac{1}{2}bh$, Area $A'B'C' = \frac{1}{2}b'h'$ (Th 12.2); $\frac{\text{Area } ABC}{\text{Area } A'B'C'} = \frac{\frac{1}{2}bh}{\frac{1}{2}b'h'}$ (div prop); $\frac{\text{Area } ABC}{\text{Area } A'B'C'} = \frac{h}{h'}$ (alg) **35.** Given: $\triangle ABC$,

median $\overline{CM}$. Prove: Area $\triangle ACM$ = Area $\triangle BCM$. $\overline{AM} \cong \overline{MB}$ (def median); $AM = MB$ (def $\cong$); Area $\triangle ACM = \frac{1}{2} AM \cdot h$, Area $\triangle BCM = \frac{1}{2} MB \cdot h$ (Th 12.2); Area $\triangle ACM$ = Area $\triangle BCM$ (subst)

Page 397

1. 30 m² **3.** 55.18 cm² **5.** 9 cm **7.** 3.39 m **9.** 9 **11.** 14.4 **13.** 30 **15.** $60\sqrt{2}$ **17.** sin $A = \frac{h}{b}$ (def); $h = b$ sin A (mult); Area $ABCD = ah$ (Th 12.5); Area $ABCD = ab$ sin A (subst) **19.** 53.528 sq units

Pages 400–401

1. 28 mm **3.** 12.6 m² **5.** 40 m² **7.** 6 cm **9.** 3 m **11.** $4x^2 - 2x - 2$ **13.** $2x - 1$ **15.** 16 m, 23 m **17.** $36\sqrt{2}$ **19.** $18\sqrt{3}$ **21.** 18.5 **23.** Given: trap $ABCD$, $RSTU$, bases $\overline{AB} \cong \overline{RS}$, $\overline{DC} \cong \overline{UT}$, alts h, h'. Prove: $\frac{\text{Area } ABCD}{\text{Area } RSTU} = \frac{h}{h'}$. $AB = RS = b_1 DC = UT = b_2$ (def $\cong$ seg); Area $ABCD = \frac{1}{2} h(b_1 + b_2)$, Area $RSTU = \frac{1}{2} h' (b_1 + b_2)$ (Th 12.6); $\frac{\text{Area } ABCD}{\text{Area } RSTU} = \frac{\frac{1}{2} h(b_1 + b_2)}{\frac{1}{2} h'(b_1 + b_2)}$ (div prop); $\frac{\text{Area } ABCD}{\text{Area } RSTU} = \frac{h}{h'}$ (alg) **25.** Constr a seg of length = sum of bases of given trap; bisect this seg to get length of median; constr rect with base $\cong$ to med and alt $\cong$ to alt of given trap.

Cumulative Review

1. m $\angle B = 60 =$ m $\angle D$; m $\angle C = 120$ **2.** $\frac{AB}{DE} = \frac{BC}{EF}$, $\frac{AB}{DE} = \frac{CA}{FD}$, $\frac{BC}{EF} = \frac{CA}{FD}$

Page 404

1. $\frac{64}{49}$; $\frac{8}{7}$ **3.** $\frac{25}{16}$; $\frac{5}{4}$ **5.** $\frac{4}{1}$; $\frac{2}{1}$ **7.** 21 cm **9.** 18.2 cm **11.** 68 cm **13.** $16\sqrt{2}$ cm **15.** 36 cm **17.** $(21 + 7\sqrt{3})$ m **19.** 15 **21.** 12 cm; 8 cm **23.** Given: $\triangle ABC \sim \triangle A'B'C'$. Prove: $\frac{\text{Area } ABC}{\text{Area } A'B'C'} = \frac{b^2}{b'^2}$. Area $ABC = \frac{1}{2} bh$, Area $A'B'C' = \frac{1}{2} b'h'$ (Th 12.2); $\frac{h}{h'} = \frac{b}{b'}$ (Th 9.6); $\frac{\text{Area } ABC}{\text{Area } A'B'C'} = \frac{\frac{1}{2} bh}{\frac{1}{2} b'h'}$

(div prop); $\frac{\text{Area } ABC}{\text{Area } A'B'C'} = \frac{b}{b'} \cdot \frac{b}{b'}$ or $\frac{b^2}{b'^2}$ (subst)

Page 407

1. 7 **3.** 484 **5.** $14\sqrt{3}$, 14 **7.** 12, $6\sqrt{2}$ **9.** $5\sqrt{3}$, 10 **11.** $48\sqrt{3}$ cm² **13.** 36 mm² **15.** $150\sqrt{3}$ cm² **17.** 2, 4, $4\sqrt{3}$ **19.** 2, $\frac{4\sqrt{3}}{3}$, $\frac{4\sqrt{3}}{3}$ **21.** Given: reg poly $YABX$ . . ., rad $\overline{OB}$. Prove: $\overline{OB}$ bis $\angle ABX$. Draw rad $\overline{OA}$, $\overline{OX}$, $\overline{OA} \cong \overline{OX}$ (def rad); $\overline{AB} \cong \overline{BX}$ (def reg poly); $\overline{OB} \cong \overline{OB}$ (reflex); $\triangle ABO \cong \triangle XBO$ (Post 16), $\angle 1 \cong \angle 2$ (CPCTC) $\overline{OB}$ bis $\angle ABX$ (def $\angle$ bis) **23.** For inscr sq, $s = r\sqrt{2}$; for circum sq $s' = 2r$; $\frac{A}{A'} = \frac{(r\sqrt{2})^2}{(2r)^2} = \frac{2r^2}{4r^2}; \frac{1}{2}$ **25.** Given: reg polys $XABC$ . . ., $X'A'B'C'$ with apothems $\overline{OD}$, $\overline{O'D'}$. Prove: $\frac{\text{Area } XABC}{\text{Area } X'A'B'C'} = \frac{(OD)^2}{(O'D')^2}$. Draw $\overline{OA}$, $\overline{OB}$, $\overline{O'A'}$, $\overline{O'B'}$, $\overline{OA} \cong \overline{OB}$, $\overline{O'A'} \cong \overline{O'B'}$ (def rad); $\angle OAD \cong \angle OBD$, $\angle O'A'D' \cong \angle O'B'D'$ (Th 5.1), $\overline{OA}$ bis $\angle A$, $\overline{O'A'}$ bis $\angle A'$ (ex 21); m $\angle OAD = \frac{1}{2}$ m $\angle XAD$, m $\angle O'A'D' = \frac{1}{2}$ m $\angle X'A'D'$ (def bis); $\angle XAD \cong \angle ABC$, $\angle X'A'D' \cong \angle A'B'C'$, $\angle XAD \cong \angle X'A'D'$ (def $\sim$ poly) $\angle XAD \cong \angle X'A'D' \cong \angle ABC \cong \angle A'B'C'$ (trans prop); $\frac{1}{2}$ m $\angle XAD = \frac{1}{2}$ m $\angle X'A'D'$ (mult); $\angle OAD \cong \angle O'A'D' \cong \angle OBD \cong \angle O'B'D'$ (trans prop); $\triangle OAB \sim \triangle O'A'B'$ (Post 21); $\frac{OD}{O'D'} = \frac{AB}{A'B'}$ (Th 9.6); Area $XABC = \frac{1}{2}(OD \cdot (n \cdot AB)$, Area $X'A'B'C' = \frac{1}{2} O'D'$ (n $\cdot A'B'$) (Th 12.9); $\frac{\text{Area } XABC}{\text{Area } X'A'B'C'} = \frac{\frac{1}{2} n \cdot OD \cdot AB}{\frac{1}{2} n \cdot O'D' \cdot A'B'}$ (div prop); $\frac{\text{Area } XABC}{\text{Area } X'A'B'C'} = \frac{OD}{O'D'} \cdot \frac{AB}{A'B'}$ (alg); $\frac{\text{Area } XABC}{\text{Area } X'A'B'C'} = \frac{OD}{O'D'} \cdot \frac{OD}{O'D'}$ or $\frac{(OD)^2}{(O'D')^2}$ (subst) **27.** 4.94; 58.12 **29.** 5.64; 104.16 **31.** 2.03; 1.91

Page 411

1. 4 m; 4π m; 12.56 m **3.** 6 mm; 12 mm; 37.68 mm **5.** 64 mm; 64π mm; 200.96 mm **7.** 2.6 mm; 5.2π mm; 16.33 mm **9.** 0.12 m; 0.75 m **11.** 0.28 mm; 1.73 mm **13.** $3\frac{1}{7}$

15. $2\pi d$ **17.** $S = \sqrt{2}$ cm; $c > p$ **19.** $2\pi r = 4s$, $r = \dfrac{2s}{\pi}$

Page 413

1. 4π m²   **3.** 4π km²   **5.** 5 m   **7.** 7 mm
9. 6 m   **11.** 24 mm   **13.** 1.13 m²
15. 1.77 cm²   **17.** 7.065 cm²   **19.** 0.07065 m²   **21.** 10 cm; 20 cm   **23.** 0.6 mm; 1.2 mm
25. 50.24 mm²   **27.** 6.449 m²   **29.** Asq = 4; $AC = 3.14$; Area of sq. is 0.86 m² greater than area of $\odot$.   **31.** $(4 - \pi)$ cm²   **33.** $\left(\sqrt{3} - \dfrac{1}{3}\pi\right)$ cm²   **35.** $12\dfrac{1}{2}\pi$ **37.** $4 - \pi$ **39.** $C_1 = 2\pi r_1$, $C_2 = 2\pi r_2$ (Th 12.10, Cor); $\dfrac{C_1}{C_2} = \dfrac{2\pi r_1}{2\pi r_2}$ (div); $\dfrac{C_1^2}{C_2^2} = \dfrac{R_1^2}{R_2^2}$ (alg); $\dfrac{A_1}{A_2} = \dfrac{R_1^2}{R_2^2}$ (ex. 38) $\dfrac{C_1^2}{C_2^2} = \dfrac{A_1}{A_2}$ (subst)   **41.** 1 to 2

Pages 416–417

1. 20 mm; 2.5π mm   **3.** 5 cm; $\dfrac{5\pi}{3}$ cm
5. 3.6 cm; 3π cm   **7.** 24 mm; 4π mm
9. 13 cm   **11.** 1 km; 2 km   **13.** $22\dfrac{1}{2}$; 16 m
15. 360; 5 mm   **17.** 12π **19.** $\dfrac{88\pi}{15}$ **21.** $\dfrac{35\pi}{9}$

Algebra Review

1. $\dfrac{7 - \sqrt{7}}{7}$ **2.** $\dfrac{12 + 2\sqrt{3}}{3}$ **3.** $\dfrac{10 - \sqrt{5}}{5}$
4. $3\sqrt{3} + \sqrt{2}$ **5.** $-3 + 3\sqrt{2}$ **6.** $\dfrac{12 + 3\sqrt{2}}{7}$
7. $-8 + 4\sqrt{5}$ **8.** $-\dfrac{2 + 2\sqrt{6} + \sqrt{3} + 3\sqrt{2}}{5}$
9. $3 - 2\sqrt{2}$ **10.** $\sqrt{2} + 1$ **11.** $\dfrac{18\sqrt{2} + 3\sqrt{3}}{23}$
12. $\dfrac{13 + 4\sqrt{3}}{11}$

Pages 419–420

1. 10π **3.** 15π **5.** 50π **7.** 75π
9. 72π cm²   **11.** 36π cm²   **13.** 60; $\dfrac{25\pi}{6}$ cm²; $\dfrac{50\pi - 75\sqrt{3}}{12}$ cm²   **15.** 120; $\dfrac{64\pi}{3}$ mm²; $\dfrac{64\pi - 48\sqrt{3}}{3}$ mm²   **17.** 120; 6 m; $12\pi - 9\sqrt{3}$ m²   **19.** 20π cm²   **21.** $\dfrac{54\pi - 81\sqrt{3}}{4}$ m²
23. $4\sqrt{7}$ m   **25.** Area is 4 times as large.
27. $A = \pi(R^2 - r^2)$ **29.** $\left(\dfrac{170\pi}{9} - 46.36\right)$ cm²

Cumulative Review

1. 120   **2.** 80

Page 422

1. 120 m²   **3.** 252 cm²   **5.** 150 cm²   **7.** 28 sq units   **9.** $\dfrac{64\pi}{5}$ cm²   **11.** 44 m²
13. 32π cm²   **15.** 14π cm   **17.** $3\sqrt{3}$ cm
19. 54 units   **21.** 240°   **23.** $\dfrac{3}{2}$

Cumulative Review

1. b   **2.** d   **3.** a   **4.** b   **5.** c   **6.** a
7. c   **8.** b   **9.** a   **10.** c   **11.** a   **12.** b
13. F   **14.** F   **15.** T   **16.** F   **17.** T
18. T   **19.** F   **20.** T   **21.** T   **22.** 9.5 cm
23. 60, 24   **25.** 89   **26.** 43   **27.** 19
28. $6\dfrac{2}{3}$ **29.** 12   **30.** 81 m²   **31.** $44\sqrt{2}$ cm²
32. $\dfrac{25}{4}\sqrt{3}$ cm²   **33.** 14π m   **34.** 12π cm²
35. 12.4   **36.** 13.1   **37.** 4.62

Page 431

1. right 2, up 3; left 4, up 2; right 6, down 4; left 3, down 5; up 8; down 3   **3.** vrt
5. neither   **7.** vrt   **9.** vrt   **11.** neither
13. horiz   **15.** 2   **17.** 3   **19.** -3 **21.** I, II
23. IV   **25.** II   **27.** (1, 5)   **29.** (4, 3)
31. $(4, -2)$, $(-3, 5)$ **33.** (4, 3), $(-1, 3)$; $(4, -7)$, $(-1, -7)$; $\left(1\dfrac{1}{2}, \dfrac{1}{2}\right)$, $\left(1\dfrac{1}{2}, -4\dfrac{1}{2}\right)$

Page 434

1. 2   **3.** 12   **5.** $\sqrt{13}$ **7.** $2\sqrt{2}$ **9.** $3\sqrt{10}$
11. $4\sqrt{13}$ **13.** $\sqrt{178}$
15. $\sqrt{(2 - m)^2 + (5 - n)^2}$ **17.** $AB = BC = \sqrt{29}$, $AC = 4$; isos   **19.** $2\sqrt{53}$, $\sqrt{74}$, $\sqrt{29}$; scal   **21.** $\sqrt{130}$, $\sqrt{26}$, $2\sqrt{26}$; scal   **23.** $RS = \sqrt{104}$, $ST = \sqrt{32}$, $RT = \sqrt{72}$; $(\sqrt{104})^2 = (\sqrt{32})^2 + (\sqrt{72})^2$; $104 = 32 + 72$ **25.** $\left(4\dfrac{1}{2}, \dfrac{1}{2}\right)$; $\left(4\dfrac{1}{2}, 5\dfrac{1}{2}\right)$ **27.** 2, -4 **29.** Given: pts $P(X_1, Y_1)$ and $Q(X_2, Y_2)$, $PQ = d$. Prove: $d = \sqrt{(X_2 - Y_1)^2 + (Y_2 - Y_1)^2}$. Draw $\overleftrightarrow{QN} \parallel \overleftrightarrow{OY}$ and $\overleftrightarrow{PN} \parallel \overleftrightarrow{OX}$ (Post 15); $\overleftrightarrow{OX} \perp \overleftrightarrow{QN}$, $\overleftrightarrow{QN} \perp \overleftrightarrow{PN}$ ($\bot \perp 1$ of $2 \parallel$s is $\perp$ other); $(PQ)^2 = (PN)^2 + (QN)^2$ (Pyth Th); $QN = |Y_2 - Y_1|$ $PN = |X_2 - X_1|$ (def) $d^2 = (X_2 - X_1)^2 + (Y_2 - Y_1)^2$ (subst); $d = \sqrt{(X_2 - X_1)^2 + (Y_2 - Y_1)^2}$ (alg)

Cumulative Review

1. 3, 12   **2.** 10, 7

Page 437

1. (2, 3)   **3.** (1, 6)   **5.** $\left(\dfrac{1}{2}, \dfrac{1}{2}\right)$ **7.** $\left(4, 1\dfrac{1}{2}\right)$
9. $\left(0, 4\dfrac{1}{2}\right)$ **11.** $\left(3\dfrac{1}{2}, -7\right)$ **13.** $(-10, -3)$

15. $(-12, -7)$ 17. $(6, 6)$ 19. $(18, -2)$
21. $(2, -3), (4, 2), (0, 1); 9$ 23. $\left(1\frac{1}{2}, -1\frac{1}{2}\right)$,
$\left(4\frac{1}{2}, 1\right), \left(2, 1\frac{1}{2}\right); \frac{1}{2}\sqrt{170}$ 25. $PR = \sqrt{61}$,
$MN = \frac{1}{2}\sqrt{61}$ 27. $MN = AB = CD = 3\sqrt{5}$
29. $MN = PQ = \sqrt{41}$; $PN = QM = \sqrt{26}$
31. Given: 2 pts $P(X_1, Y_1)$ and $Q(X_2, Y_2)$
with M the midpt of $\overline{PQ}$. Prove: $M =$
$\left(\frac{X_1 + X_2}{2}, \frac{Y_1 + Y_2}{2}\right)$. Locate $R(X_2, Y_1)$ by
drawing $\overleftrightarrow{QR} \parallel \overleftrightarrow{OY}$ and $\overleftrightarrow{PR} \parallel \overleftrightarrow{OX}$ (Post 15);
midpt of $\overline{QR}$ is $T\left(X_2, \frac{Y_2 + Y_1}{2}\right)$ (def of midpt of
vert seg); midpt of $\overline{PR}$ is $S\left(\frac{X_2 + X_1}{2}, Y_1\right)$ (def of
midpt of horiz seg); $\overline{MT} \parallel \overline{PR}$ and $\overline{MS} \parallel \overline{QR}$
(Th 7.7); $M(x, y) = M\left(\frac{X_2 + X_1}{2}, \frac{Y_2 + Y_1}{2}\right)$ (props
of horiz and vert lines)

Page 440
1. -6; dn rt   3. 0; horiz   5. undef; vert
7. 0; horiz   9. -1; dn rt   11. undef; vert
13. undef; vert   15. -1; dn rt   17. $-\frac{1}{2}$; dn rt
19. 0   21. 11   23. -3 25. -2 27. 6
29. slope $\overleftrightarrow{AB} =$ slope $\overleftrightarrow{CD} = \frac{-3}{4}$; collinear
31. slope $\overleftrightarrow{AB} =$ slope $\overleftrightarrow{CD} = -\frac{2}{3}$; parallel

Algebra Review
1. $x^2 + 4x + 4$ 2. $x^2 - 6x + 9$ 3. $y^2 + 10y + 25$ 4. $a^2 - 16a + 64$ 5. $4x^2 + 4x + 1$
6. $9y^2 - 12y + 4$ 7. $4c^2 - 20c + 25$
8. $16x^2 + 8x + 1$ 9. $9a^2 + 6ab + b^2$
10. $x^2 + 6xy + 9y^2$ 11. $4c^2 - 4cd + d^2$
12. $25x^2 - 40xy + 16y^2$ 13. $x^2 + 2x + 1$
14. $y^2 - 4y + 4$ 15. $m^2 - 8m + 16$ 16. $a^2 + 12a + 36$ 17. $x^2 + 5x + \frac{25}{4}$ 18. $y^2 - 9y + \frac{81}{4}$
19. $z^2 - 24z + 144$ 20. $a^2 + 15a + \frac{225}{4}$
21. $x^2 - 25x + \frac{625}{4}$ 22. $a^2 + 6ab + 9b^2$
23. $x^2 - 12xy + 36y^2$ 24. $c^2 + 7cd + \frac{49}{4}d^2$

Page 445
Line will pass through the given points.
1. $(-4, 0)(-2, -4)(0, -8)$ 3. $(-2, 2)(-1, 0)$
$(0, -2)$ 5. $(4, 0)(2, -6)(0, -12)$ 7. $(-3, 0)$
$\left(0, \frac{9}{5}\right)(2, 3)$ 9. $(4, 3)(0, 0)(-4, -3)$

11. $-4x + y = -7$ 13. $-3x + y = 14$
15. $-x - 3y = 9$ 17. $2x + 6y = -3$
19. $(3, 8); -3x + y = -1$ 21. $(-2, 1)$;
$6x + y = 11$ 23. $(-3, 5); \frac{4}{3}x + y = -9$
25. $(0, -6); y + 6 = 0$ 27. $(-1, 1); y = -x$
29. $m = \frac{-2 - 2}{3 - (-5)}; \frac{-1}{2}; y - 2 = \frac{-1}{2}(x + 5)$;
$x + 2y = -1$ 31. $m = -2; y + 1 = -2(x - 3)$;
$2x + y = 5$ 33. $m = \frac{1}{3}; y + 1 = \frac{1}{3}(x - 6)$;
$x - 3y = 9$ 35. $m = 1; y + 2 = 1(x + 7)$;
$-x + y = 5$ 37. For $\overline{AB}$: $m = -5; y + 4 =$
$-5(x + 2); 5x + y = -14$. For $\overline{BC}$: $m = 1$;
$y - 1 = 1(x + 3); -x + y = 4$. For $\overline{AC}$: $m = \frac{5}{2}$;
$y + 4 = \frac{5}{2}(x + 2); -5x + 2y = 2$.
39. $R = (0, 4); S = \left(3, \frac{8 + 4}{2}\right); (3, 6); T = (3, 2)$.
For $\overline{GS}$: $m = 2; y = 2x; -2x + y = 0$. For $\overline{HT}$:
$m = -2; y - 8 = -2x; 2x + y = 8$. For $\overline{IR}$:
$m = 0; y = 4$.   41. $m = \frac{y_2 - y_1}{x_2 - x_1}$;
$y - y_1 = \frac{y_2 - y_1}{x_2 - x_1}(x - x_1); \frac{y - y_1}{x - x_1} = \frac{y_2 - y_1}{x_2 - x_1}$
43. The $\triangle$s formed are 30-60 rt $\triangle$s. For l_1:
$m = \frac{0 - a}{a - 0}\sqrt{3}; -\sqrt{3}$. For l_2: $m = \frac{a\sqrt{3} - 0}{0 - (-a)}$;
$\sqrt{3}$.   45. $m = 1$ or $m = -1; y - 3 = 1(x - 4)$;
$-x + y = -1; y - 3 = -1(x - 4); x + y = 7$

Page 448
1. $y = 3x + 5$ 3. $y = 7x - 2$ 5. $y = \frac{-1}{2}$
7. $y = -x + \frac{1}{4}$ 9. $y = 2x + 4; 2; 4$
11. $y = -5x - 2; -5; -2$ 13. $y = 5; 0; 5$
15. $y = \frac{-1x}{3} - \frac{1}{2}; \frac{-1x}{3}, \frac{-1x}{2}$ Line will pass
through the given points.   17. $(1, 4)(0, 1)$
19. $(-3, 2)(0, -2)$ 21. $(3, 1)(0, 0)$
23. $(2, -3)(0, -3)$ 25. $(0, -4)(2, -2)$
27. $(-2, -1)(0, 4)$ 29. $y = -2x + 6; -2; 6$
31. $y = -x + 3; -1; 3$ 33. $y = \frac{-3}{2}x - 1; \frac{-3}{2}$;
-1 35. $y = x; 1; 0$ 37. $(-1, 6)$ 39. $(2, 0)$
41. Let $Q(0, b)$ be the pt where the nonvert line
int y-axis. Then slope $\overleftrightarrow{PQ} = \frac{0 - b}{a - 0}$, or $\frac{-b}{a}$ (def);
equa $\overleftrightarrow{PQ}$ is $y = mx + b$ (Th 13.5); $y = \frac{-b}{a}x + b$
(subst); $ay = -bx + ab$ (mult); $x = \frac{-ay}{b} + a$
(alg) $x = \frac{1}{m}y + a$ (subst)

Page 451

1. $1; -1$ **3.** $\frac{5}{2}; \frac{-2}{5}$ **5.** undef; 0 **7.** $\frac{-7}{8}; \frac{8}{7}$

9. $-7\frac{(1)}{7} = -1$ **11.** slope of $\overleftrightarrow{AB}$ = slope of $\overleftrightarrow{CD} = 1$; slope of $\overleftrightarrow{AD}$ = slope of $\overleftrightarrow{BC} = -4$ **13.** slope of $\overleftrightarrow{AB}$ = slope $\overleftrightarrow{CD} = 1$; slope of $\overleftrightarrow{BC}$ = slope of $\overleftrightarrow{AD} = -7$ **15.** slope of $\overleftrightarrow{EF}$ = slope of $\overleftrightarrow{GH} = \frac{-2}{3}$; slope of $\overleftrightarrow{EH}$ = slope of $\overleftrightarrow{FG} = \frac{3}{2}$; $\frac{-2}{3} \cdot \frac{3}{2} = -1$ (Th 13.8) **17.** $-7 \cdot \frac{1}{7} = -1$ **19.** $y = -6x + 28$ **21.** $y = \frac{-3}{2}x - \frac{7}{2}$ **23.** $x + 3y = 13$ **25.** $3x + 5y = 13$ **27.** Given: L_1 with slope m_1; L_2 with slope m_2; $m_1 \cdot m_2 = -1$. Prove $L_1 \perp L_2$. Draw $\overleftrightarrow{AB} \parallel$ x-axis (Post 15); $(AC)^2 = (x_3 - x_1)^2 + (y_3 - y_1)^2$; $(BC)^2 = (x_3 - x_2)^2 + (y_3 - y_2)^2$, $(AB)^2 = (x_2 - x_1)^2$ (Th 13.1); $(AC)^2 + (BC)^2 = (x_3 - x_1)^2 + (y_3 - y_1)^2 + (x_3 - x_2)^2 + (y_3 - y_2)^2$ (add); $m_1 = \frac{y_3 - y_1}{x_3 - x_1}$, $m_2 = \frac{y_3 - y_2}{x_3 - x_2}$ (def); $\frac{y_3 - y_1}{x_3 - x_1} \cdot \frac{y_3 - y_2}{x_3 - x_2} = -1$ (subst); $(y_3 - y_1)(y_3 - y_2) = -1 \cdot (x_3 - x_1)(x_3 - x_2)$; $2(y_3 - y_1)(y_3 - y_2) = -2(x_3 - x_1)(x_3 - x_2)$ Consider only y's: m $(AC)^2$ + m $(BC)^2 = (y_3 - y_1)^2 - 2(y_3 - y_1)(y_3 - y_2) + (y_3 - y_2)^2 = [(y_3 - y_1) - (y_3 - y_2)]^2 = 0$. Consider only x's: m $(AC)^2$ + m $(BC)^2 = (x_3 - x_1)^2 - 2(x_3 - x_1)(x_3 - x_2) + (x_3 - x_2)^2$ (subst); m $(AC)^2$ + m $(BC)^2 = [(x_3 - x_1) - (x_3 - x_2)]^2$ (distr); m $(AC)^2$ + m $(BC)^2 = (x_2 - x_1)^2$ = m $(AB)^2$; m $(AC)^2$ + m $(BC)^2$ = m $(AB)^2$ (subst); m $\angle C = 90$ (Th 10.3); $L_1 \perp L_2$ (def of rt $\angle$)

Page 454

1. $(0, a)$ **3.** $\frac{a}{2}$ **5.** $\left(\frac{a}{2}, 0\right); \left(\frac{b}{2}, \frac{c}{2}\right); \left(\frac{a+b}{2}, \frac{c}{2}\right)$

7. $(-a, 0)$ **9.** midpt $\overline{AC} = \left(\frac{a+b}{2}, \frac{c}{2}\right)$; midpt $BD = \left(\frac{a+b}{2}, \frac{c}{2}\right)$; M is midpt of both diags, so they bisect each other. **11.** Given: isos trap $ABCD$, $\overline{AB} \parallel \overline{CD}$, $\overline{AD} \cong \overline{BC}$ diags $\overline{AC}$, $\overline{BD}$. Prove: $\overline{AC} \cong \overline{BD}$, $AC = \sqrt{(a - b - 0)^2 + (c - 0)^2}$; $AC = \sqrt{(a - b)^2 + c^2}$; $BD = \sqrt{(a - b)^2 + (0 - c)^2}$; $BD = \sqrt{(a - b)^2 + c^2}$; $AC = BD$; $\overline{AC} \cong \overline{BD}$

13. Given: $ABCD$ with midpts $Z\left(\frac{a}{2}, 0\right)$, $W\left(\frac{a+d}{2}, \frac{e}{2}\right)$, $X\left(\frac{b+d}{2}, \frac{c+e}{2}\right)$, $Y\left(\frac{b}{2}, \frac{c}{2}\right)$. Prove: XZ, WY bisect each other. Midpt of $\overline{WY} = $

$\frac{\left(\frac{a+d}{2} + \frac{b}{2}, \frac{e}{2} + \frac{c}{2}\right)}{2}; \left(\frac{a+b+d}{4}, \frac{c+e}{4}\right);$ midpt $\overline{XZ} = \frac{\left(\frac{a}{2} + \frac{b+d}{2}, 0 + \frac{c+e}{2}\right)}{2};$ $\left(\frac{a+b+d}{4}, \frac{c+e}{4}\right)$ since both midpts have same coords, diag bisect each other. **15.** Given: trap $ABCD$, $\overline{AB} \parallel \overline{CD}$, $m\left(\frac{d}{2}, \frac{c}{2}\right)$ midpt diag $\overline{AC}$, $N\left(\frac{a+b}{2}, \frac{c}{2}\right)$ midpt diag $\overline{BD}$. Prove: $MN = \frac{1}{2}(AB - CD)$. $MN = \frac{a+b}{2} - \frac{d}{2}$; $MN = \frac{a+b-d}{2}$; $AB = a$; $CD = d - b$; $AB - CD = a - (d - b)$; $AB - CD = a + b - d$; $MN = \frac{1}{2}(AB - CD)$

Algebra Review

1. $9, -5$ **2.** $4, -16$ **3.** $3, 11$ **4.** $7, -11$ **5.** $5, 1$ **6.** $\frac{-2}{3}, 4$ **7.** $\frac{15}{2}, \frac{13}{2}$ **8.** $\frac{-6}{5}, 2$ **9.** $\frac{8}{3}, -4$ **10.** -2 **11.** $\frac{3}{5}, \frac{-9}{5}$ **12.** $2, \frac{2}{3}$

Page 458

1. $(x - 0)^2 + (y - 0)^2 = 3^2$ **3.** $(x - (-1))^2 + (y - 4)^2 = 1^2$ **5.** $(x - 6)^2 + (y - (-1))^2 = 7^2$ **7.** $(x - 5)^2 + (y - 5)^2 = 8^2$ **9.** $(x - 3)^2 + (y - 1)^2 = 4^2$; $x^2 - 6x + y^2 - 2y = 6$ **11.** $x^2 + (y + 4)^2 = 4$; $x^2 + y^2 + 8y = -12$ **13.** $(x + 8)^2 + (y + 1)^2 = 15$; $x^2 + 16x + y^2 + 2y = -50$ **15.** $(x + 2)^2 + (y + 9)^2 = 7$; $x^2 + 4x + y^2 + 18y = -78$ **17.** $4^2 + 0^2 = 16$ **19.** $(5 - 1)^2 + (-3)^2 = 16 + 9 = 25$ **21.** $(-\sqrt{3})^2 + (-2)^2 + 6(-2) = 3 + 4 - 12 = -5$ **23.** $(0, 0); 4$ **25.** $(0, 0); \sqrt{10}$ **27.** $(3, -4); 4$ **29.** $3\sqrt{2}$ **31.** $(-1, 5); 3\sqrt{3}$ **33.** $(8, 3); 1$ **35.** $(x - 4)^2 + (y - 3)^2 = 25$ **37.** $(x + 2)^2 + (y + \sqrt{5})^2 = 9$ **39.** $(x - 2)^2 + (y + 3)^2 = 20$ **41.** $x^2 + 4x + 4 + y^2 = x^2 - 2x - 1 + y^2 + 6y + 9 = 6$ **43.** $(3, -2)$ is center of both $\odot$s. **45.** $(4, -1)$

47. $-4x + 3y = 42$

Page 460

1. right 3, forward 1, up 2 **3.** left 2, forward 1, up 5 **5.** left 3, back 2, down 1 **7.** no move, back 3, up 4 **9.** left 1, no move, no move **11.** x = axis **13.** z = axis **15.** x and y **17.** $\sqrt{94}$ **19.** $\sqrt{161}$ **21.** $\sqrt{202}$ **23.** $\sqrt{113}$ **25.** $\sqrt{35}$ **27.** $(3, 2, 2)$ **29.** $\left(\frac{9}{2}, \frac{-7}{2}, 1\right)$

Page 462

1. right 3, up 6 **3.** left 4, down 3 **5.** vrt
7. $\sqrt{17}$ **9.** (2, 4) **11.** (−13, 2) **13.** $\sqrt{116}$;
$2\sqrt{29}$ **15.** −3; dn to rt; line will pass through
given points **17.** (3, 0)(0, −2) **19.** (−4, 0)
(0, −8) **21.** $y - 3 = 2(x - 1)$ **23.** $y + 5 =$
$\frac{1}{3}(x - 4)$ **25.** $4x - 3y = 5$ **27.** $y = 3x - 5$

29. 6; −4 **31.** $\frac{7}{5} \cdot \frac{-5}{7} = -1$

Page 469

1. A line $\parallel$ to a given line, midway bet them
3. 2 lines each $\parallel$ to given line l and 8 mm from it
5. $\perp$ bis of $\overline{RS}$ (see ex. 2) **7.** $\odot$, rad 2.5 cm,
given pt is ctr **9.** interior of $\odot$, rad = 2 cm
11. ext of $\odot$ of rad 4 cm, ctr at given pt
13. line $\parallel$ to given line l at a given dist from it
equal to the rad of the given $\odot$. **15.** $\odot$
concentric to given, rad of length = sum of radii
of given $\odot$ and rolling $\odot$.

Cumulative Review

1. 8 cm **2.** 65 cm²

Page 473

1. bis of given $\angle$ (Th 14.2) **2.** See Post 28.
3. See Post 28. **5.** diam $\perp$ to chords at their
midpt **7.** See ex. 5; diam $\perp$ to given chord,
but not including endpts of that diam (Th 14.1).

9. concentric $\odot$ with rad $\frac{1}{2}$ of given $\odot$.

i. The midpt of any rad of a $\odot$ is on the $\odot$

concentric to given $\odot$ and having a rad $\frac{1}{2}$ the rad

of given $\odot$. *ii.* Every point of a $\odot$ concentric to

a given $\odot$ and of rad $= \frac{1}{2}$ rad of the given $\odot$ is a

midpt of a rad of the given $\odot$. **11.** a line $\perp$
to a given line at the given pt. *i.* The center of a
$\odot$ tangent to a given line at a given pt is on
$\perp$ the line at the given pt. *ii.* Any pt on the $\perp$
a line at a given pt is the center of a $\odot$ tangent
to the line at the given pt. **13.** *i.* Given:
$\odot O$, O a pt on $\overleftrightarrow{QP}$, $\overleftrightarrow{QP} \perp l$ at P. Prove: Line
tangent to $\odot O$ at P. Since line $\perp$ rad $\overline{OP}$ at
its endpt on the $\odot$, line tangent $\odot O$ (Th 11.6).
ii. Given: $\odot O$, rad $\overline{OP}$, l tangent $\odot O$ at P.
Prove: $\overline{OP} \perp l$. Since l tangent $\odot O$ at P,
$OP \perp l$ (Th 11.5). **15.** *i:* $\overline{PA} \cong \overline{PB}$ (Th 5.7)
ii: Draw $\overline{PD}$ to midpt D of $\overline{AB}$; then $\overrightarrow{PD}$ is
the $\perp$ bis of $\overline{AB}$ (Th 5.8).

Algebra Review

1. $(x + 7)(x - 4) = 0$;
−7, 4 **2.** $(x + 2)(x + 3) = 0$;
−2, −3
3. $(x - 3)(x - 5) = 0$;
3, 5 **4.** $(x - 2)(x - 7) = 0$;
2, 7

5. $(x + 5)^2 = 0$; −5 **6.** $(x + 7)(x - 7) = 0$;
−7, 7
7. $(2x - 1)(x - 5) =$
0; $\frac{1}{2}$, 5 **8.** $(3x - 1)(x + 3) =$
0; $\frac{1}{3}$, −3
9. $(2x - 3)(x + 3) =$
0; $\frac{3}{2}$, −3 **10.** $(x + 8)(x - 3) = 0$;
−8, 3
11. $(x - 4)(x - 6) = 0$;
4, 6 **12.** $(x + 5)(x + 7) = 0$;
−5, −7

Page 477

1. concentric $\odot$ of 9 cm rad, 6 cm from OQ
3. 2 concentric $\odot$'s, radii 4 cm and 1 cm.
5. pt of intersection of $\odot A$ and $\odot B$; $\odot A$ with
rad 1 cm, $\odot B$ with rad 5 cm **7.** 4 pts of
intersection of $\odot O$, rad 2 cm with the bisectors
of the $\angle$s **9.** 2 pts, each 4 cm from P and on
the line $\parallel r$ and s and midway bet them.
11. 1 pt, on $\perp$ from P to l, 3 cm from P, 2 cm
from l **13.** 4 pts., $\odot P$, rad 9 cm, and 2 lines
$\parallel l$, 2 cm from l **15.** concentric $\odot$, rad. = 8 cm
17. 2 concentric $\odot$'s to given $\odot$, rad 4 cm and
10 cm **19.** 2 pts of intersection of $\odot$'s; ctr A,
rad = 3 cm, and ctr B, rad = 2 cm. **21.** 4 pts.
intersections of $\angle$ bis with lines $\parallel$ to r, 5 cm
above r and 1 cm below r **23.** 2 pts,
intersections of $\odot P$ and line midway between m
and n and parallel to them

Cumulative Review

1. $\frac{8}{3}\sqrt{3}$ cm. **2.** 196 m²

Page 481

1. 4 pts, intersection of $\angle$ bis with 2 lines $\parallel r$,
y units on either side of r **3.** no pts, 1 or 2 pts
of intersection of $\odot A$ with $l \parallel m$, n and midway
bet them $\left(d < \frac{1}{2}f, d = \frac{1}{2}f, d > \frac{1}{2}f\right)$ **5.** See
p. 480, ex 3. **7.** intersection of $\odot$ and $\angle$ bis;
0, 1, 2 pts **9.** intersection of line midway
between parallel lines and concentric locus
circle, rad $= \frac{r_1 + r_2}{2}$ no pts; 1 pt; 2 pts.

11. no pt, 1 pt, 2 pts, 3 pts, 4 pts **13.** no pts, 1 pt,
ray **15.** 1 pt **17.** 2 pts, 3 pts, no pt, 1 pt

Algebra Review

1. −3, 1 **2.** −3, 2 **3.** 13, −1 **4.** $\frac{3}{2}$, 4

5. −2, $\frac{1}{3}$ **6.** 1, $\frac{-2}{5}$ **7.** $3 \pm \sqrt{19}$

8. $\frac{-5 \pm \sqrt{73}}{4}$ **9.** $\frac{7 \pm \sqrt{13}}{6}$ **10.** $\frac{-2 \pm \sqrt{10}}{3}$

11. 1, $\frac{-6}{5}$ **12.** −1, $\frac{5}{3}$

Page 486

1. See constr pp 10, 49.   3. See ex 2.
5. See ex. 1.   7. in center, int of $\angle$ bis; circumcenter, int of $\perp$ bis of sides; they coincide   9. Draw 2 chords; constr their $\perp$ bis, which meet at ctr.   11. interior, always
13. See Th 14.4; incenter   15. 3, Post 12; 4, Th 14.2; 5, Trans; 6, Th 14.2   17. intersection of $\angle A$, $\angle D$ 19. r_i (inscr) $= \frac{1}{3} \cdot$ alt;

r_c (circum) $= \frac{2}{3} \cdot$ alt; $\frac{r_i}{r_c} = \frac{1}{3} \div \frac{2}{3} = \frac{1}{2}$ 21. $h =$

$\frac{1}{2} \cdot 24\sqrt{3}$; $h = 12\sqrt{3}$; $r_i = 4\sqrt{3}$; $r_c = 8\sqrt{3}$;

$A_i = 48\pi$ cm²; $A_c = 192\pi$ cm²

Page 489

1. See ex 1, p 174.   3. on $\perp$ bis of base
5. interior, on, exterior   7. 12   9. 10

11. $16\frac{1}{2}$ 13. 8, 12   15. 15; 45   17. 9

19. 1, given; 3, Post 8, 4, Post 1; 5, Th 7.7; 6, Th 7.7; 7, Th 3.7, Trans. 8, Th 7.5; 9, Th 7.2; 10, def of midpt: 11, Trans   21. $\frac{5}{3}\sqrt{3}$;

$\frac{10}{3}\sqrt{3}$ 23. $\angle CED$, $\angle PFD$ are rt $\angle$'s. (def, altitude); $\angle CED \cong \angle PFD$ (all rt $\angle$'s $\cong$); $\angle D \cong \angle D$ (reflex); $\triangle PFD \sim \triangle CED$ (Post 21); $\frac{PF}{CE} = \frac{PD}{CD}$ (def $\sim$ poly); $\frac{PD}{CD} = \frac{1}{3}$ (def, centroid); $\frac{PF}{CE} = \frac{1}{3}$ (subst)   25. All 6 $\triangle$s have same area; thus, their weights are equal, and the common pt. acts as the ctr. of balance.   27. Constr a $\square$ with sides S_1, S_2, by constructing a $\triangle$ with sides S_1, S_2, and 2 m; the seg 2 m is diag d_1 of $\square$; complete the $\square$; draw other diag, d_2: $\triangle$ with sides S_1, S_2, and d_2 is req $\triangle$.

Page 492

1. sphere, ctr Q, $r = 5$ cm   3. pl $r \parallel$ pl t, pl $r \parallel$ pl s, pl r midway bet pl s and pl t 5. 2 pl s, $\parallel$ to given pl, 3 m from it.   7. pl midway and $\parallel$ to $\parallel$ lines   9. l $\perp$ pl of $\triangle$ and passing through intersection of $\angle$ bis   11. pts in interior of sphere p, $r = 5$ cm   13. pl $\perp$ l at Q, except Q.   15. Cyl plus 2 hemispheres

Page 494

1. $\odot$, ctr A, $r = 1$ cm   3. region bet 2 l's, each $\parallel$ to given l and 2 cm from it   5. line $\perp$ to

given line at given pt.   7. pt on $\perp$ from A to l, 2 cm from A 9. no pts, 1 pt, 2 pts, 1 pt
11. Constr $\angle$ bis for 2 $\angle$'s.   13. Constr 2 $\perp$ lines; form a rt $\triangle$; constr $\perp$ bis of hypotenuse; midpt of hypotenuse is centroid.   15. 24
17. alt $= 6$ cm; 2 cm

Page 501

1. mult prop of ineq   3. add prop of ineq.
5. trichotomy   7. m $\angle z <$ m $\angle w$ (subtr prop of ineq)   9. $AB < BC$ (add prop of ineq)
11. $\frac{1}{2} AB > \frac{1}{2} CD$ (mult prop of ineq); $CF = \frac{1}{2} CD$, $AE = \frac{1}{2} AB$ (Th 11.2); $AE > CF$ (subst); $CF < AE$ (def)   13. m $\angle D +$ m $\angle B = 180$, m $\angle C +$ m $\angle A = 180$ (Th 11.11, Cor 4); m $\angle D +$ m $\angle B =$ m $\angle C +$ m $\angle A$ (subst); m $\angle D <$ m $\angle C$ (subtr prop ineq)   15. m $\angle DAB =$ m $\angle DBA$ (Th 5.1); m $\angle DAE <$ m $\angle EBD$ (subtr prop ineq); m $\angle DAE <$ m $\angle DBF$ (trans prop ineq); m $\angle FCB$ (Th 5.1); m $\angle DBF <$ m $\angle FCD$ (subtr prop ineq); m $\angle DAE <$ m $\angle FCD$ (tran prop ineq)

Algebra Review

1. $x > -2$ 2. $z < -1$ 3. $x \geq -\frac{1}{3}$

4. $x < \frac{11}{7}$ 5. $x \leq 6$ 6. $x \geq -6$ 7. $z > 0$
8. $x \leq 4$ 9. $y > -3$ 10. $x < 3$ 11. $z > 4$
12. $y < 4$

Pages 505–506

1. Direct path is shorter (Th 15.1).   3. Th 15.1
5. $AB + BC > AC$, $AD + DC > AC$, (Th 15.1); $AB + BC + AD + DC > 2 AC$ (add prop ineq); $AB + AD > BD$, $BC + DC > BD$ (Th 15.1); $AB + BC + AD + DC > 2 BD$ (add prop ineq); $2 (AB + BC + AD + DC) > 2 (AC) + 2 (BD)$ (add); $AB + BC + AD + DC > AC + BD$ (div prop ineq)   7. $AB + AD > BD$, $BE + EC > BC$ (Th 15.1); $BD = BE + ED$ (bet'ness); $BD = BE + EC$ (subst); $BD > BC$ (subst); $AB + AD > BC$ (trans prop ineq)   9. $AP + BP > AB$, $BP + CP > BC$, $AP + CP > AC$ (Th 15.1); $AP + BP + BP + CP + AP + CP > AB + BC + AC$ (add prop ineq), $2 (AP + BP + CP) > AB + BC + AC$ (subst); $AP + BP + CP > \frac{1}{2} (AB + BC + AC)$ (mult prop ineq)   11. $AB + AD > BD$, $BD + CB > DC$ (Th 15.1); $BD > DC - CB$ (subtr prop ineq); $AB + AD > DC - CB$ (trans prop ineq)
13. Given: $\triangle ABC$ with P on $\overline{AB}$. Prove: $CP <$

628

$\frac{1}{2}(AB + BC + AC)$. $AP + PB = AB$ (betweenness), $CP < CA + AP$, $CP < CB + PB$ (Th 15.1); $2(CP) < CA + AP + CB + PB$ (add prop ineq); $2\,CP < CA + BC + AB$ (subst); $CP < \frac{1}{2}(AB + BC + AC)$ (div prop of ineq)

Cumulative Review
1. 8   **2.** 15

Page 509
1. m $\angle A >$ m $\angle B$ (Th 15.2); m $\angle C >$ m $\angle B$ (trans)   **3.** m $\angle B > 90$ (def); m $\angle A +$ m $\angle B +$ m $\angle C = 180$ (Th 3.5); m $\angle A +$ m $\angle C < 90$ (subtr prop ineq); m $\angle A < 90$, m $\angle C < 90$ (def, angle add); m $\angle B >$ m $\angle C$ (trans ineq); $AC > BC$, $AC > AB$ (Th 15.3)   **5.** m $\angle CBA >$ m $\angle CAB$ (Th 15.2) $\frac{1}{2}$m $\angle CBA > \frac{1}{2}$m $\angle CAB$ (mult prop ineq);
m $\angle DBA = \frac{1}{2}$m $\angle CBA$, m $\angle DAB = \frac{1}{2}$m $\angle CAB$ (def, $\angle$ bis); m $\angle DBA >$ m $\angle DAB$ (subst); $AD > DB$ (Th 15.3)   **7.** m $\angle DBC >$ m $\angle A$ (Th 4.1); m $\angle DBC >$ m $\angle C$ (trans ineq); $DC > DB$ (Th 15.3)   **9.** m $\angle CAB =$ m $\angle CBA$ (Th 5.1); m $\angle CAB =$ m $\angle w +$ m $\angle x$, m $\angle CBA =$ m $\angle y +$ m $\angle z$ (Post 10); m $\angle w +$ m $\angle x =$ m $\angle y +$ m $\angle z$ (subst); m $\angle x >$ m $\angle y$ (Th 15.2); m $\angle w <$ m $\angle z$ (subtr prop ineq)   **11.** m $\angle BCD =$ m $\angle D$ (Th 5.1); $AB < BC$ (subst); m $\angle ACB <$ m $\angle A$ (Th 15.2); m $\angle ACB +$ m $\angle BCD <$ m $\angle D +$ m $\angle A$ (add prop ineq); m $\angle ACB +$ m $\angle BCD =$ m $\angle ACD$ (Post 10); m $\angle ACD <$ m $\angle D +$ m $\angle A$ (subst)

Pages 514-515
1. $\overline{AB} \cong \overline{CD}$, $\overline{AD} \cong \overline{BC}$ (Th 7.1, Cor); $BD > AC$ (Th 15.4)   **3.** $\overline{BD} \cong \overline{BD}$ (reflex); m $\angle ADB >$ m $\angle CDB$ (Th 15.5)   **5.** $\overline{CD} \cong \overline{CD}$ (reflex); $AD > DB$ (Th 15.4)   **7.** $\overline{RU} \cong \overline{SU}$ (def med), $\overline{TU} \cong \overline{TU}$ (reflex); $RT > ST$ (Th 15.4); m $\angle S >$ m $\angle R$ (Th 15.2)   **9.** $\overline{AB} \cong \overline{AB}$ (reflex); $\overline{AD} \cong \overline{EB}$ (def $\cong$); $CB > CA$ (Th 15.3)   **11.** $CD < AC$ (Th 15.3); $\overline{AB} \cong \overline{DB}$ (Th 5.1); $\overline{CB} \cong \overline{CB}$ (reflex); m $\angle DBC <$ m $\angle ABC$ (Th 15.4)

Cumulative Review
1. $7^2 + x^2 = 113$; $x = 8$; 56 cm²   **2.** $30 = 6x$; $x = 5$; $5^2 + 6^2 = d^2$; $\sqrt{61}$ cm

Algebra Review
1. $-6z < -96$; $z > 16$ **2.** $-x > -5$; $x < 5$
3. $-8x > 32$; $x < -4$ **4.** $-4x < -40$; $x > 10$
5. $-7x > -63$; $x < 9$ **6.** $-7x < 14$; $x > -2$

7. $-5x \leq -10$; $x \geq 2$ **8.** $2x > -14$; $x > -7$
9. $-4x < -8$; $x > 2$ **10.** $-3x \geq 9$; $x \leq -3$
11. $\frac{-3}{5} x \leq 10$; $x \geq \frac{-50}{3}$
12. $\frac{-2}{3} x \geq -14$; $x \leq 21$

Page 518
1. $\overline{OC} \cong \overline{OA}$, $\overline{OD} \cong \overline{OB}$ (Th 11.1); $CD < AB$ (Th 15.4); $OF > OE$ (Th 15.6)   **3.** $\triangle OFE$ is a rt $\triangle$ (def); $OE > OF$ (Th 15.3); $AB < CD$ (Th 15.7)   **5.** m $\angle B = \frac{1}{2} \overset{\frown}{AC}$, m $\angle A = \frac{1}{2} \overset{\frown}{BC}$ (Th 11.11); $\frac{1}{2}$ m$\overset{\frown}{AC} > \frac{1}{2}$ m$\overset{\frown}{BC}$ (subst); m$\overset{\frown}{AC} >$ m$\overset{\frown}{BC}$ (mult)   **7.** m $\angle AOB =$ m$\overset{\frown}{AB}$, m $\angle BOC =$ m$\overset{\frown}{BC}$ (def); m $\angle AOB <$ m $\angle BOC$ (subst); $AB < BC$ (Th 15.4); $OD > OE$ (Th 15.6)   **9.** Draw $\overline{OD} \perp \overline{AC}$; $\overline{OD}$ bis $\overline{AC}$ (Th 11.2); $AD = \frac{1}{2} AC$ (def); $AO = \frac{1}{2} AB$ (def); $\angle ADO$ is a rt $\angle$ (def $\perp$); $AO > AD$ (Th 15.3); $\frac{1}{2} AB > \frac{1}{2} AC$ (subst); $AB > AC$ **11.** Given: $\odot O$, P a noncentered interior pt; $\overline{AB} \perp \overline{OP}$, ch $\overline{CPD}$. Prove: $AB < CD$. Draw $\overline{OE} \perp \overline{CD}$; then see ex 3.   **13.** Given: $\odot O \cong \odot O'$, $AB > CD$, $\overline{OE} \perp \overline{AB}$, $\overline{OF} \perp \overline{CD}$; Prove: $OE < O'F$; In $\odot O$, draw $\overline{AG} \cong \overline{CD}$, $\overline{OH} \perp \overline{AG}$; $AB > AG$ (subst); $OE < OH$ (Th 15.6); $OH = O'F$ (Th 11.3); $OE < O'F$ (subst)

Page 520
1. $WX > YZ$ (subtr prop ineq)   **3.** $AM > ND$ (mult prop ineq)   **5.** No, $1 + 3 \not> 5$ **7.** $\angle F$, $\angle E$, $\angle D$ (Th 15.2)   **9.** $\overline{JK}$, $\overline{JL}$, $\overline{LK}$ (Th 15.3)   **11.** $AB > CD$ (Th 15.5)   **13.** $AD < AE + ED$, $EB < EC + CB$ (Th 15.1); $AD - AE < ED$, (subtr prop ineq); $EB = ED + DB$ (between-ness); $ED + DB < CB + EC$ (subst); $ED < CB + EC - DB$ (subtr prop); $AD - AE < CB + EC - DB$ (trans prop ineq); $AD + DB < CB + EC + AE$ (add prop ineq); $EC + AE = AC$ (betweenness); $AD + DB < CB + AC$ (subst)   **15.** $AB = DB$ (Th 5.2); $\overline{BC} = \overline{BC}$ (reflex); $AC > CD$ (Th 15.3); m $\angle ABC >$ m $\angle DBC$ (Th 15.5)

Page 527
1. 4, 12, 2, 4, 6; quad   **3.** 6, 18, 12, 6, 8; hex
5. 10, 30, 20, 2, 12; deca   **13.** F   **15.** T
17. T   **19.** $V = 2n$; $F = n + 2$; $E = 3n$; $V + F = 2n + n + 2$; $V + F = 3n + 2$; $V + F = E + 2$ **21.** 90

Cumulative Review
1. 4π **2.** $4\sqrt{2}$

Page 531
1. 84 **3.** 110 **5.** 150 cm² **7.** 240 + 32$\sqrt{3}$ cm² **9.** 404 mm² **11.** 384 m²
13. 768 + 192$\sqrt{3}$ cm² **15.** 156 **17.** 36$\sqrt{3}$ + 444 + 6$\sqrt{133}$

Page 534
1. 108 **3.** 89 **5.** 180 **7.** 308 **9.** 396
11. 800 m³ **13.** 1680 kg **15.** 6 units
17. 5,400 **19.** 1800$\sqrt{3}$ cm³ **21.** 434$\sqrt{2}$ cm³
23. 320 cm³

Pages 537–538
1. 20π; 22π; 10π **3.** 48π m²; 80π m²; 96π m³
5. 500π m³ **7.** 192π cm² **9.** 125π cm²
11. 150π **13.** 8:3 **15.** 1:1 **17.** π:4
19. cyl in 17, 54π cu units; cube, 216 cu units; cyl in 18, $27\sqrt{2}\pi$ cu units; cube, $54\sqrt{2}$ cu units

Page 542
1. 135; 192; 152 **3.** 260; 360; 400
5. 70 cm² **7.** 36 + 9$\sqrt{3}$ m² **9.** 192 cm²
11. 8 m **13.** 1040 cm²; 1440 cm²; 3200 cm³
15. 60 cm²; 96 cm²; **17.** 36$\sqrt{6}$ + 36$\sqrt{3}$; 108
19. 2; 3π

Cumulative Review
1. 16$\sqrt{3}$ **2.** 25$\sqrt{3}$ **3.** 196 **4.** 200

Algebra Review
1. (8.1) **2.** (−1, 4) **3.** (2, 1) **4.** (4, 2)
5. (4, 0) **6.** (2, 5) **7.** $\left(\dfrac{20}{9}, \dfrac{13}{9}\right)$ **8.** (−1, −2)

Page 546
1. 60π; 96π; 96π **3.** 136π; 200π; 320π
5. 9$\sqrt{3}$ m **7.** 6$\sqrt{5}$ cm **9.** 960π m³
11. $V_{cone} = \dfrac{1}{3} V_{cyl}$ **13.** 3$\sqrt{39}$ units **15.** 9:4
17. 4:1 **19.** $36\pi\sqrt{2}$ cm³ **21.** $\dfrac{48}{5}\pi$ **23.** 1:3
25. ($\sqrt{5}$ + 1):6

Pages 551–552
1. 144π sq units 288π cu units **3.** 100π sq units $\dfrac{500}{3}\pi$ cu units **5.** 196π cm²
7. 216π cm³ **9.** 64 m² $\dfrac{256\pi}{3}$ m³ **11.** 7 cm
13. 9 cm **15.** 3 **17.** 5 cm **19.** π:6

Page 554
1. 12 edges, 8 vertices, 6 faces **3.** 380; 500; 600 **5.** 360 m²; 468 m²; 540 m³ **7.** 360 m²; 432 cm²; 384 cm² **9.** 65π; 90π; 100π
11. 144π cm² **13.** 5 m **15.** 72 + 36$\sqrt{3}$ cm²; 24$\sqrt{3}$ cm³